Instructor's Manual

to accompany

Introduction to Management Science
A Modeling and Case Studies Approach with Spreadsheets

Frederick S. Hillier
Stanford University

Mark S. Hillier
University of Washington

Gerald J. Lieberman
Late of Stanford University

Prepared by
Christine Hillier

Some case solutions provided by
Karl Schmedders and
Molly Stephens

Boston   Burr Ridge, IL   Dubuque, IA   Madison, WI   New York   San Francisco   St. Louis
Bangkok   Bogotá   Caracas   Lisbon   London   Madrid
Mexico City   Milan   New Delhi   Seoul   Singapore   Sydney   Taipei   Toronto

McGraw-Hill Higher Education

A Division of The McGraw·Hill Companies

Instructor's Manual to accompany
INTRODUCTION TO MANAGEMENT SCIENCE: A Modeling and
Case Studies Approach with Spreadsheets

1 2 3 4 5 6 7 8 9 0 HAM/HAM 9 0 9 8 7 6 5 4 3 2 1 0 9

ISBN 0-07-037817-7

http://www.mhhe.com

IRWIN/McGRAW-HILL

Instructor's Manual to accompany Introduction to Management Science, by Hillier, Hillier, and Lieberman.

Please use this postage-paid form to report any errors that you find in this material. Be as complete as possible noting specifically which changes should be made. We will address them in subsequent printings and future editions. Thank You.

NOTE: Extra copies of this form appear at the end of this manual.

Attention: Scott Isenberg

Name _____   School _____

Office Phone _____

Please fold and seal so that our address is visible.

BUSINESS REPLY MAIL

FIRST-CLASS MAIL   PERMIT NO. 204   OAKBROOK, IL

POSTAGE WILL BE PAID BY ADDRESSEE

ATTENTION: Scott Isenberg

THE McGRAW-HILL COMPANIES
RICHARD D. IRWIN
1333 BURR RIDGE PKY.
BURR RIDGE, IL 60521-0085

(fold)

(fold)

TABLE OF CONTENTS

TEACHING RESOURCES ACCOMPANYING THE BOOK

The three key emphases of the book are summarized in its subtitle: a *modeling* and *case studies* approach with *spreadsheets*. We invite you to read the book's preface for a description of these emphases and the underlying teaching philosophy.

To support this approach to teaching management science, the wealth of resources described below are being provided with the book.

Spreadsheet Material

The CD-ROM shrink-wrapped with the book features a software package called *MS Courseware* that includes a separate Excel file for each chapter. These Excel files include numerous spreadsheets that show the formulation and solution for the various examples and case studies in the book. In contrast to the spreadsheets appearing on the printed pages, these are *live* spreadsheets that can be used to further investigate the examples and case studies. They also can be used as templates to formulate and solve similar problems.

Dozens of Excel templates also are provided in these Excel files for solving various models in the book. The Excel file for the computer simulation chapter even includes a Queueing Simulator routine for simulating queueing systems in a spreadsheet format.

In addition, several Excel add-ins are included on the CD-ROM. One is Frontline Systems' *Premium Solver*, which provides an enhancement of the standard Excel Solver (also a Frontline Systems product) for efficiently solving a variety of mathematical programming spreadsheet models. Others are TreePlan (for decision analysis), SensIt (for stochastic sensitivity analysis), and RiskSim (for computer simulation). These three add-ins are very nice shareware developed by Professor Michael R. Middleton, who is in the McLaren School of Business at the University of San Francisco. A trial version of Microsoft Project has been included on the CD-ROM as well for use with the project management chapter.

Two additional Excel add-ins, PrecisionTree and @RISK from Palisade Corporation have been thoroughly integrated into the decision analysis and computer simulation chapters, respectively. These two chapters were completed after agreement had been reached to include professional versions of these two add-ins on the CD-ROM for a limited access period. Unfortunately, this decision was reversed just before the book went to press, so these add-ins will not be as conveniently available as anticipated. However, they can still be obtained for a 10-day free trial period from the Palisade Web site, www.Palisade.com, either through downloading or by requesting a free demonstration CD-ROM that includes a package of Palisade products. Students wanting the demonstration CD-ROM should be advised to request it somewhat in advance of when it is needed. Because of the very limited access period, students also should be advised not to download or open up either PrecisionTree or @RISK until course work requiring its use begins. Another option for the instructor is to arrange a site license for the course through a link on the Palisade Web site.

Case Material

Except for Chapter 1, every chapter in the book includes at least one case study to convey the whole process of applying management science while using the techniques covered in that chapter. A few of the chapters revolve almost entirely around carrying a case study from beginning to end. Although the names and data are hypothetical and the specific problems have been reduced to textbook size for clarity, the case studies have been patterned after actual applications such as those presented in *Interfaces*. Although the case study presentations are self-contained in working through one approach to the problem, an instructor has the option of using some class time for further discussion of the cases.

In addition to the case studies within the chapters, 34 full-fledged cases are included at the end of the chapters. Like the case studies, these end-of-chapter cases employ a stimulating story-telling approach. However, the students now are asked to work out how they would address the issues in the cases. Therefore, the cases can be assigned as interesting and challenging projects for either individual students or teams of students. Again, an instructor has the option of using some class time for further discussion of the cases. Complete "solutions" or teaching notes are included in this Instructor's Manual.

Most of these cases at the end of the chapters have been developed by Karl Schmedders (a faculty member at the Kellogg School of Management at Northwestern University) and Molly Stephens (recently a management science consultant with Andersen Consulting). (The front of the book provides more information about these talented case writers.) In addition, two INFORMS teaching cases are included, one for the chapter on formulation and applications of linear programming models and the other for the queueing models chapter. These teaching cases were developed under the leadership of Professor Peter Bell of the Richard Ivey School of Business at the University of Western Ontario. They are drawn directly from real applications presented in *Interfaces* and are designed to lead to classroom discussion.

Supplementary Text Material

As listed at the end of the book's Table of Contents, some supplementary text material is included on the CD-ROM. Included are supplements to the chapters on project management, binary integer programming, decision analysis, and queueing models. The respective topics are (1) the procedure for constructing a project network, (2) some perspectives on solving binary integer programming problems, (3) decision criteria without probabilities, and (4) finite queue and finite calling population variations of the *M/M/s* model. In addition, a complete chapter on solution concepts for linear programming is available on the CD-ROM. In most cases, these supplements include problems, with solutions provided in this Instructor's Manual.

Although the topics covered in these supplements are not central to the emphases of the book, they are being made available for instructors and students who want a broader treatment of management science.

Solutions for Review Questions, Problems, and Cases

Review questions are included at the end of essentially every section of the book to assist students in reviewing the key information. Instructors have the option of assigning these review questions as part of the homework and/or using some of the questions in class as a vehicle for highlighting key material and eliciting class participation. Answers for all the review questions are included in this Instructor's Manual. Also included are complete solutions for all the problems and cases at the end of the chapters, as well as at the end of the supplements on the CD-ROM.

A Test Bank and Self-Testing Quizzes

For the instructor's exclusive use, a complete test bank is provided in a separate booklet. This test bank includes many hundred multiple-choice questions and true-false questions that provide a substantial coverage of all the chapters of the book. In addition, a Computest for computer implementation of this test bank also is available.

For the student's use, the CD-ROM provides a tutorial with sample test questions (different from those in the instructor's test bank) for self-testing quizzes on the various chapters. Each chapter's quiz has about 10 questions.

PowerPoint Slides

The CD-ROM includes an extensive set of PowerPoint slides for use by the instructor and for subsequent review by the students. The slides include class-tested lecture material to accompany nearly all the chapters. Also provided are slides of some figures in the book (including spreadsheets) in case the instructor wants to show any of these figures in class.

Teaching Notes

In addition to these PowerPoint slides, the next section of this Instructor's Manual provides several class-tested teaching notes. The topics covered are (1) using Lego® to introduce linear programming, (2) using the Excel Solver to solve linear programming problems, (3) using Lego® to introduce what-if analysis, and (4) using Excel data tables for sensitivity analysis.

A Web Site

Finally, we invite you to visit our Web page at www.mhhe.com/hilliermgmtsci/. Over time, this Web page will provide updates about the book, including errata.

In addition, you might find it interesting to visit the publisher's operations management supersite at www.mhhe.com/pom/. This supersite links to many resources on the internet that are of some relevance to the book.

Teaching Note for Chapter 2: Using Lego® to Introduce Linear Programming

Norman Pendegraft developed a new way of introducing linear programming to students using Lego® building blocks. For more information, see Norman Pendegraft's article in OR/MS Today, February 1997, Vol. 24 entitled "Lego of my simplex". I describe below how I have used Lego® in my courses at the University of Washington to introduce linear programming. I use Lego® again to introduce "what-if?" or sensitivity analysis (see the first teaching note for Chapter 4).

Begin by distributing a package of raw materials to the students—one packet for every 2-4 students (or so) works fairly well. These are their working materials. The raw materials consist of 6 large Lego® bricks (2 by 4) and 8 small Lego® bricks (2 by 2), as shown below.

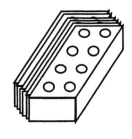

6 Large Bricks

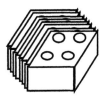

8 Small Bricks

Next, describe the two products of the company—a table and a chair. Each table consists of two large bricks and two small bricks, while a chair consists of one large brick and two small bricks. The tables and chairs are constructed out of the Lego® as shown below.

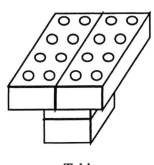

Table

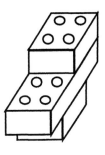

Chair

Each table produced generates $20 in profit, while each chair produced generates $15 in profit. At this point, the students are asked how they would like to use their raw materials to produce the two products in order to generate as much profit as possible.

Some students invariably begin by thinking that all tables should be produced (after all, they make the most profit). Three tables can be produced for a profit of $60. Similarly, a maximum of four chairs can be produced for a profit of $60. The optimal solution is two tables and two chairs, for a profit of $70. The students eventually stumble upon this solution.

The students (without realizing it) have now solved a linear programming problem. They have allocated scarce resources (the bricks) to a set of activities (building tables and chairs), so as to maximize profit. After having done this, explaining the concepts of linear programming, such as decision variables, objective functions, and constraints, is much easier because the students can relate it to the hands-on problem they have already solved.

Powerpoint slides for a lecture that starts with using Lego to introduce linear programming are included on the CD-ROM packaged with the text.

Teaching Note for Chapter 2: Using the Excel® Solver® to Solve Linear Programming Problems

The next eight pages give a step-by-step guide for using the Solver® to solve linear programming problems. It can be used to make overheads, or can serve as a handout for students.

It is based upon solving the following example problem. Powerpoint slides containing this example problem and the notes for using the Solver (with the Lego example) are included on the CD-ROM packaged with the text.

The Quality Furniture Corporation produces benches and picnic tables. The firm has two main resources: its labor force and a supply of redwood for use in the furniture. During the next production period, 1200 hours of manpower are available under a union agreement. The firm also has a stock of 5000 pounds of quality redwood. Each bench that Quality Furniture produces requires 4 labor hours and 10 pounds of redwood; each picnic table takes 7 labor hours and 35 pounds of redwood. Completed benches yield a profit of $9 each, and tables a profit of $20 each. What product mix will maximize total profit?

Following is the algebraic formulation of a linear programming model for this problem:

Let B = number of benches to produce

T = number of tables to produce

Maximize Profit = $(\$9)B + (\$20)T$

subject to

Labor: $4B + 7T \leq 1200$ hours

Wood: $10B + 35T \leq 5000$ pounds

and

$B \geq 0, \ T \geq 0.$

Formulating and Solving Linear Programming Models with Excel

Enter the input data and construct relationships among data elements in a readable, easy to understand way. When building this foundation for your model, think ahead about the optimization model you will be developing. Make sure there is a cell in your spreadsheet for each of the following:

- Every relevant piece of data (see cells B5:C5, B8:C9, and F8:F9). These cells are the "data cells."
- Every decision variable (for now, just label the cells, and enter an initial value for each decision variable — see cells B3 and C3). These cells are the "changing cells."
- The quantity (objective function) you wish to maximize or minimize (this must be an equation that calculates the profit or cost, based on the value of the decision variables). The cell containing this quantity (see cell D5) is the "target cell."
- Every quantity that you might want to constrain (include both sides of the constraint—an equation for the left-hand-side representing the amount of the resource used, and a number for the right-hand-side representing the amount of the resource available). The left-hand-side totals being constrained (see cells D8:D9) are the "output cells."

If you don't have any particular initial values you want to enter for your decision variables, you can start by just entering a value of 0 in each changing cell. (Note that the following spreadsheet places the changing cells and profits at the top, whereas the textbook places them at the bottom. Either location is fine.)

	A	B	C	D	E	F
1						
2		Benches	Tables			
3	Solution:	0	0			
4				Totals		
5	Profit	$9.00	$20.00	$0.00		
6						
7				LHS		RHS
8	Labor	4	7	0	≤	1200
9	Wood	10	35	0	≤	5000

The Formulas in the Spreadsheet

The formulas in the spreadsheet are shown next. Note the use of the SUMPRODUCT function. SUMPRODUCT sums the products of individual cells in two ranges. For example, SUMPRODUCT(B5:C5, B3:C3) sums the products B5*B3 plus C5*C3. The two specified ranges must be the same shape (same number of rows *and* columns). For linear programming, you should try to always use the SUMPRODUCT function (or SUM) for the objective function and constraints, as this guarantees that the equations will be linear.

	A	B	C	D	E	F
1						
2		**Benches**	**Tables**			
3	**Solution:**	0	0			
4				**Totals**		
5	Profit	9	20	=SUMPRODUCT(B5:C5,B3:C3)		
6						
7				LHS		RHS
8	Labor	4	7	=SUMPRODUCT(B8:C8,B3:C3)	≤	1200
9	Wood	10	35	=SUMPRODUCT(B9:C9,B3:C3)	≤	5000

Defining the Target Cell (Objective Function)

Once you are satisfied that the spreadsheet model is complete, and so includes all four of the elements of the linear programming model (data, decision variables, objective function, constraints), then

- Choose Solver under the Tools menu.

To select the cell you wish to optimize, select the "Set Target Cell" window within the Solver dialogue box, and then either

- Click on the cell you wish to optimize, or
- Type the address of the cell you wish to optimize.
- Choose either "Max" or "Min" depending on whether the objective is to maximize or minimize the target cell.

	A	B	C	D	E	F
1						
2		Benches	Tables			
3	Solution:	0	0			
4				Totals		
5	Profit	$9.00	$20.00	$0.00		
6						
7				LHS		RHS
8	Labor	4	7	0	≤	1200
9	Wood	10	35	0	≤	5000

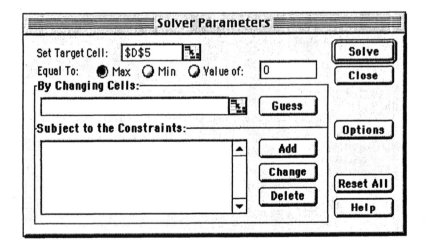

Note:

- The target cell must be a single cell (there can only be one objective).
- The target cell should contain an equation that defines the objective and depends on the decision variables.

Identifying the Changing Cells (Decision Variables)

You next tell Solver which cells are decision variables—i.e., which cells Excel is allowed to change when trying to optimize. Move the cursor to the "By Changing Cells" window, and either

- Drag the cursor across all cells you wish to treat as decision variables, or
- Type the addresses of every cell you wish to treat as a decision variable, separating them by commas.

	A	B	C	D	E	F
1						
2		Benches	Tables			
3	Solution:	0	0			
4				Totals		
5	Profit	$9.00	$20.00	$0.00		
6						
7				LHS		RHS
8	Labor	4	7	0	≤	1200
9	Wood	10	35	0	≤	5000

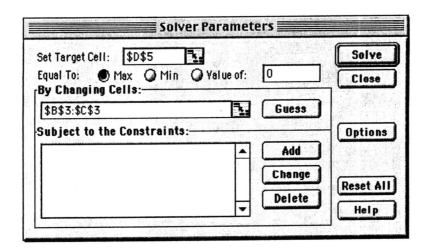

If you wish to use the "dragging" method, but the decision variables do not all lie in a connected rectangle in the spreadsheet, you can "drag" them in one group at a time:

- Drag the cursor across one group of decision variables,
- Put a comma after that group in the "By Changing Cells" window,
- Drag the cursor across the next group of decision variables,
- etc....

Adding Constraints

To begin entering constraints, click on the "Add" button to the right of the constraints window. A new dialogue box will appear. The cursor will be in the "Cell Reference" window within this dialogue box.

- Click on the cell that contains the quantity you want to constrain, or
- Type the cell address that contains the quantity you want to constrain.

The default inequality that first appears for a constraint is "<=". If you wish to change this,

- Click on the arrow beside the "<=" sign, and then
- Select the inequality (or equality) you wish from the list provided.

Notice that you may also force a decision variable to be an integer or binary (i.e., either 0 or 1) using this window. These features fall outside the realm of linear programming.

After setting the inequality, move the cursor to the "Constraint" window.

- Click on the cell you want to use as the constraining value for that constraint, or
- Type the number or the cell reference you want to use as the constraining value for that constraint, or
- Type a number that you want to use as the constraining value.

	A	B	C	D	E	F
1						
2		**Benches**	**Tables**			
3	**Solution:**	0	0			
4				**Totals**		
5	Profit	$9.00	$20.00	$0.00		
6						
7				LHS		RHS
8	Labor	4	7	0	≤	1200
9	Wood	10	35	0	≤	5000

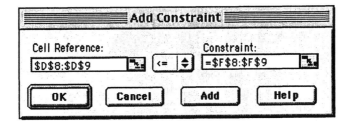

You may define a set of similar constraints (e.g., all <= constraints, or all >= constraints) in one step if they are in adjacent rows (as was done here). Simply select the range of cells for the set of constraints in both the "Cell Reference" and "Constraint" window.

After you are satisfied with the constraint(s),

- Click the "Add" button if you want to add another constraint, or
- Click the "OK" button if you want to go back to the original dialogue box.

Some Important Options

The Solver dialogue box now contains the optimization model, including the target cell (objective function), changing cells (decision variables), and constraints.

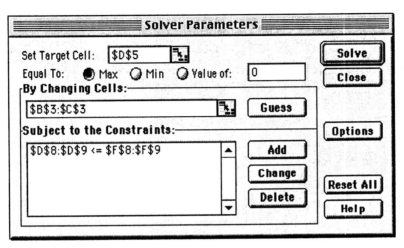

Once you are satisfied with this optimization model, there is one more very important step. Click on the "Options" button in the Solver dialogue box, and click in both the "Assume Linear Model" and the "Assume Non-Negative" box.

The "Assume Linear Model" option tells the Excel Solver that it is a *linear* programming model that is being solved. This speeds the solution process, makes it more accurate, and enables a more informative sensitivity report.

The "Assume Non-Negative" box adds non-negativity constraints to *all* the decision variables.

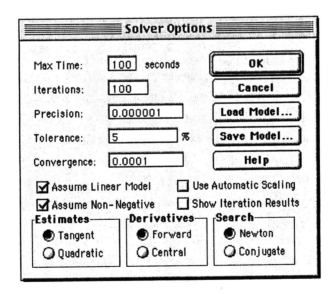

The Solution

After setting up the model and selecting the appropriate options, it is time to click "Solve". You then will receive one of four messages:

- "Solver found a solution. All constraints and optimality conditions are satisfied". This means that Solver has found an optimal solution.
- "Cell values did not converge". This means that the objective function can be improved to infinity. You may have forgotten a constraint (perhaps the non-negativity constraints) or made a mistake in a formula.
- "Solver could not find a feasible solution". This means that Solver could not find a feasible solution to the constraints you entered. You may have made a mistake in typing the constraints or in entering a formula in your spreadsheet.
- "Conditions for Assume Linear Model not satisfied". You may have included a formula in your model that is nonlinear. There is also a slim chance that Solver has made an error. (This bug shows up occasionally.)

If Solver finds an optimal solution, you have some options. First, you must choose whether you want Solver to keep the optimal values in the spreadsheet (you usually want this one) or go back to the original numbers you typed in. Click the appropriate box to make your selection. You also get to choose what kind of reports you want. You will often want to select "Sensitivity Report". Once you have made your selections, click on "OK". To view the sensitivity report, click on the "Sensitivity Report" tab in the lower-left-hand corner of the window.

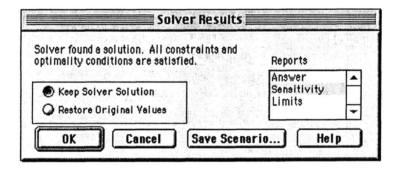

	A	B	C	D	E	F
1						
2		Benches	Tables			
3	Solution:	100	114.285714			
4				Totals		
5	Profit	$ 9.00	$ 20.00	$ 3,185.71		
6						
7				LHS		RHS
8	Labor	4	7	1200	≤	1200
9	Wood	10	35	5000	≤	5000

Teaching Note for Chapter 4: Using Lego® to Introduce What-If Analysis

Norman Pendegraft developed a new way of introducing what-if analysis to students using Lego® building blocks. For more information, see Norman Pendegraft's article in OR/MS Today, February 1997, Vol. 24 entitled "Lego of my simplex". I describe how I use Lego® in my courses at the University of Washington to introduce linear programming in the first teaching note for Chapter 2. Lego® can also be used to introduce "what-if?" or sensitivity analysis, as described below.

The following discussion assumes that this is the first time using Lego®. If Lego® was used to introduce linear programming (as described in the first teaching note for Chapter 2), then proceed through the next five paragraphs very quickly, reminding the students of the problem and what the original optimal solution was.

Begin by distributing a package of raw materials to the students—one packet for every 2-4 students (or so) works fairly well. These are their working materials. The raw materials consist of 6 large Lego® bricks (2 by 4) and 8 small Lego® bricks (2 by 2), as shown below. Three additional large bricks should also be passed out (for a total of 9), but put aside until later (see the last four paragraphs of this teaching note).

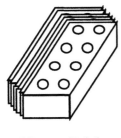

6 Large Bricks

8 Small Bricks

Next, describe the two products of the company—a table and a chair. Each table consists of two large bricks and two small bricks, while a chair consists of one large brick and two small bricks. The tables and chairs are constructed out of the Lego® as shown below.

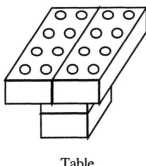

Table

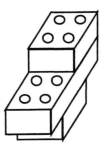

Chair

Each table produced generates $20 in profit, while each chair produced generates $15 in profit. At this point, the students are asked how they would like to use their raw materials to produce the two products in order to generate as much profit as possible.

Some students invariably begin by thinking that all tables should be produced (after all, they make the most profit). Three tables can be produced for a profit of $60. Similarly, a maximum of four chairs can be produced for a profit of $60. The optimal solution is two tables and two chairs, for a profit of $70. The students eventually stumble upon this solution.

The students (without realizing it) have now solved a linear programming problem. They have allocated scarce resources (the bricks) to a set of activities (building tables and chairs), so as to maximize profit. After having done this, explaining the concepts of linear programming, such as decision variables, objective functions, and constraints, is much easier because the students can relate it to the hands-on problem they have already solved.

We then begin what-if analysis by discussing the possibility that the unit profit per chair ($15) or table ($20) might be inaccurate. We first consider the possibility that the profit per table might really be $25 instead. If so, what should they do? After some thought they discover their optimal solution doesn't change. We then consider the possibility that the profit per table is really $35. They soon discover that it is now optimal to produce 3 tables and 0 chairs. Hence, they have discovered that there is a range of values for changes in the objective function where the optimal solution does not change.

We next consider the possibility of additional large bricks becoming available. I ask the students how much they would be willing to pay for one additional large brick. (This is where the additional large bricks that were initially set aside will become useful.) At first, the students don't think this would be worth anything, because without additional small bricks, they can't build any more product. However, someone eventually figures out that you can change one of the chairs into tables and make an additional $5 profit. Hence, they discover the shadow price for large bricks.

We then consider the possibility of getting three extra large bricks rather than just one, and wonder if these are each worth $5 as well. They soon discover that only two more large bricks (total) are useful. After that, they can no longer turn a chair into a table (because they are producing all tables). Hence, they discover that there is a range of feasibility for the shadow price for large bricks.

Using Lego® to introduce what-if analysis has proven to be extremely successful in my courses. When we later discuss the sensitivity report, the meaning behind all the numbers is much easier to understand, because they have "seen it" already. They can easily relate all of the concepts (range of optimality, shadow price, range of feasibility) back to the Lego® example.

Powerpoint slides for a lecture that uses Lego® to introduce what-if analysis are included on the CD-ROM packaged with the text.

Teaching Note for Chapters 4, 10, 11, 14 and 15: Using Excel® Data Tables for Sensitivity Analysis

A useful feature in Excel® for doing sensitivity analysis on various parameters is the data table. A data table is used to show the results in an output cell (or cells) for various trial values in a data cell (or cells). We will demonstrate using the EOQ model for determining the optimal inventory policy (see Chapter 11).

A spreadsheet formulation of the basic EOQ model for the Atlantic Coast Tire Corp. problem (introduced in Section 11.1) is shown below.

	A	B	C	D	E	F	G
1		Basic EOQ Model for Atlantic Coast Tire Corp. (Before Solving)					
2							
3			Data			Results	
4		D =	6000	(demand/year)		Reorder Point =	216
5		K =	$115	(setup cost)			
6		h =	$4.20	(unit holding cost)		Annual Setup Cost =	$690.00
7		L =	9	(lead time in days)		Annual Holding Cost =	$2,100.00
8		WD =	250	(working days/year)		Total Variable Cost =	$2,790.00
9							
10			Decision				
11		Q =	1000	(order quantity)			

	G
4	=C7*C4/C8
5	
6	=C5*C4/C11
7	=C6*C11/2
8	=SUM(G6:G7)

We can use a data table to see how the various costs (setup cost, holding cost, and total cost) vary with different order quantities. To create a data table, make a table with headings as shown on the next page. In the first column of the table, insert all the different values for the data cell (the order quantity) for which you would like to see the results, except leave the first row blank. The headings of the next columns specify the types of output data to be considered. Then, in the first row of the table, write an equation that refers to each of the output cells for which you are interested in seeing results (the setup cost in G6, the holding cost in G7, and the total cost in G8).

	A	B	C	D	E
14	Data Table for ACT Corp.				
15					
16		Order	Setup	Holding	Total
17		Quantity	Cost	Cost	Cost
18			=G6	=G7	=G8
19		1000			
20		900			
21		800			
22		700			
23		600			
24		500			
25		400			
26		300			
27		200			
28		100			

Next, select the entire table by clicking and dragging from cells B18 through E28, and choose Table from the Data menu. In the table dialogue box (as shown below), you indicate the column input cell (C11), which refers to the data cell that is being changed in the first column of the table.

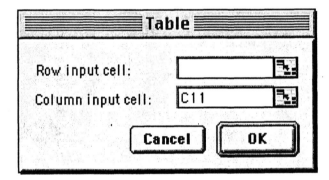

The data table shown on the next page is then generated. For each value of the input cell indicated in the first column of the table, Excel determines the corresponding value of the output cells referred to in the first row of the table (the setup cost in G6, the holding cost in G7, and the total cost in G8).

	A	B	C	D	E
14		**Data Table for ACT Corp.**			
15					
16		Order	Setup	Holding	Total
17		Quantity	Cost	Cost	Cost
18			$690	$2,100	$2,790
19		1000	$690	$2,100	$2,790
20		900	$767	$1,890	$2,657
21		800	$863	$1,680	$2,543
22		700	$986	$1,470	$2,456
23		600	$1,150	$1,260	$2,410
24		500	$1,380	$1,050	$2,430
25		400	$1,725	$840	$2,565
26		300	$2,300	$630	$2,930
27		200	$3,450	$420	$3,870
28		100	$6,900	$210	$7,110

We next show how two-way data tables can be used to simultaneously vary two data cells and see the effect on a single output cell. We will again demonstrate using the EOQ model for determining the optimal inventory policy (see Chapter 11).

A spreadsheet formulation of the basic EOQ model for the Atlantic Coast Tire Corp. problem (introduced in Section 11.1) is shown below, this time with the optimal order quantity calculated using the square root formula in cell C11.

	A	B	C	D	E	F	G
1		**Basic EOQ Model for Atlantic Coast Tire Corp.**					
2							
3			Data			Results	
4		D =	6000	(demand/year)		Reorder Point =	216
5		K =	$115	(setup cost)			
6		h =	$4.20	(unit holding cost)		Annual Setup Cost =	$1,203.74
7		L =	9	(lead time in days)		Annual Holding Cost =	$1,203.74
8		WD =	250	(working days/year)		Total Variable Cost =	$2,407.49
9							
10			Decision				
11		Q =	573.21	(order quantity)			

	C
11	=SQRT(2*C4*C5/C6)

	G
4	=C7*C4/C8
5	
6	=C5*C4/C11
7	=C6*C11/2
8	=SUM(G6:G7)

We can use a data table to see how the optimal order quantity varies with simultaneous changes in the setup cost and unit holding cost. To create a two-way data table, make a table with column and row headings as shown on the next page. In the upper-left-hand corner of the table, write an equation that refers to the output cell for which you are interested in seeing results (the optimal order quantity in C11). To the left of the table, insert all the different values for the first

19

changing data cell (the setup cost). Above the table, insert all the different values for the second changing data cell (the unit holding cost).

	A	B	C	D	E	F	G	H
14	Data Table for ACT Corp.							
15								
16						Unit Holding Cost		
17			=C11	$3.78	$3.99	$4.20	$4.41	$4.62
18			$103.50					
19		Setup	$109.25					
20		Cost	$115.00					
21			$120.75					
22			$126.50					

Next, select the entire table (cells C17 through H22), and choose Table from the Data menu. In the table dialogue box (shown below), you indicate which data cells are being changed simultaneously. The column input cell refers to the data cell whose various values are indicated in the column to the left of the table (the setup costs), while the row input cell refers to the data cell whose various values are indicated in the row above the table (the unit holding cost).

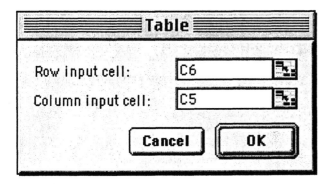

The data table shown below is then generated. For each value of the data cells to the left of the table (the setup cost in C5) and above the table (the unit holding cost in C6), Excel determines the corresponding value of the output cell referred to in the upper-left-hand corner of the table (the optimal order quantity in C11).

	A	B	C	D	E	F	G	H
14	Sensitivity Analysis for Atlantic Coast Tire Corp.							
15								
16						Unit Holding Cost		
17			573	$3.78	$3.99	$4.20	$4.41	$4.62
18			$103.50	573	558	544	531	518
19		Setup	$109.25	589	573	559	545	533
20		Cost	$115.00	604	588	573	559	547
21			$120.75	619	603	587	573	560
22			$126.50	634	617	601	587	573
23					Optimal Order Quantity			

These examples were from inventory management (Chapter 11). Data tables are also useful for performing sensitivity analysis in decision analysis (Chapter 10), queueing models (Chapter 14), and simulation (Chapter 15).

It can also be instructive to perform sensitivity analysis on various parameters in a linear programming model (Chapter 4). However, Excel data tables do not re-solve the model automatically for each value of the input parameter. Therefore, to create a data table for a linear programming model, one must manually re-solve the model using the Solver for each combination of input parameters.

CHAPTER 1
INTRODUCTION

Review Questions

1.1-1   The rapid development of the discipline began in the 1940's and 1950's.

1.1-2   The traditional name given to the discipline is operations research.

1.1-3   A management science study provides an analysis and recommendations, based on the quantitative factors involved in the problem, as input to the managers.

1.1-4   Management science is based strongly on some scientific fields, including mathematics and computer science. It also draws upon the social sciences, especially economics.

1.1-5   A decision support system is an interactive computer-based system that aids managerial decision-making. The system draws current data from databases or management information systems and then solves the various versions of the model specified by the manager.

1.1-6   Many managerial problems revolve around such quantitative factors as production quantities, revenues, costs, the amounts available of needed resources, etc.

1.1-7   The production and sales volume needs to exceed the break-even point to make it worthwhile to introduce a product.

1.2-1   These applications typically resulted in annual savings in the millions of dollars.

Problems

1.1   Answers will vary.

1.2   Answers will vary.

1.3   a)

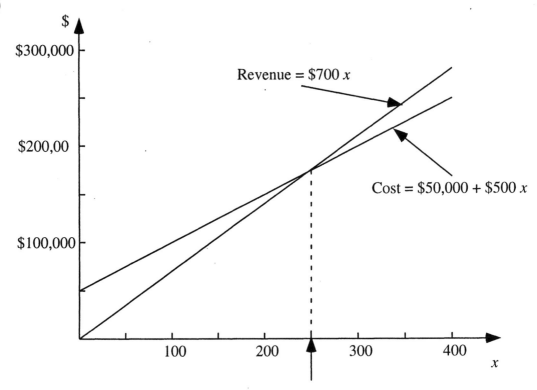

Break-even point = 250 units

b) Profit = -$50,000 + $200 x = 0
    $200 x = $50,000
    x = 250

c)
$$\text{Maximize Profit} = \begin{cases} 0, & \text{if } x = 0 \\ -\$50,000 + \$200x & \text{if } x > 0, \end{cases}$$

subject to

$$x \leq s,$$
$$x \geq 0.$$

d)

Data	
Unit Revenue =	$700
Fixed Cost =	$50,000
Marginal Cost =	$500
Sales Forecast =	300

Production Quantity =	300

Results	
Total Revenue =	$210,000
Total Fixed Cost =	$50,000
Total Variable Cost =	$150,000
Profit (Loss) =	$10,000

Break-Even Point =	250

e)

Data	
Unit Revenue =	$700
Fixed Cost =	$50,000
Marginal Cost =	$500
Sales Forecast =	200

| Production Quantity = | 0 |

Results	
Total Revenue =	$0
Total Fixed Cost =	$0
Total Variable Cost =	$0
Profit (Loss) =	$0

| Break-Even Point = | 250 |

1.4 a)

Data	
Unit Revenue =	$900
Fixed Cost =	$0
Marginal Cost =	$650
Sales Forecast =	300

| Production Quantity = | 300 |

Results	
Total Revenue =	$270,000
Total Fixed Cost =	$0
Total Variable Cost =	$195,000
Profit (Loss) =	$75,000

| Break-Even Point = | 0 |

b) The make option appears to be better ($100,000 profit for the *make option* vs. $75,000 profit for the *buy option*).

c) x = number of grandfather clocks to produce for sale

$$\text{Make option:} \quad \text{Profit} = \begin{cases} 0, & \text{if } x = 0 \\ -\$50,000 + \$500x & \text{if } x > 0 \end{cases}$$

Buy option: Profit = ($900 - 650)$x$ = 250x$.

Incremental profit from choosing make option rather than buy option =

$$\begin{cases} 0, & \text{if } x = 0 \\ -\$50,000 + \$500x - \$250x = -\$50,000 + \$250x, & \text{if } x > 0 \end{cases}$$

Mathematical model:
Now interpret x as the number to produce with the make option. The model is to find the value of x so as to

$$\text{Maximize Incremental Profit} = \begin{cases} 0, & \text{if } x = 0 \\ -\$50,000 + \$250x & \text{if } x > 0 \end{cases}$$

subject to

$x \leq s$, (sales forecast)

$x \geq 0$.

d)

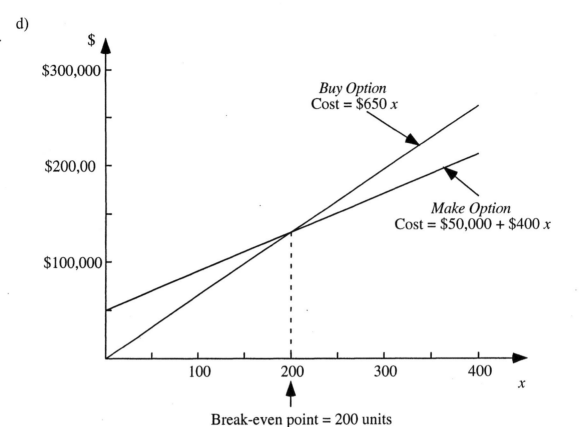

Break-even point = 200 units

e) Make-option cost = $50,000 + $400x
Buy-option cost = $650x

$$\text{Break - even point} = \frac{\$50,000}{\$650 - \$400} = 200 \text{ units.}$$

f)

Data	
Unit Revenue =	$900
Fixed Cost (Make) =	$50,000
Marginal Cost (Make) =	$400
Marginal Cost (Buy) =	$650
Sales Forecast =	300

Production Quantity =	300

Results	
Total Revenue =	$270,000
Total Fixed Cost =	$50,000
Total Variable Cost =	$120,000
Profit (Loss) =	$100,000
Break-Even Point =	200

If s ≤ 200, then set $x = 0$ (so buy s instead of make).
If s > 200, then set $x = s$ (so make option with $x = s$).
Since s = 300, use make option and produce 300 grandfather clocks.

CHAPTER 2
LINEAR PROGRAMMING: BASIC CONCEPTS

Teaching notes for this chapter are available in the Teaching Notes section near the front of this Instructor's Manual.

Review Questions

2.1-1   Ponderosa Industrial uses linear programming monthly to guide the product-mix decision.

2.1-2   Overall profitability has increased by 20%. Better utilization of raw material, capital equipment, and personnel also resulted.

2.1-3   The goal was to improve the utilization of reservation personnel by matching work schedules to customer needs.

2.1-4   United Airlines saved more than $6 million annually in direct salary and benefit costs. Customer service also improved and workloads were reduced for support staff.

2.1-5   The SDM system is used to coordinate the supply, distribution and marketing of each of Citgo's major products throughout the United States.

2.1-6   Citgo saved about $14 million annually in interest expenses. Improvements in coordination, pricing, and purchasing decisions added at least $2.5 million more to annual profits.

2.2-1   They provide the highest quality available in the industry for the most discriminating buyers.

2.2-2   1) Should the company launch the two new products?

   2) What should be the product mix for the two new products?

2.2-3   The group was asked to analyze product mix.

2.2-4   Which combination of production rates for the two new products would maximize the total profit from both of them.

2.2-5   1) available production capacity in each of the plants

   2) how much of the production capacity in each plant would be needed by each product

   3) profitability of each product

2.3-1   1) What are the decisions to be made?

   2) What are the constraints on these decisions?

   3) What is the overall measure of performance for these decisions?

2.3-2   When formulating a linear programming model on a spreadsheet, the cells showing the data for the problem, or levels of a number of activities, are called the data cells. The changing cells are the cells that contain the decisions to be made. The output cells are the cells that provide output that depends on the changing cells. The target cell is a special kind of output cell that shows the overall measure of performance of the decision to be made.

2.3-3   The Excel equation for each output cell can be expressed as a SUMPRODUCT function, where each term in the sum is the product of a data cell and a changing cell.

2.4-1　1)　Gather the relevant data.

2)　Identify the decisions to be made.

3)　Identify the constraints on these decisions.

4)　Identify the overall measure of performance for these decisions.

5)　Convert the verbal description of the constraints and measure of performance into quantitative expressions in terms of the data and decisions

2.4-2　When formulating a linear programming model algebraically, algebraic symbols need to be introduced to represents the measure of performance and the decisions.

2.4-3　A decision variable is an algebraic variable that represents a decision regarding the level of a particular activity. The objective function is the part of a linear programming model that expresses what needs to be either maximized or minimized, depending on the objective for the problem. A nonnegativity constraint is a constraint that express the restriction that a particular decision variable must be greater than or equal to zero. All constraints that are not nonnegativity constraints are referred to as functional constraints.

2.4-4　A feasible solution is one that satisfies all the constraints of the problem. The best feasible solution is called the optimal solution.

2.5-1　The graphical method is used for problems having only two decision variables.

2.5-2　The axes represent production rates for product 1 and product 2.

2.5-3　The line forming the boundary of what is permitted by a constraint is called a constraint boundary line. Its equation is called a constraint boundary equation.

2.5-4　The coefficient of x_1 gives the slope of the constraint boundary line. The constant term gives the value of x_2 where the line intercepts the x_2-axis.

2.5-5　The easiest way to determine which side of the line is permitted is to check whether the origin (0,0) satisfies the constraint. If it does, then the permissible region lies on the side of the constraint where the origin is. Otherwise it lies on the other side.

2.6-1　The "Solver" dialogue box is used to enter the addresses for the target cell and the changing cells.

2.6-2　The "Add Constraint" dialogue box is used to specify the functional constraints for the model.

2.6-3　The Assume Linear Model option and the Assume Non-Negative option normally need to be chosen to solve a linear programming model.

2.7-1　The Profit & Gambit Co. produces cleaning products for home use.

2.7-2　Both television and print media are being considered.

2.7-3　Management's objective is to determine how much to advertise in each medium to meet the market share goals at a minimum total cost.

2.7-4　The rational for the placement of the changing cells is that it is a natural placement since each one is in the column for the corresponding advertising medium and directly under its unit cost. The rationale for the placement of the target cell is that the natural location for this cell is in the Cost row and Totals column.

2.7-5　The objective is to minimize total cost rather than maximize profit. The functional constraints contain $\geq$ rather than $\leq$.

2.7-6　No, the origin (0,0) does not satisfy a $\geq$ functional constraint with a positive right-hand side.

2.7-7 The objective function lines passing through the feasible region should be moved closer to the origin to reach the optimal solution.

2.8-1 No, management generally does not get involved with the technical details of a study.

2.8-2 The graphical method helps a manager develop a good intuitive feeling for the linear programming is.

2.8-3 1) where linear programming is applicable

2) where it should not be applied

3) distinguish between competent and shoddy studies using linear programming.

4) how to interpret the results of a linear programming study.

Problems

2.1 a) The two factors that often hinder the use of optimization models by managers are cultural differences and response time. Cultural differences cause managers and model developers to often have a hard time understanding each other. Response time is often slow due to the time to translate, formulate, and solve the manger's problem using optimization systems.

b) The company shifted from an emphasis on the manufacture of thicker plywoods to thinner plywoods.

c) Ponderosa plans to use optimization in the use of timber for other products also. In addition, optimization may be used for raw material and inventory management and for financial planning.

2.2 a) The shift schedules at airports and reservation offices were done by hand prior to this study.

b) The project requirements were:
(i)   to determine the needs for increased manpower,
(ii) to identify excess manpower for reallocation,
(iii) to reduce the time required for preparing schedules,
(iv) to make manpower allocation more day- and time-sensitive, and
(v)   to quantify the cost associated with scheduling.

c) Flexibility, such as the number of start times, the preferred shift lengths, the length of breaks, the preferred days-off combinations, etc. were considered. This versatility was necessary to satisfy the group culture at each office, which was necessary to gather field support.

d) Benefits included:
(i)   significant labor cost savings,
(ii) improved customer service,
(iii) improved employee schedules,
(iv) quantified manpower planning and evaluation.

2.3 a) During the years preceding this study, the price of crude oil increased tenfold and short-term interest rates more than tripled.

b) Citgo's distribution network of pipelines, tankers, and barges spanned the eastern two-thirds of the United States. They market their products in all of the 48 contiguous states.

c) An 11-week planning horizon, partitioned into six one-week periods and one five-week period, was used.

d) Citgo used an IBM 4381. Typical run times for model generation, solution, and reports were two minutes, half a minute, and seven minutes, respectively.

e) The four types of model users were the product managers, the pricing manager, the product traders, and the budget manager. Product managers compared the model recommendations to the actual operational decisions to determine the existence and cause of discrepancies. They also used the model's what-if capabilities to generate economically viable alternatives to current and forecasted operations. The pricing manager used the model to set ranges for terminal prices for each product and to help set prices and recommend volumes for bulk sales made to reduce excess inventories. Product traders used the model to determine which side of the trading board they should be on for each product. They also used the model's what-if capabilities to determine the sensitivity of spot prices to the required purchases or sales volumes as prices fluctuated during the week. The budget manager used the Financial Summary Report to generate various components of the monthly and quarterly budgets.

f) The major reports generated by the SDM system are:
   (i) Infeasibility report,
   (ii) In-transit, Terminal, Exchange, Inventory reports,
   (iii) Spot recommendation report,
   (iv) Purchases, Sales, Trades reports,
   (v) Wholesale report,
   (vi) Volume summary report,
   (vii) Financial summary report.

g) The education of the users was a challenge in addition to the collection, validation, and correction of input data for the model. Another challenge concerned the forecasting sales volumes and wholesales prices. Citgo forecasted for monthly and quarterly budgets, while SDM systems needed weekly forecasts.

h) Direct benefits were:
   (i) the reduction in Citgo's product inventory with no drop in service levels, and
   (ii) operational decision making improved.

   Indirect benefits were:
   (i) the establishment of a corporate database, which provided common, up-to-date, on-line, operational information for current decision, support
   (ii) the utilization of a single forecast throughout the different departments, which kept the entire organization, focused,
   (iii) the closed-loop planning process fostered by the continual feedback provided by the project manager, when comparing actual decision to model recommended decision,
   (iv) increased interdepartmental communication, and
   (v) the insight gained from the modeling process itself.

2.4 a & b)

	Hours Used Per Unit Produced				Hours Available
	Doors	Windows	Totals		
Plant 1	1	0	4	≤	4
Plant 2	0	2	6	≤	12
Plant 3	3	2	18	≤	18
Unit Profit	$600	$300	$3,300		
Solution	4	3			

c)

Maximize $P = 600D + 300W$,

subject to

$D \leq 4$

$2W \leq 12$

$3D + 2W \leq 18$

and

$D \geq 0, \ W \geq 0.$

d) Optimal Solution: $(D, W) = (x_1, x_2) = (4, 3)$ and $P = 3300$.

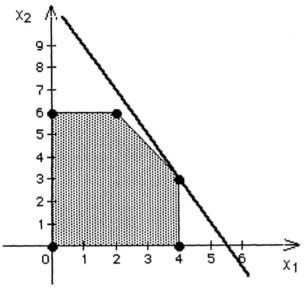

2.5 a) Optimal Solution: $(D, W) = (x_1, x_2) = \left(1\frac{2}{3}, 6\frac{1}{2}\right)$ and $P = 3750$.

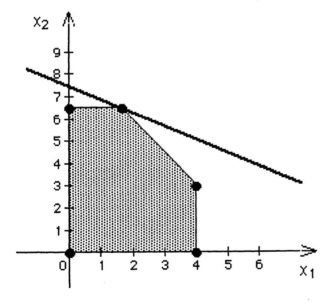

b) Optimal Solution: $(D, W) = (x_1, x_2) = \left(1\frac{1}{3}, 7\right)$ and $P = 3900$.

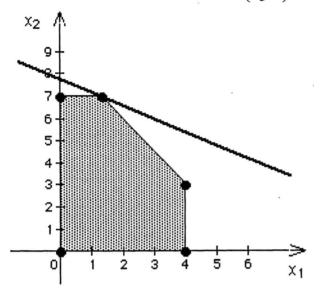

c) Optimal Solution: $(D, W) = (x_1, x_2) = \left(1, 7\frac{1}{2}\right)$ and $P = 4050$.

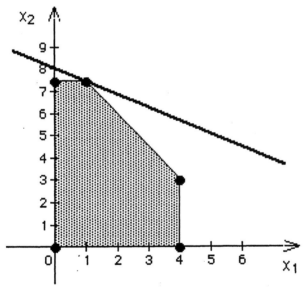

d) Each additional hour per week would increase total profit by $150.

2.6 a)

| | Hours Used Per Unit Produced | | | | Hours |
	Doors	Windows	Totals		Available
Plant 1	1	0	1.6667	≤	4
Plant 2	0	2	13	≤	13
Plant 3	3	2	18	≤	18
Unit Profit	$300	$500	$3,750		
Solution	1.667	6.5			

b)

	Hours Used Per Unit Produced				Hours
	Doors	Windows	Totals		Available
Plant 1	1	0	1.3333	≤	4
Plant 2	0	2	14	≤	14
Plant 3	3	2	18	≤	18
Unit Profit	$300	$500	$3,900		
Solution	1.333	7			

c)

	Hours Used Per Unit Produced				Hours
	Doors	Windows	Totals		Available
Plant 1	1	0	1	≤	4
Plant 2	0	2	15	≤	15
Plant 3	3	2	18	≤	18
Unit Profit	$300	$500	$4,050		
Solution	1	7.5			

d) Each additional hour per week would increase total profit by $150.

2.7   a & b)

	Resources Used Per Unit Produced				Resource
Resource	Product A	Product B	Totals		Available
Q	2	1	2	≤	2
R	1	2	2	≤	2
S	3	3	4	≤	4
Unit Profit	$3,000	$2,000	$3,333		
Solution	1	0.667			

c)

Maximize $P = 3A + 2B,$

subject to $2A + B \le 2$

              $A + 2B \le 2$

              $3A + 3B \le 4$

and $A \ge 0, \ B \ge 0.$

d) Optimal Solution: $(A, B) = (x_1, x_2) = \left(\frac{2}{3}, \frac{2}{3}\right)$ and $P = 3.33$.

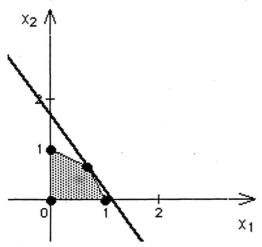

2.8 a) As in the Wyndor Glass Co. problem, we want to find the optimal levels of two activities that compete for limited resources. We want to find the optimal mix of the two activities. Let x_1 be the fraction purchased of the partnership in the first friends venture. Let x_2 be the fraction purchased of the partnership in the second friends venture. The following table gives the data for the problem:

Resource	Resource Usage per Unit of Activity		Amount of Resource Available
	1	2	
Fraction of partnership in first friends venture	1	0	1
Fraction of partnership in second friends venture	0	1	1
Money	$5000	$4000	$6000
Summer Work Hours	400	500	600
Unit Profit	$4500	$4500	

b) The decisions to be made are how much, if any, to participate in each venture. The constraints on the decisions are that you can't become more than a full partner in either venture, that your money is limited to $6,000, and time is limited to 600 hours. In addition, negative involvement is not possible. The overall measure of performance for the decisions is the profit to be made.

c) First venture: (fraction of 1st) ≤ 1
    Second venture: (fraction of 2nd) ≤ 1
    Money: 5000 (fraction of 1st) + 4000 (fraction of 2nd) ≤ 6000
    Hours: 400 (fraction of 1st) + 500 (fraction of 2nd) ≤ 600
    Nonnegativity: (fraction of 1st) ≥ 0, (fraction of 2nd) ≥ 0

    Profit = $4500 (fraction of 1st) + $4500 (fraction of 2nd)

d & e)

	A	B	C	D	E	F
1		Resource Usage Per Unit of Each Activity				
2		Activity				Resource
3	Resource	1	2	Totals		Available
4	Fraction of 1st	1	0	0.667	≤	1
5	Fraction of 2nd	0	1	0.667	≤	1
6	Money	5000	4000	6000.00	≤	6000
7	Work Hours	400	500	600	≤	600
8	Unit Profit	4500	4500	$ 6,000.00		
9	Solution	0.667	0.667			

Data cells: B4:C8 and F4:F7
Changing cells: B9:C9
Target cell: D8
Output cells: D4:D7

	D
4	=SUMPRODUCT(B4:C4,B9:C9)
5	=SUMPRODUCT(B5:C5,B9:C9)
6	=SUMPRODUCT(B6:C6,B9:C9)
7	=SUMPRODUCT(B7:C7,B9:C9)
8	=SUMPRODUCT(B8:C8,B9:C9)

f) This is a linear programming model because the decisions are represented by changing
cells that can have any value that satisfy the constraints. Each constraint has an output
cell on the left, a mathematical sign in the middle, and a data cell on the right. The overall
level of performance is represented by the target cell and the objective is to maximize that
cell. Also, the Excel equation for each output cell is expressed as a SUMPRODUCT
function where each term in the sum is the product of a data cell and a changing cell.

g)

Maximize $P = 4500x_1 + 4500x_2$,

subject to $x_1 \leq 1$

$x_2 \leq 1$

$5000x_1 + 4000x_2 \leq 6000$

$400x_1 + 500x_2 \leq 600$

and $x_1 \geq 0, \; x_2 \geq 0.$

h) Algebraic Version
   decision variables: x_1, x_2
   functional constraints:

$$x_1 \le 1$$

$$x_2 \le 1$$

$$5000x_1 + 4000x_2 \le 6000$$

$$400x_1 + 500x_2 \le 600$$

   objective function: Maximize $P = 4500x_1 + 4500x_2$,
   parameters: all of the numbers in the above algebraic model
   nonnegativity constraints: $x_1 \ge 0,\ x_2 \ge 0$

   Spreadsheet Version
   decision variables: B9:C9
   functional constraints: D4:F7
   objective function: D8
   parameters: B4:C8 and F4:F7
   nonnegativity constraints: "Assume nonnegativity" in the Options of the Solver

i) Optimal Solution: $(x_1, x_2) = \left(\dfrac{2}{3}, \dfrac{2}{3}\right)$ and $P = 6000$.

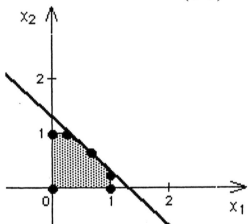

2.9   a) objective function $P = x_1 + 2x_2$
   functional constraints

$$x_1 + x_2 \le 5$$

$$x_1 + 3x_2 \le 9$$

   nonnegativity constraints $x_1 \ge 0, x_2 \ge 0$

   b & e)

Resource Usage Per Unit of Each Activity

Resource	Activity 1	2	Totals		Resource Available
1	1	1	5	≤	5
2	1	3	9	≤	9
Unit Profit	1	2	$ 7.00		
Solution	3	2			

c) Yes.

d) No.

f) Optimal Solution: $(x_1, x_2) = (3, 2)$ and $P = 7$.

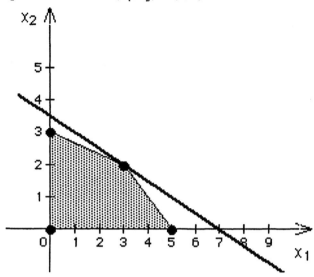

2.10 a) objective function $P = 3x_1 + 2x_2$
   functional constraints
   $$3x_1 + x_2 \leq 9$$
   $$x_1 + 2x_2 \leq 8$$
   nonnegativity constraints $x_1 \geq 0,\ x_2 \geq 0$

b & f)

	Resource Usage Per Unit of Each Activity				
	Activity			Resource	
Resource	1	2	Totals	Available	
1	3	1	9	$\leq$	9
2	1	2	8	$\leq$	8
Unit Profit	3	2	$ 12.00		
Solution	2	3			

c) Yes.

d) Yes.

e) No.

g) Optimal Solution: $(x_1, x_2) = (2,3)$ and $P = 12$.

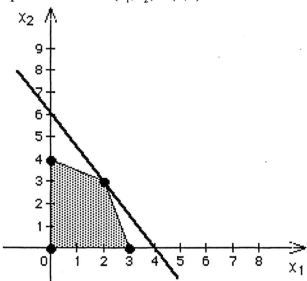

2.11 a) As in the Wyndor Glass Co. problem, we want to find the optimal levels of two activities that compete for limited resources. We want to find the optimal mix of the two activities.

Let W be the number of wood-framed windows to produce.
Let A be the number of aluminum-framed windows to produce.

The following table gives the data for the problem:

Resource	Resource Usage per Unit of Activity		Amount of Resource Available
	wood-framed	aluminum-framed	
glass	6	8	48
aluminum	0	1	4
wood	1	0	6
Unit Profit	$60	$30	

b) The decisions to be made are how many windows of each type to produce. The constraints on the decisions are the amounts of glass, aluminum and wood available. In addition, negative production levels are not possible. The overall measure of performance for the decisions is the profit to be made.

c) glass: 6 (#wood-framed) + 8 (# aluminum-framed) ≤ 48
   aluminum: 1 (# aluminum-framed) ≤ 4
   wood: 1 (#wood-framed) ≤ 6
   Nonnegativity: (#wood-framed) ≥ 0, (# aluminum-framed) ≥ 0

Profit = $60 (#wood-framed) + $30 (# aluminum-framed)

d & e)

	A	B	C	D	E	F
1		Resources Used Per Unit Produced				Resource
2	Resource	wood-framed	aluminum-framed	Totals		Available
3	glass	6	8	48	≤	48
4	aluminum	0	1	1.5	≤	4
5	wood	1	0	6	≤	6
6	Unit Profit	$60	$30	$405		
7	Solution	6	1.500			

Data cells: B3:C6 and F3:F5
Changing cells: B7:C7
Target cell: D6
Output cells: D3:D6

	D
3	=SUMPRODUCT(B3:C3,B7:C7)
4	=SUMPRODUCT(B4:C4,B7:C7)
5	=SUMPRODUCT(B5:C5,B7:C7)
6	=SUMPRODUCT(B6:C6,B7:C7)

f) This is a linear programming model because the decisions are represented by changing cells that can have any value that satisfy the constraints. Each constraint has an output cell on the left, a mathematical sign in the middle, and a data cell on the right. The overall level of performance is represented by the target cell and the objective is to maximize that cell. Also, the Excel equation for each output cell is expressed as a SUMPRODUCT function where each term in the sum is the product of a data cell and a changing cell.

g)

Maximize $P = 60W + 30A$,

subject to $6W + 8A \le 48$

$W \le 6$

$A \le 4$

and $W \ge 0, \ A \ge 0.$

h) Algebraic Version
decision variables: W, A
functional constraints:

$6W + 8A \le 48$

$W \le 6$

$A \le 4$

objective function: Maximize $P = 60W + 30A$
parameters: all of the numbers in the above algebraic model
nonnegativity constraints: $W \ge 0, \ A \ge 0$

Spreadsheet Version
decision variables: B7:C7
functional constraints: D3:F6
objective function: D6
parameters: B3:C6 and F3:F5
nonnegativity constraints: "Assume nonnegativity" in the Options of the Solver

i) Optimal Solution: $(W, A) = (x_1, x_2) = \left(6, 1\frac{1}{2}\right)$ and $P = 405$.

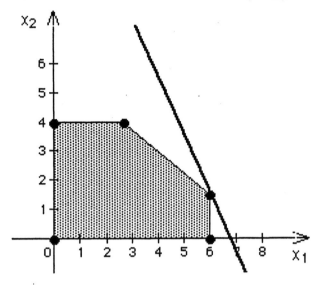

j)

Resource	Resources Used Per Unit Produced		Totals		Resource Available
	wood-framed	aluminum-framed			
glass	6	8	48	≤	48
aluminum	0	1	1.5	≤	4
wood	1	0	6	≤	6
Unit Profit	$40	$30	$285		
Solution	6	1.5			

Resource	Resources Used Per Unit Produced		Totals		Resource Available
	wood-framed	aluminum-framed			
glass	6	8	48	≤	48
aluminum	0	1	4	≤	4
wood	1	0	2.66667	≤	6
Unit Profit	$20	$30	$173		
Solution	3	4			

k)

Resource	Resources Used Per Unit Produced		Totals		Resource Available
	wood-framed	aluminum-framed			
glass	6	8	48	≤	48
aluminum	0	1	2.25	≤	4
wood	1	0	5	≤	5
Unit Profit	$60	$30	$368		
Solution	5	2.25			

2.12 a)

	27" sets	20" sets	Totals		
work hours	20	10	500	≤	500
27" sales	1	0	20	≤	40
20" sales	0	1	10	≤	10
Unit Profit	$120	$80	$3,200		
Solution	20	10			

b) Let x_1 = number of 27" TV sets to be produced per month
   Let x_2 = number of 20" TV sets to be produced per month
   Maximize $P = 120x_1 + 80x_2$,

   subject to $\quad 20x_1 + 10x_2 \le 500$

   $\qquad\qquad\quad x_1 \le 40$

   $\qquad\qquad\quad x_2 \le 10$

   and $\qquad\quad x_1 \ge 0, \ x_2 \ge 0.$

c) Optimal Solution: $(x_1, x_2) = (20, 10)$ and $P = 3200$.

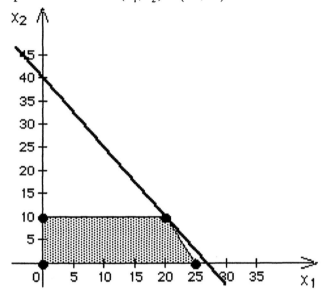

2.13 a) If $x_2 = 0$ then $x_1 = 2$. If $x_1 = 0$ then $x_2 = 4$.

   b)

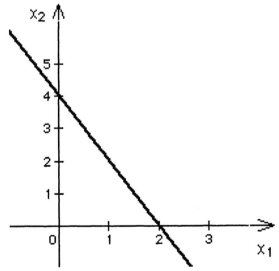

   c) slope = -2

d) $x_2 = -2x_1 + 4$ slope = -2 x_2 intercept = 4

2.14   a)   If $x_2 = 0$ then $x_1 = 5$. If $x_1 = 0$ then $x_2 = 2$.

      b)

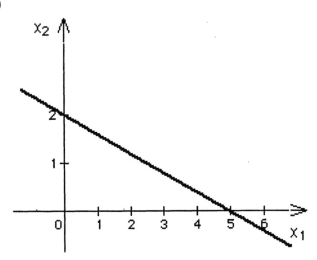

      c)   slope = $-\dfrac{2}{5}$

      d) $x_2 = -\dfrac{2}{5}x_1 + 2$ slope = $-\dfrac{2}{5}$ x_2 intercept = 2

2.15   a)   If $x_2 = 0$ then $x_1 = 6$. If $x_1 = 0$ then $x_2 = -4$.

      b)

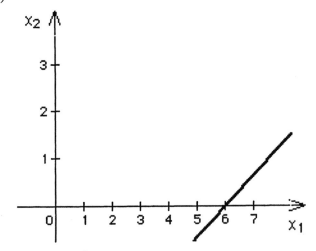

      c)   slope = $-\dfrac{2}{3}$

      d) $x_2 = -\dfrac{2}{3}x_1 - 4$ slope = $-\dfrac{2}{3}$ x_2 intercept = -4

2.16   a)

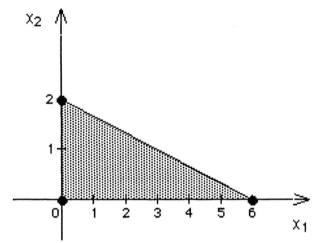

b)

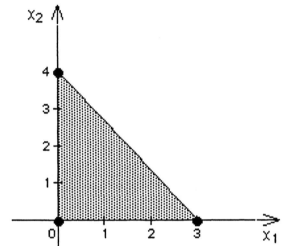

c)

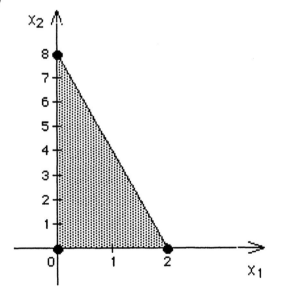

d)

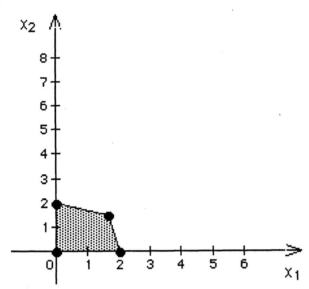

2.17   a)

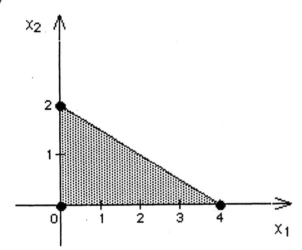

b)

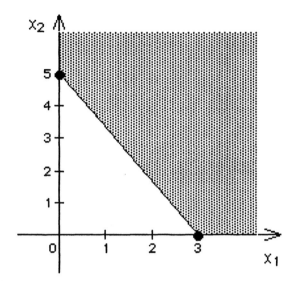

c)

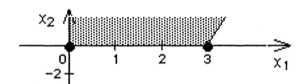

d)

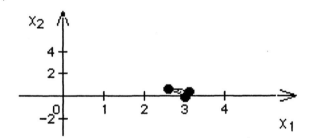

2.18   a)

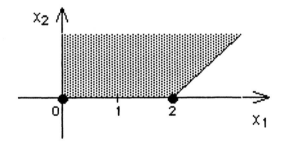

b)

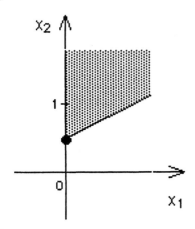

c)

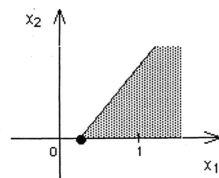

d)

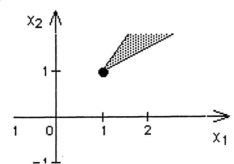

2.19 a) The decisions to be made are how many of each light fixture to produce. The constraints on the decisions are the amounts of frame parts and electrical components available, and the maximum number of product 2 that can be sold (60 units). In addition, negative production levels are not possible. The overall measure of performance for the decisions is the profit to be made.

      b) frame parts: 1 (# product 1) + 3 (# product 2) $\leq$ 200
          electrical components: 2 (# product 1) + 2 (# product 2) $\leq$ 300
          product 2 max.:   1 (# product 2) $\leq$ 60
          Nonnegativity: (# product 1) $\geq$ 0, (# product 2) $\geq$ 0

      Profit = \$1 (# product 1) + \$2 (# product 2)

c)

	product 1	product 2	Totals		
frame parts	1	3	200	≤	200
electrical components	2	2	300	≤	300
product 2 sales	0	1	25	≤	60
Unit Profit	$1	$2	$175		
Solution	125	25			

d) Let x_1 = number of units of product 1 to produce
Let x_2 = number of units of product 2 to produce
Maximize $P = x_1 + 2x_2$,

subject to $\qquad x_1 + 3x_2 \le 200$

$\qquad\qquad\quad 2x_1 + 2x_2 \le 300$

$\qquad\qquad\quad x_2 \le 60$

and $\qquad\qquad x_1 \ge 0,\ x_2 \ge 0.$

e) Optimal Solution: $(x_1, x_2) = (125, 25)$ and $P = 175$.

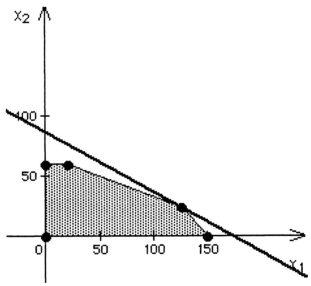

2.20 a) The decisions to be made are what quotas to establish for the two product lines. The constraints on the decisions are the amounts of work hours available in underwriting, administration, and claims. In addition, negative levels are not possible. The overall measure of performance for the decisions is the profit to be made.

b) underwriting: 3 (# special risk) + 2 (# mortgage) ≤ 2400
administration: 1 (# mortgage) ≤ 800
claims: 2 (# special risk) ≤ 1200
Nonnegativity: (# special risk) ≥ 0, (# mortgage) ≥ 0

Profit = $5 (# special risk) + $2 (# mortgage)

c)

| | Hours Used Per Unit | | | | Hours |
	special risk	mortgage	Totals		Available
underwriting	3	2	2400	≤	2400
administration	0	1	300	≤	800
claims	2	0	1200	≤	1200
Unit Profit	$5	$2	$3,600		
Solution	600	300			

d)

Maximize $P = 5S + 2M$,

subject to $\quad 3S + 2M \leq 2400$

$$M \leq 800$$

$$2S \leq 1200$$

and $\quad S \geq 0, \ M \geq 0.$

e) Optimal Solution: $(S, M) = (x_1, x_2) = (600, 300)$ and $P = 3600$.

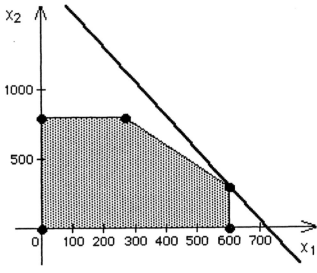

2.21 a)

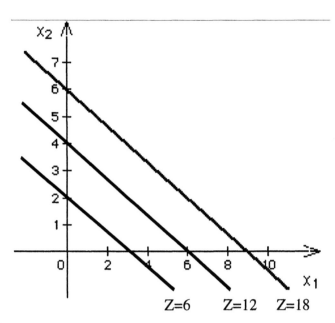

Z=6   Z=12   Z=18

b)

	slope-intercept form	slope	x_2 intercept
Z=6	$x_2 = -\dfrac{2}{3}x_1 + 2$	$-\dfrac{2}{3}$	2
Z=12	$x_2 = -\dfrac{2}{3}x_1 + 4$	$-\dfrac{2}{3}$	4
Z=18	$x_2 = -\dfrac{2}{3}x_1 + 6$	$-\dfrac{2}{3}$	6

2.22 a)

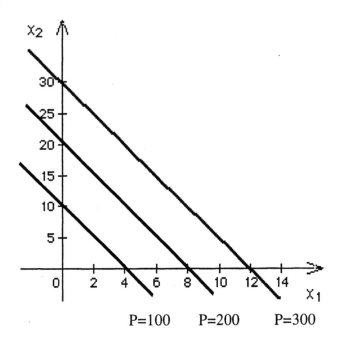

P=100   P=200   P=300

b)

	slope-intercept form	slope	x_2 intercept
Z=100	$x_2 = -\dfrac{5}{2}x_1 + 10$	$-\dfrac{5}{2}$	10
Z=200	$x_2 = -\dfrac{5}{2}x_1 + 20$	$-\dfrac{5}{2}$	20
Z=300	$x_2 = -\dfrac{5}{2}x_1 + 30$	$-\dfrac{5}{2}$	30

2.23 a)

Cost=100   200   300

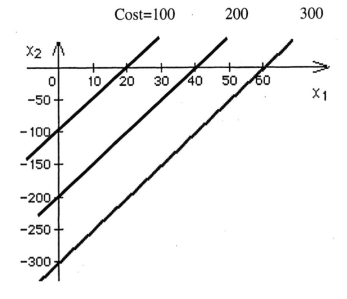

b)

	slope-intercept form	slope	x_2 intercept
Z=300	$x_2 = 5x_1 - 300$	5	-300
Z=200	$x_2 = 5x_1 - 200$	5	-200
Z=100	$x_2 = 5x_1 - 100$	5	-100

2.24 a) $x_2 = -\dfrac{1}{2}x_1 + 10$

b) slope $= -\dfrac{1}{2}$ x_2 intercept $= 10$

c)

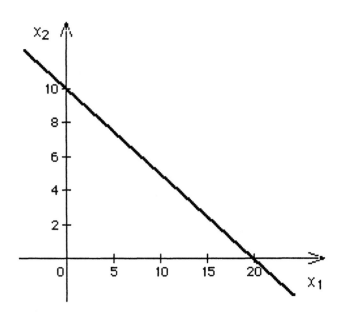

2.25 $x_2 = -\dfrac{8}{5}x_1 + 8$

2.26 a) $x_2 = -2x_1 + 4$

b) $x_2 = \dfrac{2}{3}x_1 + 2$

c) $x_2 = 2\dfrac{1}{2}x_1 - 5$

2.27 a) $x_1 - 2x_2 = 0$

b) $x_2 = \dfrac{1}{2}x_1$

c) slope $= \dfrac{1}{2}$ x_2 intercept $= 0$

d)

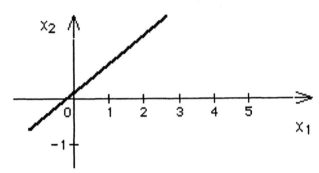

e) The area above the constraint boundary line is permitted by the constraint.

2.28   a)   Optimal Solution: $(x_1, x_2) = (0, 7)$ and $P = 70$.

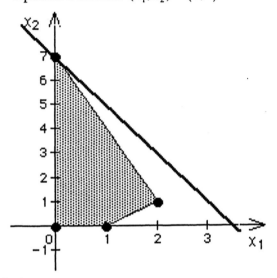

b & c)

Resource	Resources Used Per Unit Produced 1	2	Totals		Resource Available
A	1	-1	-7	≤	1
B	3	1	7	≤	7
Unit Profit	$20	$10	$70		
Solution	0	7			

2.29 a) Optimal Solution: $(x_1, x_2) = (13, 5)$ and $P = 31$.

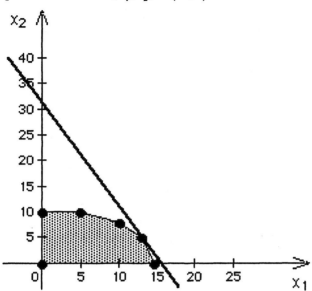

b & c)

	Resource Usage Per Unit of Each Activity				
	Activity				Resource
Resource	1	2	Totals		Available
1	0	1	5	≤	10
2	2	5	51	≤	60
3	1	1	18	≤	18
4	3	1	44	≤	44
Unit Profit	2	1	$ 31.00		
Solution	13	5			

2.30 a) Optimal Solution: $(x_1, x_2) = (2, 6)$ and $P = 18$.

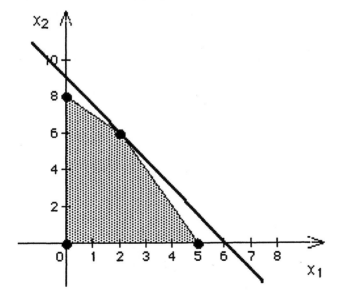

b & c)

Resource Usage Per Unit of Each Activity

Resource	Activity 1	2	Totals		Resource Available
1	1	1	8	≤	8
2	2	1	1 0	≤	1 0
Unit Profit	3	2	$ 18.00		
Solution	2	6			

2.31 a) Optimal Solution: $(x_1, x_2) = (3,9)$ and $P = 210$.

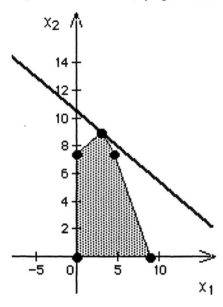

b & c)

Resource Usage Per Unit of Each Activity

Resource	Activity 1	2	Totals		Resource Available
1	-1	2	15	≤	1 5
2	1	1	12	≤	1 2
3	5	3	42	≤	4 5
Unit Profit	10	20	$ 210.00		
Solution	3	9			

2.32   Optimal Solution: $(x_1, x_2) = \left(3\frac{1}{3}, 3\frac{1}{3}\right)$ and $P = 3000$.

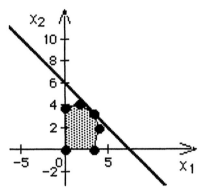

2.33   a)   The decisions to be made are how many hotdogs and buns should be produced. The constraints on the decisions are the amounts of flour and pork available, and the hours available to work. In addition, negative production levels are not possible. The overall measure of performance for the decisions is the profit to be made.

b)   flour: 0.1 (# buns) ≤ 200
     pork: 0.25 (# hotdogs) + ≤ 800
     work hours: 3 (# hotdogs) + 2 (# buns) ≤ 12,000
     Nonnegativity: (# hotdogs) ≥ 0, (# buns) ≥0

     Profit = 0.2 (# hotdogs) + 0.1 (# buns)

c)

Resource Usage Per Unit of Each Activity

| | Activity | | | | Resource |
Resource	Hotdogs	Buns	Totals		Available
flour	0	0.1	120	≤	200
pork	0.25	0	800	≤	800
work hours	3	2	12000	≤	12000
Unit Profit	0.2	0.1	$ 760.00		
Solution	3200	1200			

d)

   Maximize $P = 0.2H + 0.1B$,

   subject to $0.1B \le 200$

                    $0.25H \le 800$

                    $3H + 2B \le 12,000$

   and $H \ge 0, \ B \ge 0$.

e) Optimal Solution: $(H, B) = (x_1, x_2) = (3200, 1200)$ and $P = 760$.

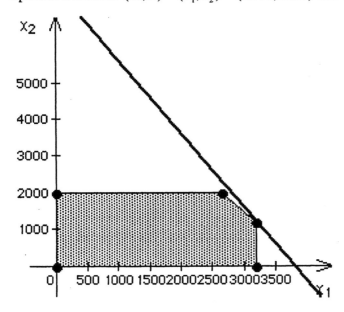

2.34 a)

	Tables	Chairs	Totals		
Oak	50	25	2500	≤	2500
Labor hours	6	6	450	≤	480
Ratio	2	-1	-2.09184E-09	≤	0
Unit Profit	400	100	$ 15,000.00		
Solution	25	50			

b)

Maximize $P = 400T + 100C$,

subject to $\quad 50T + 25C \leq 2500$

$\qquad\qquad 6T + 6C \leq 480$

$\qquad\qquad 2T - C \leq 0$

and $\qquad T \geq 0, \ C \geq 0$.

c) Optimal Solution: $(T, C) = (x_1, x_2) = (25, 50)$ and $P = 15,000$.

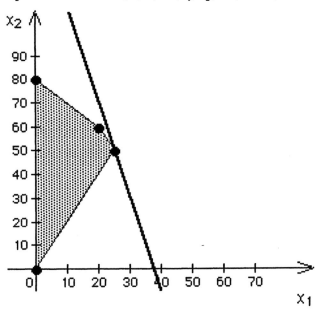

2.35 a)

	Beef	Gravy	Peas	Carrots	Roll	Totals		
Calories	54	20	15	8	40	320	≤	320
Fat Calories	2.8	9	-4.5	-2.4	-2	-43	≤	0

	Beef	Gravy	Peas	Carrots	Roll	Totals		
Calories	54	20	15	8	40	320	≥	280
Vitamin A	0	0	15	350	0	8400	≥	600
Vitamin C	0	1	3	1	0	25	≥	10
Protein	8	0	1	1	1	40	≥	30
Beef	1	0	0	0	0	2	≥	2
Gravy	-0.5	1	0	0	0	0	≥	0
Unit Cost	0.4	0.35	0.15	0.18	0.1	$ 5.47		
Solution	2	1	0	24	0			

2-31

b) Let B = ounces of beef tips,

       G = ounces of gravy,

       P = ounces of peas,

       C = ounces of carrots,

       R = ounces of roll.

Minimize $Z = 0.4B + 0.35G + 0.15P + 0.18C + 0.1R$

subject to

$$54B + 20G + 15P + 8C + 40R \geq 280$$

$$54B + 20G + 15P + 8C + 40R \leq 320$$

$$2.8B + 9G - 4.5P - 2.4C - 2R \leq 0$$

$$15P + 350C \geq 600$$

$$G + 3P + C \geq 10$$

$$8B + P + C + R \geq 30$$

$$B \geq 2$$

$$G - 0.5B \geq 0$$

and

$$B \geq 0, \ G \geq 0, \ P \geq 0, \ C \geq 0, \ R \geq 0.$$

2.36 When $c < \dfrac{1}{2}$ then the optimal solution is $(x_1, x_2) = (0,5)$.

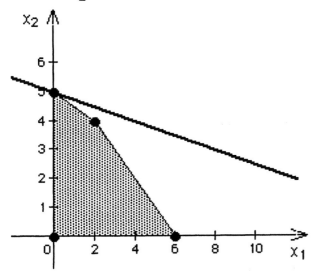

When $c = \dfrac{1}{2}$ then the optimal solutions are $(x_1, x_2) = (0,5)(2,4)$,

and all points on the connecting line.

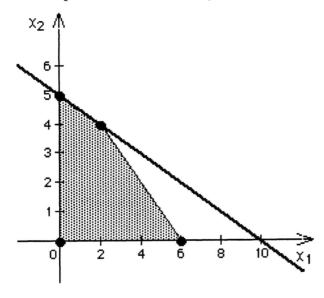

When $\dfrac{1}{2} < c < 1$ then the optimal solution is $(x_1 , x_2) = (2,4)$.

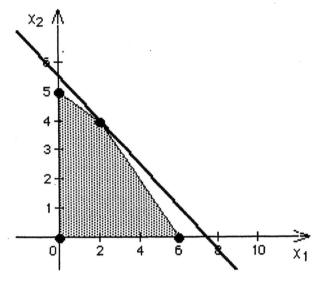

When $c = 1$ then the optimal solutions are $(x_1 , x_2) = (6,0)(2,4)$, and all points on the connecting line.

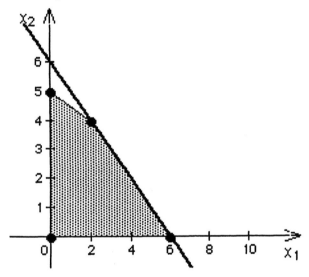

When c > 1 then the optimal solution is $(x_1, x_2) = (6,0)$.

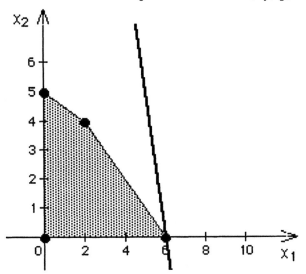

2.37   When $c < -2$ then the optimal solution is $(x_1, x_2) = (2,0)$.

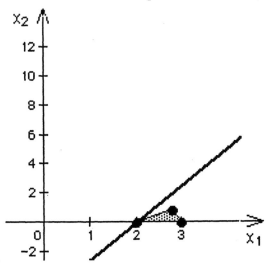

When $c = -2$ then the optimal solutions are $(x_1, x_2) = (2,0), \left(\dfrac{14}{5}, \dfrac{4}{5}\right)$,

and all points on the connecting line.

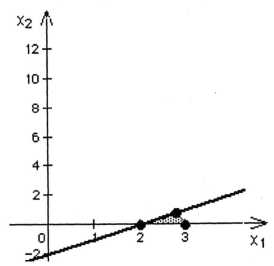

When $-2 < c < 8$ then the optimal solution is $(x_1, x_2) = \left(\dfrac{14}{5}, \dfrac{4}{5}\right)$.

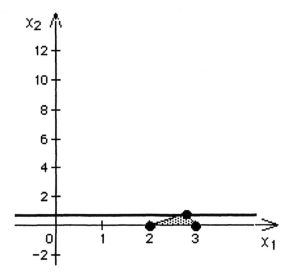

When $c = 8$ then the optimal solutions are $(x_1, x_2) = (3,0), \left(\dfrac{14}{5}, \dfrac{4}{5}\right)$,

and all points on the connecting line.

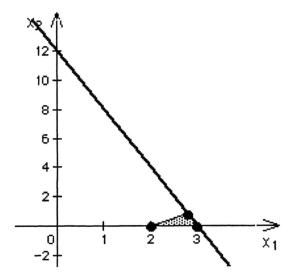

When c > 8 then the optimal solution is $(x_1, x_2) = (3,0)$.

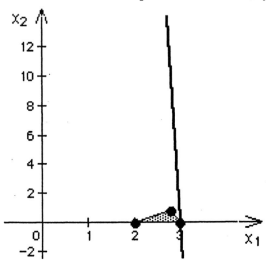

2.38

When $k < \dfrac{1}{2}$ $\left(\text{for example, } k = \dfrac{1}{4} \text{ is graphed below}\right)$ then the optimal solution is

$(x_1, x_2) = \left(\dfrac{2k+3}{k}, 0\right)$. Thus, $(2,3)$ is not optimal for these values of k.

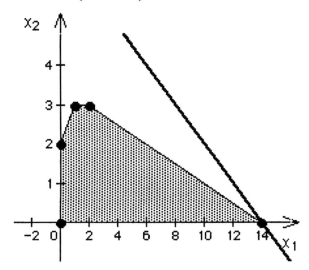

When $k \geq \dfrac{1}{2}$ (for example, $k = 1$ is graphed below) then the

optimal solution is $(x_1, x_2) = (2,3)$.

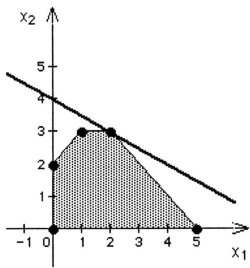

2.39   a)   The decisions to be made are how many servings of steak and potatoes are needed. The constraints on the decisions are the amounts of carbohydrates, protein, and fat that are needed. In addition, negative levels are not possible. The overall measure of performance for the decisions is the cost.

b) carbohydrates: 5 (# steak) + 15 (# potatoes) $\geq$ 50

   protein: 20 (# steak) + 5 (# potatoes) $\geq$ 40

   fat: 15 (# steak) + 2 (# potatoes) $\leq$ 60

   Nonnegativity: (# steak) $\geq$0, (# potatoes) $\geq$ 0

Cost = 4 (# steak) + 2 (# potatoes)

c)

	Contribution Per Unit		Totals		Level
	Steak	Potato			
Carbohydrate	5	15	50	$\geq$	50
Protein	20	5	40	$\geq$	40
Fat	15	2	24.91	$\leq$	60
Unit Cost	4	2	$ 10.91		
Solution	1.3	2.9			

d)

Minimize $C = 4S + 2P$,

   subject to $5S + 15P \geq 50$

                   $20S + 5P \geq 40$

                   $15S + 2P \leq 60$

   and $S \geq 0, \ P \geq 0.$

e)   Optimal Solution: $(S, P) = (x_1, x_2) = (1.3, 2.9)$ and $C = 10.91$.

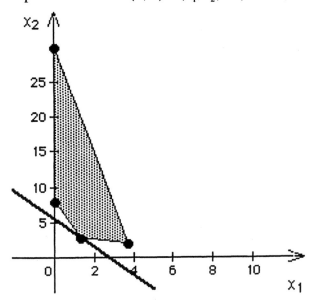

2.40   a)   Optimal Solution: $(x_1, x_2) = (2, 4)$ and $C = 110$.

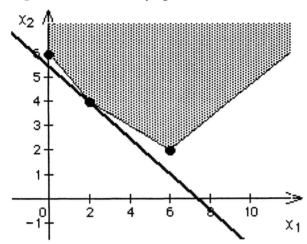

b & c)

Benefit	Activity		Totals		Level
	1	2			
A	1	2	10	≥	10
B	2	-3	-8	≤	6
C	1	1	6	≥	6
Unit Cost	15	20	$ 110.00		
Solution	2	4			

2.41   a)   The decisions to be made are what combination of feed types to use. The constraints on the decisions are the amounts of calories and vitamins needed, and a maximum level for feed type A. In addition, negative levels are not possible. The overall measure of performance for the decisions is the cost.

b)   Calories: 800 (amt. Type A) + 1000 (amt. Type B) ≥ 8000
       Vitamins: 140 (amt. Type A) + 70 (amt. Type B) ≥ 700
       Type A maximum: 0.667 (amt. Type A) – 0.333 (amt. Type B) ≤ 0
       Nonnegativity: (amt. Type A) ≥ 0, (amt. Type B) ≥ 0

       Cost = 0.4 (amt. Type A) + 0.8 (amt. Type B)

c)

	Feed Type A	Feed Type B	Totals		
Calories	800	1000	8000	≥	8000
Vitamins	140	70	799.7429	≥	700
Type A max.	0.667	-0.333	0	≤	0
Unit Cost	0.4	0.8	$ 5.72		
Solution	2.85	5.72			

d)

Minimize $C = 0.4A + 0.8B,$

subject to $\quad 800A + 1000B \geq 8000$

$$140A + 70B \geq 700$$

$$\frac{2}{3}A - \frac{1}{3}B \leq 0$$

and $\quad A \geq 0, \ B \geq 0.$

e) Optimal Solution: $(A, B) = (x_1, x_2) = (2.85, 5.72)$ and $C = 5.72.$

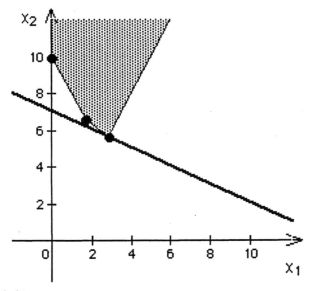

2.42   a & b)

| | Increase in Market Share per Unit of Advertising | | | | Minimum |
| | Advertising Media | | | | Required |
	Television	Print Media	Totals		Increase
Stain Remover	0%	1.5%	5%	$\geq$	3%
Liquid Detergent	3%	4%	18%	$\geq$	18%
Powder Detergent	-1%	2%	4%	$\geq$	4%
Unit Cost ($millions)	1	2	8		
Solution	2	3			

c)

Minimize $C = T + 2P,$

subject to $\quad 1.5P \geq 3$

$$3T + 4P \geq 18$$

$$-1T + 2P \geq 4$$

and $\quad T \geq 0, \ P \geq 0.$

d) Optimal Solution: $(x_1, x_2) = (2,3)$, and $C = 8$.

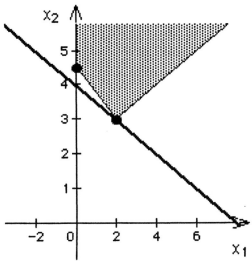

e) Management changed their assessment of how much each type of ad would change market share. For print media, market share will now increase by 1.5% for product 1, 2% for product 2, and 2% for product 3.

f) Given the new data on advertising, I recommend that there be 2 units of advertising on television and 3 units of advertising in the print media. This will minimize cost, with a cost of $8 million, while meeting the minimum increase requirements. Further refining the data may allow us to rework the problem and save even more money while maintaining the desired increases in market share. In addition, when negotiating a decrease in the unit cost of television ads, point out that our new data shows that we should purchase fewer television ads at the current price so they might want to reduce the current price.

2.43 a) Optimal Solution: $(x_1, x_2) = \left(7\frac{1}{2}, 5\right)$ and $C = 550$.

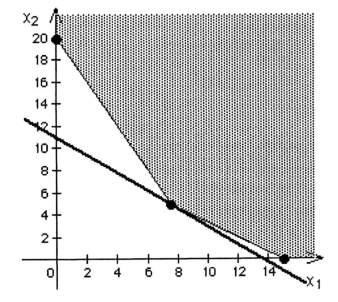

b) Optimal Solution: $(x_1, x_2) = (15, 0)$ and $C = 600$.

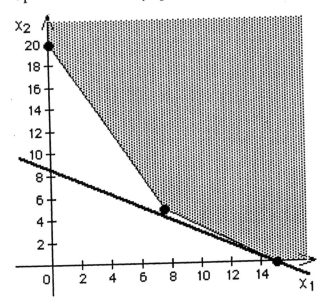

c) Optimal Solution: $(x_1, x_2) = (6, 6)$ and $C = 540$.

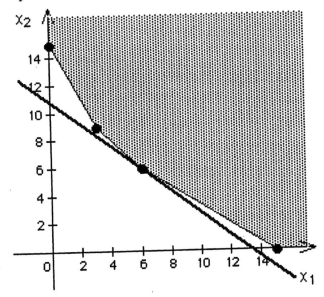

d & e)

	1	2	Totals		
1	2	3	30	$\geq$	30
2	1	1	12	$\geq$	12
3	2	1	20	$\geq$	20
Unit Cost	40	50	550		
Solution	7.5	5			

f) Part b)

	1	2	Totals		
1	2	3	30	≥	30
2	1	1	15	≥	12
3	2	1	30	≥	20
Unit Cost	40	70	600		
Solution	15	0			

Part c)

	1	2	Totals		
1	2	3	30	≥	30
2	1	1	12	≥	12
3	2	1	18	≥	15
Unit Cost	40	50	540		
Solution	6	6			

2.44 a) Optimal Solution: $(x_1, x_2) = (3, 2)$ and $C = 13$.

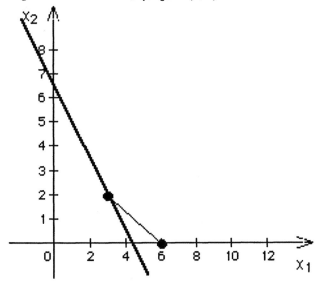

b & c)

	1	2	Totals		
1	1	2	7	≤	12
2	2	3	12	=	12
3	2	1	8	≥	8
Unit Cost	3	2	13		
Solution	3	2			

2.45 a)

Resource	Bread	PB	Jelly	Apples	Milk	Juice	Totals		Maximum Level
Calories	80	100	70	90	120	110	443.0769	≤	500
Fat Calories	15	80	0	0	60	0	128.462	≤	132.923

Benefit	Bread	PB	Jelly	Apples	Milk	Juice	Totals		Minimum Level
Calories	80	100	70	90	120	110	443.0769	≥	300
Vitamin C	0	0	4	6	2	80	60	≥	60
Fiber	4	0	3	10	0	1	11.69231	≥	10
Bread	1	0	0	0	0	0	2	≥	2
Peanut Butter	0	1	0	0	0	0	1	≥	1
Jelly	0	0	1	0	0	0	1	≥	1
Liquid	0	0	0	0	1	1	1	≥	1

	Bread	PB	Jelly	Apples	Milk	Juice		
Unit Cost	6	5	8	35	20	40	$ 58.85	
Solution	2.000	1	1	0	0.30769	0.69231		

b) Let B = slices of bread,
P = Tbsp. of peanut butter,
J = Tbsp. of jelly,
A = number of apples,
M = cups of milk,
C = cups of cranberry juice.

Minimize $C = 6B + 5P + 8J + 35A + 20M + 40C$

subject to

$$80B + 100P + 70J + 90A + 120M + 110C \geq 300$$

$$80B + 100P + 70J + 90A + 120M + 110C \leq 500$$

$$15B + 80P + 60M$$
$$\leq 0.3(80B + 100P + 70J + 90A + 120M + 110C)$$

$$4J + 6A + 2M + 80C \geq 60$$

$$4B + 3J + 10A + C \geq 10$$

$$B \geq 2$$

$$P \geq 1$$

$$J \geq 1$$

$$M + C \geq 1$$

and $B \geq 0,\ P \geq 0,\ J \geq 0,\ A \geq 0,\ M \geq 0,\ C \geq 0.$

Cases

2.1   a)   In this case, we have two decision variables: one variable to determine the number of Family Thrillseekers we should assemble and one variable to determine the number of Classy Cruisers we should assemble. We also have the following three constraints:

1. The plant has a maximum of 48,000 labor hours. Each Thrillseeker requires six labor hours, and each Cruiser requires 10.5 labor hours. The sum of the total number of labor hours required to assemble all Thrillseekers and all Cruisers must be less than or equal to 48,000 hours.

2. The plant has a maximum of 20,000 doors available. Each Thrillseeker requires four doors, and each Cruiser requires two doors. The sum of the total number of doors required to assemble all Thrillseekers and all Cruisers must be less than or equal to 20,000 doors.

3. Because the demand for Cruisers is limited to 3,500 cars, the decision variable for the number of Cruisers we should assemble must be less than or equal to 3,500.

The formulas used in the problem formulation follow.

	A	B	C	D	E	F	G	H
3			Thrillseeker	Cruiser	Totals			Right-Hand
4		Constraint						Side
5		Labor Hours	6	10.5	=SUMPRODUCT(C5:D5,C9:D9)	<	=	48000
6		Doors	4	2	=SUMPRODUCT(C6:D6,C9:D9)	<	=	20000
7		Cruiser Demand	0	1	=SUMPRODUCT(C7:D7,C9:D9)	<	=	3500
8		Profit ($thousands)	3.6	5.4	=SUMPRODUCT(C8:D8,C9:D9)			
9		Solution	3800	2400				

The values used in the problem formulation follow.

	A	B	C	D	E	F	G	H
3			Thrillseeker	Cruiser	Totals			Right-Hand
4		Constraint						Side
5		Labor Hours	6	10.5	48000	<	=	48000
6		Doors	4	2	20000	<	=	20000
7		Cruiser Demand	0	1	2400	<	=	3500
8		Profit ($thousands)	3.6	5.4	26640			
9		Solution	3800	2400				

We specify the following Solver settings.

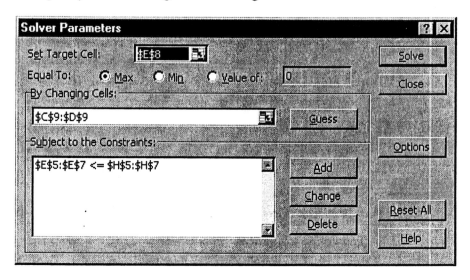

Finally, throughout this case we use the following solver options.

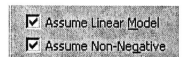

Rachel's plant should assemble 3,800 Thrillseekers and 2,400 Cruisers to obtain a maximum profit of $26,640,000.

b) In part (a) above, we observed that the Cruiser demand constraint was not binding. Therefore, raising the demand for the Cruiser will not change the optimal solution. The marketing campaign should not be undertaken.

c) The new value of the right-hand side of the labor constraint becomes 48,000 * 1.25 = 60,000 labor hours. All formulas and Solver settings used in part (a) remain the same. The values for the problem formulation follow.

	A	B	C	D	E	F	G	H
3			Thrillseeker	Cruiser	Totals			Right-Hand
4		Constraint						Side
5		Labor Hours	6	10.5	56250	<	=	60000
6		Doors	4	2	20000	<	=	20000
7		Cruiser Demand	0	1	3500	<	=	3500
8		Profit ($thousands)	3.6	5.4	30600			
9		Solution	3250	3500				

Rachel's plant should now assemble 3,250 Thrillseekers and 3,500 Cruisers to achieve a maximum profit of $30,600,000.

d) Using over time labor increases the profit by $30,600,000 – $26,640,000 = $3,960,000. Rachel should therefore be willing to pay at most $3,960,000 extra for overtime labor beyond regular time rates.

e) The value of the right-hand side of the Cruiser demand constraint is 3,500 * 1.20 = 4,200 cars. The value of the right-hand side of the labor hour constraint is 48,000 * 1.25 = 60,000 hours. All formulas and Solver settings used in part (a) remain the same. Ignoring the costs of the advertising campaign and overtime labor, the values for the problem formulation follow.

	A	B	C	D	E	F	G	H
3			Thrillseeker	Cruiser	Totals			Right-Hand
4		Constraint						Side
5		Labor Hours	6	10.5	60000	<	=	60000
6		Doors	4	2	20000	<	=	20000
7		Cruiser Demand	0	1	4000	<	=	4200
8		Profit ($thousands)	3.6	5.4	32400			
9		Solution	3000	4000				

Rachel's plant should produce 3,000 Thrillseekers and 4,000 Cruisers for a maximum profit of $32,400,000. This profit excludes the costs of advertising and using overtime labor.

f) The advertising campaign costs $500,000. In the solution to part (e) above, we used the maximum overtime labor available, and the maximum use of overtime labor costs $1,600,000. Thus, our solution in part (e) required an extra $500,000 + $1,600,000 = $2,100,000. We perform the following cost/benefit analysis:

Profit in part (e):	$32,400,000
− Advertising and overtime costs:	$ 2,100,000
	$30,300,000

We compare the $30,300,000 profit with the $26,640,000 profit obtained in part (a) and conclude that the decision to run the advertising campaign and use overtime labor is a very wise, profitable decision.

g) Because we consider this question independently, the values of the right-hand sides for the Cruiser demand constraint and the labor hour constraint are the same as those in part (a). We now change the profit for the Thrillseeker from 3.6 to 2.8 in the problem formulation. All formulas and Solver settings used in part (a) remain the same. The values for the problem formulation follow.

	A	B	C	D	E	F	G	H
3			Thrillseeker	Cruiser	Totals			Right-Hand
4		Constraint						Side
5		Labor Hours	6	10.5	48000	<	=	48000
6		Doors	4	2	14500	<	=	20000
7		Cruiser Demand	0	1	3500	<	=	3500
8		Profit ($thousands)	2.8	5.4	24150			
9		Solution	1875	3500				

Rachel's plant should assemble 1,875 Thrillseekers and 3,500 Cruisers to obtain a maximum profit of $24,150,000.

h) Because we consider this question independently, the profit for the Thrillseeker remains the same as the profit specified in part (a). The labor hour constraint changes. Each Thrillseeker now requires 7.5 hours for assembly. All formulas and Solver settings used in part (a) remain the same. The values for the new problem formulation follow.

	A	B	C	D	E	F	G	H
3			Thrillseeker	Cruiser	Totals			Right-Hand
4		Constraint						Side
5		Labor Hours	7.5	10.5	48000	<	=	48000
6		Doors	4	2	13000	<	=	20000
7		Cruiser Demand	0	1	3500	<	=	3500
8		Profit ($thousands)	3.6	5.4	24300			
9		Solution	1500	3500				

Rachel's plant should assemble 1,500 Thrillseekers and 3,500 Cruisers for a maximum profit of $24,300,000.

i) Because we consider this question independently, we use the problem formulation used in part (a). In this problem, however, the number of Cruisers assembled has to be strictly equal to the total demand. We use the following new Solver settings:

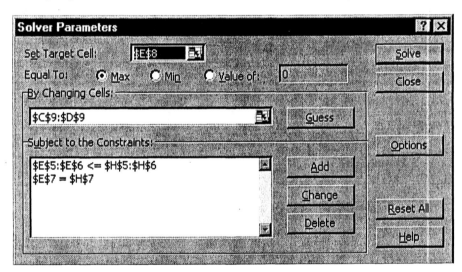

The formulas used in the problem formulation remain the same as those used in part (a). The values used in the problem follow.

	A	B	C	D	E	F	G	H
3			Thrillseeker	Cruiser	Totals			Right-Hand
4		Constraint						Side
5		Labor Hours	6	10.5	48000	<	=	48000
6		Doors	4	2	14500	<	=	20000
7		Cruiser Demand	0	1	3500		=	3500
8		Profit ($thousands)	3.6	5.4	25650			
9		Solution	1875	3500				

The new profit is $25,650,000, which is $26,640,000 – $25,650,000 = $990,000 less than the profit obtained in part (a). This decrease in profit is less than $2,000,000, so Rachel should meet the full demand for the Cruiser.

j) We now combine the new considerations described in parts (f), (g), and (h). In part (f), we decided to use both the advertising campaign and the overtime labor. The advertising campaign raises the demand for the Cruiser to 4,200 sedans, and the overtime labor increases the labor hour capacity of the plant to 60,000 labor hours. In part (g), we decreased the profit generated by a Thrillseeker to $2,800. In part (h), we increased the time to assemble a Thrillseeker to 7.5 hours. Including the increased demand for Cruisers, the increased plant capacity, the decreased unit profit for a Thrillseeker, and the increased time to assemble a Thrillseeker, the new problem is formulated as follows:

	A	B	C	D	E	F	G	H
3			Thrillseeker	Cruiser	Totals			Right-Hand
4		Constraint						Side
5		Labor Hours	7.5	10.5	60000	<	=	60000
6		Doors	4	2	16880	<	=	20000
7		Cruiser Demand	0	1	4200	<	=	4200
8		Profit ($thousands)	2.8	5.4	28616			
9		Solution	2120	4200				

The formulas and Solver settings used for this problem are the same as those used in part (a). Rachel's plant should assemble 2,120 Thrillseekers and 4,200 Cruisers for a maximum profit of $28,616,000 – $2,100,000 = $26,516,000.

2.2   a)   We want to determine the amount of potatoes and green beans Maria should purchase to minimize ingredient costs. We have two decision variables: one variable to represent the amount (in pounds) of potatoes Maria should purchase and one variable to represent the amount (in pounds) of green beans Maria should purchase. We also have constraints on nutrition, taste, and weight.

Nutrition Constraints
1. We first need to ensure that the dish has 180 grams of protein. We are told that 100 grams of potatoes have 1.5 grams of protein and 10 ounces of green beans have 5.67 grams of protein. Since we have decided to measure our decision variables in pounds, however, we need to determine the grams of protein in one pound of each ingredient.

We perform the following conversion for potatoes:

$$100\text{g of potatoes}\left(\frac{1\text{ lb}}{453.6\text{g}}\right) = 0.220459 \text{ lb of potatoes}$$

$$\frac{1.5\text{g of protein}}{0.22046\text{ lb of potatoes}} = \frac{6.804\text{g of protein}}{1\text{ lb of potatoes}}$$

We perform the following conversion for green beans:

$$10\text{ oz of green beans}\left(\frac{28.35\text{ g}}{1\text{ oz}}\right) = 283.5 \text{ g of green beans}$$

$$283.5\text{ g of green beans}\left(\frac{1\text{ lb}}{453.6\text{ g}}\right) = 0.625 \text{ lb of green beans}$$

$$\frac{5.67\text{ g of protein}}{0.625\text{ lb of green beans}} = \frac{9.072\text{ g of protein}}{1\text{ lb of green beans}}$$

The total grams of protein in the potatoes and green beans Maria purchases for the casserole must be greater than or equal to 180 grams.

2. We next need to ensure that the dish has 80 milligrams of iron. We are told that 100 grams of potatoes have 0.3 milligrams of iron and 10 ounces of green beans have 3.402 milligrams of iron. Since we have decided to measure our decision variables in pounds, however, we need to determine the milligrams of iron in one pound of each ingredient.

We perform the following conversion for potatoes:

$$\frac{0.3\text{ mg of iron}}{0.22046\text{ lb of potatoes}} = \frac{1.3608\text{ mg of iron}}{1\text{ lb of potatoes}}$$

We perform the following conversion for green beans:

$$\frac{0.3402\text{ mg of iron}}{0.625\text{ lb of green beans}} = \frac{5.4432\text{ mg of iron}}{1\text{ lb of green beans}}$$

The total milligrams of iron in the potatoes and green beans Maria purchases for the casserole must be greater than or equal to 80 milligrams.

3. We next need to ensure that the dish has 1,050 milligrams of vitamin C. We are told that 100 grams of potatoes have 12 milligrams of vitamin C and 10 ounces of green beans have 28.35 milligrams of vitamin C. Since we have decided to measure our decision variables in pounds, however, we need to determine the milligrams of vitamin C in one pound of each ingredient.

We perform the following conversion for potatoes:

$$\frac{12 \text{ mg of vitamin C}}{0.22046 \text{ lb of potatoes}} = \frac{54.432 \text{ mg of vitamin C}}{1 \text{ lb of potatoes}}$$

We perform the following conversion for green beans:

$$\frac{28.35 \text{ mg of vitamin C}}{0.625 \text{ lb of green beans}} = \frac{45.36 \text{ mg of vitamin C}}{1 \text{ lb of green beans}}$$

The total milligrams of vitamin C in the potatoes and green beans Maria purchases for the casserole must be greater than or equal to 1,050 milligrams.

Taste Constraint
Edson requires that the casserole contain at least a six to five ratio in the weight of potatoes to green beans. We have:

$$\frac{\text{pounds of potatoes}}{\text{pounds of green beans}} > \frac{6}{5}$$

$$5 \text{ (pounds of potatoes)} > 6 \text{ (pounds of green beans)}$$

Weight Constraint
Finally, Maria requires a minimum of 10 kilograms of potatoes and green beans together. Because we measure potatoes and green beans in pounds, we must perform the following conversion:

$$10 \text{ kg of potatoes and green beans} \left(\frac{1000 \text{ g}}{1 \text{ kg}} \right) \left(\frac{1 \text{ lb}}{453.6 \text{ g}} \right)$$

$$= 22.046 \text{ lb of potatoes and green beans}$$

The amount of potatoes and green beans Maria purchases must weigh 22.046 pounds or more.

The formulas used in the problem formulation follow.

	A	B	C	D	E	F	G	H
3			Potatoes	Green Beans	Totals			Right-Hand
4		Constraint						Side
5		Protein (g)	6.804	9.072	=SUMPRODUCT(C5:D5,C11:D11)	>	=	180
6		Iron (mg)	1.3608	5.4432	=SUMPRODUCT(C6:D6,C11:D11)	>	=	80
7		Vitamin C (mg)	54.432	45.36	=SUMPRODUCT(C7:D7,C11:D11)	>	=	1050
8		Taste	5	-6	=SUMPRODUCT(C8:D8,C11:D11)	>	=	0
9		Amount (lb)	1	1	=SUMPRODUCT(C9:D9,C11:D11)	>	=	22.046
10		Cost (per lb)	0.4	1	=SUMPRODUCT(C10:D10,C11:D11)			
11		Solution (lb)	13.5667	11.3056				

The values for the problem and solution follow.

	A	B	C	D	E	F	G	H
3			Potatoes	Green Beans	Totals			Right-Hand
4		Constraint						Side
5		Protein (g)	6.804	9.072	194.8717949	>	=	180
6		Iron (mg)	1.3608	5.4432	80	>	=	80
7		Vitamin C (mg)	54.432	45.36	1251282051	>	=	1050
8		Taste	5	-6	0	>	=	0
9		Amount (lb)	1	1	24.8722470.9	>	=	22.046
10		Cost (per lb)	0.4	1	16.73223895			
11		Solution (lb)	13.567	11.306				

The Solver settings used to solve the problem follow.

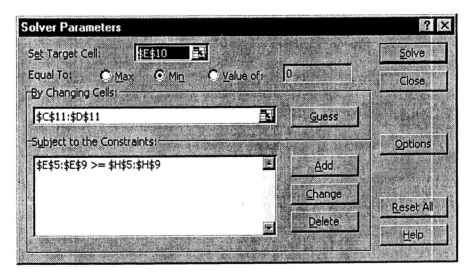

Finally, throughout this case we use the following Solver options.

☑ Assume Linear Model
☑ Assume Non-Negative

Maria should purchase 13.567 lb of potatoes and 11.306 lb of green beans to obtain a minimum cost of $16.73.

b) The taste constrint changes. The new constraint is now.

$$\frac{\text{pounds of potatoes}}{\text{pounds of green beans}} > \frac{1}{2}$$

2 (pounds of potatoes) > 1 (pounds of green beans)

The formulas and Solver settings used to solve the problem remain the same as in part (a). The values for the problem and solution follow.

	A	B	C	D	E	F	G	H
3			Potatoes	Green Beans	Totals			Right-Hand
4		Constraint						Side
5		Protein (g)	6.804	9.072	180	>	=	180
6		Iron (mg)	1.3608	5.4432	80	>	=	80
7		Vitamin C (mg)	54.432	45.36	1110	>	=	1050
8		Taste	2	-1	8.45091122	>	=	0
9		Amount (lb)	1	1	22.4132863	>	=	22.046
10		Cost (per lb)	0.4	1	16.2404468			
11		Solution (lb)	10.288	12.125				

Maria should purchase 10.288 lb of potatoes and 12.125 lb of green beans to obtain a minimum cost of $16.24.

c) The right-hand side of the iron constraint changes from 80 mg to 65 mg. The formulas and Solver settings used in the problem remain the same as in part (a). The values for the new problem formulation and solution follow.

	A	B	C	D	E	F	G	H
3			Potatoes	Green Beans	Totals			Right-Hand
4		Constraint						Side
5		Protein (g)	6.804	9.072	180	>	=	180
6		Iron (mg)	1.3608	5.4432	65	>	=	65
7		Vitamin C (mg)	54.432	45.36	1222.5	>	=	1050
8		Taste	5	-6	31.0479129	>	=	0
9		Amount (lb)	1	1	23.7911522	>	=	22.046
10		Cost (per lb)	0.4	1	14.3114345			
11		Solution (lb)	15.800	7.992				

Maria should purchase 15.8 lb of potatoes and 7.992 lb of green beans to obtain a minimum cost of $14.31.

d) The iron requirement remains 65 mg. We need to change the price per pound of green beans from $1.00 per pound to $0.50 per pound. The formulas and Solver settings used in the problem remain the same as in part (a). The values for the new problem formulation and solution follow.

	A	B	C	D	E	F	G	H
3			Potatoes	Green Beans	Totals			Right-Hand
4		Constraint						Side
5		Protein (g)	6.804	9.072	180	>	=	180
6		Iron (mg)	1.3608	5.4432	73.8947368	4	=	65
7		Vitamin C (mg	54.432	45.36	1155.789474	4	=	1050
8		Taste	5	-6	0	>	=	0
9		Amount (lb)	1	1	22.9741019	2	=	22.046
10		Cost (per lb)	0.4	0.5	10.2339181	3		
11		Solution (lb)	12.531	10.443				

Maria should purchase 12.531 lb of potatoes and 10.443 lb of green beans to obtain a minimum cost of $10.23.

e) We still have two decision variables: one variable to represent the amount (in pounds) of potatoes Maria should purchase and one variable to represent the amount (in pounds) of lima beans Maria should purchase. To determine the grams of protein in one pound of lima beans, we perform the following conversion:

$$\frac{22.68 \text{ g of protein}}{0.625 \text{ lb of lima beans}} = \frac{36.288 \text{ g of protein}}{1 \text{ lb of lima beans}}$$

To determine the milligrams of iron in one pound of lima beans, we perform the following conversion:

$$\frac{6.804 \text{ mg of iron}}{0.625 \text{ lb of lima beans}} = \frac{10.8864 \text{ mg of iron}}{1 \text{ lb of lima beans}}$$

Lima beans contain no vitamin C, so we do not have to perform a measurement conversion for vitamin C.

We change the decision variable from green beans to lima beans and insert the new parameters for protein, iron, vitamin C, and cost. The formulas and Solver settings used in the problem remain the same as in part (a). The values for the new problem formulation and solution follows.

	A	B	C	D	E	F	G	H
			Potatoes	Lima Beans	Totals			Right-Hand
3								
4		Constraint						Side
5		Protein (g)	6.804	36.288	260.41666667		=	180
6		Iron (mg)	1.3608	10.8864	65	>	=	65
7		Vitamin C (mg)	54.432	0	1050	>	=	1050
8		Taste	5	-6	75.094	>	=	0
9		Amount (lb)	1	1	22.84961052	>	=	22.046
10		Cost (per lb)	0.4	0.6	9.851741623			
11		Solution (lb)	19.290	3.559				

Maria should purchase 19.29 lb of potatoes and 3.559 lb of lima beans to obtain a minimum cost of $9.85.

f) Edson takes pride in the taste of his casserole, and the optimal solution from above does not seem to preserve the taste of the casserole. First, Maria forces Edson to use lima beans instead of green beans, and lima beans are not an ingredient in Edson's original recipe. Second, although Edson places no upper limit on the ratio of potatoes to beans, the above recipe uses an over five to one ratio of potatoes to beans. This ratio seems unreasonable since such a large amount of potatoes will overpower the taste of beans in the recipe.

g) We only need to change the values on the right-hand side of the iron and vitamin C constraints. The formulas and Solver settings used in the problem remain the same as in part (a). The values used in the new problem formulation and solution follow.

	A	B	C	D	E	F	G	H
3			Potatoes	Lima Beans	Totals			Right-Hand
4		Constraint						Side
5		Protein (g)	6.804	36.288	428.5718034		=	180
6		Iron (mg)	1.3608	10.8864	120		>=	120
7		Vitamin C (mg)	54.432	0	685.7232823		=	500
8		Taste	5	-6	6.300		>=	0
9		Amount (lb)	1	1	22.046		>=	22.046
10		Cost (per lb)	0.4	0.6	10.70804061			
11		Solution (lb)	12.598	9.448				

Maria should purchase 12.598 lb of potatoes and 9.448 lb of lima beans to obtain a minimum cost of $10.71.

2.3   a) The number of operators that the hospital needs to staff the call center during each two-hour shift can be found in the following table:

	A	B	C	D	E	F
	work	average number of	number of calls from	number of calls from	number of operators	number of operators
1		calls per hour				
2	shift	calls per hour	English speakers	Spanish speakers	speaking English	speaking Spanish
3	7am to 9am	40	32	8	6	2
4	9am to 11am	85	68	17	12	3
5	11am to 1pm	70	56	14	10	3
6	1pm to 3pm	95	76	19	13	4
7	3pm to 5pm	80	64	16	11	3
8	5pm to 7pm	35	28	7	5	2
9	7pm to 9pm	10	8	2	2	1

For example, the average number of phone calls per hour during the shift from 7am to 9am equals 40. Since, on average, 80% of all phone calls are from English speakers, there is an average number of 32 phone calls per hour from English speakers during that shift. Since one operator takes, on average, 6 phone calls per hour, the hospital needs 32/6 = 5.333 English-speaking operators during that shift. The hospital cannot employ fractions of an operator and so needs 6 English-speaking operators for the shift from 7am to 9am.

b) The problems of determining how many Spanish-speaking operators and English-speaking operators Lenny needs to hire to begin each shift are independent. Therefore we can formulate two smaller linear programming models instead of one large model. We are going to have one model for the scheduling of the Spanish-speaking operators and another one for the scheduling of the English-speaking operators.

Lenny wants to minimize the operating costs while answering all phone calls. For the given scheduling problem we make the assumption that the only operating costs are the wages of the employees for the hours that they answer phone calls. The wages for the hours during which they perform paperwork are paid by other cost centers. Moreover, it does not matter for the callers whether an operator starts his or her work day with phone calls or with paperwork. For example, we do not need to distinguish between operators who start their day answering phone calls at 9am and operators who start their day with paperwork at 7am, because both groups of operators will be answering phone calls at the same time. And only this time matters for the analysis of Lenny's problem.

We define the decision variables according to the time when the employees have their first shift of answering phone calls. For the scheduling problem of the English-speaking operators we have 7 decision variables. First, we have 5 decision variables for full-time employees.

The number of operators having their first shift on the phone from 7am to 9am.
The number of operators having their first shift on the phone from 9am to 11am.
The number of operators having their first shift on the phone from 11am to 1pm.
The number of operators having their first shift on the phone from 1pm to 3pm.
The number of operators having their first shift on the phone from 3pm to 5pm.

In addition, we define 2 decision variables for part-time employees.

The number of part-time operators having their first shift from 3pm to 5pm.
The number of part-time operators having their first shift from 5pm to 7pm.

The unit cost coefficients in the objective function are the wages operators earn while they answer phone calls.   All operators who have their first shift on the phone from 7am to 9am, 9am to 11am, or 11am to 1pm finish their work on the phone before 5pm. They earn 4*$10 = $40 during their time answering phone calls. All operators who have their first shift on the phone from 1pm to 3pm or 3pm to 5pm have one shift on the phone before 5pm and another one after 5pm. They earn 2*$10+2*$12 = $44 during their time answering phone calls. The second group of part-time operators, those having their first shift from 5pm to 7pm, earn 4*$12 = $48 during their time answering phone calls.

There are 7 constraints, one for each two-hour shift during which phone calls need to be answered. The right-hand sides for these constraints are the number of operators needed to ensure that all phone calls get answered in a timely manner. On the left-hand side we determine the number of operators on the phone during any given shift. For example, during the 11am to 1pm shift the total number of operators answering phone calls equals the sum of the number of operators who started answering calls at 7am and are currently in their second shift of the day and the number of operators who started answering calls at 11am.

The following spreadsheet describes the entire problem formulation for the English-speaking employees:

	A	B	C	D	E	F	G	H	I	J	K
1											
2	Shifts of	Number of operators whose first shift of answering phone calls in English is from									Required number
3	phone operators	7am to 9am	9am to 11am	11am to 1 pm	1pm to 3pm	3pm to 5pm	3pm to 5pm (P)	5pm to 7pm (P)	Totals		of operators
4	7am to 9am	1	0	0	0	0	0	0	6	>=	6
5	9am to 11am	0	1	0	0	0	0	0	13	>=	12
6	11am to 1 pm	1	0	1	0	0	0	0	10	>=	10
7	1pm to 3pm	0	1	0	1	0	0	0	13	>=	13
8	3pm to 5pm	0	0	1	0	1	1	0	11	>=	11
9	5pm to 7pm	0	0	0	1	0	1	1	5	>=	5
10	7pm to 9pm	0	0	0	0	1	0	1	2	>=	2
11	Unit cost	40	40	40	44	44	44	48	1228	=	Total cost
12	Solution	6	13	4	0	2	5	0			

The following formulas are used in the problem formulation:

	I
1	
2	
3	Totals
4	=SUMPRODUCT(B4:H4,B12:H12)
5	=SUMPRODUCT(B5:H5,B12:H12)
6	=SUMPRODUCT(B6:H6,B12:H12)
7	=SUMPRODUCT(B7:H7,B12:H12)
8	=SUMPRODUCT(B8:H8,B12:H12)
9	=SUMPRODUCT(B9:H9,B12:H12)
10	=SUMPRODUCT(B10:H10,B12:H12)
11	=SUMPRODUCT(B11:H11,B12:H12)
12	

The solver appears as follows:

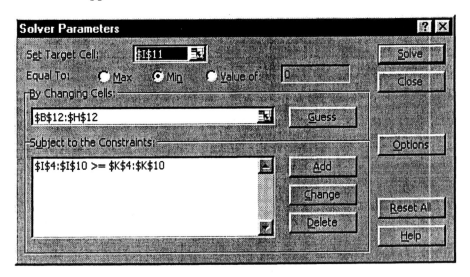

Throughout this analysis we use the following solver options:

☑ Assume Linear Model

☑ Assume Non-Negative

The linear programming model for the Spanish-speaking employees can be developed in a similar fashion.

	A	B	C	D	E	F	G	H	I	J
1										
2		Shifts of	Number of operators whose first shift of answering phone calls in Spanish is from							Required number
3		phone operators	7am to 9am	9am to 11am	11am to 1 pm	1pm to 3pm	3pm to 5pm	Totals		of operators
4		7am to 9am	1	0	0	0	0	2	>=	2
5		9am to 11am	0	1	0	0	0	3	>=	3
6		11am to 1 pm	1	0	1	0	0	4	>=	3
7		1pm to 3pm	0	1	0	1	0	5	>=	4
8		3pm to 5pm	0	0	1	0	1	3	>=	3
9		5pm to 7pm	0	0	0	1	0	2	>=	2
10		7pm to 9pm	0	0	0	0	1	1	>=	1
11		Unit cost	40	40	40	44	44	412	=	Total cost
12		Solution	2	3	2	2	1			

	H
1	
2	
3	Totals
4	=SUMPRODUCT(C4:G4,C12:G12)
5	=SUMPRODUCT(C5:G5,C12:G12)
6	=SUMPRODUCT(C6:G6,C12:G12)
7	=SUMPRODUCT(C7:G7,C12:G12)
8	=SUMPRODUCT(C8:G8,C12:G12)
9	=SUMPRODUCT(C9:G9,C12:G12)
10	=SUMPRODUCT(C10:G10,C12:G12)
11	=SUMPRODUCT(C11:G11,C12:G12)
12	

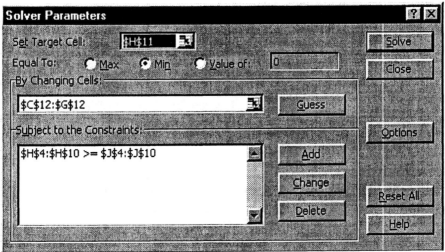

c) Lenny should hire 25 full-time English-speaking operators. Of these operators, 6 have their first phone shift from 7am to 9am, 13 from 9am to 11am, 4 from 11am to 1pm, and 2 from 3pm to 5pm. Lenny should also hire 5 part-time operators who start their work at 3pm. In addition, Lenny should hire 10 Spanish-speaking operators. Of these operators, 2 have their first shift on the phone from 7am to 9am, 3 from 9am to 11am, 2 from 11am to 1pm and 1pm to 3pm, and 1 from 3pm to 5pm. The total (wage) cost of running the calling center equals $1640 per day.

d) The restriction that Lenny can find only one English-speaking operator who wants to start work at 1pm affects only the linear programming model for English-speaking operators. This restriction does not put a bound on the number of operators who start their first phone shift at 1pm because those operators can start work at 11am with paperwork. However, this restriction does put an upper bound on the number of operators having their first phone shift from 3pm to 5pm. The new worksheet appears as follows.

	A	B	C	D	E	F	G	H	I	J	K	L
1												
2		Shifts of	Number of operators whose first shift of answering phone calls in English is from									Required number
3		phone operators	7 am to 9am	9am to 11am	11am to 1 pm	1pm to 3pm	3pm to 5pm	3pm to 5pm (P)	5 pm to 7pm (P)	Totals		of operators
4		7am to 9am	1	0	0	0	0	0	0	6	>=	6
5		9am to 11am	0	1	0	0	0	0	0	13	>=	12
6		11am to 1 pm	1	0	1	0	0	0	0	12	>=	10
7		1pm to 3pm	0	1	0	1	0	0	0	13	>=	13
8		3pm to 5pm	0	0	1	0	1	1	0	11	>=	11
9		5pm to 7pm	0	0	0	1	0	1	1	5	>=	5
10		7pm to 9pm	0	0	0	0	1	0	1	2	>=	2
11		Unit cost	40	40	40	44	44	44	48	1268	=	Total cost
12		Solution	6	13	6	0	1	4	1			
13		Upper bounds					1					

The Solver dialogue box displays the additional constraint.

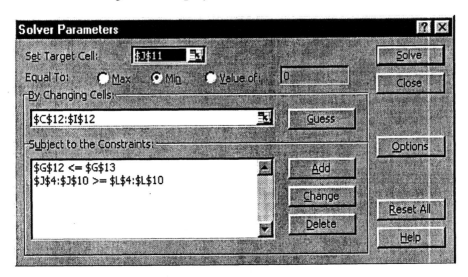

Lenny should hire 26 full-time English-speaking operators. Of these operators, 6 have their first phone shift from 7am to 9am, 13 from 9am to 11am, 6 from 11am to 1pm, and 1 from 3pm to 5pm. Lenny should also hire 4 part-time operators who start their work at 3pm and 1 part-time operator starting work at 5pm. The hiring of Spanish-speaking operators is unaffected. The new total (wage) costs equal $1680 per day.

e) For each hour, we need to divide the average number of calls per hour by the average processing speed, which is 6 calls per hour. The number of bilingual operators that the hospital needs to staff the call center during each two-hour shift can be found in the following table:

	A	B	C
1	work	average number of	number of operators
2	shift	calls per hour	speaking English
3	7am to 9am	40	7
4	9am to 11am	85	15
5	11am to 1pm	70	12
6	1pm to 3pm	95	16
7	3pm to 5pm	80	14
8	5pm to 7pm	35	6
9	7pm to 9pm	10	2

f) The linear programming model for Lenny's scheduling problem can be found in the same way as before, only that now all operators are bilingual.

	A	B	C	D	E	F	G	H	I	J	K
1											
2	Shifts of		Number of operators whose first shift of answering phone calls in both languages is from								Required number
3	phone operators	7am to 9am	9am to 11am	11am to 1pm	1pm to 3pm	3pm to 5pm	3pm to 5pm (P)	5pm to 7pm (P)	Totals		of operators
4	7am to 9am	1	0	0	0	0	0	0	7	>=	7
5	9am to 11am	0	1	0	0	0	0	0	16	>=	15
6	11am to 1pm	1	0	1	0	0	0	0	13	>=	12
7	1pm to 3pm	0	1	0	1	0	0	0	16	>=	16
8	3pm to 5pm	0	0	1	0	1	1	0	14	>=	14
9	5pm to 7pm	0	0	0	1	0	1	1	6	>=	6
10	7pm to 9pm	0	0	0	0	1	0	1	2	>=	2
11	Unit cost	40	40	40	44	44	44	48	1512	=	Total cost
12	Solution	7	16	6	0	2	6	0			

(The formulas and the solver dialogue box are identical to those in part (b).)

Lenny should hire 31 full-time bilingual operators. Of these operators, 7 have their first phone shift from 7am to 9am, 16 from 9am to 11am, 6 from 11am to 1pm, and 2 from 3pm to 5pm. Lenny should also hire 6 part-time operators who start their work at 3pm. The total (wage) cost of running the calling center equals $1512 per day.

g) The total cost of part (f) is $1512 per day; the total cost of part (b) is $1640. Lenny could pay an additional $1640-$1512 = $128 in total wages to the bilingual operators without increasing the total operating cost beyond those for the scenario with only monolingual operators. The increase of $128 represents a percentage increase of 128/1512 = 8.466%.

h) Creative Chaos Consultants has made the assumption that the number of phone calls is independent of the day of the week. But maybe the number of phone calls is very different on a Monday than it is on a Friday. So instead of using the same number of average phone calls for every day of the week, it might be more appropriate to determine whether the day of the week affects the demand for phone operators. As a result Lenny might need to hire more part-time employees for some days with an increased calling volume.

Similarly, Lenny might want to take a closer look at the length of the shifts he has scheduled. Using shorter shift periods would allow him to "fine tune" his calling centers and make it more responsive to demand fluctuations.

Lenny should investigate why operators are able to answer only 6 phone calls per hour. Maybe additional training of the operators could enable them to answer phone calls quicker and so increase the number of phone calls they are able to answer in an hour.

Finally, Lenny should investigate whether it is possible to have employees switching back and forth between paperwork and answering phone calls. During slow times phone operators could do some paperwork while they are sitting next to a phone, while in times of sudden large call volumes employees who are scheduled to do paperwork could quickly switch to answering phone calls.

Lenny might also want to think about the installation of an automated answering system that gives callers a menu of selections. Depending upon the caller's selection, the call is routed to an operator who specializes in answering questions about that selection.

Case 2.4

KUWAIT'S AL-MANAKH STOCK MARKET
Teaching Note

Basic Issue

Traders caught in a web of post-dated checks and IOUs following the crash of the al-Manakh stock market must be disentangled in order to bring stability to the Kuwait economy and legal system.

Techniques and concepts

Optimization and solving linear equations.

Suggested Assignment Questions

1. Determine a method of allocating payments between traders using the example given in the case, while ignoring the asset breakdown.
2. How should the total payments be allocated among asset classes?

Suggested Discussion Questions

1. What OR/MS tools can be used to help resolve this problem?
2. What is the advantage of a model-based approach over a legal or political procedure?
3. What is the most appropriate and fair rationale (or objective) to guide disentangling payments?
4. What constraints must be taken into account?
5. How should different assets be treated?

Professor Peter C. Bell, Richard Ivey School of Business, prepared this teaching note, with assistance from Sam Ridesic, as an aid to instructors in the classroom use of the case *Kuwait's al-Manakh Stock Market* © INFORMS, 1998.

Analysis

The disentanglement problem is most easily handled in two stages. First, assume that all assets are equivalent and determine the total payments for each trader (and also the total receipts for each trader). Second, determine how these total payments are broken down by asset type.

The most contentious part of the solution procedure is determining an appropriate objective. Several possibilities are listed in the case, and most have strengths and weaknesses. The Finance Minister of Kuwait decided that simultaneously determining traders' payments to each other, asset by asset, so as to maximize the sum of the insolvent trader's DSRs was the appropriate objective from the government's perspective. This is the objective modeled here.

Problem formulation

Decision Variables

Let:

λ_i = The fraction of payments made by trader i to all his debtors, (by definition $0 \leq \lambda_i \leq 1$).

λ_{ik} = The portion of asset type k trader i uses to settle his debt.

Parameters

All in Kuwaiti Dinars *(KD)*.

n = number of traders to be disentangled,

K = number of different types of assets,

a_i = total assets of trader i,

p_i = total payables of trader i,

C_i = objective function coefficient or weight of trader i debt due from trader j,

r_{ij} = receivables of trader i due from trader j,

A_k = a vector of asset type k for all traders, $(k = 1, 2, ..., K)$.

A = a vector of total assets, where $A = \sum_{k=1}^{K} A_k$.

a_{ik} = the amount of asset type k that belongs to trader i,

$\tilde{\lambda}$ = vector of debt settlement ratios for all traders.

$\tilde{\lambda}_k$ = vector of asset type k portion used for debt settlement ratios for all traders.

D = matrix of all traders payables and receivables, where D is defined as follows:

$$D = \begin{bmatrix} p_1 & -r_{12} & -r_{13} & \cdots & -r_{1n} \\ -r_{12} & p_2 & & & -r_{2n} \\ -r_{31} & & p_3 & & \\ & & & \ddots & \\ -r_{n1} & & & & p_n \end{bmatrix}$$

Elements of the main diagonal in D provide the total payables of a trader while the off-diagonal elements in the ith row represent the negative of the receivables of trader i. Off-diagonal elements in the jth column represent the payables of the jth trader to others in the system.

The Linear Programming Model

This linear programming model identifies solvent from insolvent traders and determines the debt settlement ratio of all traders.

$$\text{Maximize } \sum_{i=1}^{n} C_i \lambda_{ir}$$

Subject to

$$p_i \lambda_i - \sum_{\substack{j=1 \\ j \neq i}}^{n} r_{ij} \lambda_j \leq a_i \quad i = 1, \ldots, n,$$

$$\lambda_i \leq 1 \quad i = 1, \ldots, n.$$
$$\lambda_i \geq 0 \quad i = 1, \ldots, n.$$

Solving this model determines the fraction of his assets that each trader pays into the settlement account. If this fraction is 1, the trader is insolvent, if less than 1, the trader is solvent.

Solvent traders are now removed from the analysis by requiring these debtors to adjust their asset portfolios such that they can pay off the required amount in cash. The cash assets of each insolvent trader are augmented by the amounts paid by solvent traders.

System of Linear Equations for Debt Payment by Type of Asset

Setting the LP inequalities to equalities gives:

$$D \tilde{\lambda} = A.$$

Substituting for $A = \sum_{k=1}^{K} A_k$:

$$D\tilde{\lambda} = \sum_{k=1}^{K} A_k.$$

Multiplying through by D^{-1} provides the expression:

$$\tilde{\lambda} = D^{-1}A_1 + D^{-1}A_2 + \cdots + D^{-1}A_K.$$

By setting

$$\tilde{\lambda}_k = D^{-1}A_k \ \ k = 1, ..., K.$$

then

$$\tilde{\lambda} = \tilde{\lambda}_1 + \tilde{\lambda}_2 + \cdots \tilde{\lambda}_K.$$

That is, the debt settlement ratio of a trader equals the sum of the debt settlement ratios for each type of asset owned by that trader. Clearly D^{-1} is independent of the asset type, and one needs only a single inversion of matrix D.

Results for example in case using Solver:

			Trader				
Maximize sum of "DSR"s			A				
=	4		B				
			C				
			D				

			Receipts				
Trader	Assets	Payments	From A	From B	From C	From D	Payments-Receipts
A	10	83		42	5	15	21
B	3	65	9		40	15	1
C	85	45	74	23		20	-72
D	30	50	0	0	0		50

Table 1: Solver Model.

A "Solver" model is shown in Table 1 before optimization. The "Changing Cells" are the "DSR"s and the "Target Cell" to be maximized contains the sum of the DSRs. Note that the "DSR"s in the Solver model are the λ's in the above formulation. The Solver model assumes that all traders are weighted equally (that is $C_i = 1$ for $i = 1,2,3,4$.).

The second table in the Solver model lists the assets for each trader, the receipts of each trader from each other trader (= the receivables multiplied by the "DSR" for the paying trader), and the total payments each trader makes (= the sum of the column of receipts "From" that trader). The right-hand column of this table computes the (Payments-receipts) for each trader. There are three sets of constraints.

1. Each DSR must be ≥ 0,
2. Each DSR must be ≤ 1, and
3. For each trader, (Payments - Receipts) must be ≤ Assets.

							Trader	"DSR"
Maximize sum of "DSR"s							A	0.746263
	=	3.2495917					B	0.903329
							C	1
							D	0.6

			Receipts					
Trader	Assets	Payments	From A	From B	From C	From D	Payments-Receipts	
A	10	61.93982697		37.9398	5	9	10.00002074	
B	3	58.71636678	6.71637		40	9	3	
C	85	45	55.2235	20.7766		12	-43.00002074	
D	30	30	0	0	0		30	

Table 2: Solver Model after optimization.

Table 2 shows the same model after optimization. Trader C is solvent (optimized "DSR" = 1), the other three traders are insolvent.

Table 3 shows the determination of each trader's DSR for each asset type. This calculation begins by constructing the "D" matrix (above) where the diagonal elements are the payables for each trader and the off-diagonal elements are the receivables due to each trader from each insolvent trader. The "D" matrix is inverted (MINVERSE(array) function in Excel) and then multiplied by the matrix of assets for each insolvent trader (A,B, and D), where the new cash assets of each insolvent include the receipts from solvent trader C. This multiplication yields the asset DSRs for A, B, and D which sum to the overall DSRs determined in the Solver model (above). For ease of display, the individual asset DSRs are displayed in Table 3 in transposed form.

Trader	D matrix			DSRs
	A	B	D	
A	83	-42	-15	0.7463
B	-9	65	-15	0.9033
D	0	0	50	0.6

Trader	D^-1 matrix		
A	0.012956	0.0084	0.0064
B	0.001794	0.0165	0.0055
D	0	0	0.02

Insolvent traders' assets after cash payments from Trader C

Cash	Land	Rec'bles	Shares
6	4	3	2
40.6	1.2	0.2	1
5	7	3	15

Proportion of debt covered by each trader' assets

	A	B	C	D
Cash and KSE shares	0.4496	0.7099	1	0.1
Real Estate	0.1067	0.0655	0	0.14
Receivables	0.0597	0.0252	0	0.06
Shares in Gulf companies	0.1303	0.1027	0	0.3
Total (Trader DSR)	0.7463	0.9033	1	0.6

Table 3: Computation of DSRs for four traders for four asset types.

Impact of the Work

The model described above was used to generate results which were presented to an arbitration panel. These results established figures for all the involved parties which were used to resolve the entanglements starting in 1983.

His Excellency Shaikh Ali Al-Khalifa Al-Sabah, former Minister of Finance and Oil of Kuwait has provided an over view of the benefits of this work.

"Had we not resorted to this model, the social and economic consequences to Kuwait would have been catastrophic in the sense that the legal system would have been blocked by the claims and counterclaims of about 20,000 claimants. The legal system would have no way of resolving each and every case individually. According to Kuwaiti law, they had to issue a judgment on each and every check. So, it would have been arbitrary, it would have led to results that would have been capricious, benefiting those who were solvent against those whose claims came later on.

"The societal impact of this on society knowing that the judiciary system did not produce an equitable solution would have been also tremendous since a lot of the people who were involved in these transactions were from the same family.

"The political consequences would have been just as serious. I leave it to your imagination (to consider) the political consequences when members of the society believe that the judiciary system did not give them their due right.

"The economic situation, overall, would have been much slower (which would have caused) asset values to drop tremendously bringing more suffering to the Kuwaiti economy.

"Thank God, as a result of the solution, while not everybody was satisfied, everybody knew that the system was fair. So, I would not be too complimentary to the gentlemen involved in the study in saying that their model was the cornerstone that we have used in solving a very complicated debt crisis that involved so many people in a small society."

Some basic facts put the minister's comments in perspective. For each of the 29 000 post dated checks, three court cases would have been required to settle the debt. A criminal case for issuing a check with insufficient funds, a commercial case for violating banking regulations, and finally, a bankruptcy case to verify debts and distribute assets. Since each case would take approximately five years, the court system would have had to function at eighteen times capacity for five years before the situation could have been resolved. The cost to the court system was estimated to exceed $380 million.

Thanks to the LP model, no court ordered bankruptcies took place. Since the solution to the problem was generated long before the courts would have completed their work, the economy was able to recover without having to spend years of further instability. Less apparent was the social strife that would have persisted. With males over the age of 25 accounting for only 16% of the total Kuwaiti population, many families were pitted against each other, as most of the entangled traders fell in this demographic category. Prolonged and bitter trials would have led to a high level of social tension within this small society.

Another benefit to the solution was that through netting intertrader debts and credits, the gross debt of the al-Manakh crash fell from $94 billion to $20 billion. Also, the DSRs that were generated by the optimization model slowed down and in some cases arrested the downslide in asset value that precipitated from the crash. The optimization model quickly, efficiently, and fairly disentangled the web of IOUs and brought stability to the devastated Kuwaiti economy.

Available Videotape:

A short videotape is available on which Minister of Finance, His Excellency Shaikh Ali Al-Khalifa Al-Sabah talks about the work and its impact on Kuwait. (Run time, about 10 mins).

Sources:

A.A. Elimam, M. Girgis and S. Kotob, A Solution to Post Crash Debt Entanglements in Kuwait's al-Manakh Stock Market, **Interfaces** 27: 1 January-February 1997, pp.89-106.

Videotape: 96.02 Al-Manakh Stock market (Kuwait), INFORMS/CPMS Edelman Award for Management Science Achievement, INFORMS, 1997 (46:28 mins).

CHAPTER 3
LINEAR PROGRAMMING: FORMULATION AND APPLICATIONS

Review Questions

3.1-1 The problem is to determine which levels should be chosen of different advertising media to obtain the most effective advertising mix for the new cereal.

3.1-2 The overall measure of performance being used is expected exposure.

3.1-3 Claire is concerned about the plan because TV commercials are not being used and that is the primary method of reaching young children.

3.1-4 The management science team needs to check the assumption that fractional solutions are allowed and the assumption of proportionality to evaluate the adequacy of using a linear programming model to represent the problem.

3.2-1 The identifying feature for a resource-allocation problem is that each functional constraint in the linear programming model is a resource constraint.

3.2-2 Amount of resource used ≤ Amount of resource available.

3.2-3 1) The amount available of each limited resource for the collective use of all the activities being considered in the study.

2) The amount of each resource needed by each activity. Specifically, for each combination of resource and activity, the amount of resource used per unit of activity must be estimated.

3) The contribution per unit of activity to the overall measure of performance represented by the objective function.

3.2-4 The data in the parameter table are the parameters for the linear programming model. The data in the Contribution per unit row become the coefficients of the decision variables in the objective function and are placed in the changing cells. The data in each Resource row become the numbers in the corresponding resource constraints and are placed in the data cells.

3.2-5 The three activities in the examples are determining the most profitable mix of production rates for two new products, capital budgeting, and choosing the mix of advertising media.

3.2-6 The resources in the examples are available production capacities of different plants, cumulative investment capital available by certain times, financial allocations for advertising and for planning purposes, and TV commercial spots available for purchase.

3.3-1 For resource-allocation problems, limits are set on the use of various resources, and then the objective is to make the most effective use of these given resources. For cost-benefit-tradeoff problems, management takes a more aggressive stance, prescribing what benefits must be achieved by the activities under consideration, and then the objective is to achieve all these benefits with minimum cost.

3.3-2 The identifying feature for a cost-benefit-tradeoff problem is that each functional constraint is a benefit constraint.

3.3-3 Level achieved ≥ Minimum acceptable level.

3.3-4   1) For each benefit, an estimate of how much each activity contributes to that benefit.

2) The minimum acceptable level for each benefit.

3) The cost per unit of each activity.

3.3-5   The linear programming model can be written directly from the parameter table to a spreadsheet. The Unit cost row provides the coefficients of the decision variables for the objective function and is placed in the changing cells. The data in each Benefit row provides both the coefficients and the right-hand side for a benefit constraint and are placed in the data cells.

3.3-6   The activities for the examples are choosing the mix of advertising media, personnel scheduling, and controlling air pollution.

3.3-7   The benefits for the examples are increased market share, minimizing total personnel costs while meeting service requirements, and reductions in the emission of pollutants.

3.4-1   Distribution-network problems deal with the distribution of goods through a distribution network at minimum cost.

3.4-2   The identifying feature for a distribution-network problem is that each functional constraint is a fixed-requirement constraint.

3.4-3   In contrast to the ≤ form for resource constraints and the ≥ form for benefit constraints, fixed-requirement constraints have an = form.

3.4-4   F1 Amount, F2 Amount, W1 Amount, W2 Amount, and DC Amount all have fixed requirements.

3.5-1   Two new goals need to be incorporated into the study. The first is that the advertising should be seen by at least 5 million young children. The second is that the advertising should be seen by at least 5 million parents of young children.

3.5-2   Two benefit constraints and a fixed-requirement constraint are included in the new linear programming model.

3.5-3   Management decided to adopt the new plan because it does a much better job of meeting all of management's goals for the campaign.

3.6-1   Mixed problems may contain all three types of functional constraints: resource constraints, benefit constraints, and fixed-requirement constraints.

3.6-2   The Save-It Co. problem is an example of a blending problem where the objective is to find the best blend of ingredients into final products to meet certain specifications.

3.7-1   A linear programming model must accurately reflect the managerial view of the problem.

3.7-2   Linear programming models generally are formulated by management science teams.

3.7-3   The line of communication between the management science team and the manager is vital.

3.7-4   Model validation is a testing process used on an initial version of a model to identify the errors and omissions that inevitably occur when constructing large models.

3.7-5   The process of model enrichment involves beginning with a relatively simple version of the model and then using the experience gained with this model to evolve toward more elaborate models that more nearly reflect the complexity of the real problem.

3.7-6 What-if analysis is an important part of a linear programming study because an optimal solution can only be solved for with respect to one specific version of the model at a time. Management may have "what-if" questions about how the solution will change given changes in the model formulation.

3.8-1 The Ponderosa problem falls into the mixed problem category. The United Airlines problem is basically a cost-benefit-tradeoff problem. The Citgo problem is a distribution-network problem.

3.8-2 The Ponderosa problem has 90 decision variables, the United Airlines problem has over 20,000 decision variables, and the Citgo problem has about 15,000 decision variables.

3.8-3 Two factors helped make the Ponderosa application successful. One is that they implemented a financial planning system with a natural-language user interface, with the optimization codes operating in the background. The other success factor was that the optimization system used was interactive.

3.8-4 The most important success factor in the United Airlines application was the support of operational managers and their staffs.

3.8-5 The factors that helped make the Citgo application successful were developing output reports in the language of managers to meet their needs, using "what-if" analysis, the support of operational managers, and, most importantly, the unlimited support provided the management science task force by top management.

Problems

3.1 a & b)

	A	B	C	D	E	F	G	H
1		Resource Usage Per Unit of Each Activity						
2		Activity						Resource
3	Resource	TV Commercials	Magazine Ads	Radio Ads	SS Ads	Totals		Available
4	Ad Budget	300	150	200	100	4000	≤	4000
5	Planning Budget	90	30	50	40	1000	≤	1000
6	TV Spots	1	0	0	0	0	≤	5
7	Radio Spots	0	0	1	0	10	≤	10
8	Unit Exposure	140	60	90	50	1766.667		
9	Solution	3.333	6.667	10	0			

Data cells: B4:E8 and H4:H7
Changing cells: B9:E9
Target cell: F8

	F
4	=SUMPRODUCT(B4:E4,B9:E9)
5	=SUMPRODUCT(B5:E5,B9:E9)
6	=SUMPRODUCT(B6:E6,B10:E10)
7	=SUMPRODUCT(B7:E7,B9:E9)
8	=SUMPRODUCT(B8:E8,B9:E9)

c) This is a linear programming model because the decisions are represented by changing cells that can have any value that satisfy the constraints. Each constraint has an output cell on the left, a mathematical sign in the middle, and a data cell on the right. The overall level of performance is represented by the target cell and the objective is to maximize that cell. Also, the Excel equation for each output cell is expressed as a SUMPRODUCT function where each term in the sum is the product of a data cell and a changing cell.

d)

Maximize $E = 140T + 60M + 90R + 50S$,

subject to $\quad 300T + 150M + 200R + 100S \le 4000$

$\quad\quad\quad\quad 90T + 30M + 50R + 40S \le 1000$

$\quad\quad\quad\quad T \le 5$

$\quad\quad\quad\quad R \le 10$

and $\quad\quad\quad T \ge 0, \ M \ge 0, \ R \ge 0, \ S \ge 0.$

3.2 a & c)

Resource	Resource Usage Per Unit of Each Activity		Totals		Resource Available
	Activity 1	Activity 2			
1	2	1	10	$\le$	10
2	3	3	20	$\le$	20
3	2	4	20	$\le$	20
Unit Profit	20	30	$166.67		
Solution	3.333	3.333			

b)

(x_1, x_2)	Feasible?	P	
(2,2)	Yes	$100	
(3,3)	Yes	$150	
(2,4)	Yes	$160	Best
(4,2)	Yes	$140	
(3,4)	No		
(4,3)	No		

d)

Maximize $P = 20x_1 + 30x_2$,

subject to $\quad 2x_1 + x_2 \le 10$

$\quad\quad\quad\quad 3x_1 + 3x_2 \le 20$

$\quad\quad\quad\quad 2x_1 + 4x_2 \le 20$

and $\quad\quad\quad x_1 \ge 0, \ x_2 \ge 0.$

e) Optimal Solution: $(x_1, x_2) = \left(3\frac{1}{3}, 3\frac{1}{3}\right)$ and $P = 166.67$.

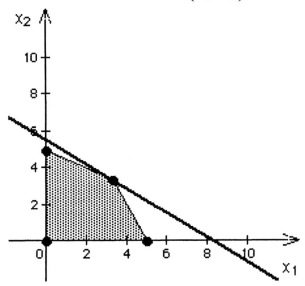

3.3   a)

	Resource Usage Per Unit of Each Activity					Resource
Resource	Activity 1	Activity 2	Activity 3	Totals		Available
A	30	20	0	500	≤	500
B	0	10	40	600	≤	600
C	20	20	30	783.3333333	≤	1000
Unit Profit	50	40	70	$ 1,883.33		
Solution	16.667	0	15			

b)

Maximize $P = 50x_1 + 40x_2 + 70x_3,$

subject to $30x_1 + 20x_2 \le 500$

$10x_2 + 40x_3 \le 600$

$20x_1 + 20x_2 + 30x_3 \le 1000$

and $x_1 \ge 0, \ x_2 \ge 0, \ x_3 \ge 0.$

3.4   a & c)

	Resource Usage Per Unit of Each Activity						Resource
Resource	Activity 1	Activity 2	Activity 3	Activity 4	Totals		Available
P	3	5	-2	4	400	≤	400
Q	4	-1	3	2	0	≤	300
R	6	3	2	-1	400	≤	400
S	-2	2	5	3	300	≤	300
Unit Profit	11	9	8	9	$ 1,703.48		
Solution	64.677	0	42.289	72.637			

b)

(x_1, x_2, x_3, x_4)	Feasible?	P	
(30,30,30,30)	Yes	$1110	
(40,40,40,40)	No		
(35,39,30,40)	Yes	$1336	
(35,39,34,40)	Yes	$1368	
(37,39,35,40)	Yes	$1398	Best

Many answers are possible.

3.5 a) The activities are the production of products 1, 2, and 3. The limited resources are hours available on the milling machine, lathe, and grinder.

b)

Resource	Resource Usage Per Unit of Each Activity			Resource Available
	Product 1	Product 2	Product 3	
Milling Machine	9	3	5	500 hours
Lathe	5	4	0	350 hours
Grinder	3	0	2	150 hours
Sales Potential	0	0	1	20 units
Unit Profit	$50	$20	$25	

c) The decisions to be made are how many of each product should be produced. The constraints on these decisions are the number of hours available on the milling machine, lathe, and grinder as well as the sales potential of product 3. The overall measure of performance is profit, which is to be maximized.

d) milling machine: $9(\text{\# units of } 1) + 3(\text{\# units of } 2) + 5(\text{\# units of } 3) \le 500$
lathe: $5(\text{\# units of } 1) + 4(\text{\# units of } 2) \le 350$
grinder: $3(\text{\# units of } 1) + 2(\text{\# units of } 3) \le 150$
sales: $(\text{\# units of } 3) \le 20$
Nonnegativity: $(\text{\# units of } 1) \ge 0, (\text{\# units of } 2) \ge 0, (\text{\# units of } 3) \ge 0$

Profit $= \$50(\text{\# units of } 1) + \$20(\text{\# units of } 2) + \$25(\text{\# units of } 3)$

e & f)

	A	B	C	D	E	F	G
1		Resource Usage Per Unit of Each Activity					Resource
2	Resource	Product 1	Product 2	Product 3	Totals		Available
3	Milling Machine	9	3	5	500	≤	500
4	Lathe	5	4	0	0	≤	350
5	Grinder	3	0	2	0	≤	150
6	Sales Potential	0	0	1	0	≤	20
7	Unit Profit	50	20	25	$ 3,333.33		
8	Solution	0	166.667	0			

Data cells: B3:E7 and G3:G6
Changing cells: B8:D8
Target cell: E7
Output cells: E3:E6

	E
3	=SUMPRODUCT(B3:D3,B8:D8)
4	=SUMPRODUCT(B4:D4,B9:D9)
5	=SUMPRODUCT(B5:D5,B8:D8)
6	=SUMPRODUCT(B6:D6,B8:D8)
7	=SUMPRODUCT(B7:D7,B8:D8)

g)

Maximize $P = 50x_1 + 20x_2 + 25x_3$,

subject to $\quad 9x_1 + 3x_2 + 5x_3 \le 500$

$\qquad\qquad 5x_1 + 4x_2 \le 350$

$\qquad\qquad 3x_1 + 2x_3 \le 150$

$\qquad\qquad x_3 \le 20$

and $\qquad x_1 \ge 0, \ x_2 \ge 0, \ x_3 \ge 0.$

3.6 a)

Resource	Resource Usage Per Unit of Each Activity			Resource Available
	Part A	Part B	Part C	
Machine 1	.02	.03	.05	40 hours
Machine 2	.05	.02	.04	40 hours
Unit Profit	50	40	30	

b & d)

Resource	Resource Usage Per Unit of Each Activity			Totals		Resource Available
	Part A	Part B	Part C			
Machine 1	0.02	0.03	0.05	40	≤	40
Machine 2	0.05	0.02	0.04	40	≤	40
Unit Profit	50	40	30	$61,818.18		
Solution	363.636	1090.909	0			

c)

(x_1, x_2, x_3)	Feasible?	P	
(500,500,300)	No		
(350,1000,0)	Yes	$57,500	
(400,1000,0)	Yes	$60,000	Best

Many answers are possible.

e)

Maximize $P = 50A + 40B + 30C$,

subject to $.02A + .03B + .05C \le 40$

$.05A + .02B + .04C \le 40$

and $A \ge 0,\ B \ge 0,\ C \ge 0.$

3.7 a)

Resource	Resource Usage Per Unit of Each Activity			Resource Available
	A1	A2	A3	
1	3	5	4	400
2	1	1	1	100
3	1	3	2	200
Unit Profit	20	40	30	

b)

Resource Usage Per Unit of Each Activity

Resource	Activity			Totals		Resource Available
	A1	A2	A3			
1	3	5	4	400	≤	400
2	1	1	1	100	≤	100
3	1	3	2	200	≤	200
Unit Profit	20	40	30	$ 3,000		
Solution	50	50	0			

3.8 a & c)

Benefit	Benefit Contribution Per Unit of Each Activity		Totals		Minimum Level
	Activity 1	Activity 2			
1	5	3	60	≥	60
2	2	2	31	≥	30
3	7	9	126	≥	126
Unit Cost	60	50	$842.50		
Solution	6.75	8.75			

b)

(x_1, x_2)	Feasible?	C	
(7,7)	No		
(7,8)	No		
(8,7)	No		
(8,8)	Yes	$880	Best
(8,9)	Yes	$930	
(9,8)	Yes	$940	

d)

Minimize $C = 60x_1 + 50x_2$,

subject to $\quad 5x_1 + 3x_2 \geq 60$

$\qquad\qquad 2x_1 + 2x_2 \geq 30$

$\qquad\qquad 7x_1 + 9x_2 \geq 126$

and $\qquad\qquad x_1 \geq 0, \; x_2 \geq 0.$

e) Optimal Solution: $(x_1, x_2) = (6.75, 8.75)$ and $C = 842.50$.

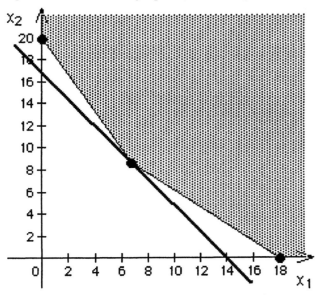

3.9 a & c)

Benefit	Benefit Contribution Per Unit of Each Activity				Totals		Minimum Level
	Activity 1	Activity 2	Activity 3	Activity 4			
P	2	- 1	4	3	80	≥	80
Q	1	4	- 1	2	60	≥	60
R	3	5	4	- 1	110	≥	110
Unit Cost	400	600	500	300	$ 17,125.00		
Solution	32.5	3.75	0	6.25			

b)

(x_1, x_2, x_3, x_4)	Feasible?	C	
(32,4,0,6)	No		
(33,4,0,6)	Yes	$17,400	Best
(33,5,0,6)	No		
(33,4,1,6)	Yes	$17,900	
(33,4,1,7)	Yes	$18,200	

Many answers are possible.

3.10 a)

Ingredient	Benefit Contribution Per Unit of Each Activity			Minimum Daily Requirement
	kg of Corn	kg of Tankage	kg of Alfalfa	
Carbohydrates	90	20	40	200
Protein	30	80	60	180
Vitamins	10	20	60	150
Unit Cost	84	72	60	

b & e)

Nutritional Ingredient	Kilogram of			Totals	Minimum Level
	Corn	Tankage	Alfalfa		
Carbohydrates	90	20	40	200 ≥	200
Proteins	30	80	60	180 ≥	180
Vitamins	10	20	60	157 ≥	150
Unit Cost	84	72	60	$ 242	
Solution	1	0	2		

c) $(x_1, x_2, x_3) = (1,2,2)$ is a feasible solution with a daily cost of $348.00. This diet will provide 210 kg of carbohydrates, 310 kg of protein, and 170 kg of vitamins daily.

d) Answers will vary.

f)

Minimize $Cost = 84C + 72T + 60A$,

subject to $\quad 90C + 20T + 40A \geq 200$

$\qquad\qquad\quad 30C + 80T + 60A \geq 180$

$\qquad\qquad\quad 10C + 20T + 60A \geq 150$

and $\qquad\quad C \geq 0, \ T \geq 0, \ A \geq 0.$

3.11 a)

Year	Benefit Contribution Per Unit of Asset			Minimum Cash Flow Required
	Asset 1	Asset 2	Asset 3	
5	$2 million	$1 million	$0.5 million	$400 million
10	$0.5 million	$0.5 million	$1 million	$100 million
20	0	$1.5 million	$2 million	$300 million
Unit Cost	$1 million	$1 million	$1 million	

b & e)

	Benefit Contribution Per Unit of Each Asset				Minimum Cash Flow Required
Year	Asset 1	Asset 2	Asset 3	Totals	
5	2	1	0.5	400 ≥	400
10	0.5	0.5	1	150 ≥	100
20	0	1.5	2	300 ≥	300
Unit Cost	1	1	1	$ 300	
Solution	100	200	0		

c) $(x_1, x_2, x_3) = (100,100,200)$ is a feasible solution. This would generate \$400 million in 5 years, \$300 million in 10 years, and \$550 million in 20 years. The total invested will be \$400 million.

d) Answers will vary.

f)

Minimize $C = x_1 + x_2 + x_3$,

subject to
$$2x_1 + x_2 + .5x_3 \geq 400$$
$$.5x_1 + .5x_2 + x_3 \geq 100$$
$$1.5x_2 + 2x_3 \geq 300$$

and
$$x_1 \geq 0, \ x_2 \geq 0, \ x_3 \geq 0.$$

3.12 a) The activities are leasing space for a number of months. The benefit is meeting the space requirements.

b)

Month	\multicolumn{8}{c}{Contribution Toward Required Amount}							
	1-1	1-2	1-3	1-4	1-5	2-1	2-2	2-3
1	1	1	1	1	1			
2		1	1	1	1	1	1	1
3			1	1	1		1	1
4				1	1			1
5					1			
Unit Cost	\$650	\$1000	\$1350	\$1600	\$1900	\$650	\$1000	\$1350

Month	\multicolumn{7}{c}{Contribution Toward Required Amount}							Resource Required
	2-4	3-1	3-2	3-3	4-1	4-2	5-1	
1								30,000
2	1							20,000
3	1	1	1	1				40,000
4	1		1	1	1	1		10,000
5	1			1		1	1	50,000
Unit Cost	\$1600	\$650	\$1000	\$1350	\$650	\$1000	\$650	

c) The decisions to be made are how much space to lease and for how many months. The constraints on these decisions are the minimum required space. The overall measure of performance is cost which is to be minimized.

d) month 1: 9(# units of 1) + 3(# units of 2) + 5(# units of 3) ≤ 500
   month 2: 5(# units of 1) + 4(# units of 2) ≤ 350
   month 3: 3(# units of 1) + 2(# units of 3) ≤ 150
   month 4: (# units of 3) ≤ 20
   month 5:
   Nonnegativity: (# units of 1) ≥ 0, (# units of 2) ≥ 0, (# units of 3) ≥ 0

   Profit = \$50(# units of 1) + \$20(# units of 2) + \$25(# units of 3)

e & f)

	A	B	C	D	E	F	G	H	I
1		Contribution Toward Required Amount							
2	Month	1-1	1-2	1-3	1-4	1-5	2-1	2-2	2-3
3	1	1	1	1	1	1			
4	2		1	1	1	1	1	1	1
5	3			1	1	1		1	1
6	4				1	1			1
7	5					1			
8	Unit Cost	$ 650	$ 1,000	$ 1,350	$ 1,600	$ 1,900	$ 650	$ 1,000	$ 1,350
9	Solution	0	0	0	0	30000	0	0	0

	J	K	L	M	N	O	P	Q	R	S
1		Contribution Toward Required Amount								Resource
2	2-4	3-1	3-2	3-3	4-1	4-2	5-1	Totals		Available
3								30000	≥	30000
4	1							30000	≥	20000
5	1	1	1	1				40000	≥	40000
6	1		1	1	1	1		30000	≥	10000
7	1			1		1	1	50000	≥	50000
8	$ 1,600	$ 650	$ 1,000	$ 1,350	$ 650	$ 1,000	$ 650	76499994		
9	0	10000	0	0	0	0	20000			

Data cells: B3:P8 and S3:S7
Changing cells: B9:P9
Target cell: Q8
Output cells: Q3:Q7

	Q
3	=SUMPRODUCT(B3:P3,B9:P9)
4	=SUMPRODUCT(B4:P4,B9:P9)
5	=SUMPRODUCT(B5:P5,B9:P9)
6	=SUMPRODUCT(B6:P6,B9:P9)
7	=SUMPRODUCT(B7:P7,B9:P9)
8	=SUMPRODUCT(B8:P8,B9:P9)

g)

Let x_{ij} = the amount of space leased in month i for a period of j months

for $i = 1,...,5$ and $j = 1,...,6-i.$

Minimize $C = 650(x_{11} + x_{21} + x_{31} + x_{41} + x_{51}) + 1000(x_{12} + x_{22} + x_{32} + x_{42})$

$+1350(x_{13} + x_{23} + x_{33}) + 1600(x_{14} + x_{24}) + 1900x_{15}$

subject to $x_{11} + x_{12} + x_{13} + x_{14} + x_{15} \geq 30,000$

$x_{12} + x_{13} + x_{14} + x_{15} + x_{21} + x_{22} + x_{23} + x_{24} \geq 20,000$

$x_{13} + x_{14} + x_{15} + x_{22} + x_{23} + x_{24} + x_{31} + x_{32} + x_{33} \geq 40,000$

$x_{14} + x_{15} + x_{23} + x_{24} + x_{32} + x_{33} + x_{41} + x_{42} \geq 10,000$

$x_{15} + x_{24} + x_{33} + x_{42} + x_{51} \geq 50,000$

and $x_{ij} \geq 0,$ for $i = 1,...,5$ and $j = 1,...,6-i.$

3.13   a)

Benefit	Benefit Contribution Per Unit of Each Activity				Minimum Requirement
	A1	A2	A3	A4	
1	3	2	-2	5	80
2	1	-1	0	1	10
3	1	1	-1	2	30
Unit Cost	2	1	-1	3	

b)

	Benefit Contribution Per Unit of Each Activity						Minimum Acceptable Level
Benefit	Activity				Totals		
	1	2	3	4			
A	3	2	-2	5	80	≥	80
B	1	-1	0	1	10	≥	10
C	1	1	-1	2	32.857	≥	30
Unit Cost	2	1	-1	3	$ 47.14		
Solution	0	4.286	0	14.2857			

3.14   a) This is a cost-benefit-tradeoff problem because it asks you to meet required benefit levels at minimum cost.

b)

Time	Benefit Contribution Per Unit of Activity							Minimum Requirement
	FT1	FT2	FT3	PT1	PT2	PT3	PT4	
8am-noon	1			1				4
	1			-2				0
noon-4pm	1	1			1			8
	1	1			-2			0
4pm-8pm		1	1			1		10
		1	1			-2		0
8pm-midnight			1				1	6
			1				-2	0
unit cost	$14	$14	$14	$12	$12	$12	$12	

c & d)

Time	Benefit Contribution Per Unit of Each Activity							Totals		Minimum Required
	FT 1	FT 2	FT 3	PT 1	PT 2	PT 3	PT 4			
8 am-12 noon	1	0	0	1	0	0	0	4	≥	4
	1	0	0	-2	0	0	0	4	≥	0
noon-4 pm	1	1	0	0	1	0	0	8	≥	8
	1	1	0	0	-2	0	0	8	≥	0
4 pm-8 pm	0	1	1	0	0	1	0	10	≥	10
	0	1	1	0	0	-2	0	10	≥	0
8 pm-midnight	0	0	1	0	0	0	1	6	≥	6
	0	0	1	0	0	0	-2	6	≥	0
Unit Cost	14	14	14	12	12	12	12	$ 196.00		
Solution	4	4	6	0	0	0	0			

e) Let f_1 = number of full-time consultants working the morning shift (8 a.m.-4 p.m.),
f_2 = number of full-time consultants working the afternoon shift (12 p.m.-8 p.m.),
f_3 = number of full-time consultants working the evening shift (4 p.m.-midnight),
p_1 = number of part-time consultants working the first shift (8 a.m.-12 p.m.),
p_2 = number of part-time consultants working the second shift (12 p.m.-4 p.m.),
p_3 = number of part-time consultants working the third shift (4 p.m.-8 p.m.),
p_4 = number of part-time consultants working the fourth shift (8 p.m.-midnight).

Minimize $C = (\$14 / \text{hour})(8 \text{ hours})[f_1 + f_2 + f_3] +$

$$(\$5 / \text{hour})(4 \text{ hours})[p_1 + p_2 + p_3 + p_4],$$

subject to

$$f_1 + p_1 \geq 4$$
$$f_1 + f_2 + p_2 \geq 8$$
$$f_2 + f_3 + p_3 \geq 10$$
$$f_3 + p_4 \geq 6$$
$$f_1 \geq 2p_1$$
$$f_1 + f_2 \geq 2p_2$$
$$f_2 + f_3 \geq 2p_3$$
$$f_3 \geq 2p_4$$

and

$$f_1 \geq 0, \ f_2 \geq 0, \ f_3 \geq 0, \ p_1 \geq 0, \ p_2 \geq 0, \ p_3 \geq 0, \ p_4 \geq 0.$$

3.15 a) This is a distribution-network problem because it deals with the distribution of goods through a distribution network at minimum cost.

b)

Require-ment	Contribution Toward Required Amount Per Unit Shipped						Required Amount
	F1-C1	F1-C2	F1-C3	F2-C1	F2-C2	F2-C3	
F1 Amt	1	1	1	0	0	0	400
F2 Amt	0	0	0	1	1	1	500
C1 Amt	1	0	0	1	0	0	300
C2 Amt	0	1	0	0	1	0	200
C3 Amt	0	0	1	0	0	1	400
Unit Cost	$600	$800	$700	$400	$200	$400	

c)

	Contribution Toward Required Amount Per Unit Shipped							Required
	Shipping Lane							
Requirement	F1-C1	F1-C2	F1-C3	F2-C1	F2-C2	F2-C3	Totals	Amount
F1 Amount	1	1	1	0	0	0	400 =	400
F2 Amount	0	0	0	1	1	1	500 =	500
C1 Amount	1	0	0	1	0	0	300 =	300
C2 Amount	0	1	0	0	1	0	200 =	200
C3 Amount	0	0	1	0	0	1	400 =	400
Unit Cost	600	800	700	400	200	400	$ 410,000	
Solution	300	0	100	0	200	300		

d) Let

$$x_{F1\text{-}C1} = \text{number of units shipped from Factory 1 to Customer 1,}$$
$$x_{F1\text{-}C2} = \text{number of units shipped from Factory 1 to Customer 2,}$$
$$x_{F1\text{-}C3} = \text{number of units shipped from Factory 1 to Customer 3,}$$
$$x_{F2\text{-}C1} = \text{number of units shipped from Factory 2 to Customer 1,}$$
$$x_{F2\text{-}C2} = \text{number of units shipped from Factory 2 to Customer 2,}$$
$$x_{F2\text{-}C3} = \text{number of units shipped from Factory 2 to Customer 3.}$$

Minimize $C = 600x_{F1-C1} + 800x_{F1-C2} + 700x_{F1-C3} +$
$$400x_{F2-C1} + 900x_{F2-C2} + 600x_{F2-C3}$$

subject to
$$x_{F1-C1} + x_{F1-C2} + x_{F1-C3} = 400$$
$$x_{F2-C1} + x_{F2-C2} + x_{F2-C3} = 500$$
$$x_{F1-C1} + x_{F2-C1} = 300$$
$$x_{F1-C2} + x_{F2-C2} = 200$$
$$x_{F1-C3} + x_{F2-C3} = 400$$

and
$$x_{F1-C1} \geq 0, \ x_{F1-C2} \geq 0, \ x_{F1-C3} \geq 0,$$
$$x_{F2-C1} \geq 0, \ x_{F2-C2} \geq 0, \ x_{F2-C3} \geq 0.$$

3.16 a) Requirement 1: The total amount shipped from Mine 1 must be 40 tons.
Requirement 2: The total amount shipped from Mine 2 must be 60 tons.
Requirement 3: The total amount shipped to the Plant must be 100 tons.
Requirement 4: For Storage 1, the amount shipped out minus the amount in = 0.
Requirement 5: For Storage 2, the amount shipped out minus the amount in = 0.

b)

Require- ment	Contribution Toward Required Amount Per Unit Shipped						Required Amount
	M1-S1	M1-S2	M2-S1	M2-S2	S1-P	S2-P	
M1 Amt	1	1	0	0	0	0	40
M2 Amt	0	0	1	1	0	0	60
S1 Amt	1	0	1	0	-1	0	0
S2 Amt	0	1	0	1	0	-1	0
P Amt	0	0	0	0	1	1	100
Capacity	30	30	50	50	70	70	
Unit Cost	$2000	$1700	$1600	$1100	$400	$800	

c)

Requirement	M1-S1	M1-S2	M2-S1	M2-S2	S1-P	S2-P	Totals		Required Amount
				Contribution Toward Required Amount Per Unit Shipped					
M1 Amount	1	1	0	0	0	0	40	=	40
M2 Amount	0	0	1	1	0	0	60	=	60
S1 Amount	1	0	1	0	-1	0	0	=	0
S2 Amount	0	1	0	1	0	-1	0	=	0
P Amount	0	0	0	0	1	1	100	=	100
Capacity	30	30	50	50	70	70			
Unit Cost	2000	1700	1600	1100	400	800	$ 194,000		
Solution	10	30	10	50	70	30			

d) Let

$x_{M1\text{-}S1}$ = number of units shipped from Mine 1 to Storage 1,

$x_{M1\text{-}S2}$ = number of units shipped from Mine 1 to Storage 2,

$x_{M2\text{-}S1}$ = number of units shipped from Mine 2 to Storage 1,

$x_{M2\text{-}S2}$ = number of units shipped from Mine 2 to Storage 2,

$x_{S1\text{-}P}$ = number of units shipped from Storage 1 to the Plant,

$x_{S2\text{-}P}$ = number of units shipped from Storage 2 to the Plant.

$$\text{Minimize } C = 2000x_{M1-S1} + 1700x_{M1-S2} + 1600x_{M2-S1} +$$
$$1100x_{M2-S2} + 400x_{S1-P} + 800x_{S2-P}$$

subject to
$$x_{M1-S1} + x_{M1-S2} = 40$$
$$x_{M2-S1} + x_{M2-S2} = 60$$
$$x_{M1-S1} + x_{M2-S1} - x_{S1-P} = 0$$
$$x_{M1-S2} + x_{M2-S2} - x_{S2-P} = 0$$
$$x_{S1-P} + x_{S2-P} = 100$$
$$x_{M1-S1} \le 30, \ x_{M1-S2} \le 30$$
$$x_{M2-S1} \le 50, \ x_{M2-S2} \le 50$$
$$x_{S1-P} \le 70, \ x_{S2-P} \le 70$$

and
$$x_{M1-S1} \ge 0, \ x_{M1-S2} \ge 0, \ x_{M2-S1} \ge 0,$$
$$x_{M2-S2} \ge 0, \ x_{S1-P} \ge 0, \ x_{S2-P} \ge 0.$$

3.17 a)

$$A_1 + B_1 + R_1 = 60{,}000$$
$$A_2 + B_2 + C_2 + R_2 = R_1$$
$$A_3 + B_3 + R_3 = R_2 + 1.40A_1$$
$$A_4 + R_4 = R_3 + 1.40A_2 + 1.70B_1$$
$$D_5 + R_5 = R_4 + 1.40A_3 + 1.70B_2$$

b)

Let A_t = amount invested in investment A at the beginning of year t

B_t = amount invested in investment A at the beginning of year t

C_t = amount invested in investment A at the beginning of year t

D_t = amount invested in investment A at the beginning of year t

R_t = amount not invested at the beginning of year t.

Maximize $P = 1.40A_4 + 1.70B_3 + 1.90C_2 + 1.30D_5 + R_5$

subject to
$$A_1 + B_1 + R_1 = 60{,}000$$
$$A_2 + B_2 + C_2 - R_1 + R_2 = 0$$
$$-1.40A_1 + A_3 + B_3 - R_2 + R_3 = 0$$
$$-1.40A_2 + A_4 - 1.70B_1 - R_3 + R_4 = 0$$
$$-1.40A_3 - 1.70B_2 + D_5 - R_4 + R_5 = 0$$

and
$$A_t \geq 0,\ B_t \geq 0,\ C_t \geq 0,\ D_t \geq 0,\ R_t \geq 0.$$

c & d)

Contribution Toward Required Amount Per Unit

				Investment						Remainder							Required
Year	A1	A2	A3	A4	B1	B2	B3	C2	D5	R1	R2	R3	R4	R5	Totals		Amount
1	1	0	0	0	1	0	0	0	0	1	0	0	0	0	60000	=	60000
2	0	1	0	0	0	1	0	1	0	-1	1	0	0	0	0	=	0
3	-1.4	0	0	0	0	0	1	0	0	0	-1	1	0	0	0	=	0
4	0	-1.4	0	1	-1.7	0	0	0	0	0	0	-1	1	0	-1.33577E-12	=	0
5	0	0	-1.4	0	0	-1.7	0	0	1	0	0	0	-1	1	1.45519E-11	=	0
Unit Profit	0	0	0	1.4	0	0	1.7	1.9	1.3	0	0	0	0	1	$ 152,880		
Solution	60000	0	84000	0	0	0	0	0	117600	0	0	0	0	0			

3.18 a)

$$60x_1 + 25x_2 + 45x_3 + 20x_4 + 50x_5 = 40$$
$$10x_1 + 15x_2 + 45x_3 + 50x_4 + 40x_5 = 35$$
$$30x_1 + 60x_2 + 10x_3 + 30x_4 + 10x_5 = 25$$
$$x_1 + x_2 + x_3 + x_4 + x_5 = 1$$

b)

Require- ment	Contribution Toward Required Amount					Required Amount
	Alloy 1	Alloy 2	Alloy 3	Alloy 4	Alloy 5	
% tin	60	25	45	20	50	40
% zinc	10	15	45	50	45	35
% lead	30	60	10	30	10	25
% total	1	1	1	1	1	1
Unit Cost	$22	$20	$25	$24	$27	

c)

Requirement	Contribution Toward Required Amount					Totals		Required Amount
	Alloy 1	Alloy 2	Alloy 3	Alloy 4	Alloy 5			
% tin	60	25	45	20	50	40	=	40
% zinc	10	15	45	50	45	35	=	35
% lead	30	60	10	30	10	25	=	25
% total	1	1	1	1	1	1	=	1
Unit Cost	22	20	25	24	27	$ 23.46		
Solution	0.0435	0.2826	0.6739	0	3E-15			

d) Let x_1 = amount of Alloy 1 used,
x_2 = amount of Alloy 2 used,
x_3 = amount of Alloy 3 used,
x_4 = amount of Alloy 4 used,
x_5 = amount of Alloy 5 used.

Minimize $C = 22x_1 + 20x_2 + 25x_3 + 24x_4 + 27x_5$

subject to $\quad 60x_1 + 25x_2 + 45x_3 + 20x_4 + 50x_5 = 40$

$\quad\quad\quad\quad 10x_1 + 15x_2 + 45x_3 + 50x_4 + 40x_5 = 35$

$\quad\quad\quad\quad 30x_1 + 60x_2 + 10x_3 + 30x_4 + 10x_5 = 25$

$\quad\quad\quad\quad x_1 + x_2 + x_3 + x_4 + x_5 = 1$

and $\quad x_1 \geq 0, \ x_2 \geq 0, \ x_3 \geq 0, \ x_4 \geq 0, \ x_5 \geq 0.$

3.19 a)

Resource	Resource Usage Per Unit of Each Activity									Resource Available
	P1-L	P1-M	P1-S	P2-L	P2-M	P2-S	P3-L	P3-M	P3-S	
Capacity P1	1	1	1	0	0	0	0	0	0	750 units
Capacity P2	0	0	0	1	1	1	0	0	0	900 units
Capacity P3	0	0	0	0	0	0	1	1	1	450 units
Space P1	20	15	12	0	0	0	0	0	0	13000 sf
Space P2	0	0	0	20	15	12	0	0	0	12000 sf
Space P3	0	0	0	0	0	0	20	15	12	5000 sf
Sales P1	1	0	0	1	0	0	1	0	0	900 units
Sales P2	0	1	0	0	1	0	0	1	0	1200 units
Sales P3	0	0	1	0	0	1	0	0	1	750 units
Unit Profit	$42	$36	$30	$42	$36	$30	$42	$36	$30	
	0	0	0	0	0	0	0	0	0	

Requirement	Contribution Toward Required Amount									Required Amount
	P1-L	P1-M	P1-S	P2-L	P2-M	P2-S	P3-L	P3-M	P3-S	
% P1=%P2	1/750	1/750	1/750	-1/900	-1/900	-1/900	0	0	0	0
%P1=%P3	1/750	1/750	1/750	0	0	0	-1/450	-1/450	-1/450	0

b & c)

Resource	Resource Usage Per Unit of Each Activity									Totals		Resource Available
	P1-L	P1-M	P1-S	P2-L	P2-M	P2-S	P3-L	P3-M	P3-S			
Capacity P1	1	1	1	0	0	0	0	0	0	694.444	≤	750
Capacity P2	0	0	0	1	1	1	0	0	0	833.333	≤	900
Capacity P3	0	0	0	0	0	0	1	1	1	416.667	≤	450
Space P1	20	15	12	0	0	0	0	0	0	13000	≤	13000
Space P2	0	0	0	20	15	12	0	0	0	12000	≤	12000
Space P3	0	0	0	0	0	0	20	15	12	5000	≤	5000
Sales P1	1	0	0	1	0	0	1	0	0	516.667	≤	900
Sales P2	0	1	0	0	1	0	0	1	0	844.444	≤	1200
Sales P3	0	0	1	0	0	1	0	0	1	583.333	≤	750

Requirement	Contribution Toward Required Amount									Totals		Required Amount
	P1-L	P1-M	P1-S	P2-L	P2-M	P2-S	P3-L	P3-M	P3-S			
%P1=%P2	0.00133	0.00133	0.00133	-0.0011	-0.0011	-0.0011	0	0	0	0	=	0
%P1=%P3	0.00133	0.00133	0.00133	0	0	0	-0.0022	-0.0022	-0.0022	0	=	0
Unit Profit	420	360	300	420	360	300	420	360	300	$ 696,000		
Solution	516.667	177.778	0	0	666.667	166.667	0	0	416.667			

d) Let

x_{P1L} = number of large units produced at Plant 1,

x_{P1M} = number of medium units produced at Plant 1.

x_{P1S} = number of small units produced at Plant 1,

x_{P2L} = number of large units produced at Plant 2,

x_{P2M} = number of medium units produced at Plant 2.

x_{P2S} = number of small units produced at Plant 2,

x_{P3L} = number of large units produced at Plant 3,

x_{P3M} = number of medium units produced at Plant 3.

x_{P3S} = number of small units produced at Plant 3.

Maximize $P = 420x_{P1L} + 360x_{P1M} + 300x_{P1S} + 420x_{P2L} + 360x_{P2M} +$
$$300x_{P2S} + 420x_{P3L} + 360x_{P3M} + 300x_{P3S}$$

subject to $\quad x_{P1L} + x_{P1M} + x_{P1S} \le 750$

$$x_{P2L} + x_{P2M} + x_{P2S} \le 900$$

$$x_{P3L} + x_{P3M} + x_{P3S} \le 450$$

$$20x_{P1L} + 15x_{P1M} + 12x_{P1S} \le 13000$$

$$20x_{P2L} + 15x_{P2M} + 12x_{P2S} \le 12000$$

$$20x_{P3L} + 15x_{P3M} + 12x_{P3S} \le 5000$$

$$x_{P1L} + x_{P2L} + x_{P3L} \le 900$$

$$x_{P1M} + x_{P2M} + x_{P3M} \le 1200$$

$$x_{P1S} + x_{P2S} + x_{P3S} \le 750$$

$$\frac{1}{750}x_{P1L} + \frac{1}{750}x_{P1M} + \frac{1}{750}x_{P1S} - \frac{1}{900}x_{P2L} - \frac{1}{900}x_{P2M} - \frac{1}{900}x_{P2S} = 0$$

$$\frac{1}{750}x_{P1L} + \frac{1}{750}x_{P1M} + \frac{1}{750}x_{P1S} - \frac{1}{450}x_{P3L} - \frac{1}{450}x_{P3M} - \frac{1}{450}x_{P3S} = 0$$

and $\quad x_{P1L} \ge 0, \; x_{P1M} \ge 0, \; x_{P1S} \ge 0, \; x_{P2L} \ge 0, \; x_{P2M} \ge 0,$

$$x_{P2S} \ge 0, \; x_{P3L} \ge 0, \; x_{P3M} \ge 0, \; x_{P3S} \ge 0.$$

3.20   a)

Resource	Resource Usage Per Unit of Each Activity												Resource Available
	1F	1C	1B	2F	2C	2B	3F	3C	3B	4F	4C	4B	
Front Wt.	1	0	0	1	0	0	1	0	0	1	0	0	12 tons
Center Wt.	0	1	0	0	1	0	0	1	0	0	1	0	18 tons
Back Wt.	0	0	1	0	0	1	0	0	1	0	0	1	10 tons
Cargo 1 Wt.	1	1	1	0	0	0	0	0	0	0	0	0	20 tons
Cargo 2 Wt.	0	0	0	1	1	1	0	0	0	0	0	0	16 tons
Cargo 3 Wt.	0	0	0	0	0	0	1	1	1	0	0	0	25 tons
Cargo 4 Wt	0	0	0	0	0	0	0	0	0	1	1	1	13 tons
Front Space	500	0	0	700	0	0	600	0	0	400	0	0	7000 cf
Center Space	0	500	0	0	700	0	0	600	0	0	400	0	9000 cf
Back Space	0	0	500	0	0	700	0	0	600	0	0	400	5000 cf
Unit Profit ($)	320	320	320	400	400	400	360	360	360	290	290	290	

Req'm't	Contribution Toward Required Amount												Reqd Amt
	1F	1C	1B	2F	2C	2B	3F	3C	3B	4F	4C	4B	
%F=%C	1/12	-1/18	0	1/12	-1/18	0	1/12	-1/18	0	1/12	-1/18	0	0
%F=%B	1/12	0	-1/10	1/12	0	-1/10	1/12	0	-1/10	1/12	0	-1/10	0

b)

Resource	Resource Usage Per Unit of Each Activity												Totals		Resource Available
	1F	1C	1B	2F	2C	2B	3F	3C	3B	4F	4C	4B			
Front Wt.	1	0	0	1	0	0	1	0	0	1	0	0	12	≤	12
Center Wt.	0	1	0	0	1	0	0	1	0	0	1	0	18	≤	18
Back Wt.	0	0	1	0	0	1	0	0	1	0	0	1	10	≤	10
Cargo 1 Wt.	1	1	1	0	0	0	0	0	0	0	0	0	15	≤	20
Cargo 2 Wt.	0	0	0	1	1	1	0	0	0	0	0	0	12	≤	16
Cargo 3 Wt.	0	0	0	0	0	0	1	1	1	0	0	0	0	≤	25
Cargo 4 Wt.	0	0	0	0	0	0	0	0	0	1	1	1	13	≤	13
Space Front	500	0	0	700	0	0	600	0	0	400	0	0	7000	≤	7000
Space Center	0	500	0	0	700	0	0	600	0	0	400	0	9000	≤	9000
Space Back	0	0	500	0	0	700	0	0	600	0	0	400	5000	≤	5000

Requirement	Contribution Toward Required Amount												Totals		Required Amount
	1F	1C	1B	2F	2C	2B	3F	3C	3B	4F	4C	4B			
%F=%C	0.0833	-0.0556	0	0.0833	-0.0556	0	0.0833	-0.0556	0	0.08333	-0.0556	0	0	=	0
%F=%B	0.0833	0	-0.1	0.0833	0	-0.1	0.0833	0	-0.1	0.0833	0	-0.1	0	=	0
Unit Profit	320	320	320	400	400	400	360	360	360	290	290	290	$ 13,330		
Solution	0	5	10	7.33333	4.167	0.000	0	0	0	4.66667	8.333	0.000			

c) Let

x_{1F} = number of tons of cargo type 1 stowed in the front compartment,

x_{1C} = number of tons of cargo type 1 stowed in the center compartment

x_{1B} = number of tons of cargo type 1 stowed in the back compartment,

x_{2F} = number of tons of cargo type 2 stowed in the front compartment,

x_{2C} = number of tons of cargo type 2 stowed in the center compartment

x_{2B} = number of tons of cargo type 2 stowed in the back compartment,

x_{3F} = number of tons of cargo type 3 stowed in the front compartment,

x_{3C} = number of tons of cargo type 3 stowed in the center compartment

x_{3B} = number of tons of cargo type 3 stowed in the back compartment,

x_{4F} = number of tons of cargo type 4 stowed in the front compartment,

x_{4C} = number of tons of cargo type 4 stowed in the center compartment

x_{4B} = number of tons of cargo type 4 stowed in the back compartment.

Maximize $P = 320x_{1F} + 320x_{1C} + 320x_{1B} + 400x_{2F} + 400x_{2C} + 400x_{2B} +$

$\qquad 360x_{3F} + 360x_{3C} + 360x_{3B} + 290x_{4F} + 290x_{4C} + 400x_{4B}$

subject to

$$x_{1F} + x_{2F} + x_{3F} + x_{4F} \le 12$$

$$x_{1C} + x_{2C} + x_{3C} + x_{4C} \le 18$$

$$x_{1B} + x_{2B} + x_{3B} + x_{4B} \le 10$$

$$x_{1F} + x_{1C} + x_{1B} \le 20$$

$$x_{2F} + x_{2C} + x_{2B} \le 16$$

$$x_{3F} + x_{3C} + x_{3B} \le 25$$

$$x_{4F} + x_{4C} + x_{4B} \le 13$$

$$500x_{1F} + 700x_{2F} + 600x_{3F} + 400x_{4F} \le 7000$$

$$500x_{1C} + 700x_{2C} + 600x_{3C} + 400x_{4C} \le 9000$$

$$500x_{1B} + 700x_{2B} + 600x_{3B} + 400x_{4B} \le 5000$$

$$\frac{1}{12}x_{1F} + \frac{1}{12}x_{2F} + \frac{1}{12}x_{3F} + \frac{1}{12}x_{4F} - \frac{1}{18}x_{1C} - \frac{1}{18}x_{2C} - \frac{1}{18}x_{3C} - \frac{1}{18}x_{4C} = 0$$

$$\frac{1}{12}x_{1F} + \frac{1}{12}x_{2F} + \frac{1}{12}x_{3F} + \frac{1}{12}x_{4F} - \frac{1}{10}x_{1B} - \frac{1}{10}x_{2B} - \frac{1}{10}x_{3B} - \frac{1}{10}x_{4B} = 0$$

and

$$x_{1F} \ge 0,\ x_{1C} \ge 0,\ x_{1B} \ge 0,\ x_{2F} \ge 0,\ x_{2C} \ge 0,\ x_{2B} \ge 0,$$

$$x_{3F} \ge 0,\ x_{3C} \ge 0,\ x_{3B} \ge 0,\ x_{4F} \ge 0,\ x_{4C} \ge 0,\ x_{4B} \ge 0.$$

3.21 a)

Resource	Men's	Women's	Children's	Full-Time	Part-Time	Totals		Resource Available
Leather	2	1.5	1	0	0	5000	≤	5000
Labor	30	45	40	-2400	-1200	0	≤	0
Full-Time Employees	0	0	0	1	0	25	≥	20
Employee Ratio	0	0	0	1	-2	0	≥	0
Unit Profit	8	10	6	-520	-200	4500		
Solution	2500	0	0	25	12.5			

(Resource Usage Per Unit of Each Activity)

b) Let M = number of men's gloves to produce per week,
W = number of women's gloves to produce per week,
C = number of children's gloves to produce per week,
F = number of full-time workers to employ,
PT = number of part-time workers to employ.

Maximize $P = 8M + 10W + 6C - 13(40)F - 10(20)PT$

subject to

$$2M + 1.5W + C \le 5000$$
$$30M + 45W + 40C \le 40(60)F + 20(60)PT$$
$$F \ge 20$$
$$F \ge 2PT$$

and $M \ge 0,\ W \ge 0,\ C \ge 0,\ F \ge 0,\ PT \ge 0.$

3.22

Resource Usage Per Unit of Each Activity

Resource	KC,M	KC,W	KC,F	DH,Tu	DH,Th	HB,M	HB,Tu	HB,W	HB,F	SC,M	SC,Tu	SC,W	SC,F	KS,M	KS,W	KS,Th	NK,Th	NK,F	Totals		Resource Available
KC Knowledge	1	1	1																9	≥	8
DH Knowledge				1	1														8	≥	8
HB Knowledge						1	1	1	1										19	≥	8
SC Knowledge										1	1	1	1						20	≥	8
KS Knowledge														1	1	1			7	≥	7
NK Knowledge																	1	1	7	≥	7
Mon Hours	1					1				1				1					14	≥	14
Tues Hours				1			1				1								14	≥	14
Wed Hours		1						1				1			1				14	≥	14
Thurs Hours					1											1	1		14	≥	14
Fri Hours			1						1				1					1	14	≥	14
Availability KC,M	1																		4	≤	6
Availability KC,W		1																	2	≤	6
Availability KC,F			1																3	≤	6
Availability DH,Tu				1															2	≤	6
Availability DH,TH					1														6	≤	6
Availability HB,M						1													4	≤	4
Availability HB,Tu							1												7	≤	8
Availability HB,W								1											4	≤	4
Availability HB,F									1										4	≤	4
Availability SC,M										1									5	≤	5
Availability SC,Tu											1								5	≤	5
Availability SC,W												1							5	≤	5
Availability SC,F													1						5	≤	5
Availability KS,M														1					1	≤	3
Availability KS,W															1				3	≤	3
Availability KS,Th																1			3	≤	8
Availability NK,Th																	1		5	≤	6
Availability NK,F																		1	2	≤	2
Unit Cost	10	10	10	10.1	10.1	9.9	9.9	9.9	9.9	9.8	9.8	9.8	9.8	10.8	10.8	10.8	11.3	11.3	710		
Solution	4	2	3	2	6	4	7	4	4	5	5	5	5	1	3	3	5	2			

3.23　a)　<u>Resource Constraints:</u>
Calories must be no more than 420.
No more than 20% of total calories from fat.

<u>Benefit Constraints:</u>
Calories must be at least 380
There must be at least 50 mg of vitamin content.
There must be at least 2 times as much strawberry flavoring as sweetener.

<u>Fixed-Requirement Constraints:</u>
There must be 15 mg of thickeners.

b)

| | Resource Usage Per Unit of Each Activity | | | | | | | Resource |
Resource	Strawberry	Cream	Vitamin	Sweetener	Thickener	Totals		Available
Min Calories	50	100	0	120	80	380	≥	380
Max Calories	50	100	0	120	80	380	≤	420
Fat	-9	55	0	-24	14	-73	≤	0
Vitamin	20	0	50	0	2	128	≥	50
Taste	1	0	0	-2	0	0	≥	0
Thickness	3	8	1	2	25	15	=	15
Unit Cost	10	8	25	15	6	90		
Solution	3.455	0	1	2	0			

c)　Let　S = Tablespoons of strawberry flavoring,
CR = Tablespoons of cream,
V = Tablespoons of vitamin supplement,
A = Tablespoons of artificial sweetener,
T = Tablespoons of thickening agent,

Minimize $C = 10S + 8CR + 25V + 15A + 6T$

subject to　$50S + 100CR + 120A + 80T \geq 380$

$50S + 100CR + 120A + 80T \leq 420$

$S + 75CR + 30T \leq 0.2(50S + 100C + 120A + 80T)$

$20S + 50V + 2T \geq 50$

$S \geq 2A$

$3S + 8CR + V + 2A + 25T = 15$

and　$S \geq 0, \; CR \geq 0, \; V \geq 0, \; A \geq 0, \; T \geq 0.$

3.24 a) Resource Constraints:
Calories must be no more than 600.
No more than 30% of total calories from fat.

Benefit Constraints:
Calories must be at least 400
There must be at least 60 mg of vitamin C.
There must be at least 12 g of protein.
There must be at least 2 times as much peanut butter as jelly.
There must be at least 1 cup of liquid

Fixed-Requirement Constraints:
There must be 2 slices of bread.

b & c)

Resource	Resource Usage Per Unit of Each Activity						Totals		Resource Available
	Bread	PB	Jelly	Crackers	Milk	Juice			
Min Calories	70	100	50	60	150	100	600	≥	400
Max Calories	70	100	50	60	150	100	600	≤	600
Fat	-11	45	-15	2	25	-30	-145	≤	0
Vitamin C	0	0	3	0	2	120	514	≥	60
Protein	3	4	0	1	8	1	12	≥	12
Bread	1	0	0	0	0	0	2	=	2
PB&J	0	1	-2	0	0	0	0	≥	0
Liquid	0	0	0	0	1	1	4	≥	1
Unit Cost	5	4	7	8	15	35	163		
Solution	2	0	0	0	0	4			

d) Let B = slices of bread,
P = Tablespoons of peanut butter,
S = Tablespoons of strawberry jelly,
G = graham crackers,
M = cups of milk,
J = cups of juice.

Minimize $C = 5B + 4P + 7S + 8G + 15M + 35J$

subject to $70B + 100P + 50S + 60G + 150M + 100J \geq 400$

$70B + 100P + 50S + 60G + 150M + 100J \leq 600$

$10B + 75P + 20G + 70M \leq$

$.3(70B + 100P + 50S + 60G + 150M + 100J)$

$3S + 2M + 120J \geq 60$

$3B + 4P + G + 8M + J \geq 12$

$B = 2$

$P \geq 2S$

$M + J \geq 1$

and $B \geq 0, \ P \geq 0, \ S \geq 0, \ G \geq 0, \ M \geq 0, \ J \geq 0.$

Cases

3.1 a) The fixed design and fashion costs are sunk costs and therefore should not be considered when setting the production now in July. Since the velvet shirts have a positive contribution to covering the sunk costs, they should be produced or at least considered for production according to the linear programming model. Had Ted raised these concerns before any fixed costs were made, then he would have been correct to advise against designing and producing the shirts. With a contribution of $22 and a demand of 6000 units, maximum expected profit will be only $132,000. This amount will not be enough to cover the $500,000 in fixed costs directly attributable to this product.

b) The following insight greatly simplifies the analysis of the problem. The production processes of the various clothing items are not all linked together. We can separate the clothing items according to the materials that are used in their production and instead of one large linear programming problem we can formulate 4 smaller problems.

We use the term net contribution of a sales item to describe the difference between its total revenues and variable costs. The net contribution does not reflect any part of the fixed costs.

The cashmere sweater is the only item consisting of cashmere. The net contribution of one cashmere sweater equals $450 - $150 – 1.5*$60 = $210. TrendLines can sell at most 4000 sweaters and has 9000 yards of cashmere as raw material. It is optimal to produce 4000 sweaters using 6000 yards of cashmere yielding a net contribution of 4000*$210 = $840,000.

The silk blouse and camisole are the only items using silk and no other materials are used for these items. We can determine the optimal production amounts of these two items through a simple linear program. The first constraint models the resource limitation in the production process that Katherine has ordered 18,000 yards of silk. The second constraint models the production condition that whenever a silk blouse is produced automatically also a silk camisole is produced. Finally we must include the stated upper bounds on the number of silk items we can sell.

	A	B	C	D	E	F	G
1							
2							
3			Activity				
4		Constraint	silk blouse	silk camisole	Totals		Constraint RHS
5		silk	1.5	0.5	18000	<=	18000
6		production	1	-1	-8000	<=	0
7		unit profit	60.5	53.5	1226000		
8		Solution	7000	15000			
9		Maximum	12000	15000			

	E
3	
4	Totals
5	=SUMPRODUCT(C5:D5,C8:D8)
6	=SUMPRODUCT(C6:D6,C8:D8)
7	=SUMPRODUCT(C7:D7,C8:D8)
8	

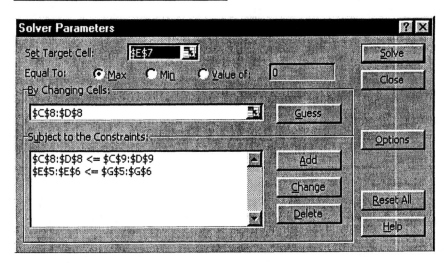

Throughout this case we use the following solver options.

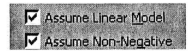

TrendLines should produce 7000 silk blouses and 15000 silk camisoles yielding a net contribution of $1,226,000.

We can determine the optimal production plan for the items made from cotton in a similar fashion. There are no demand limitations for the cotton items.

	A	B	C	D	E	F	G
1							
2							
3			Activity				
4		Constraint	cotton sweater	cotton m-s	Totals		Constraint RHS
5		wool	1.5	0.5	30000	<=	30000
6		production	1	-1	-60000	<=	0
7		unit profit	66.25	33.75	2025000		
8		Solution	0	60000			

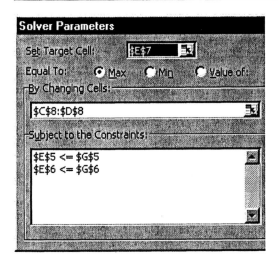

TrendLines should produce 60000 cotton mini-skirts but no cotton sweaters yielding a net contribution of $2,025,000.

It remains to develop a linear programming problem for determining the optimal production quantities of the tailored wool slacks, the tailored skirt, the wool blazer, the velvet pants and shirts, and the button-down blouse. We include four constraints for the resource limitations on wool, velvet, rayon, and acetate. Upper and lower bounds are given for many items. When there is no lower bound, we insert 0, when there is no upper bound, we determine a safe upper bound as a consequence of the resource limitations.

	A	B	C	D	E	F	G	H	I	J	K
1											
2											
3			Resource Usage Per Unit of Each Activity								
4			Activity								Resource
5		Resource	tail.wool slacks	tail.skirt	wool blazer	velvet pants	velvet shirt	b.-d. blouse	Totals		Available
6		wool	3	0	2.5	0	0	0	25100	<=	45000
7		acetate	2	1.5	1.5	2	0	0	28000	<=	28000
8		rayon	0	2	0	0	0	1.5	30000	<=	30000
9		velvet	0	0	0	3	1.5	0	9000	<=	20000
10		unit profit	110	143.25	155.25	136	22	26.625	2771933.333		
11		Solution	4200	8066.666667	5000	0	6000	9244.444444			
12		Minimum	4200	2800	3000	0	0	0			
13		Maximum	7000	20000	5000	5500	6000	20000			

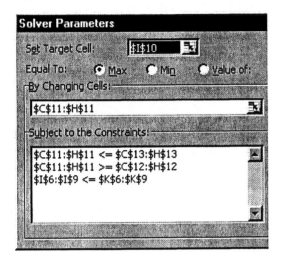

	I
4	
5	Totals
6	=SUMPRODUCT(C6:H6,C11:H11)
7	=SUMPRODUCT(C7:H7,C11:H11)
8	=SUMPRODUCT(C8:H8,C11:H11)
9	=SUMPRODUCT(C9:H9,C11:H11)
10	=SUMPRODUCT(C10:H10,C11:H11)
11	

Solver Parameters

Set Target Cell: $I$10

Equal To: ● Max   ○ Min   ○ Value of:

By Changing Cells:

$C$11:$H$11

Subject to the Constraints:

$C$11:$H$11 <= $C$13:$H$13
$C$11:$H$11 >= $C$12:$H$12
$I$6:$I$9 <= $K$6:$K$9

TrendLines should produce 4200 wool slacks, 8066.67 skirts, 5000 wool blazers, no velvet pants, 6000 velvet shirts, and 9244.44 button-down blouses. The net contribution of these items equals $2,771,933.33. (Of course, TrendLines cannot produce two-thirds of a skirt, so the actual solution should be integer. You will learn about integer programming in chapter 8.)

The net contribution of all clothing items equals $840,000 + $1,226,00 + $ 2,025,000 + $2,771,933.33 = $6,862,933.33. So far we have not considered the sunk costs for the three fashion shows and the designers which total $8,960,000. The total profit equals $6,862,933.33 - $8,960,000 = -$2,097,066.67. So, TrendLines actually loses almost $2.1 million.

c) If velvet cannot be sent back to the textile wholesaler, then the whole quantity will be considered as a sunk cost and therefore added to the fixed costs. The objective function coefficients of items using velvet will no longer include the material cost. The objective function coefficients of the velvet pants and shirts are now $175 and $40, respectively.

	A	B	C	D	E	F	G	H		I	J	K
1												
2												
3					Resource Usage Per Unit of Each Activity							
4					Activity							Resource
5		Resource	tail.wool slacks	tail.skirt	wool blazer	velvet pants	velvet shirt	b.-d. blouse		Totals		Available
6		wool	3	0	2.5	0	0	0		25100	<=	45000
7		acetate	2	1.5	1.5	2	0	0		28000	<=	28000
8		rayon	0	2	0	0	0	1.5		30000	<=	30000
9		velvet	0	0	0	3	1.5	0		20000	<=	20000
10		unit profit	110	143.25	155.25	172	40	26.625		2983822.22		
11		Solution	4200	3177.777778	5000	3666.666667	6000	15762.96296				
12		Minimum	4200	2800	3000	0	0	0				
13		Maximum	7000	20000	5000	5500	6000	20000				

The production plan changes considerably. TrendLines should produce 4200 wool slacks, 3177.77 skirts, 5000 wool blazers, 3666.67 velvet pants, 6000 velvet shirts, and 15762.92 button-down blouses. The production decisions for all other items are unaffected by the change. The net contribution of all clothing items equals $840,000 + $1,226,00 + $ 2,025,000 + $2,983,822.22 = $7,074,822.22. The sunk costs now include the material cost for velvet and total $9,200,000. The loss equals $9,200,000 - $7,074,822.22 = $2,125,177.78.

d) When TrendLines cannot return the velvet to the wholesaler, the costs for velvet cannot be recovered. These cost are no longer variable cost but now are sunk cost. As a consequence the increased net contribution of the velvet items makes them more attractive to produce. This way the revenues from selling these items can contribute to the recovery of at least some of the fixed costs. Instead of zero TrendLines produces now 3666.67 velvet pants. These pants also require some acetate and thus their production affects the production plan for all other items. Since it is not optimal to make full use of the ordered velvet in part (b) it comes as no surprise that the loss in part (c) is even bigger than in part (b).

e) The unit contribution of a wool blazer changes to $75.25.

	A	B	C	D	E	F	G	H		I	J	K
1												
2												
3					Resource Usage Per Unit of Each Activity							
4					Activity							Resource
5		Resource	tail.wool slacks	tail.skirt	wool blazer	velvet pants	velvet shirt	b.-d. blouse		Totals		Available
6		wool	3	0	2.5	0	0	0		20100	<=	45000
7		acetate	2	1.5	1.5	2	0	0		28000	<=	28000
8		rayon	0	2	0	0	0	1.5		30000	<=	30000
9		velvet	0	0	0	3	1.5	0		9000	<=	20000
10		unit profit	110	143.25	75.25	136	22	26.625		2436933.333		
11		Solution	4200	10066.66667	3000	0	6000	6577.777778				
12		Minimum	4200	2800	3000	0	0	0				
13		Maximum	7000	20000	5000	5500	6000	20000				

TrendLines should produce 4200 wool slacks, 10066.67 skirts, the minimum of 3000 wool blazers, no velvet pants, 6000 velvet shirts, and 6577.78 button-down blouses. The production decisions for all other items are unaffected by the change. The net contribution of all clothing items equals $840,000 + $1,226,00 + $ 2,025,000 + $2,436,933.33 = $6,527,933.33. The loss equals $8,960,000 - $6,527,933.33= $2,432,066.67.

f) The right-hand-side of the acetate constraint changes.

	A	B	C	D	E	F	G	H	I	J	K
1											
2											
3					Resource Usage Per Unit of Each Activity						
4					Activity						Resource
5		Resource	tail.wool slacks	tail.skirt	wool blazer	velvet pants	velvet shirt	b.-d. blouse	Totals		Available
6		wool	3	0	2.5	0	0	0	25100	<=	45000
7		acetate	2	1.5	1.5	2	0	0	38000	<=	38000
8		rayon	0	2	0	0	0	1.5	30000	<=	30000
9		velvet	0	0	0	3	1.5	0	9000	<=	20000
10		unit profit	110	143.25	155.25	136	22	26.625	3490266.667		
11		Solution	4200	14733.33333	5000	0	6000	355.5555556			
12		Minimum	4200	2800	3000	0	0	0			
13		Maximum	7000	15000	5000	5500	6000	20000			

TrendLines should produce 4200 wool slacks, 14733.33 skirts, the minimum of 5000 wool blazers, no velvet pants, 6000 velvet shirts, and 355.55 button-down blouses. The production decisions for all other items are unaffected by the change. The net contribution of all clothing items equals $840,000 + $1,226,00 + $ 2,025,000 + $3,490,266.67 = $7,581,266.67. The loss equals $8,960,000 - $7,581,266.67 = $1,378,733.33.

g) The net contribution of one cashmere sweater sold in the November sale equals 0.6*$450 - $150 – 1.5*$60 = $30. After producing 4000 sweaters to be sold in September and October TrendLines has 3000 yards of cashmere as raw material left. It is optimal to produce 2000 more sweaters using the remaining 3000 yards of cashmere yielding an additional contribution of 2000*$30 = $60,000.

For the three linear programming problems determining the production plans for all other clothing items we need to include new decision variables representing the number of clothing items that are sold during the November sale. Clearly TrendLines does not want to produce items with a negative net contribution. Therefore, we need to consider only those clothing items that have a positive net contribution after taking the sales price into account.

	A	B	C	D	E	F	G	H
1								
2								
3				Activity				
4		Constraint	silk blouse	silk camisole	silk camisole(sale)	Totals		Constraint RHS
5		silk	1.5	0.5	0.5	18000	<=	18000
6		production	1	-1	-1	-8000	<=	0
7		unit profit	60.5	53.5	5.5	1226000		
8		Solution	7000	15000	0			
9		Maximum	12000	15000	36000			

	A	B	C	D	E	F	G	H	I
1									
2									
3				Activity					
4		Constraint	cotton sweater	sweater(sale)	cotton m-s	m-s (sale)	Totals		Constraint RHS
5		wool	1.5	1.5	0.5	0.5	30000	<=	30000
6		production	1	1	-1	-1	-60000	<=	0
7		unit profit	66.25	14.25	33.75	3.75	2025000		
8		Solution	0	0	60000	0			

	A	B	C	D	E	F	G	H	I	J	K	L	M
1													
2													
3					Resource Usage Per Unit of Each Activity								
4					Activity								Resource
5		Resource	tail.wool slacks	tail.skirt	skirt (sale)	wool blazer	blazer (sale)	velvet pants	velvet shirt	b.-d. blouse	Totals		Available
6		wool	3	0	0	2.5	2.5	0	0	0	25100	<=	45000
7		acetate	2	1.5	1.5	1.5	1.5	2	0	0	28000	<=	28000
8		rayon	0	2	2	0	0	0	0	1.5	30000	<=	30000
9		velvet	0	0	0	0	0	3	1.5	0	9000	<=	20000
10		unit profit	110	143.25	35.25	155.25	27.25	136	22	26.625	2771933.333		
11		Solution	4200	8066.666667	0	5000	0	0	6000	9244.444444			
12		Minimum	4200	2800	0	3000	0	0	0	0			
13		Maximum	7000	15000	15000	5000	20000	5500	6000	20000			

It only pays to produce 2000 more Cashmere sweaters. The production plan for all other items is the same as in part (b). The sale of the Cashmere sweaters reduces the loss by $60,000 to $2,037,066.67.

3.2   a) We define 12 decision variables, one for each age group surveyed in each region. Rob's restrictions are easily modeled as constraints. For example, his condition that at least 20 percent of the surveyed customers have to be from the first age group requires that the sum of the variables for the age group "18 to 25" across all three regions is at least 400. All his other requirements are modeled similarly. Finally, the sum of all variables has to equal 2000, because that is the number of customers Rob wants to have interviewed.

	A	B	C	D	E	F	G	H	I	J	K
1											
2					Cost per Person						
3					Age Group						
4				18 to 25	26 to 40	41 to 50	51 and over				
5			Silicon Valley	$4.75	$6.50	$6.50	$5.00				
6		Region	Big Cities	$5.25	$5.75	$6.25	$6.25				
7			Small Towns	$6.50	$7.50	$7.50	$7.25				
8											
9											
10											
11					Number of People Surveyed						
12					Age Group						
13				18 to 25	26 to 40	41 to 50	51 and over	Totals		Survey restrictions	
14			Silicon Valley	600	0	0	300	900	>=	300	
15		Region	Big Cities	0	550	150	0	700	>=	700	
16			Small Towns	250	0	160	0	400	>=	400	
17		Totals		850	550	300	300	$ 11,200	=	Total Cost	
18				>=	>=	>=	>=	$12,880.00	=	Bid	
19	Survey restrictions			400	550	300	300			Total Surveys	
20								2000	=	2000	
21											
22			Formula in cell H14:	=SUM(D14:G14)							
23			Formula in cell H15:	=SUM(D15:G15)							
24			Formula in cell H16:	=SUM(D16:G16)							
25			Formula in cell D17:	=SUM(D14:D16)							
26			Formula in cell E17:	=SUM(E14:E16)							
27			Formula in cell F17:	=SUM(F14:F16)							
28			Formula in cell G17:	=SUM(G14:G16)							
29			Formula in cell H20:	=SUM(D14:G16)							
30			Formula in cell H17:	=SUMPRODUCT(D5:G7,D14:G16)							
31			Formula in cell H18:	=1.15*H17							

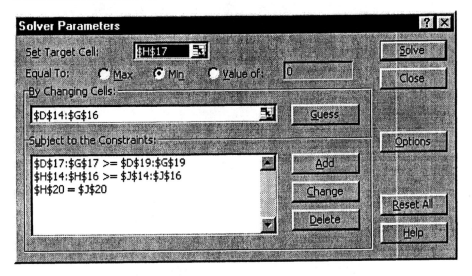

The cost of conducting the survey meeting all constraints imposed by AmeriBank incurs cost of $11,200. The mix of customers is displayed in the spreadsheet above.

b) Sophisticated Surveys will submit a bid of 1.15*$11200 = $12,880.

c) We need to include the new lower-bound constraint on all variables.

	A	B	C	D	E	F	G	H	I	J	K
1											
2					Cost per Person						
3					Age Group						
4				18 to 25	26 to 40	41 to 50	51 and over				
5			Silicon Valley	$4.75	$6.50	$6.50	$5.00				
6		Region	Big Cities	$5.25	$5.75	$6.25	$6.25				
7			Small Towns	$6.50	$7.50	$7.50	$7.25				
8											
9											
10											
11					Number of People Surveyed						
12					Age Group						
13				18 to 25	26 to 40	41 to 50	51 and over	Totals		Survey restrictions	
14			Silicon Valley	600	50	50	200	900	>=	300	
15		Region	Big Cities	150	450	50	50	700	>=	700	
16			Small Towns	100	50	200	50	400	>=	400	
17		Totals		850	550	300	300	11387.5	=	Total Cost	
18				>=	>=	>=	>=	$13,095.62	=	Bid	
19		Survey restrictions		400	550	300	300	Total Surveys			
20								2000	=	2000	
21								Minimum value for each variable			
22			Formula in cell H14:		"=SUM(D14:G14)"					50	
23			Formula in cell H15:		"=SUM(D15:G15)"						
24			Formula in cell H16:		"=SUM(D16:G16)"						
25			Formula in cell D17:		"=SUM(D14:D16)"						
26			Formula in cell E17:		"=SUM(E14:E16)"						
27			Formula in cell F17:		"=SUM(F14:F16)"						
28			Formula in cell G17:		"=SUM(G14:G16)"						
29			Formula in cell H20:		"=SUM(D14:G16)"						
30			Formula in cell H17:		"=SUMPRODUCT(D5:G7,D14:G16)"						
31			Formula in cell H18:		"=1.15*H17"						

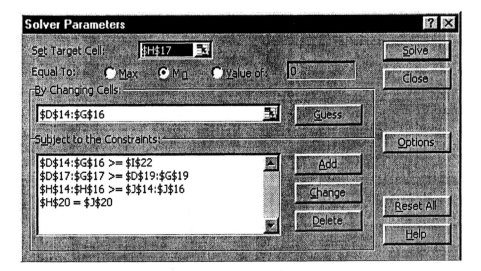

The new requirement increases the bid to $13,095.62.

d) We include upper bounds on the total number of people surveyed in Silicon Valley and from the age group of 18 to 25 year-olds.

	A	B	C	D	E	F	G	H	I	J	K	L
1												
2					Cost per Person							
3					Age Group							
4				18 to 25	26 to 40	41 to 50	51 and over					
5			Silicon Valley	$4.75	$6.50	$6.50	$5.00					
6		Region	Big Cities	$5.25	$5.75	$6.25	$6.25					
7			Small Towns	$6.50	$7.50	$7.50	$7.25					
8												
9												
10												
11					Number of People Surveyed							
12					Age Group							
13				18 to 25	26 to 40	41 to 50	51 and over	Totals		Survey restrictions		
14			Silicon Valley	100	50	50	450	650	>=	300	<=	650
15		Region	Big Cities	400	450	50	50	950	>=	700		
16			Small Towns	100	50	200	50	400	>=	400		
17		Totals		600	550	300	550	$ 11,575	=	Total Cost		
18				>=	>=	>=	>=	$13,311.25	=	Bid		
19	Survey restrictions			400	550	300	300	Total Surveys				
20				<=				2000	=	2000		
21				600				Minimum value for each variable				
22										50		
23												
24			Formula in cell H14:	"=SUM(D14:G14)"								
25			Formula in cell H15:	"=SUM(D15:G15)"								
26			Formula in cell H16:	"=SUM(D16:G16)"								
27			Formula in cell D17:	"=SUM(D14:D16)"								
28			Formula in cell E17:	"=SUM(E14:E16)"								
29			Formula in cell F17:	"=SUM(F14:F16)"								
30			Formula in cell G17:	"=SUM(G14:G16)"								
31			Formula in cell H20:	"=SUM(D14:G16)"								
32			Formula in cell H17:	"=SUMPRODUCT(D5:G7,D14:G16)"								
33			Formula in cell H18:	"=1.15*H17"								

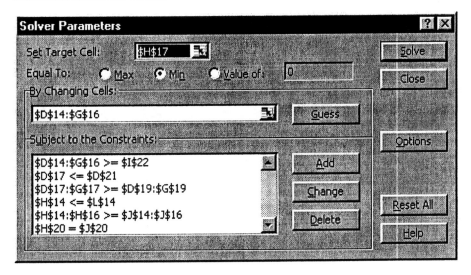

The new requirements increase the bid to $13,311.25.

e) The three cost factors for the age group "18 to 25" are changed.

	A	B	C	D	E	F	G	H	I	J	K	L
1												
2					Cost per Person							
3					Age Group							
4				18 to 25	26 to 40	41 to 50	51 and over					
5			Silicon Valley	$6.50	$6.50	$6.50	$5.00					
6		Region	Big Cities	$6.75	$5.75	$6.25	$6.25					
7			Small Towns	$7.00	$7.50	$7.50	$7.25					
8												
9												
10												
11					Number of People Surveyed							
12					Age Group							
13				18 to 25	26 to 40	41 to 50	51 and over	Totals		Survey restrictions		
14			Silicon Valley	50	50	50	500	650	>=	300	<=	650
15		Region	Big Cities	100	600	200	50	950	>=	700		
16			Small Towns	250	50	50	50	400	>=	400		
17		Totals		400	700	300	600	$ 12,025	=	Total Cost		
18				>=	>=	>=	>=	$13,828.75	=	Bid		
19		Survey restrictions		400	550	300	300	Total Surveys				
20				<=				2000	=	2000		
21				600				Minimum value for each variable				
22								50				
23												
24			Formula in cell H14:	"=SUM(D14:G14)"								
25			Formula in cell H15:	"=SUM(D15:G15)"								
26			Formula in cell H16:	"=SUM(D16:G16)"								
27			Formula in cell D17:	"=SUM(D14:D16)"								
28			Formula in cell E17:	"=SUM(E14:E16)"								
29			Formula in cell F17:	"=SUM(F14:F16)"								
30			Formula in cell G17:	"=SUM(G14:G16)"								
31			Formula in cell H20:	"=SUM(D14:G16)"								
32			Formula in cell H17:	"=SUMPRODUCT(D5:G7,D14:G16)"								
33			Formula in cell H18:	"=1.15*H17"								

With the new cost factors the bid increases to $13,828.75.

f) We eliminate all lower and upper bounds on the age groups and regions and replace them with Rob's strict requirements. These requirements also ensure that exactly 2000 people are surveyed so that we can drop that constraint too.

	A	B	C	D	E	F	G	H	I	J	K
1											
2					Cost per Person						
3					Age Group						
4				18 to 25	26 to 40	41 to 50	51 and over				
5			Silicon Valley	$6.50	$6.50	$6.50	$5.00				
6		Region	Big Cities	$6.75	$5.75	$6.25	$6.25				
7			Small Towns	$7.00	$7.50	$7.50	$7.25				
8											
9											
10											
11					Number of People Surveyed						
12					Age Group						
13				18 to 25	26 to 40	41 to 50	51 and over	Totals		Survey restrictions	
14			Silicon Valley	50	50	50	250	400	=	400	
15		Region	Big Cities	50	600	300	50	1000	=	1000	
16			Small Towns	400	50	50	100	600	=	600	
17		Totals		500	700	400	400	$ 12,475	=	Total Cost	
18				=	=	=	=	$14,346.25	=	Bid	
19		Survey restrictions		500	700	400	400				
20											
21								Minimum value for each variable			
22			Formula in cell H14:	"=SUM(D14:G14)"					50		
23			Formula in cell H15:	"=SUM(D15:G15)"							
24			Formula in cell H16:	"=SUM(D16:G16)"							
25			Formula in cell D17:	"=SUM(D14:D16)"							
26			Formula in cell E17:	"=SUM(E14:E16)"							
27			Formula in cell F17:	"=SUM(F14:F16)"							
28			Formula in cell G17:	"=SUM(G14:G16)"							
29			Formula in cell H20:	"=SUM(D14:G16)"							
30			Formula in cell H17:	"=SUMPRODUCT(D5:G7,D14:G16)"							
31			Formula in cell H18:	"=1.15*H17"							

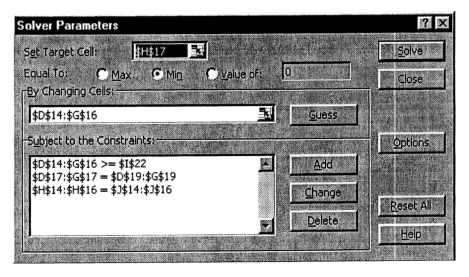

Solver Parameters

Set Target Cell: $H$17
Equal To: ○ Max ⦿ Min ○ Value of: 0
By Changing Cells: $D$14:$G$16

Subject to the Constraints:
$D$14:$G$16 >= $I$22
$D$17:$G$17 = $D$19:$G$19
$H$14:$H$16 = $J$14:$J$16

Solve Close Guess Options Add Change Delete Reset All Help

Rob's strict requirements increase the cost of the survey by $450. The new bid of Sophisticated Surveys is $14,346.25.

3.3 a & b)

Data:

Area	Number of Students	Percentage in 6th Grade	Percentage in 7th Grade	Percentage in 8th Grade	Bussing Cost ($/Student) School 1	School 2	School 3
1	450	0.32	0.38	0.3	300	0	700
2	600	0.37	0.28	0.35	-	400	500
3	550	0.3	0.32	0.38	600	300	200
4	350	0.28	0.4	0.32	200	500	-
5	500	0.39	0.34	0.27	0	-	400
6	450	0.34	0.28	0.38	500	300	0
				Capacity:	900	1100	1000

Solution:

Number of Students Assigned

	School 1	School 2	School 3	Total		
Area 1	0	450	0	450	=	450
Area 2	0	422.222222	177.777778	600	=	600
Area 3	0	227.777778	322.222222	550	=	550
Area 4	350	0	0	350	=	350
Area 5	366.666667	0	133.333333	500	=	500
Area 6	83.3333333	0	366.666667	450	=	450
Total	800	1100	1000			
	≤	≤	≤			
Capacity	900	1100	1000			

Total Bussing Cost = $ 555,555.56

Grade Constraints:

	School 1	School 2	School 3
6th Graders	269.333333	368.555556	339.111111
7th Graders	288	362.111111	300.888889
8th Graders	242.666667	369.333333	360
30% of Total	240	330	300
36% of Total	288	396	360

c) The recommendation to the school board is to assign students to schools as shown in the above solution section of the spreadsheet. Quantities that are not integers must be rounded since partial students cannot be sent.

d) The following solution decreases total bussing costs by over $135,000 but violates the grade constraints that were imposed. Solutions will vary and those than satisfy the grade constraints will be likely to increase the total bussing costs.

Data:

Area	Number of Students	Percentage in 6th Grade	Percentage in 7th Grade	Percentage in 8th Grade	Bussing Cost ($/Student) School 1	School 2	School 3
1	450	0.32	0.38	0.3	300	0	700
2	600	0.37	0.28	0.35	-	400	500
3	550	0.3	0.32	0.38	600	300	200
4	350	0.28	0.4	0.32	200	500	-
5	500	0.39	0.34	0.27	0	-	400
6	450	0.34	0.28	0.38	500	300	0
				Capacity:	900	1100	1000

Solution:

	Number of Students Assigned School 1	School 2	School 3	Total		
Area 1	0	450	0	450	=	450
Area 2	0	600	0	600	=	600
Area 3	0	0	550	550	=	550
Area 4	350	0	0	350	=	350
Area 5	500	0	0	500	=	500
Area 6	0	0	450	450	=	450
Total	850	1050	1000			
	≤	≤	≤			
Capacity	900	1100	1000			

Total Bussing Cost = $ 420,000.00

Grade Constraints:

	School 1	School 2	School 3
6th Graders	293	366	318
7th Graders	310	339	302
8th Graders	247	345	380
30% of Total	255	315	300
36% of Total	306	378	360

e) The number of students assigned from each area to each school changes to the solution shown below and the total bussing cost is reduced by almost $162,000.

Data:

Area	Number of Students	Percentage in 6th Grade	Percentage in 7th Grade	Percentage in 8th Grade	Bussing Cost ($/Student)		
					School 1	School 2	School 3
1	450	0.32	0.38	0.3	300	0	700
2	600	0.37	0.28	0.35	-	400	500
3	550	0.3	0.32	0.38	600	300	0
4	350	0.28	0.4	0.32	0	500	-
5	500	0.39	0.34	0.27	0	-	400
6	450	0.34	0.28	0.38	500	300	0
				Capacity:	900	1100	1000

Solution:

Number of Students Assigned

	School 1	School 2	School 3	Total		
Area 1	0	450	0	450	=	450
Area 2	0	600	0	600	=	600
Area 3	0	0	550	550	=	550
Area 4	350	0	0	350	=	350
Area 5	318.181818	0	181.818182	500	=	500
Area 6	131.818182	50	268.181818	450	=	450
Total	800	1100	1000			
	≤	≤	≤			
Capacity	900	1100	1000			

Total Bussing Cost = $ 393,636.36

Grade Constraints:

	School 1	School 2	School 3
6th Graders	266.909091	383	327.090909
7th Graders	285.090909	353	312.909091
8th Graders	248	364	360
30% of Total	240	330	300
36% of Total	288	396	360

f) The number of students assigned from each area to each school changes to the solution shown below and the total bussing cost is reduced by over $215,000.

Data:

Area	Number of Students	Percentage in 6th Grade	Percentage in 7th Grade	Percentage in 8th Grade	Bussing Cost ($/Student)		
					School 1	School 2	School 3
1	450	0.32	0.38	0.3	0	0	700
2	600	0.37	0.28	0.35	-	400	500
3	550	0.3	0.32	0.38	600	0	0
4	350	0.28	0.4	0.32	0	500	-
5	500	0.39	0.34	0.27	0	-	400
6	450	0.34	0.28	0.38	500	0	0
				Capacity:	900	1100	1000

Solution:

	Number of Students Assigned					
	School 1	School 2	School 3	Total		
Area 1	38.7096771	411.290323	0	450	=	450
Area 2	0	236.559139	363.440861	600	=	600
Area 3	0	77.95699	472.04301	550	=	550
Area 4	350	0	0	350	=	350
Area 5	435.483871	0	64.5161288	500	=	500
Area 6	75.8064517	374.193548	0	450	=	450
Total	900	1100	900			
	≤	≤	≤			
Capacity	900	1100	1000			

Total Bussing Cost = $ 340,053.76

Grade Constraints:

	School 1	School 2	School 3
6th Graders	306	369.752688	301.247312
7th Graders	324	352.247312	274.752688
8th Graders	270	378	324
30% of Total	270	330	270
36% of Total	324	396	324

g)

Option	Cost	# students walking 1 to 1.5 miles	# students walking more than 1.5 miles
current	$555,555.56	0	0
1	$393,636.36	900	0
2	$340,053.76	900	491

h) Answers will vary.

Teaching notes for this chapter are available in the Teaching Notes section near the front of this Instructor's Manual.

Review Questions

4.1-1   The parameters of a linear programming model are the constants (coefficients or right-hand sides) in the functional constraints and the objective function.

4.1-2   Many of the parameters of a linear programming model are only estimates of quantities that cannot be determined precisely and thus result in inaccuracies.

4.1-3   What-if analysis reveals how close each of these estimates needs to be to avoid obtaining an erroneous optimal solution, and therefore pinpoints the sensitive parameters where extra care is needed to refine their estimates.

4.1-4   No, if the optimal solution will remain the same over a wide range of values for a particular coefficient, then it may be appropriate to make only a fairly rough estimate for a parameter of a model.

4.1-5   Conditions that impact the parameters of a model, such as unit profit, may change over time and render them inaccurate.

4.1-6   If conditions change, what-if analysis leaves signposts that indicate whether a resulting change in a parameter of the model changes the optimal solution.

4.1-7   Sensitivity analysis is studying how changes in the parameters of a linear programming model affect the optimal solution.

4.1-8   What-if analysis provides guidance about what the impact would be of altering policy decisions that are represented by parameters of a model.

4.2-1   The estimates of the unit profits for the two products are most questionable.

4.2-2   The number of hours of production time that is being made available per week in the three plants might change after analysis.

4.3-1   The range of optimality for a coefficient in the objective function is the range of values over which the optimal solution for the original model remains optimal.

4.3-2   If the true value for a coefficient in the objective function lies outside its range of optimality then the optimal solution would not hold and the problem would need to be resolved.

4.3-3   The Objective Coefficient column gives the current value of each coefficient. The Allowable Increase column and the Allowable Decrease Column give the amount that each coefficient may differ from these values to remain within the range of optimality.

4.4-1   The 100% rule considers the percentage of the allowable change (increase or decrease) for each coefficient in the objective function.

4.4-2   If the sum of the percentage changes do not exceed 100% then the original optimal solution definitely will still be optimal.

4.4-3   No, exceeding 100% may or may not change the optimal solution depending on the directions of the changes in the coefficients.

4.5-1 The right-hand side of a functional constraint might be altered if it represents managerial policy decisions rather than quantities that are largely outside of the control of management.

4.5-2 Given an optimal solution and the corresponding value of the objective function, the shadow price for a functional constraint is the rate at which the value of the objective function can be increased by increasing the right-hand side of the constraint by a small amount.

4.5-3 Shadow price analysis provides valuable guidance to managers about the effects of altering policy decisions.

4.5-4 Yes, shadow prices are valid for determining the effects of decreases as well as increases in the right-hand side.

4.5-5 A shadow price of 0 tells a manager that a small change in the right-hand side of the constraint will not change Z at all.

4.6-1 The range of feasibility for the right-hand side of a functional constraint is found in the Solver's sensitivity report by using the columns labeled "Constraint R.H. Side", "Allowable increase", and "Allowable decrease".

4.6-2 The ranges of feasibility are of interest to managers because they tell them how large changes in the right-hand sides can be before the shadow prices are no longer applicable.

4.7-1 Managerial decisions regarding right-hand sides are interrelated and so frequently are considered simultaneously.

4.7-2 The data needed to apply the 100% rule for simultaneous changes in right-hand sides are given by the Sensitivity Report (Constraint R.H. Side, Allowable Increase, and Allowable Decrease).

4.7-3 If the sum of the percentage changes does not exceed 100%, the shadow prices definitely will still be valid.

4.7-4 If the sum of the percentages of allowable changes in the right-hand sides does exceed 100%, then we cannot be sure if the shadow prices will still be valid.

Problems

4.1   a)

Resource	Resource Usage Per Unit of Each Activity		Totals		Resource Available
	Produce Toys	Produce Subassemblies			
Sub A	2	-1	3000	≤	3000
Sub B	1	-1	1000	≤	1000
Unit Profit	3	-2.5	$ 3,500.00		
Solution	2000	1000			

b)

Unit Profit for Toys	Optimal Production Rates Toys	Subassemblies	Total Profit
$2.00	1000	0	$2000
$2.50	1000	0	$2500
$3.00	2000	1000	$3500
$3.50	2000	1000	$4500
$4.00	2000	1000	$5500

The estimate of the unit profit for toys can decrease by somewhere between $0 and $0.50 before the optimal solution will change. We can not determine what will happen when the unit profit for toys increases since it is not shown in the table.

c)

Unit Profit for Subassemblies	Optimal Production Rates Toys	Subassemblies	Total Profit
-$3.50	1000	0	$3000
-$3.00	1000	0	$3000
-$2.50	2000	1000	$3500
-$2.00	2000	1000	$4000
-$1.50	2000	1000	$4500

The estimate of the unit profit for subassemblies can decrease by somewhere between $0 and $0.50 before the optimal solution will change. We can not determine what will happen when the unit profit for toys increases since it is not shown in the table.

d)

Adjustable Cells

Cell	Name	Final Value	Reduced Cost	Objective Coefficient	Allowable Increase	Allowable Decrease
$B$6	Solution Produce Toys	2000	0	3	2	0.5
$C$6	Solution Produce Subassemblies	1000	0	-2.5	1	0.5

Constraints

Cell	Name	Final Value	Shadow Price	Constraint R.H. Side	Allowable Increase	Allowable Decrease
$D$3	Sub A Totals	3000	0.5	3000	1E+30	1000
$D$4	Sub B Totals	1000	2	1000	500	1E+30

Based on the allowable increase and decrease in the Excel sensitivity report,

Current value of P_T: 3.
Allowable increase in P_T: 2.   So, $P_T \leq 3 + 2 = 5$.
Allowable decrease in P_T: 0.5.   So, $P_T \geq 3 - 0.5 = 2.5$.
Range of optimality for P_T: $2.5 \leq P_T \leq 5$.

Current value of P_S: -2.5.
Allowable increase in P_S: 1.   So, $P_S \leq -2.5 + 1 = -1.5$.
Allowable decrease in P_S: 0.5.   So, $P_S \geq -2.5 - 0.5 = -3$.
Range of optimality for P_S: $-3 \leq P_S \leq -1.5$

4.2 a)

Resource	Resource Usage Per Unit of Each Activity 1	2	Totals		Resource Available
1	1	2	10	≤	10
2	1	3	12	≤	12
Unit Profit	2	5	$ 22.00		
Solution	6	2			

Adjustable Cells

Cell	Name	Final Value	Reduced Cost	Objective Coefficient	Allowable Increase	Allowable Decrease
$B$6	Solution Activity 1	6	0	2	0.5	0.333333333
$C$6	Solution Activity 2	2	0	5	1	1

Constraints

Cell	Name	Final Value	Shadow Price	Constraint R.H. Side	Allowable Increase	Allowable Decrease
$D$3	Totals	10	1	10	2	2
$D$4	Totals	12	1	12	3	2

b)

Resource	Activity 1 1	Activity 2 2	Totals		Resource Available
1	1	2	8	≤	10
2	1	3	12	≤	12
Unit Profit	1	5	$ 20.00		
Solution	0	4			

Resource	Activity 1 1	Activity 2 2	Totals		Resource Available
1	1	2	10	≤	10
2	1	3	10	≤	12
Unit Profit	3	5	$ 30.00		
Solution	10	0			

c)

Resource	Activity 1 1	Activity 2 2	Totals		Resource Available
1	1	2	10	≤	10
2	1	3	10	≤	12
Unit Profit	2	2.5	$ 20.00		
Solution	10	0			

Resource	1	2	Totals		Available
1	1	2	8	≤	10
2	1	3	12	≤	12
Unit Profit	2	7.5	$ 30.00		
Solution	0	4			

d) Based on the allowable increase and decrease in the Excel sensitivity report,

Current value of P_1: 2.
Allowable increase in P_1: 0.5. So, $P_1 \leq 2 + 0.5 = 2.5$.
Allowable decrease in P_1: 0.333. So, $P_1 \geq 2 - 0.333 = 1.667$.
Range of optimality for P_1: $1.667 \leq P_1 \leq 2.5$.

Current value of P_2: 5.
Allowable increase in P_2: 1. So, $P_2 \leq 5 + 1 = 6$.
Allowable decrease in P_2: 1. So, $P_2 \geq 5 - 1 = 4$.
Range of optimality for P_2: $4 \leq P_2 \leq 6$

This fits with what we saw in parts b) and c). All of the new profits are outside the range of optimality so the optimal solution changes in each case.

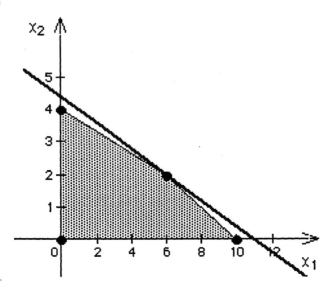

Graphical analysis of part b)
This optimal solution changes in both cases.
When the coefficient of Activity 1 changes to 1, then the objective function line in the graph becomes flatter, and the optimal solution switches to (0,4).

When the coefficient of Activity 1 changes to 3, then the objective function line in the graph becomes steeper, and the optimal solution switches to (10,0).

Graphical analysis of part c)
This optimal solution changes in both cases.
When the coefficient of Activity 2 changes to 2.5, then the objective function line in the graph becomes steeper and the optimal solution switches to (10,0).

When the coefficient of Activity 2 changes to 7.5, then the objective function line in the graph becomes flatter and the optimal solution switches to (0,4).

Graphical analysis of part d)
When the coefficient of Activity 1 decreases or the coefficient of Activity 2 increases, then the objective function line becomes flatter. When the coefficient of Activity 1 decreases by more than 0.333 or the coefficient of Activity 2 increases more than 1, then the optimal solution switches to (0,4).

When the coefficient of Activity 1 increases or the coefficient of Activity 2 decreases, then the objective function line becomes steeper. When the coefficient of Activity 1 increases by more than 0.5 or the coefficient of Activity 2 decreases more than 1, then the optimal solution switches to (10,0).

4.3

Adjustable Cells

Cell	Name	Final Value	Reduced Cost	Objective Coefficient	Allowable Increase	Allowable Decrease
$B$11	Solution F1-DC	50	-200	300	200	1E+30
$C$11	Solution F2-DC	30	0	400	100	1E+30
$D$11	Solution F1-W1	30	0	700	1E+30	200
$E$11	Solution F2-W1	40	0	900	1E+30	100
$F$11	Solution DC-W1	30	0	200	200	1E+30
$G$11	Solution DC-W2	50	-100	400	100	1E+30

a) F2-DC, F2-W1, and DC-W2 have the smallest margins for error (100). The greatest effort in estimating the unit shipping costs should be placed on these shipping lanes.

b)

The range of optimality for C_{F1-DC} is $C_{F1-DC} \leq 500$.

The range of optimality for C_{F2-DC} is $C_{F2-DC} \leq 500$.

The range of optimality for C_{F1-W1} is $C_{F1-W1} \geq 500$.

The range of optimality for C_{F2-W1} is $C_{F2-W1} \geq 800$.

The range of optimality for C_{DC-W1} is $C_{DC-W1} \leq 400$.

The range of optimality for C_{DC-W2} is $C_{DC-W2} \leq 500$.

c) The range of optimality for each unit shipping cost indicates how much that shipping cost can change before you would want to change the shipping quantities used in the optimal solution.

d) Use the 100% rule for simultaneous changes in objective function coefficients. If the sum of the percentage changes does not exceed 100%, the optimal solution definitely will still be optimal. If the sum does exceed 100%, then we cannot be sure.

4.4

a) Optimal solution does not change.

b) Optimal solution does change to:

Benefit	Benefit Contribution Per Unit of Each Activity					Totals		Minimum Acceptable Level
	6am Shift	8am Shift	Noon Shift	4pm Shift	10pm Shift			
Serve 6-8am	1	0	0	0	0	48	≥	48
Serve 8-10am	1	1	0	0	0	79	≥	79
Serve 10-12am	1	1	0	0	0	79	≥	65
Serve 12-2pm	1	1	1	0	0	112	≥	87
Serve 2-4pm	0	1	1	0	0	64	≥	64
Serve 4-6pm	0	0	1	1	0	82	≥	73
Serve 6-8pm	0	0	1	1	0	82	≥	82
Serve 8-10pm	0	0	0	1	0	49	≥	43
Serve 10-12pm	0	0	0	1	1	64	≥	52
Serve 12-6am	0	0	0	0	1	15	≥	15
Unit Cost	170	160	175	170	195	$ 30,150.00		
Solution	48	31	33	49	15			

c) Optimal Solution will change to:

Benefit	6am Shift	8am Shift	Noon Shift	4pm Shift	10pm Shift	Totals		Minimum Acceptable Level
Serve 6-8am	1	0	0	0	0	48	≥	48
Serve 8-10am	1	1	0	0	0	79	≥	79
Serve 10-12am	1	1	0	0	0	79	≥	65
Serve 12-2pm	1	1	1	0	0	112	≥	87
Serve 2-4pm	0	1	1	0	0	64	≥	64
Serve 4-6pm	0	0	1	1	0	82	≥	73
Serve 6-8pm	0	0	1	1	0	82	≥	82
Serve 8-10pm	0	0	0	1	0	49	≥	43
Serve 10-12pm	0	0	0	1	1	64	≥	52
Serve 12-6am	0	0	0	0	1	15	≥	15
Unit Cost	170	165	175	170	195	$ 30,305.00		
Solution	48	31	33	49	15			

Benefit Contribution Per Unit of Each Activity — Activity

d) Optimal Solution does not change.

e) Optimal Solution does not change.

f)

Cell	Name	Final Value	Reduced Cost	Objective Coefficient	Allowable Increase	Allowable Decrease
$B$15	Solution 6am Shift	48	0	170	1E+30	10
$C$15	Solution 8am Shift	31	0	160	10	160
$D$15	Solution Noon Shift	39	0	175	5	175
$E$15	Solution 4pm Shift	43	0	180	1E+30	5
$F$15	Solution 10pm Shift	15	0	195	1E+30	195

Part a)
Optimal solution does not change (within allowable increase of $10).

Part b)
Optimal solution does change (outside of allowable decrease of $5).

Part c)
By the 100% rule for simultaneous changes in the objective function, the optimal solution may or may not change.

C_{8AM}: $160 \to $165.   % of allowable increase $= 100\left(\dfrac{165-160}{10}\right) = 50\%$

C_{4PM}: $180 \to $170.   % of allowable decrease $= 100\left(\dfrac{180-170}{5}\right) = \underline{200\%}$

$$\text{Sum} = 250\%.$$

Part d)
By the 100% rule for simultaneous changes in the objective function, the optimal solution does not change.

C_{6AM}: $170 \to $166.   % of allowable decrease $= 100\left(\dfrac{170-166}{10}\right) = 50\%$

C_{8AM}: $160 \to $164.   % of allowable increase $= 100\left(\dfrac{164-160}{10}\right) = 40\%$

C_{noon}: $175 \to $171.   % of allowable decrease $= 100\left(\dfrac{175-171}{175}\right) = 2\%$

C_{4PM}: $180 \to $184.   % of allowable increase $= 100\left(\dfrac{184-180}{\infty}\right) = 0\%$

C_{10PM}: $195 \to $199.   % of allowable increase $= 100\left(\dfrac{199-195}{\infty}\right) = \underline{0\%}$

$$\text{Sum} = 92\%.$$

Part e)
By the 100% rule for simultaneous changes in the objective function, the optimal solution may or may not change.

C_{6AM}: $170 \rightarrow$ \$173.40. % of allowable increase $= 100\left(\dfrac{173.40-170}{\infty}\right) = 0\%$

C_{8AM}: $160 \rightarrow$ \$163.20. % of allowable increase $= 100\left(\dfrac{163.20-160}{10}\right) = 32\%$

C_{noon}: $175 \rightarrow$ \$178.50. % of allowable increase $= 100\left(\dfrac{178.50-175}{5}\right) = 70\%$

C_{4PM}: $180 \rightarrow$ \$183.60. % of allowable increase $= 100\left(\dfrac{183.60-180}{\infty}\right) = 0\%$

C_{10PM}: $195 \rightarrow$ \$198.90. % of allowable increase $= 100\left(\dfrac{198.9-195}{\infty}\right) = \underline{0\%}$

Sum $= 102\%$.

4.5 a) Optimal solution changes to:

Resource Usage Per Unit of Each Activity
(cumulative investment per 1% share)

Resource	Activity Project 1	Project 2	Project 3	Totals		Resource Available
Capital Now	0.4	0.8	0.9	24.2985612	≤	25
Capital End Year 1	1	1.6	1.4	45.00	≤	45
Capital End Year 2	1.9	2.4	1.6	65.00	≤	65
Capital End Year 3	2	3.1	2.2	80	≤	80
Unit Profit	0.452	0.7	0.5	$ 18.12		
Solution	13.8093525	6.115	15.647			

b) Optimal solution does not change.

c) Optimal solution does not change.

d) Optimal solution does not change.

e) Optimal solution changes to:

Resource Usage Per Unit of Each Activity
(cumulative investment per 1% share)

Resource	Activity Project 1	Project 2	Project 3	Totals		Resource Available
Capital Now	0.4	0.8	0.9	20.6451613	≤	25
Capital End Year 1	1	1.6	1.4	41.29	≤	45
Capital End Year 2	1.9	2.4	1.6	61.94	≤	65
Capital End Year 3	2	3.1	2.2	80	≤	80
Unit Profit	0.4	0.702	0.498	$ 18.12		
Solution	0	25.806	0.000			

f) Optimal solution changes to:

Resource Usage Per Unit of Each Activity
(cumulative investment per 1% share)

Resource	Activity			Totals		Resource Available
	Project 1	Project 2	Project 3			
Capital Now	0.4	0.8	0.9	24.2985612	≤	25
Capital End Year 1	1	1.6	1.4	45.00	≤	45
Capital End Year 2	1.9	2.4	1.6	65.00	≤	65
Capital End Year 3	2	3.1	2.2	80	≤	80
Unit Profit	0.46	0.69	0.49	$ 18.01		
Solution	13.3093525	6.115	15.647			

g) Optimal solution does not change.

h)

Adjustable Cells

Cell	Name	Final Value	Reduced Cost	Objective Coefficient	Allowable Increase	Allowable Decrease
$B$10	Solution Project 1	0	-0.000485437	0.45	0.000485437	1E+30
$C$10	Solution Project 2	16.505	0.000	0.7	0.004545455	0.000543478
$D$10	Solution Project 3	13.107	0.000	0.5	0.001388889	0.003225806

Constraints

Cell	Name	Final Value	Shadow Price	Constraint R.H. Side	Allowable Increase	Allowable Decrease
$E$5	Capital Now Totals	25	0.009708738	25	0.304878049	4.35483871
$E$6	Capital End Year 1 Totals	44.76	0.00	45	1E+30	0.242718447
$E$7	Capital End Year 2 Totals	60.58	0.00	65	1E+30	4.417475728
$E$8	Capital End Year 3 Totals	80	0.223300971	80	0.78125	18.88888889

Part a)
Optimal solution changes (not within allowable increase of $49,000).

Part b)
Optimal solution does not change (within allowable increase of $455,000).

Part c)
Optimal solution does not change (within allowable decrease of ∞).

Part d)
Optimal solution does not change (within allowable decrease of $323,000).

Part e)
By the 100% rule for simultaneous changes in the objective function, the optimal solution may or may not change.

P_2: $70M \to \$70.2M$. % of allowable increase $= 100\left(\dfrac{0.702 - 0.70}{0.00455}\right) = 4396\%$

P_1: $45M \to \$40M$. % of allowable decrease $= 100\left(\dfrac{0.45 - 0.40}{\infty}\right) = 0\%$

P_3: $50M \to \$49.8M$. % of allowable decrease $= 100\left(\dfrac{0.50 - 0.498}{.003226}\right) = 6200\%$

Sum $= 10,596\%$.

By the 100% rule for simultaneous changes in the objective function, the optimal solution may or may not change.

P_1: $45M \rightarrow $46M.   % of allowable increase = $100\left(\dfrac{0.46 - 0.45}{0.000485}\right) = 2062\%$

P_2: $70M \rightarrow $69M.   % of allowable decrease = $100\left(\dfrac{0.70 - 0.69}{0.000543}\right) = 1842\%$

P_3: $50M \rightarrow $49M.   % of allowable decrease = $100\left(\dfrac{0.50 - 0.49}{0.00323}\right) = \underline{310\%}$

Sum = 4213%.

Part g)
By the 100% rule for simultaneous changes in the objective function, the optimal solution may or may not change.

P_1: $45M \rightarrow $54M.   % of allowable increase = $100\left(\dfrac{0.54 - 0.45}{0.000485}\right) = 1,855,770\%$

P_2: $70M \rightarrow $84M.   % of allowable increase = $100\left(\dfrac{0.84 - 0.70}{0.004545}\right) = 307,692\%$

P_3: $50M \rightarrow $60M.   % of allowable increase = $100\left(\dfrac{0.60 - 0.50}{0.001389}\right) = \underline{719,424\%}$

Sum = 2,882,886%.

4.6   a) Optimal solution: produce no chocolate ice cream, 300 gallons of vanilla ice cream, and 75 gallons of banana ice cream. Total profit will be $341.25.

b) The optimal solution will change since $1.00 is outside the allowable range. The profit will go up, but how much can't be determined without resolving.

c) The optimal solution will not change since $0.92 is within the allowable range. Total profit will decrease by $2.25 (0.03 x 75) to $339.

d) The optimal solution will change. Since the change is within the allowable range, we can calculate the change in profit using the shadow price (1 x 3 = 3). The new profit will be $338.25.

e) This increase is outside of the allowable increase so the problem will have to be resolved to determine whether this is worthwhile.

f) The final value is 180 as shown in the totals column in the solution. The shadow price is 0 since we are using less milk than we have available. The R.H.Side value is 200 as given in the problem. The allowable increase is infinity since we are already using less than is available. The allowable decrease is 20 since the solution will change once the right-hand side drops below 180.

4.7 a) Let   G = number of grandfather clocks produced
         W = number of wall clocks produced

Maximize $P = 300G + 200W$,

subject to $6G + 4W \le 40$,

              $8G + 4W \le 40$,

              $3G + 3W \le 20$,

and $G \ge 0, \ W \ge 0$.

b) Optimal Solution: $(G, W) = (x_1, x_2) = (3.333, 3.333)$ and $P = 1666.67$.

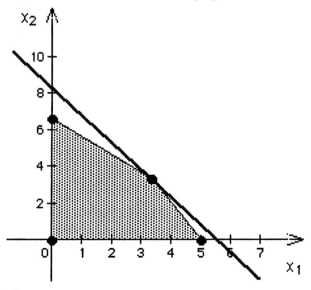

c & d)

Resource	Resource Usage Per Unit of Each Activity Grandfather	Wall	Totals	Resource Available
David	6	4	33.333 ≤	40
LaDeana	8	4	40.00 ≤	40
Lydia	3	3	20 ≤	20
Unit Profit	300	200	$ 1,666.67	
Solution	3.333	3.333		

Adjustable Cells

Cell	Name	Final Value	Reduced Cost	Objective Coefficient	Allowable Increase	Allowable Decrease
$B$7	Solution Grandfather	3.333	0	300	100	100
$C$7	Solution Wall	3.333	0.000	200	100	50

Constraints

Cell	Name	Final Value	Shadow Price	Constraint R.H. Side	Allowable Increase	Allowable Decrease
$D$3	David Totals	33.333	0	40	1E+30	6.667
$D$4	LaDeana Totals	40.00	25.00	40	13.333	13.333
$D$5	Lydia Totals	20	33.333	20	10	5

e) The optimal solution will remain the same since $75 is within the allowable increase.

f) By the 100% rule for simultaneous changes in the objective function, the optimal solution may or may not change.

C_G: $300 → $375.   % of allowable increase = $100\left(\dfrac{375-300}{100}\right) = 75\%$

C_W: $200 → $175.   % of allowable decrease = $100\left(\dfrac{200-175}{50}\right) = \underline{50\%}$

Sum $= 125\%$.

g) When the profit for grandfather clocks increases to $375, the optimal solution is still: $(G,W) = (x_1, x_2) = (3.333, 3.333)$ and $P = 1666.67$.

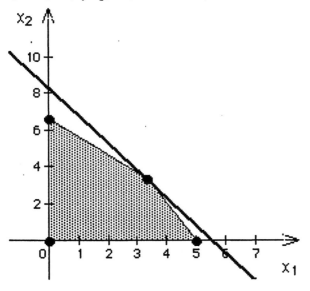

If both profit estimates change then the optimal solution changes to: $(G,W) = (x_1, x_2) = (5,0)$ and $P = 1875$. $(5,0)$ with a profit of $1875.

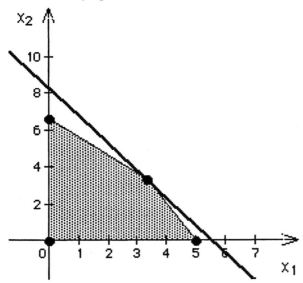

h) Lydia should increase her hours slightly since she has the highest shadow price connected to her.

i) The shadow price for David is zero because all of his available hours are not being used and consequently an increase in his hours would not impact total profit.

j) Yes, this increase is within the allowable increase. The increase in total profit will be $33.33 x 5 = $166.65.

k) By the 100% rule for simultaneous changes in right-hand sides, the optimal solution may or may not change. The shadow prices may not be used to determine the effect on profit.

C_L: $20 \rightarrow 25$.   % of allowable increase $= 100\left(\dfrac{25-20}{10}\right) = 50\%$

C_D: $40 \rightarrow 35$.   % of allowable decrease $= 100\left(\dfrac{40-35}{6.667}\right) = \underline{75\%}$

$$\text{Sum} = 125\%.$$

l) The revised graph is shown below. The optimal solution changes from (3.333,3.333) with a profit of $1666.70 to (2.5,5), (.833,7.5), and all points on the connecting line segment, with a profit of $1750.

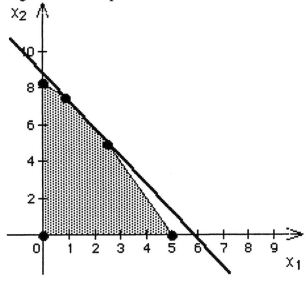

4.8   a)

Goal for Market Share	Optimal Advertising		Total Cost
	TV	Print	
18%	4	3	$10 million
21%	5	3	$11 million
24%	6	3	$12 million
27%	7	3	$13 million
30%	8	3	$14 million
33%	8.857	3.214	$15.286 million
36%	9.714	3.429	$16.571 million

b) The cost per 1% increase of market share for small increases from 18% is $333,333. The market share can be increased to somewhere between 30% and 33% before the cost per 1% goes up.

c) According to this report, the allowable increase for liquid detergent is 12%. This means that the shadow price of $333,333 remains valid until the market share increases to 30% (18%+12%).

Adjustable Cells

Cell	Name	Final Value	Reduced Cost	Objective Coefficient	Allowable Increase	Allowable Decrease
$C$10	Solution Television	4	0	1	2	1
$D$10	Solution Print Media	3	0	2	1E+30	1.333333333

Constraints

Cell	Name	Final Value	Shadow Price	Constraint R.H. Side	Allowable Increase	Allowable Decrease
$E$6	Stain Remover Totals	3%	13333%	0.03	1E+30	0.008571429
$E$7	Liquid Detergent Totals	18%	3333%	0.18	0.12	1E+30
$E$8	Powder Detergent Totals	8%	0%	0.04	0.04	1E+30

d) The optimal solution for the original problem is $(TV,P) = (x_1,x_2) = (4,3)$ and Cost=$10 million.

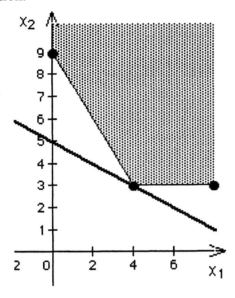

When the minimum market share increase for liquid detergent is increased by 1%, the resulting graphical solution (with cost $10.333 million) is shown below. This demonstrates that the cost per 1% increase for small increases is $0.333 million.

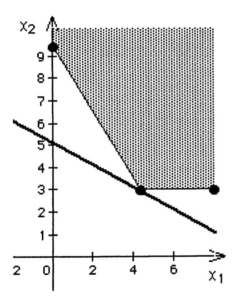

The market share can be increased by 12% before the cost per 1% goes up. The graph below shows the new optimal solution for the new minimum goal of 30%.

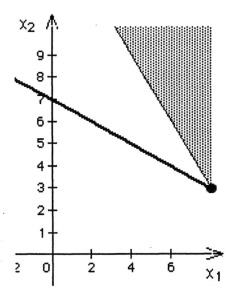

4.9 a)

| Resource | Resource Usage Per Unit of Each Activity | | Totals | | Resource Available |
	Produce Toys	Produce Subassemblies			
Sub A	2	-1	3000	≤	3000
Sub B	1	-1	1000	≤	1000
Max. Demand	1	0	2000	≤	2500
Unit Profit	3	-2.5	$ 3,500.00		
Solution	2000	1000			

b)

| Resource | Resource Usage Per Unit of Each Activity | | Totals | | Resource Available |
	Produce Toys	Produce Subassemblies			
Sub A	2	-1	3001	≤	3001
Sub B	1	-1	1000	≤	1000
Max. Demand	1	0	2001	≤	2500
Unit Profit	3	-2.5	$ 3,500.50		
Solution	2001	1001			

The shadow price for subassembly A is $0.50, which is the maximum premium that the company should be willing to pay.

c)

| Resource | Resource Usage Per Unit of Each Activity | | Totals | | Resource Available |
	Produce Toys	Produce Subassemblies			
Sub A	2	-1	3000	≤	3000
Sub B	1	-1	1001	≤	1001
Max. Demand	1	0	1999	≤	2500
Unit Profit	3	-2.5	$ 3,502.00		
Solution	1999	998			

The shadow price for subassembly B is $2.00, which is the maximum premium that the company should be willing to pay.

d)

Supply Type A	Optimal Production Rates Toys	Subassemblies	Total Profit
3000	2000	1000	$3500
3100	2100	1100	$3550
3200	2200	1200	$3600
3300	2300	1300	$3650
3400	2400	1400	$3700
3500	2500	1500	$3750
3600	2500	1500	$3750
3700	2500	1500	$3750
3800	2500	1500	$3750
3900	2500	1500	$3750
4000	2500	1500	$3750

The shadow price is still valid until the maximum supply of subassembly A is 3500.

e)

Supply Type B	Optimal Production Rates Toys	Subassemblies	Total Profit
1000	2000	1000	$3500
1100	1900	800	$3700
1200	1800	600	$3900
1300	1700	400	$4100
1400	1600	200	$4300
1500	1500	0	$4500
1600	1500	0	$4500
1700	1500	0	$4500
1800	1500	0	$4500
1900	1500	0	$4500
2000	1500	0	$4500

The shadow price is still valid until the maximum supply of subassembly B is 1500.

f)

Adjustable Cells

Cell	Name	Final Value	Reduced Cost	Objective Coefficient	Allowable Increase	Allowable Decrease
$B$7	Solution Produce Toys	2000	0	3	2	0.5
$C$7	Solution Produce Subassemblies	1000	0	-2.5	1	0.5

Constraints

Cell	Name	Final Value	Shadow Price	Constraint R.H. Side	Allowable Increase	Allowable Decrease
$D$3	Sub A Totals	3000	0.5	3000	500	1000
$D$4	Sub B Totals	1000	2	1000	500	500
$D$5	Max. Demand Totals	2000	0	2500	1E+30	500

As shown in the sensitivity report, the shadow price is $0.50 for subassembly A is $2.00 for subassembly B. According to the allowable increase and allowable decrease, the range of feasibility for the right-hand side of the subassembly A constraint is $2000 \le$ subassembly $A \le 3500$. The range of feasibility for the right-hand side of the subassembly B constraint is $500 \le$ subassembly $B \le 1500$.

4.10 a) The shadow price is $1.

Resource	Activity 1 1	Activity 2 2	Totals		Resource Available
1	1	2	11	≤	11
2	1	3	12	≤	12
Unit Profit	2	5	$ 23.00		
Solution	9	1			

b)

Resource 1 Parameter	Optimal Solution		Total Profit
	Activity 1	Activity 2	
5	0	2	$12.50
6	0	3	$15
7	0	3	$17.50
8	0	4	$20
9	3	3	$21
10	6	2	$22
11	9	1	$23
12	12	0	$24
13	12	0	$24
14	12	0	$24
15	12	0	$24

The shadow price of $1 is valid in the range of 8 to 12.

c) The shadow price is $1.

Resource	Activity 1 1	Activity 2 2	Totals		Resource Available
1	1	2	10	≤	10
2	1	3	13	≤	13
Unit Profit	2	5	$ 23.00		
Solution	4	3			

d)

Resource 2 Parameter	Optimal Solution Activity 1	Activity 2	Total Profit
6	6	0	$12
7	7	0	$14
8	8	0	$16
9	9	0	$18
10	10	0	$20
11	8	1	$21
12	6	2	$22
13	4	3	$23
14	2	4	$24
15	0	5	$25
16	0	5	$25
17	0	5	$25
18	0	5	$25

The shadow price of $1 is valid in the range of 10 to 15.

e) As shown in the sensitivity report, the shadow prices for both constraints are 1. According to the allowable increase and allowable decrease, the range of feasibility for the right-hand side of the first constraint is $8 \leq RHS_1 \leq 12$. Similarly, the range of feasibility for the right-hand side of the second constraint is $10 \leq RHS_2 \leq 15$.

Adjustable Cells

Cell	Name	Final Value	Reduced Cost	Objective Coefficient	Allowable Increase	Allowable Decrease
$B$6	Solution Activity 1	6	0	2	0.5	0.333333333
$C$6	Solution Activity 2	2	0	5	1	1

Constraints

Cell	Name	Final Value	Shadow Price	Constraint R.H. Side	Allowable Increase	Allowable Decrease
$D$3	Totals	10	1	10	2	2
$D$4	Totals	12	1	12	3	2

4.11 a) Optimal solution: $(x_1, x_2) = (2,2)$ and $P = 6$

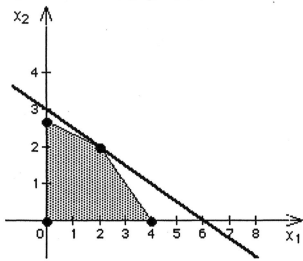

b) When the right-hand-side of the first constraint is increased to 9, the new optimal solution becomes $(x_1, x_2) = (1.5, 2.5)$ and $P = 6.5$. Hence, the shadow price for the first constraint is 6.5-6=0.5.

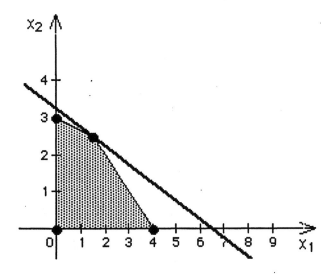

When the right-hand-side of the second constraint is increased to 5, the new optimal solution becomes $(x_1, x_2) = (3.5, 1.5)$ and $P = 6.5$. Hence, the shadow price for the second constraint is $6.5-6=0.5$.

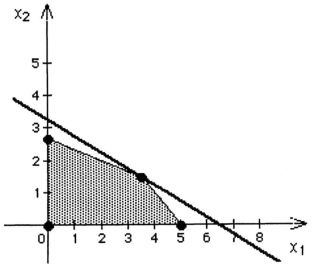

c) Original model:

Resource	Activity 1 1	Activity 2 2	Totals	Resource Available
Resource 1	1	3	8	≤ 8
Resource 2	1	1	4	≤ 4
Unit Profit	1	2	$ 6.00	
Solution	2	2		

The shadow price for resource 1 is $0.50.

Resource	Activity 1 1	Activity 2 2	Totals	Resource Available
Resource 1	1	3	9	≤ 9
Resource 2	1	1	4	≤ 4
Unit Profit	1	2	$ 6.50	
Solution	2	2		

The shadow price for resource 2 is $0.50.

Resource	Activity 1 1	Activity 2 2	Totals	Resource Available
Resource 1	1	3	8	≤ 8
Resource 2	1	1	5	≤ 5
Unit Profit	1	2	$ 6.50	
Solution	3	2		

d)

Adjustable Cells

Cell	Name	Final Value	Reduced Cost	Objective Coefficient	Allowable Increase	Allowable Decrease
$B$6	Solution Activity 1	2	0	1	1	0.333333333
$C$6	Solution Activity 2	2	0	2	1	1

Constraints

Cell	Name	Final Value	Shadow Price	Constraint R.H. Side	Allowable Increase	Allowable Decrease
$D$3	Resource 1 Totals	8	0.5	8	4	4
$D$4	Resource 2 Totals	4	0.5	4	4	1.333333333

e) These shadow prices tell management that for each one unit change of the amounts of the resources being made available, profit will change by $.50 (for small changes). Management is then able to evaluate whether or not to change the amounts of resources being made available.

4.12 a) Optimal solution: $(x_1, x_2) = (3, 4)$ and $P = 17$.

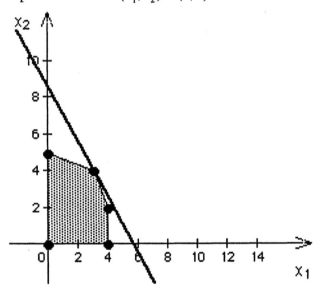

b) When the right-hand-side of the first constraint is increased to 5, the optimal solution remains the same. Hence, the shadow price for the first constraint is 0.

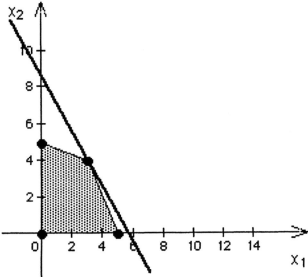

When the right-hand-side of the second constraint is increased to 16, the new optimal solution becomes $(x_1, x_2) = (2.8, 4.4)$ and $P = 17.2$. Hence, the shadow price for the second constraint is $17.2 - 17 = 0.2$.

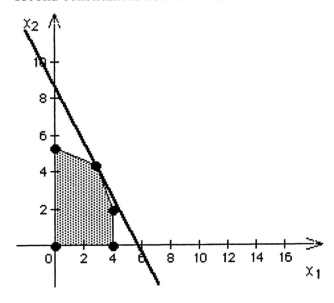

When the right-hand-side of the third constraint is increased to 11, the new optimal solution becomes $(x_1, x_2) = (3.6, 3.8)$ and $P = 18.4$. Hence, the shadow price for the third constraint is $18.4-17=1.4$.

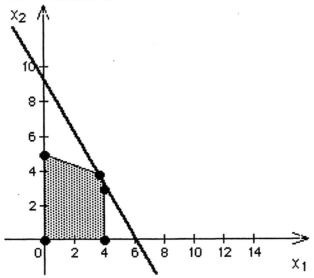

c) Original model:

Resource	Resource Usage Per Unit Activity 1	Activity 2	Totals		Resource Available
Resource 1	1	0	3	≤	4
Resource 2	1	3	15	≤	15
Resource 3	2	1	10	≤	10
Unit Profit	3	2	$ 17.00		
Solution	3	4			

The shadow price for resource 1 is $0.

Resource	Resource Usage Per Unit Activity 1	Activity 2	Totals		Resource Available
Resource 1	1	0	3	≤	5
Resource 2	1	3	15	≤	15
Resource 3	2	1	10	≤	10
Unit Profit	3	2	$ 17.00		
Solution	3	4			

The shadow price for resource 2 is $0.20.

Resource	Resource Usage Per Unit Activity 1	Activity 2	Totals		Resource Available
Resource 1	1	0	2.8	≤	4
Resource 2	1	3	16	≤	16
Resource 3	2	1	10	≤	10
Unit Profit	3	2	$ 17.20		
Solution	2.8	4			

The shadow price for resource 3 is $1.40.

Resource	Resource Usage Per Unit Activity 1	Activity 2	Totals		Resource Available
Resource 1	1	0	3.6	≤	4
Resource 2	1	3	15	≤	15
Resource 3	2	1	11	≤	11
Unit Profit	3	2	$ 18.40		
Solution	3.6	4			

d)

Adjustable Cells

Cell	Name	Final Value	Reduced Cost	Objective Coefficient	Allowable Increase	Allowable Decrease
$B$7	Solution Activity 1	3	0	3	1	2.333333333
$C$7	Solution Activity 2	4	0	2	7	0.5

Constraints

Cell	Name	Final Value	Shadow Price	Constraint R.H. Side	Allowable Increase	Allowable Decrease
$D$3	Resource 1 Totals	3	0	4	1E+30	1
$D$4	Resource 2 Totals	15	0.2	15	15	5
$D$5	Resource 3 Totals	10	1.4	10	1.666666667	5

e) These shadow prices tell management that it would a change in the amount of resource 1 available will not change profit. For resource 2, a change in the amount available will change profit by $.20. For resource 3, a change in the amount available will change profit by $1.40. The shadow prices let management evaluate the benefits of potential changes in available resource amounts.

4.13

Constraints

Cell	Name	Final Value	Shadow Price	Constraint R.H. Side	Allowable Increase	Allowable Decrease
$E$4	Ad Budget Totals	4000	0.3	4000	250	1125
$E$5	Planning Budget Totals	1000	0.5	1000	450	50
$E$6	TV Spots Totals	5	5	5	1.667	5

a) The total number of expected exposure units could be increased by 0.3 for each additional $1000 added to the advertising budget.

b) This remains valid for increases of up to $ 250,000.

c) The total number of expected exposure units could be increased by 0.5 for each additional $1000 added to the planning budget.

d) This remains valid for increases of up to $450,000.

e) By the 100% rule for simultaneous changes in right-hand sides, the shadow prices are still valid.

C_A: $4000 → $4100. % of allowable increase $= 100\left(\dfrac{4100-4000}{250}\right) = 40\%$

C_P: $1000 → $1100. % of allowable increase $= 100\left(\dfrac{1100-1000}{450}\right) = \underline{22\%}$

Sum $= 62\%$.

f) The $100,000 should be added to the planning budget since this will add 50 expected exposure units rather than 30 for the advertising budget.

g) This cannot be determined without resolving the model since the allowable decrease for the planning budget is only $50,000. For any decreases greater than this, the shadow price is no longer valid.

4.14

Constraints

Cell	Name	Final Value	Shadow Price	Constraint R.H. Side	Allowable Increase	Allowable Decrease
$E$4	Ad Budget Totals	3750	0	4000	1E+30	250
$E$5	Planning Budget Totals	1000	3.455	1000	25	45.556
$E$6	TV Spots Totals	3.030	0	5	1E+30	1.97
$E$11	Young Children Totals	5	-142.424	5	0.661	0.5
$E$12	Parents of Young Children Totals	4.621	0	4	0.621	1E+30
$E$17	Coupon Redemption Totals	1500000	-0.001	1500000	215789.474	100000

a) The total number of expected exposure units could not be increased by adding an additional $1000 to the advertising budget.

b) This remains valid for any increases.

c) The total number of expected exposure units could be increased by 3.455 for each additional $1000 added to the planning budget.

d) This remains valid for increases of up to $25,000.

e) By the 100% rule for simultaneous changes in right-hand sides, the shadow prices are not valid.

$$C_A: \quad \$4000 \rightarrow \$4100. \quad \% \text{ of allowable increase} = 100\left(\frac{4100 - 4000}{\infty}\right) = 0\%$$

$$C_P: \quad \$1000 \rightarrow \$1100. \quad \% \text{ of allowable increase} = 100\left(\frac{1100 - 1000}{25}\right) = \underline{400\%}$$

$$\text{Sum} = 400\%.$$

f) The $100,000 should be added to the planning budget since this will add 3.455 expected exposure units rather than 0 for the advertising budget.

g) This cannot be determined without resolving the model since the allowable decrease for the planning budget is only $45,556. For any decreases greater than this, the shadow price is no longer valid.

4.15

Constraints

Cell	Name	Final Value	Shadow Price	Constraint R.H. Side	Allowable Increase	Allowable Decrease
$G$4	Serve 6-8am Totals	48	10	48	6	48
$G$5	Serve 8-10am Totals	79	160	79	1E+30	6
$G$6	Serve 10-12am Totals	79	0	65	14	1E+30
$G$7	Serve 12-2pm Totals	118	0	87	31	1E+30
$G$8	Serve 2-4pm Totals	70	0	64	6	1E+30
$G$9	Serve 4-6pm Totals	82	0	73	9	1E+30
$G$10	Serve 6-8pm Totals	82	175	82	1E+30	6
$G$11	Serve 8-10pm Totals	43	5	43	6	6
$G$12	Serve 10-12pm Totals	58	0	52	6	1E+30
$G$13	Serve 12-6am Totals	15	195	15	1E+30	6

a) The following shift can be increased by the indicated amounts:
Serve 10-12 am   14
Serve 12-2 pm   31
Serve 2-4 pm   6
Serve 4-6 pm   9
Serve 10-12 pm   6

b) For each of the following shifts, total cost will increase by the amount indicated per unit increase. These costs hold for the indicated increases
Serve 6-8 am $10   6
Serve 8-10 am $160   ∞
Serve 6-8 pm $175   ∞
Serve 8-10 pm $5   6
Serve 12-6 am $195   ∞

c) By the 100% rule for simultaneous changes in right-hand sides, the shadow prices are still valid.

C_{6-8am}: $48 \to 49$.   % of allowable increase $= 100\left(\dfrac{49-48}{6}\right) = 17\%$

C_{8-10am}: $79 \to 80$ % of allowable increase $= 100\left(\dfrac{80-79}{\infty}\right) = 0\%$

C_{6-8pm}: $82 \to 83$ % of allowable increase $= 100\left(\dfrac{83-82}{\infty}\right) = 0\%$

C_{8-10pm}: $43 \to 44$ % of allowable increase $= 100\left(\dfrac{44-43}{6}\right) = 17\%$

C_{12-6am}: $15 \to 16$.   % of allowable increase $= 100\left(\dfrac{16-15}{\infty}\right) = \underline{0\%}$

Sum $= 34\%$.

d) By the 100% rule for simultaneous changes in right-hand sides, the shadow prices are still valid.

C_{6-8am}: $48 \to 49$.   % of allowable increase $= 100\left(\dfrac{49-48}{6}\right) = 17\%$

C_{8-10am}: $79 \to 80$ % of allowable increase $= 100\left(\dfrac{80-79}{\infty}\right) = 0\%$

$C_{10-12am}$: $65 \to 66$.   % of allowable increase $= 100\left(\dfrac{66-65}{14}\right) = 7\%$

C_{12-2pm}: $87 \to 88$.   % of allowable increase $= 100\left(\dfrac{88-87}{31}\right) = 3\%$

C_{2-4pm}: $64 \to 65$.   % of allowable increase $= 100\left(\dfrac{65-64}{6}\right) = 17\%$

C_{4-6pm}: $73 \to 74$.   % of allowable increase $= 100\left(\dfrac{74-73}{9}\right) = 11\%$

C_{6-8pm}: $82 \to 83$ % of allowable increase $= 100\left(\dfrac{83-82}{\infty}\right) = 0\%$

C_{8-10pm}: $43 \to 44$ % of allowable increase $= 100\left(\dfrac{44-43}{6}\right) = 17\%$

$C_{10-12pm}$: $52 \to 53$.   % of allowable increase $= 100\left(\dfrac{53-52}{6}\right) = 17\%$

C_{12-6am}: $15 \to 16$.   % of allowable increase $= 100\left(\dfrac{16-15}{\infty}\right) = \underline{0\%}$

Sum $= 89\%$.

e) All numbers can increase by $\dfrac{100}{89}$ (or 1.124) before it is no longer definite that the shadow prices remain valid.

Cases

4.1 a) The decisions to be made are how which types of abatement methods will be used and at what fractions of their abatement capacities for the blast furnaces and the open-hearth furnaces. The constraints on these decisions are the technological limits on how heavily each method can be used and the required reductions in the annual emission rate. The overall measure of performance is cost, which is to be minimized.

b and c)

	Benefit Contribution Per Unit of Abatement Method							
	Taller Smokestacks		Filters		Better Fuels			Acceptable
Constraints	Blast	Open-hearth	Blast	Open-hearth	Blast	Open-hearth	Totals	Level
reduce particulates	12	9	25	20	17	13	60 ≥	60
reduce sulfer oxides	35	42	18	31	56	49	150 ≥	150
reduce hydrocarbons	37	53	28	24	29	20	125 ≥	125
smokestacks - blast	1	0	0	0	0	0	1 ≤	1
smokestacks-open-hearth	0	1	0	0	0	0	0.6226975 ≤	1
filters - blast	0	0	1	0	0	0	0.3434794 ≤	1
filters - open-hearth	0	0	0	1	0	0	1 ≤	1
fuels - blast	0	0	0	0	1	0	0.0475728 ≤	1
fuels - open-hearth	0	0	0	0	0	1	1 ≤	1
Unit Cost	8	10	7	6	11	9	$ 32.155	
Solution	1	0.6227	0.3435	1	0.0476	1		

Adjustable Cells

Cell	Name	Final Value	Reduced Cost	Objective Coefficient	Allowable Increase	Allowable Decrease
$B$14	Solution Blast	1	0	8	0.336210968	1E+30
$C$14	Solution Open-hearth	0.6227	0.0000	10	0.429446289	0.666961637
$D$14	Solution Blast	0.3435	0.0000	7	0.381632655	2.011459969
$E$14	Solution Open-hearth	1	0	6	1.816085017	1E+30
$F$14	Solution Blast	0.0476	0.0000	11	2.975225225	0.044638358
$G$14	Solution Open-hearth	1	0	9	0.044161638	1E+30

Constraints

Cell	Name	Final Value	Shadow Price	Constraint R.H. Side	Allowable Increase	Allowable Decrease
$H$4	reduce particulates Totals	60	0.111046969	60	14.29714286	7.48
$H$5	reduce sulfer oxides Totals	150	0.126817108	150	20.453125	1.689655172
$H$6	reduce hydrocarbons Totals	125	0.069325636	125	2.041666667	21.69195612
$H$7	smokestacks - blast Totals	1	-0.336210968	1	0.246231156	0.748477435
$H$8	smokestacks - open-hearth Totals	0.622697455	0	1	1E+30	0.377302545
$H$9	filters - blast Totals	0.343479402	0	1	1E+30	0.656520598
$H$10	filters - open-hearth Totals	1	-1.816085017	1	0.110609481	1
$H$11	fuels - blast Totals	0.047572816	0	1	1E+30	0.952427184
$H$12	fuels - open-hearth Totals	1	-0.044161638	1	0.048086359	0.962708538

d) The right-hand-side of each constraint with a non-zero shadow price is sensitive, since changing its value will impact the total cost. All three required reductions in emission rates are sensitive parameters. All of the objective coefficients have an allowable range to stay optimal around them, and thus are not as sensitive. However, for some, the allowable change is small—in particular, the cost of the two better fuel options (with an allowable increase of only 0.045 and an allowable decrease of 0.044, respectively) are fairly sensitive. Thus, all five of these parameters should be estimated more closely, if possible.

e) The following table shows in which cases the optimal solution will change:

Current Value	10% Less Value	Solution Changes?	10% More Value	Solution Changes?
8	7.2	No	8.8	Yes
10	9	Yes	11	Yes
7	6.3	No	7.7	Yes
6	5.4	No	6.6	No
11	9.9	Yes	12.1	No
9	8.1	No	9.9	Yes

This suggests that focus should be put on estimating all of the costs except the one that is currently $6 million since it's optimal solution will not change with a 10% increase or decrease. Special consideration should be given to the estimate of the current $10 million cost since it affects the optimal solution for both an increase and a decrease.

f)

Pollutant	Rate that cost changes	Maximum increase before rate changes	Maximum decrease before rate changes
Particulates	0.111	14.297	7.48
Sulfur oxides	0.127	20.453	1.69
Hydrocarbons	0.069	2.042	21.692

g) Particulates and sulfur oxides:
For each unit increase in particulate reduction, cost will increase by $0.111 million.
For each unit decrease in sulfur oxide reduction, cost will decrease by $0.127 million.
Thus, cost will remain equal if for each unit increase in particulate reduction, the sulfur oxide reduction is reduced by $0.111 / $0.127 = 0.874 units.

Particulates and hydrocarbons:
For each unit increase in particulate reduction, cost will increase by $0.111 million.
For each unit decrease in hydrocarbon reduction, cost will decrease by $0.069 million.
Thus, cost will remain equal if for each unit increase in particulate reduction, the hydrocarbon reduction is reduced by $0.111 / $0.069 = 1.609 units.

Particulates and both sulfur oxides and hydrocarbons:
For each unit increase in particulate reduction, cost will increase by $0.111 million.
For each simultaneous unit decrease in sulfur oxide and hydrocarbon reduction, cost will decrease by $0.127 + $0.069 = $0.196.
Thus, cost will remain equal if for each unit increase in particulate reduction, the sulfur oxide and hydrocarbon reduction are each reduced by $0.111 / $0.196 = 0.566 units.

h) 10% increase

| | Benefit Contribution Per Unit of Abatement Method | | | | | | | | |
| Constraints | Taller Smokestacks | | Filters | | Better Fuels | | Totals | | Acceptable Level |
	Blast	Open-hearth	Blast	Open-hearth	Blast	Open-hearth			
reduce particulates	12	9	25	20	17	13	66	≥	66
reduce sulfer oxides	35	42	18	31	56	49	165	≥	165
reduce hydrocarbons	37	53	28	24	29	20	137.5	≥	137.5
smokestacks - blast	1	0	0	0	0	0	1	≤	1
smokestacks-open-hearth	0	1	0	0	0	0	0.7188402	≤	1
filters - blast	0	0	1	0	0	0	0.4359748	≤	1
filters - open-hearth	0	0	0	1	0	0	1	≤	1
fuels - blast	0	0	0	0	1	0	0.2135922	≤	1
fuels - open-hearth	0	0	0	0	0	1	1	≤	1
Unit Cost	8	10	7	6	11	9	$ 35,590		
Solution	1	0.7188	0.4360	1	0.2136	1			

20% increase

| | Benefit Contribution Per Unit of Abatement Method | | | | | | | | |
| Constraints | Taller Smokestacks | | Filters | | Better Fuels | | Totals | | Acceptable Level |
	Blast	Open-hearth	Blast	Open-hearth	Blast	Open-hearth			
reduce particulates	12	9	25	20	17	13	72	≥	72
reduce sulfer oxides	35	42	18	31	56	49	180	≥	180
reduce hydrocarbons	37	53	28	24	29	20	150	≥	150
smokestacks - blast	1	0	0	0	0	0	1	≤	1
smokestacks-open-hearth	0	1	0	0	0	0	0.8149829	≤	1
filters - blast	0	0	1	0	0	0	0.5284702	≤	1
filters - open-hearth	0	0	0	1	0	0	1	≤	1
fuels - blast	0	0	0	0	1	0	0.3796117	≤	1
fuels - open-hearth	0	0	0	0	0	1	1	≤	1
Unit Cost	8	10	7	6	11	9	$ 39,025		
Solution	1	0.8150	0.5285	1	0.3796	1			

30% increase

| | Benefit Contribution Per Unit of Abatement Method | | | | | | | | |
| Constraints | Taller Smokestacks | | Filters | | Better Fuels | | Totals | | Acceptable Level |
	Blast	Open-hearth	Blast	Open-hearth	Blast	Open-hearth			
reduce particulates	12	9	25	20	17	13	78	≥	78
reduce sulfer oxides	35	42	18	31	56	49	195	≥	195
reduce hydrocarbons	37	53	28	24	29	20	162.5	≥	162.5
smokestacks - blast	1	0	0	0	0	0	1	≤	1
smokestacks-open-hearth	0	1	0	0	0	0	0.9111257	≤	1
filters - blast	0	0	1	0	0	0	0.6209656	≤	1
filters - open-hearth	0	0	0	1	0	0	1	≤	1
fuels - blast	0	0	0	0	1	0	0.5456311	≤	1
fuels - open-hearth	0	0	0	0	0	1	1	≤	1
Unit Cost	8	10	7	6	11	9	$ 42,460		
Solution	1	0.9111	0.6210	1	0.5456	1			

40% increase

Constraints	Taller Smokestacks Blast	Taller Smokestacks Open-hearth	Filters Blast	Filters Open-hearth	Better Fuels Blast	Better Fuels Open-hearth	Totals		Acceptable Level
	Benefit Contribution Per Unit of Abatement Method								
reduce particulates	12	9	25	20	17	13	84	≥	84
reduce sulfer oxides	35	42	18	31	56	49	210	≥	210
reduce hydrocarbons	37	53	28	24	29	20	175	≥	175
smokestacks - blast	1	0	0	0	0	0	1	≤	1
smokestacks-open-hearth	0	1	0	0	0	0	1	≤	1
filters - blast	0	0	1	0	0	0	0.705282	≤	1
filters - open-hearth	0	0	0	1	0	0	1	≤	1
fuels - blast	0	0	0	0	1	0	0.7815769	≤	1
fuels - open-hearth	0	0	0	0	0	1	0.9293187	≤	1
Unit Cost	8	10	7	6	11	9	$ 45.898		
Solution	1	1.0000	0.7053	1	0.7816	0.9293187			

50% increase

Constraints	Taller Smokestacks Blast	Taller Smokestacks Open-hearth	Filters Blast	Filters Open-hearth	Better Fuels Blast	Better Fuels Open-hearth	Totals		Acceptable Level
	Benefit Contribution Per Unit of Abatement Method								
reduce particulates	12	9	25	20	17	13	93.378953	≥	90
reduce sulfer oxides	35	42	18	31	56	49	225	≥	225
reduce hydrocarbons	37	53	28	24	29	20	187.5	≥	187.5
smokestacks - blast	1	0	0	0	0	0	1	≤	1
smokestacks-open-hearth	0	1	0	0	0	0	1	≤	1
filters - blast	0	0	1	0	0	0	0.9491107	≤	1
filters - open-hearth	0	0	0	1	0	0	1	≤	1
fuels - blast	0	0	0	0	1	0	1	≤	1
fuels - open-hearth	0	0	0	0	0	1	0.8962451	≤	1
Unit Cost	8	10	7	6	11	9	$ 49.710		
Solution	1	1.0000	0.9491	1	1.0000	0.8962451			

Subtracting $3.5 for each 10% reduction gives the following costs:

10% - $32.090
20% - $32.025
30% - $31.960
40% - $31.898
50% - $32.210

To minimize the total cost of both pollution abatement and taxes, a 40% reduction should be chosen.

i) The sensitivity report for a 40% reduction is shown below.

Adjustable Cells

Cell	Name	Final Value	Reduced Cost	Objective Coefficient	Allowable Increase	Allowable Decrease
$B$14	Solution Blast	1	0	8	0.552692013	1E+30
$C$14	Solution Open-hearth	1.0000	0.0000	10	0.429446287	1E+30
$D$14	Solution Blast	0.7053	0.0000	7	0.381632653	1.292358804
$E$14	Solution Open-hearth	1	0	6	1.789231947	1E+30
$F$14	Solution Blast	0.7816	0.0000	11	0.384387352	0.044638358
$G$14	Solution Open-hearth	0.929318704	0	9	0.044161637	0.371892925

Constraints

Cell	Name	Final Value	Shadow Price	Constraint R.H. Side	Allowable Increase	Allowable Decrease
$H$4	reduce particulates Totals	84	0.099260015	84	0.264818356	0.845849802
$H$5	reduce sulfer oxides Totals	210	0.124011227	210	1.112449799	6.294117647
$H$6	reduce hydrocarbons Totals	175	0.081653483	175	0.863773966	0.253199269
$H$7	smokestacks - blast Totals	1	-0.552692013	1	0.014418823	0.043313262
$H$8	smokestacks-open-hearth Totals	1	-0.429446287	1	0.007268433	0.022703764
$H$9	filters - blast Totals	0.70528196	0	1	1E+30	0.29471804
$H$10	filters - open-hearth Totals	1	-1.789231947	1	1.174670633	0.116240034
$H$11	fuels - blast Totals	0.781576933	0	1	1E+30	0.218423067
$H$12	fuels - open-hearth Totals	0.929318704	0	1	1E+30	0.070681296

Pollutant	Rate that cost changes	Maximum increase before rate changes	Maximum decrease before rate changes
Particulates	0.099	0.265	0.846
Sulfur oxides	0.124	1.112	6.294
Hydrocarbons	0.082	0.864	0.253

Particulates and sulfur oxides:
For each unit increase in particulate reduction, cost will increase by $0.099 million.
For each unit decrease in sulfur oxide reduction, cost will decrease by $0.124 million.
Thus, cost will remain equal if for each unit increase in particulate reduction, the sulfur oxide reduction is reduced by $0.099 / $0.124 = 0.798 units.

Particulates and hydrocarbons:
For each unit increase in particulate reduction, cost will increase by $0.099 million.
For each unit decrease in hydrocarbon reduction, cost will decrease by $0.082 million.
Thus, cost will remain equal if for each unit increase in particulate reduction, the hydrocarbon reduction is reduced by $0.099 / $0.082 = 1.207 units.

Particulates and both sulfur oxides and hydrocarbons:
For each unit increase in particulate reduction, cost will increase by $0.099 million.
For each simultaneous unit decrease in sulfur oxide and hydrocarbon reduction, cost will decrease by $0.124 + $0.082 = $0.206.
Thus, cost will remain equal if for each unit increase in particulate reduction, the sulfur oxide and hydrocarbon reduction are each reduced by $0.099 / $0.206 = 0.481 units.

4.2   a)   The decisions to be made are how much acreage should be planted in each of the crops and how many cows and hens to have for the coming year. The constraints on these decisions are amount of labor hours available, the investment funds available, the number of acres available, the space available in the barn and chicken house, the minimum requirements for feed to be planted. The overall measure of performance is monetary worth, which is to be maximized.

b & c)

Resources	Resource Usage Per Unit of Activity									Totals	≤	Resource Available
	acres soybean	acres corn	acres wheat	current cows	new cows	current hens	new hens	leftover W/S Labor	leftover S/F Labor			
acreage	1	1	1	2	2	0	0	0	0	640	≤	640
barn space	0	0	0	1	1	0	0	0	0	30	≤	42
chicken house space	0	0	0	0	0	1	1	0	0	2000	≤	5000
winter/spring hours	1	0.9	0.6	60	60	0.3	0.3	1	0	4000	≤	4000
summer/fall hours	1.4	1.2	0.7	60	60	0.3	0.3	0	1	4500	≤	4500
investment fund	0	0	0	0	1500	0	3	0	0	0	≤	20000
feed for cows	0	-1	0	1	1	0	0	0	0	0	≤	0
feed for chickens	0	0	-1	0	0	0.05	0.05	0	0	0	≤	0
Net Income	$0	$0	$0	$850	$850	$4.25	$4.25	$5	$5.50	$ 46,817		
Net Value	$70	$60	$40	$1,050	$1,350	$1.88	$2.25	$0	$0	$ 72,550		
Remaining Investment										$ 20,000		
Living Expenses										$ (40,000)		
										$ 99,367		Total Monetary Worth
Solution	450	30	100	30	0	2000	0	1063	1364			

Note that the cells for current cows and current hens are not changing cells but fixed amounts.

Adjustable Cells

Cell	Name	Final Value	Reduced Cost	Objective Coefficient	Allowable Increase	Allowable Decrease
$B$17	Solution soybean	450	0	70	1E+30	8.400000002
$C$17	Solution corn	30	0	60	8.400000002	1E+30
$D$17	Solution wheat	100	0	40	17.15005129	1E+30
$F$17	Solution cows	0	-53.00000097	699.9999983	53.00000097	1E+30
$H$17	Solution hens	0	-0.857502564	3.499997547	0.857502564	1E+30
$I$17	Solution W/S Labor	1063	0	5	57.3	0.915371347
$J$17	Solution S/F Labor	1364	0	5.5	34.5	0.929824579

Constraints

Cell	Name	Final Value	Shadow Price	Constraint R.H. Side	Allowable Increase	Allowable Decrease
$K$4	acreage Totals	640	57.3	640	974.2857143	450
$K$5	barn space Totals	30	0	42	1E+30	12
$K$6	chicken house space Totals	2000	0	5000	1E+30	3000
$K$7	winter/spring hours Totals	4000	5	4000	1E+30	1063
$K$8	summer/fall hours Totals	4500	5.5	4500	1E+30	1364
$K$9	investment fund Totals	0	0	20000	1E+30	20000
$K$10	feed for cows Totals	0	8.400000002	0	30	450
$K$11	feed for chickens Totals	0	24.15	0	100	450

This model predicts that the family's monetary worth at the end of the coming year will be $99, 367.

d) Range of optimality -   soybeans: $61.6 \leq$ soybeans value $\leq \infty$
   corn: $-\infty \leq$ corn value ≤ 68.4
   wheat: $-\infty \leq$ wheat value ≤ 57.15

e) Drought

Resources	acres soybean	acres corn	acres wheat	current cows	new cows	current hens	new hens	leftover W/S Labor	leftover S/F Labor	Totals	≤	Resource Available
						Resource Usage Per Unit of Activity						
acreage	1	1	1	2	2	0	0	0	0	259.33333	≤	640
barn space	0	0	0	1	1	0	0	0	0	42	≤	42
chicken house space	0	0	0	0	0	1	1	0	0	2666.6667	≤	5000
winter/spring hours	1	0.9	0.6	60	60	0.3	0.3	1	0	4000	≤	4000
summer/fall hours	1.4	1.2	0.7	60	60	0.3	0.3	0	1	4500	≤	4500
investment fund	0	0	0	0	1500	0	3	0	0	20000	≤	20000
feed for cows	0	-1	0	1	1	0	0	0	0	4.547E-13	≤	0
feed for chickens	0	0	-1	0	0	0.05	0.05	0	0	1.705E-11	≤	0
Net Income	$0	$0	$0	$850	$850	$4.25	$4.25	$5	$5.50	$ 55,544		
Net Value	-$10	-$15	$0	$1,050	$1,350	$1.88	$2.25	$0	$0	$ 52,320		
Remaining Investment										$		
Living Expenses										$ (40,000)		
										$ 67,864		Total Monetary Worth
Solution	0	42	133	30	12	2000	667	562	1036			

Flood

Resources	acres soybean	acres corn	acres wheat	current cows	new cows	current hens	new hens	leftover W/S Labor	leftover S/F Labor	Totals	≤	Resource Available
						Resource Usage Per Unit of Activity						
acreage	1	1	1	2	2	0	0	0	0	640	≤	640
barn space	0	0	0	1	1	0	0	0	0	42	≤	42
chicken house space	0	0	0	0	0	1	1	0	0	2666.6667	≤	5000
winter/spring hours	1	0.9	0.6	60	60	0.3	0.3	1	0	4000	≤	4000
summer/fall hours	1.4	1.2	0.7	60	60	0.3	0.3	0	1	4500	≤	4500
investment fund	0	0	0	0	1500	0	3	0	0	20000	≤	20000
feed for cows	0	-1	0	1	1	0	0	0	0	-380.6667	≤	0
feed for chickens	0	0	-1	0	0	0.05	0.05	0	0	-7.11E-15	≤	0
Net Income	$0	$0	$0	$850	$850	$4.25	$4.25	$5	$5.50	$ 51,318		
Net Value	$15	$20	$10	$1,050	$1,350	$1.88	$2.25	$0	$0	$ 62,737		
Remaining Investment										$		
Living Expenses										$ (40,000)		
										$ 74,055		Total Monetary Worth
Solution	0	423	133	30	12	2000	667	220	579			

Early Frost

Resources	acres soybean	acres corn	acres wheat	current cows	new cows	current hens	new hens	leftover W/S Labor	leftover S/F Labor	Totals	≤	Resource Available
						Resource Usage Per Unit of Activity						
acreage	1	1	1	2	2	0	0	0	0	640	≤	640
barn space	0	0	0	1	1	0	0	0	0	30	≤	42
chicken house space	0	0	0	0	0	1	1	0	0	2000	≤	5000
winter/spring hours	1	0.9	0.6	60	60	0.3	0.3	1	0	4000	≤	4000
summer/fall hours	1.4	1.2	0.7	60	60	0.3	0.3	0	1	4500	≤	4500
investment fund	0	0	0	0	1500	0	3	0	0	0	≤	20000
feed for cows	0	-1	0	1	1	0	0	0	0	6.673E-11	≤	0
feed for chickens	0	0	-1	0	0	0.05	0.05	0	0	7.104E-11	≤	0
Net Income	$0	$0	$0	$850	$850	$4.25	$4.25	$5	$5.50	$ 46,817		
Net Value	$50	$40	$30	$1,050	$1,350	$1.88	$2.25	$0	$0	$ 61,950		
Remaining Investment										$ 20,000		
Living Expenses										$ (40,000)		
										$ 88,767		Total Monetary Worth
Solution	450	30	100	30	0	2000	0	1063	1364			

Drought and Early Frost

Resources	acres soybean	acres corn	acres wheat	current cows	new cows	current hens	new hens	leftover W/S Labor	leftover S/F Labor	Totals	≤	Resource Available
						Resource Usage Per Unit of Activity						
acreage	1	1	1	2	2	0	0	0	0	226	≤	640
barn space	0	0	0	1	1	0	0	0	0	42	≤	42
chicken house space	0	0	0	0	0	1	1	0	0	2000	≤	5000
winter/spring hours	1	0.9	0.6	60	60	0.3	0.3	1	0	4000	≤	4000
summer/fall hours	1.4	1.2	0.7	60	60	0.3	0.3	0	1	4500	≤	4500
investment fund	0	0	0	0	1500	0	3	0	0	18000	≤	20000
feed for cows	0	-1	0	1	1	0	0	0	0	-1.28E-12	≤	0
feed for chickens	0	0	-1	0	0	0.05	0.05	0	0	0	≤	0
Net Income	$0	$0	$0	$850	$850	$4.25	$4.25	$5	$5.50	$ 55,039		
Net Value	-$15	-$20	-$10	$1,050	$1,350	$1.88	$2.25	$0	$0	$ 49,610		
Remaining Investment										$ 2,000		
Living Expenses										$ (40,000)		
										$ 66,649		Total Monetary Worth
Solution	0	42	100	30	12	2000	0	782	1260			

Flood and Early Frost

Resources	acres soybean	acres corn	acres wheat	current cows	new cows	current hens	new hens	leftover W/S Labor	leftover S/F Labor	Totals		Resource Available
				Resource Usage Per Unit of Activity								
acreage	1	1	1	2	2	0	0	0	0	362	≤	640
barn space	0	0	0	1	1	0	0	0	0	37.333333	≤	42
chicken house space	0	0	0	0	0	1	1	0	0	5000	≤	5000
winter/spring hours	1	0.9	0.6	60	60	0.3	0.3	1	0	4000	≤	4000
summer/fall hours	1.4	1.2	0.7	60	60	0.3	0.3	0	1	4500	≤	4500
investment fund	0	0	0	0	1500	0	3	0	0	20000	≤	20000
feed for cows	0	-1	0	1	1	0	0	0	0	-2.69E-12	≤	0
feed for chickens	0	0	-1	0	0	0.05	0.05	0	0	7.671E-11	≤	0
Net Income	$0	$0	$0	$850	$850	$4.25	$4.25	$5	$5.50	$ 56,336		
Net Value	$10	$10	$5	$1,050	$1,350	$1.88	$2.25	$0	$0	$ 53,523		
Remaining Investment										$ (0)		
Living Expenses										$ (40,000)		
										$ 69,860		Total Monetary Worth
Solution	0	37.3	250	30	7.333	2000	3000	76	540			

f)

Opt. Sol. Used	Family's monetary worth at year's end if the scenario is actually:					
	Good Weather	Drought	Flood	Early Frost	Drought & Early Frost	Flood & Early Frost
Good Weather	99,367	57,117	70,417	88,767	53,717	67,367
Drought	76,348	67,864	70,668	74,174	66,321	69,581
Flood	94,962	57,929	74,055	85,175	54,482	69,162
Early Frost	99,367	57,117	70,417	88,767	53,717	67,367
Drought & Early Frost	75,009	67,859	70,329	73,169	66,649	69,409
Flood & Early Frost	80,476	67,676	71,483	77,230	64,990	69,860

The "Flood & Early Frost" solution looks like the best conservative option. The "Flood" option looks good for those who would like more risk.

g and h)

The expected net value for each of the crops is calculated as follows:

Soybeans: ($70)(0.4) + (-$10)(0.2) + ($15)(0.1) + ($50)(0.15) + (-$15)(0.1) + ($10)(0.05) = $34 million,

Corn: ($60)(0.4) + (-$15)(0.2) + ($20)(0.1) + ($40)(0.15) + (-$20)(0.1) + ($10)(0.05) = $27.5 million,

Wheat: ($40)(0.4) + ($0)(0.2) + ($10)(0.1) + ($30)(0.15) + (-$10)(0.1) + ($5)(0.05) = $20.75 million.

The resulting spreadsheet solution is shown below:

Resources	acres soybean	acres corn	acres wheat	current cows	new cows	current hens	new hens	leftover W/S Labor	leftover S/F Labor	Totals		Resource Available
acreage	1	1	1	2	2	0	0	0	0	640	≤	640
barn space	0	0	0	1	1	0	0	0	0	42	≤	42
chicken house space	0	0	0	0	0	1	1	0	0	2000	≤	5000
winter/spring hours	1	0.9	0.6	60	60	0.3	0.3	1	0	4000	≤	4000
summer/fall hours	1.4	1.2	0.7	60	60	0.3	0.3	0	1	4500	≤	4500
investment fund	0	0	0	0	1500	0	3	0	0	18000	≤	20000
feed for cows	0	-1	0	1	1	0	0	0	0	0	≤	0
feed for chickens	0	0	-1	0	0	0.05	0.05	0	0	0	≤	0
Net Income	$0	$0	$0	$850	$850	$4.25	$4.25	$5	$5.50	$ 49,781		
Net Value	$34.0	$27.5	$20.8	$1,050	$1,350	$1.88	$2.25	$0	$0	$ 68,756		
Remaining Investment										$ 2,000		
Living Expenses										$ (40,000)		
										$ 80,537		Total Monetary Worth
Solution	414	42	100	30	12	2000	0	368	680			

(Header: Resource Usage Per Unit of Activity)

Adjustable Cells

Cell	Name	Final Value	Reduced Cost	Objective Coefficient	Allowable Increase	Allowable Decrease
$B$17	Solution soybean	414	0	34	7.499999997	0.400002814
$C$17	Solution corn	42	0	27.5	4.899999997	22.49999999
$D$17	Solution wheat	100	0	20.75	0.400002814	1E+30
$F$17	Solution cows	12	0	700	1E+30	22.49999999
$H$17	Solution hens	0	-0.020000141	3.499999875	0.020000141	1E+30
$I$17	Solution W/S Labor	368	0	5	0.388601036	0.071429073
$J$17	Solution S/F Labor	680	0	5.5	0.394736842	0.075472229

Constraints

Cell	Name	Final Value	Shadow Price	Constraint R.H. Side	Allowable Increase	Allowable Decrease
$K$4	acreage Totals	640	21.3	640	368.2	414
$K$5	barn space Totals	42	22.49999999	42	1.333333333	12
$K$6	chicken house space Totals	2000	0	5000	1E+30	3000
$K$7	winter/spring hours Totals	4000	5	4000	1E+30	368.2
$K$8	summer/fall hours Totals	4500	5.5	4500	1E+30	680
$K$9	investment fund Totals	18000	0	20000	1E+30	2000
$K$10	feed for cows Totals	0	4.899999997	0	42	414
$K$11	feed for chickens Totals	0	7.399999998	0	100	414

This model predicts that the family's monetary worth at the end of the coming year will be $80,537.

i)   The shadow price for the investment constraint is zero, indicating that additional investment funds will not increase their total monetary worth at all. Thus, it is not worthwhile to obtain a bank loan. The shadow price would need to be at least $1.10 before a loan at 10% interest would be worthwhile.

j)   The expected net value for soybeans can increase up to $7.50 or decrease up to $0.40; for corn can increase up to $4.90 or decrease up to $22.50; for wheat can increase up to $0.40 or decrease any amount without changing the optimal solution. The expected net value for soybeans and wheat should be estimated most carefully.

The solution is sensitive to decreases in the expected value of soybeans and increases in the expected value of wheat. If the *cumulative* decrease in the expected value of soybeans *and* increase in the expected value of wheat exceeds $0.40, then the 100% rule will be violated, and the solution might change.

k)   Answers will vary.

4.3   a)

Data:

Area	Number of Students	Percentage in 6th Grade	Percentage in 7th Grade	Percentage in 8th Grade	Bussing Cost ($/Student) School 1	School 2	School 3
1	450	0.32	0.38	0.3	300	0	700
2	600	0.37	0.28	0.35	-	400	500
3	550	0.3	0.32	0.38	600	300	200
4	350	0.28	0.4	0.32	200	500	-
5	500	0.39	0.34	0.27	0	-	400
6	450	0.34	0.28	0.38	500	300	0
				Capacity:	900	1100	1000

Solution: Number of Students Assigned

	School 1	School 2	School 3	Total		
Area 1	0	450	0	450	=	450
Area 2	0	422.222222	177.777778	600	=	600
Area 3	0	227.777778	322.222222	550	=	550
Area 4	350	0	0	350	=	350
Area 5	366.666667	0	133.333333	500	=	500
Area 6	83.3333333	0	366.666667	450	=	450
Total	800	1100	1000			
	≤	≤	≤			
Capacity	900	1100	1000			

Total Bussing Cost = $ 555,555.56

Grade Constraints:

	School 1	School 2	School 3
6th Graders	269.333333	368.555556	339.111111
7th Graders	288	362.111111	300.888889
8th Graders	242.666667	369.333333	360
30% of Total	240	330	300
36% of Total	288	396	360

b)

Adjustable Cells

Cell	Name	Final Value	Reduced Cost	Objective Coefficient	Allowable Increase	Allowable Decrease
$B$14	Area 1 School 1	0	177.77778	300	1E+30	177.77778
$C$14	Area 1 School 2	450	0	0	177.77778	1.554E+17
$D$14	Area 1 School 3	0	266.66667	700	1E+30	266.66667
$B$15	Area 2 School 1	0	-800	0	1E+30	800
$C$15	Area 2 School 2	422.22222	0	400	34.210526	4.5454555
$D$15	Area 2 School 3	177.77778	0	500	4.5454555	34.210526
$B$16	Area 3 School 1	0	11.111114	600	1E+30	11.111114
$C$16	Area 3 School 2	227.77778	0	300	4.5454555	34.210526
$D$16	Area 3 School 3	322.22222	0	200	34.210526	7.6923092
$B$17	Area 4 School 1	350	0	200	366.66667	2.339E+16
$C$17	Area 4 School 2	0	366.66667	500	1E+30	366.66667
$D$17	Area 4 School 3	0	-433.3333	0	1E+30	433.33333
$B$18	Area 5 School 1	366.66667	0	0	16.66667	108.33333
$C$18	Area 5 School 2	0	233.33333	0	1E+30	233.33333
$D$18	Area 5 School 3	133.33333	0	400	108.33333	16.66667
$B$19	Area 6 School 1	83.333333	0	500	33.333342	166.66667
$C$19	Area 6 School 2	0	200	300	1E+30	200
$D$19	Area 6 School 3	366.66667	0	0	166.66667	33.333342

Constraints

Cell	Name	Final Value	Shadow Price	Constraint R.H. Side	Allowable Increase	Allowable Decrease
$B$30	8th Graders School 1	242.66667	0	0	1E+30	45.333333
$C$30	8th Graders School 2	369.33333	0	0	1E+30	26.666667
$D$30	8th Graders School 3	360	-6666.667	0	5.3333333	0.6666667
$B$20	Total School 1	800	0	900	1E+30	100
$C$20	Total School 2	1100	-177.7778	1100	36.363636	3.7735849
$D$20	Total School 3	1000	-144.4444	1000	42.105263	3.8834951
$B$28	6th Graders School 1	269.33333	0	0	29.333333	1E+30
$C$28	6th Graders School 2	368.55556	0	0	38.555556	1E+30
$D$28	6th Graders School 3	339.11111	0	0	39.111111	1E+30
$B$28	6th Graders School 1	269.33333	0	0	1E+30	18.666667
$C$28	6th Graders School 2	368.55556	0	0	1E+30	27.444444
$D$28	6th Graders School 3	339.11111	0	0	1E+30	20.888889
$B$29	7th Graders School 1	288	0	0	48	1E+30
$C$29	7th Graders School 2	362.11111	0	0	32.111111	1E+30
$D$29	7th Graders School 3	300.88889	0	0	0.8888889	1E+30
$B$29	7th Graders School 1	288	-2777.778	0	0.2580645	2.9090909
$C$29	7th Graders School 2	362.11111	0	0	1E+30	33.888889
$D$29	7th Graders School 3	300.88889	0	0	1E+30	59.111111
$B$30	8th Graders School 1	242.66667	0	0	2.6666667	1E+30
$C$30	8th Graders School 2	369.33333	0	0	39.333333	1E+30
$D$30	8th Graders School 3	360	0	0	60	1E+30
$E$14	Area 1 Total	450	177.77778	450	3.7735849	36.363636
$E$15	Area 2 Total	600	577.77778	600	3.7735849	36.363636
$E$16	Area 3 Total	550	477.77778	550	3.7735849	36.363636
$E$17	Area 4 Total	350	311.11111	350	72.727273	6.4516129
$E$18	Area 5 Total	500	-55.55556	500	12.903226	145.45455
$E$19	Area 6 Total	450	277.77778	450	3.2258065	36.363636

c) The bussing cost from area 6 to school 1 can increase $33.33 before the current optimal solution would no longer be optimal. The new solution with a 10% increase ($50) is shown below.

Data:

Area	Number of Students	Percentage in 6th Grade	Percentage in 7th Grade	Percentage in 8th Grade	Bussing Cost ($/Student) School 1	School 2	School 3
1	450	0.32	0.38	0.3	300	0	700
2	600	0.37	0.28	0.35	-	400	500
3	550	0.3	0.32	0.38	600	300	200
4	350	0.28	0.4	0.32	200	500	-
5	500	0.39	0.34	0.27	0	-	400
6	450	0.34	0.28	0.38	550	300	0
				Capacity:	900	1100	1000

Solution: Number of Students Assigned

	School 1	School 2	School 3	Total		
Area 1	0	450	0	450	=	450
Area 2	0	600	0	600	=	600
Area 3	72.7272726	50	427.272727	550	=	550
Area 4	350	0	0	350	=	350
Area 5	318.181818	0	181.818182	500	=	500
Area 6	59.0909093	0	390.909091	450	=	450
Total	800	1100	1000			
	≤	≤	≤			
Capacity	900	1100	1000			

Total Bussing Cost = $ 559,318.18

Grade Constraints:

	School 1	School 2	School 3
6th Graders	264	381	332
7th Graders	288	355	308
8th Graders	248	364	360
30% of Total	240	330	300
36% of Total	288	396	360

d) The bussing cost from area 6 to school 2 can increase any amount and the current optimal solution will still be optimal.

e) According to the 100% rule, the bussing cost from area 6 can increase uniformly up to 6.67% ($33 for school 1, and $20 for school 2) without changing the solution. Beyond that the solution might change. This calculation is shown below.

School 1: $500 → $533.33. % of allowable increase $= 100\left(\dfrac{533.33-500}{33.33}\right) = 100\%$

School 2: $300 → $320.   % of allowable increase $= 100\left(\dfrac{320-300}{\infty}\right) = \underline{0\%}$

$$\text{Sum} = 100\%.$$

The new spreadsheet solution is shown below.

Data:

Area	Number of Students	Percentage in 6th Grade	Percentage in 7th Grade	Percentage in 8th Grade	Bussing Cost ($/Student) School 1	School 2	School 3
1	450	0.32	0.38	0.3	300	0	700
2	600	0.37	0.28	0.35	-	400	500
3	550	0.3	0.32	0.38	600	300	200
4	350	0.28	0.4	0.32	200	500	-
5	500	0.39	0.34	0.27	0	-	400
6	450	0.34	0.28	0.38	550	330	0
				Capacity:	900	1100	1000

Solution: Number of Students Assigned

	School 1	School 2	School 3	Total		
Area 1	0	450	0	450	=	450
Area 2	0	600	0	600	=	600
Area 3	72.7272727	50	427.272727	550	=	550
Area 4	350	0	0	350	=	350
Area 5	318.181818	0	181.818182	500	=	500
Area 6	59.0909091	0	390.909091	450	=	450
Total	800	1100	1000			
	≤	≤	≤			
Capacity	900	1100	1000			

Total Bussing Cost = $ 559,318.18

Grade Constraints:

	School 1	School 2	School 3
6th Graders	264	381	332
7th Graders	288	355	308
8th Graders	248	364	360
30% of Total	240	330	300
36% of Total	288	396	360

f) The shadow price for school 1 is zero. Thus, adding a temporary classroom at school 1 would not save any money, and thus would not be worthwhile.

The shadow price for school 2 is -$177.78. Thus, adding a temporary classroom at school 2 would save ($177.78)(20) = $3555.60 in bussing cost. This is worthwhile, since it exceeds the $2500 leasing cost.

The shadow price for school 3 is -$144.44. Thus, adding a temporary classroom at school 3 would save ($144.44)(20) = $2888.80 in bussing cost. This is also worthwhile, since it exceeds the $2500 leasing cost.

g) For school 2, the allowable increase for school capacity is 36. This means the shadow price is only valid for a single additional portable classroom.

For school 3, the allowable increase for school capacity is 42. This means the shadow price is valid for up to two additional portable classrooms.

h) The following combinations do not violate the 100% rule:

Portables to add to school 2	Portables to add to school 3	100%-rule calculation	Bussing Cost Savings
1	0	(20/36) + (0/42) = 55.6%	($177.78)(20)=$2888.80
0	1	(0/36) + (20/42) = 47.6%	
0	2	(0/36) + (40/42) = 95.23%	

Each combination yields the following total savings

Portables to add to school 2	Portables to add to school 3	Bussing Cost Savings	Lease Cost	Total Savings
1	0	($177.78)(20) = $3555.60	$2500	$1055.60
0	1	($144.44)(20) = $2888.80	$2500	$388.80
0	2	($144.44)(40) = $5777.60	$5000	$777.60

Of these combinations, adding one portable to school 2 is best in terms of minimizing total cost. The spreadsheet solution is shown below.

Data:

Area	Number of Students	Percentage in 6th Grade	Percentage in 7th Grade	Percentage in 8th Grade	Bussing Cost ($/Student) School 1	School 2	School 3
1	450	0.32	0.38	0.3	300	0	700
2	600	0.37	0.28	0.35	-	400	500
3	550	0.3	0.32	0.38	600	300	200
4	350	0.28	0.4	0.32	200	500	-
5	500	0.39	0.34	0.27	0	-	400
6	450	0.34	0.28	0.38	500	300	0
				Capacity:	900	1100	1000

Solution: Number of Students Assigned

	School 1	School 2	School 3	Total		
Area 1	0	450	0	450	=	450
Area 2	0	520	80	600	=	600
Area 3	0	150	400	550	=	550
Area 4	350	0	0	350	=	350
Area 5	340	0	160	500	=	500
Area 6	90	0	360	450	=	450
Total	780	1120	1000			
	≤	≤	≤			
Capacity	900	1120	1000			

Total Bussing Cost = $ 552,000.00
Leasing Cost = $ 2,500.00
Total Cost = $ 554,500.00

Grade Constraints:

	School 1	School 2	School 3
6th Graders	261.2	381.4	334.4
7th Graders	280.8	364.6	305.6
8th Graders	238	374	360
30% of Total	234	336	300
36% of Total	280.8	403.2	360

i) Adding two portables to school 2 yields the following solution. This is the best plan.

Data:	Number of Students	Percentage in 6th Grade	Percentage in 7th Grade	Percentage in 8th Grade	Bussing Cost ($/Student)		
Area					School 1	School 2	School 3
1	450	0.32	0.38	0.3	300	0	700
2	600	0.37	0.28	0.35	-	400	500
3	550	0.3	0.32	0.38	600	300	200
4	350	0.28	0.4	0.32	200	500	-
5	500	0.39	0.34	0.27	0	-	400
6	450	0.34	0.28	0.38	500	300	0
				Capacity:	900	1100	1000

Solution:	Number of Students Assigned					
	School 1	School 2	School 3	Total		
Area 1	0	450	0	450	=	450
Area 2	0	600	0	600	=	600
Area 3	0	90	460	550	=	550
Area 4	350	0	0	350	=	350
Area 5	318.947368	0	181.052632	500	=	500
Area 6	95.2631579	0	354.736842	450	=	450
Total	764.210526	1140	995.789474			
	≤	≤	≤			
Capacity	900	1140	1000			

Total Bussing Cost = $ 549,052.63
Leasing Cost = $ 5,000.00
Total Cost = $ 554,052.63

Grade
Constraints:

	School 1	School 2	School 3
6th Graders	254.778947	393	329.221053
7th Graders	275.115789	367.8	308.084211
8th Graders	234.315789	379.2	358.484211
30% of Total	229.263158	342	298.736842
36% of Total	275.115789	410.4	358.484211

CHAPTER 5
TRANSPORTATION AND ASSIGNMENT PROBLEMS

Review Questions

5.1-1 The CEO is concerned about escalating costs, in particular the shipping costs for peas.

5.1-2 The Management Science Group is being asked to look at the current shipping plan and see if they can develop a new one that would reduce the total shipping cost to an absolute minimum.

5.2-1 Transportation problems in general are concerned with distributing any commodity from any group of supply centers, called sources, to any group of receiving centers, called destinations, in such a way as to minimize the total distribution cost.

5.2-2 The only data needed for a transportation problem are the supplies, demands, and unit costs.

5.2-3 The problem is formulated as a transportation model if it is described completely in terms of a parameter table and it satisfies both the requirements assumption and the cost assumption.

5.2-4 A transportation problem will have feasible solutions if and only if the sum of its supplies equals the sum of its demands.

5.2-5 As long as all its supplies and demands have integer values, any transportation problem with feasible solutions is guaranteed to have an optimal solution with integer values for all its decision variables.

5.2-6 The transportation simplex method and network simplex method can solve them faster.

5.3-1 To formulate the spreadsheet model, a ≤ sign instead of an = sign is used in the respective cells and the corresponding constraints in the Solver dialog box.

5.3-2 To formulate the spreadsheet model, the demand row at the bottom of the parameter table and the solution table is replaced by a minimum and maximum row. The constraints in the Solver dialog box match these range restrictions.

5.4-1 The areas of application in this section are distributing natural resources, production scheduling, designing school attendance zones, meeting energy needs, and choosing a new site location.

5.4-2 Their objective is to minimize the total cost of meeting the water needs of the four cities they serve.

5.4-3 The sources are the production of jet engines on regular time and overtime in each of the four months. The destinations are their installation in each of the four months.

5.4-4 Distances play the role of unit costs.

5.4-5 The objective of management is to minimize the total cost of meeting all the energy needs.

5.5-1 I) The cost of transporting the oil from its sources to all the refineries, including the new one.

II) The cost of transporting finished product from all the refineries, including the new one, to the distribution centers.

III) Operating costs for the new refineries.

5.5-2   The new refinery will have a great impact on the operation of the entire distribution system, including decisions on how much to ship to and from each refinery (new and old).

5.5-3   Three transportation problems were solved to compare total shipping costs for crude oil with each potential choice of a new refinery site, and three were solved to compare total shipping costs for finished product with each potential choice of a new refinery site. This resulted in six total problems.

5.5-4   Management must consider non-financial factors as well, such as closeness to corporate headquarters.

5.6-1   Given a set of tasks to be performed and a set of assignees that are available to perform these tasks, the problem is to determine which assignee should be assigned to each task.

5.6-2   I) The number of assignees and the number of tasks are the same.

   II) Each assignee is to be assigned to exactly one task.

   III) Each task is to be performed by exactly one assignee.

   IV) There is a cost associated with each combination of an assignee performing a task.

5.6-3   When the assumptions are satisfied, all that needs to be done to formulate a problem as an assignment problem is (1) to identify the assignees and tasks, and (2) to construct a cost table that gives the cost associated with each combination of an assignee performing a task.

5.6-4   When an assignment problem is described as a transportation problem, the sources are assignments, the destinations are tasks, and the supplies and demands are all equal to 1.

5.6-5   The Hungarian method solves assignment problems well.

5.7-1   When formulating the spreadsheet model, a constraint is included in the Solver dialog box that sets the assignee/task combination equal to 0.

5.7-2   If an assignee will perform more than one task, the supply is change from 1 to the greater amount that can be performed.

5.7-3   If a task will be performed by more than one assignee, the demand is changed from 1 to the greater amount.

Problems

5.1   a)

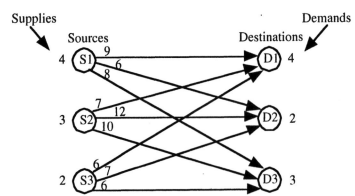

b & c)

Unit Cost ($)

		Destination			Supply
		1	2	3	
	1	9	6	8	4
Source	2	7	12	10	3
	3	6	7	6	2
Demand		4	2	3	

Shipment Quantities

		Destination			Totals		Supply
		1	2	3			
	1	0	2	2	4	=	4
Source	2	3	0	0	3	=	3
	3	1	0	1	2	=	2
Totals		4	2	3			
		=	=	=	Total Cost	=	$ 61
Demand		4	2	3			

5.2   a)

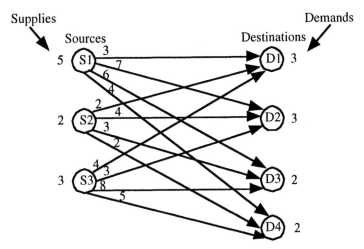

b & c)

Unit Cost ($)

		Destination 1	2	3	4	Supply
	1	3	7	6	4	5
Source	2	2	4	3	2	2
	3	4	3	8	5	3
Demand		3	3	2	2	

Shipment Quantities

		Destination 1	2	3	4	Totals		Supply
	1	3	0	0	2	5	=	5
Source	2	0	0	2	0	2	=	2
	3	0	3	0	0	3	=	3
Totals		3	3	2	2			
		=	=	=	=	Total Cost =		$ 32
Demand		3	3	2	2			

5.3   a)

Unit Cost ($)
Destination (Retail Outlet)

		1	2	3	4	Supply
	1	500	600	400	200	10
Source	2	200	900	100	300	20
(Plant)	3	300	400	200	100	20
	4	200	100	300	200	10
Demand		20	10	10	20	

b & c)

Unit Cost ($)
Destination (Retail Outlet)

		1	2	3	4	Supply
	1	500	600	400	200	10
Source	2	200	900	100	300	20
(Plant)	3	300	400	200	100	20
	4	200	100	300	200	10
Demand		20	10	10	20	

Shipment Quantities
Destination (Retail Outlet)

		1	2	3	4	Totals		Supply
	1	0	0	0	10	10	=	10
Source	2	10	0	10	0	20	=	20
(Plant)	3	10	0	0	10	20	=	20
	4	0	10	0	0	10	=	10
Totals		20	10	10	20			
		=	=	=	=	Total Cost =		$ 10,000
Demand		20	10	10	20			

5.4 a)

		Unit Cost ($) Destination (Distribution Center)				Supply
		1	2	3	4	
Source	1	500	750	300	450	12
(Plant)	2	650	800	400	600	17
	3	400	700	500	550	11
Demand		10	10	10	10	

b & c)

		Unit Cost ($) Destination (Distribution Center)				Supply
		1	2	3	4	
Source	1	500	750	300	450	12
(Plant)	2	650	800	400	600	17
	3	400	700	500	550	11
Demand		10	10	10	10	

Shipment Quantities

		Destination (Distribution Center)				Totals		Supply
		1	2	3	4			
Source	1	0	0	2	10	12	=	12
(Plant)	2	0	9	8	0	17	=	17
	3	10	1	0	0	11	=	11
Totals		10	10	10	10			
		=	=	=	=	Total Cost =		$ 20,200
Demand		10	10	10	10			

5.5

		Unit Cost ($) Destination		Supply
		Today	Tomorrow	
Source	Dick	3	2.7	5
	Harry	2.9	2.8	4
Demand		3	4	

Daily Purchase

		Destination		Totals		Supply
		Today	Tomorrow			
Source	Dick	0	4	4	≤	5
	Harry	3	0	3	≤	4
Totals		3	4			
		=	=	Total Cost =		$ 20
Demand		3	4			

5.6

Unit Cost ($)

		Destination (Product) 1	2	3	Supply
	1	31	45	38	400
Source	2	29	41	35	600
(Plant)	3	32	46	40	400
	4	28	42	-	600
	5	29	43	-	1000
Demand		600	1000	800	

Daily Production

		Destination (Product) 1	2	3	Totals		Supply
	1	0	0	200	200	≤	400
Source	2	0	0	600	600	≤	600
(Plant)	3	0	0	0	0	≤	400
	4	0	600	0	600	≤	600
	5	600	400	0	1000	≤	1000
Totals		600	1000	800			
		=	=	=	Total Cost =		$ 88,400
Demand		600	1000	800			

5.7

Unit Cost ($)

		Destination Wheat	Barley	Oats	Supply
	England	162	121.5	82.8	70
Source	France	93.6	108	75	110
	Spain	158.4	100.8	100.8	80
Demand		125	60	75	

Allocation Quantities

		Destination Wheat	Barley	Oats	Totals		Supply
	England	0	0	70	70	=	70
Source	France	110	0	0	110	=	110
	Spain	15	60	5	80	=	80
Totals		125	60	75			
		=	=	=	Total Cost =		$ 25,020
Demand		125	60	75			

5.8

		Unit Cost ($) Destination			
		1	2	3	Supply
Source	North	130	160	150	18
	South	180	150	160	14
Demand		10	5	10	

		Hauling Destination					
		1	2	3	Totals		Supply
Source	North	10	0	8	18	≤	18
	South	0	5	2	7	≤	14
Totals		10	5	10			
		=	=	=	Total Cost =		$ 3,570
Demand		10	5	10			

5.9

Adjustable Cells

Cell	Name	Final Value	Reduced Cost	Objective Coefficient	Allowable Increase	Allowable Decrease
$D$15	Bellingham Sacramento	0	14.9999999	464	1E+30	15
$E$15	Bellingham Salt Lake City	20	0	513	15	21
$F$15	Bellingham Rapid City	0	83.9999996	654	1E+30	84
$G$15	Bellingham Albuquerque	55	0	867	21	351
$D$16	Eugene Sacramento	80	0	352	15	1E+30
$E$16	Eugene Salt Lake City	45	0	416	21	15
$F$16	Eugene Rapid City	0	217	690	1E+30	217
$G$16	Eugene Albuquerque	0	20.9999997	791	1E+30	21
$D$17	Albert Lea Sacramento	0	728	995	1E+30	728
$E$17	Albert Lea Salt Lake City	0	351	682	1E+30	351
$F$17	Albert Lea Rapid City	70	0	388	84	1E+30
$G$17	Albert Lea Albuquerque	30	0	685	351	84

Constraints

Cell	Name	Final Value	Shadow Price	Constraint R.H. Side	Allowable Increase	Allowable Decrease
$D$18	Totals Sacramento	80	267	80	0	20
$E$18	Totals Salt Lake City	65	331	65	0	20
$F$18	Totals Rapid City	70	388	70	0	70
$G$18	Totals Albuquerque	85	685	85	0	30
$H$15	Bellingham Totals	75	182	75	30	0
$H$16	Eugene Totals	125	85	125	20	0
$H$17	Albert Lea Totals	100	0	100	0	1E+30

		Range of Optimality Destination			
		Sacramento	Salt Lake City	Rapid City	Albuquerque
Source	Bellingham	449 to ∞	492 to 528	570 to ∞	516 to 888
	Eugene	-∞ to 367	401 to 437	473 to ∞	770 to ∞
	Albert Lea	267 to ∞	331 to ∞	-∞ to 472	601 to 1036

These ranges tell management how much each individual cost can change without changing the optimal solution.

5.10

Adjustable Cells

Cell	Name	Final Value	Reduced Cost	Objective Coefficient	Allowable Increase	Allowable Decrease
$D$15	Colombo Berdoo	2.22045E-16	0	160	0	20
$E$15	Colombo Los Devils	5	0	130	20	1E+30
$F$15	Colombo San Go	0	10	220	1E+30	10
$G$15	Colombo Hollyglass	0	0	170	1E+30	0
$D$16	Sacron Berdoo	2	0	140	10	0
$E$16	Sacron Los Devils	0	20	130	1E+30	20
$F$16	Sacron San Go	2.5	0	190	10	10
$G$16	Sacron Hollyglass	1.5	0	150	0	1E+30
$D$17	Calorie Berdoo	0	10	190	1E+30	10
$E$17	Calorie Los Devils	0	50	200	1E+30	50
$F$17	Calorie San Go	1.5	0	230	10	20
$G$17	Calorie Hollyglass	0	-190	0	1E+30	190

Constraints

Cell	Name	Final Value	Shadow Price	Constraint R.H. Side	Allowable Increase	Allowable Decrease
$H$15	Colombo Totals	5	-20	5	1.5	0
$H$16	Sacron Totals	6	-40	6	1.5	2.5
$H$17	Calorie Totals	1.5	0.0	5	1E+30	3.5
$D$18	Totals Berdoo	2	180	2	2.5	1.5
$E$18	Totals Los Devils	5	150	5	0	1.5
$F$18	Totals San Go	4	230	4	3.5	1.5
$G$18	Totals Hollyglass	1.5	190	1.5	2.5	1.5

a) The optimal solution would change because the decrease of $30 million is outside the allowable decrease of $20 million.

b) The optimal solution would remain the same since the allowable increase is ∞.

c) By the 100% rule for simultaneous changes, the optimal solution will not change.

C_{CS}: $230 \rightarrow$ \$215   % of allowable decrease $= 100\left(\dfrac{230-215}{20}\right) = 75\%$

C_{SL}: $130 \rightarrow$ \$145   % of allowable increase $= 100\left(\dfrac{145-130}{\infty}\right) = \underline{0\%}$

$\qquad\qquad\qquad\qquad\qquad\qquad\qquad\qquad\qquad$ Sum $= 75\%$.

d) By the 100% rule for simultaneous changes, the shadow prices may or may not remain valid.

C_{Sacron}: $6 \rightarrow$ \$5.5   % of allowable decrease $= 100\left(\dfrac{6-5.5}{2.5}\right) = 20\%$

$C_{Hollyglass}$: $1.5 \rightarrow$ \$1   % of allowable decrease $= 100\left(\dfrac{1.5-1}{0}\right) = \underline{\infty\%}$

$\qquad\qquad\qquad\qquad\qquad\qquad\qquad\qquad\qquad$ Sum $= \infty\%$.

5.11

Unit Cost (Millions of Dollars)

		Berdoo	Los Devils	San Go	Hollyglass	Supply
		Destination (City)				
Source	Colombo	160	130	220	170	5
(River)	Sacron	140	130	190	150	6
	Calorie	190	200	230	-	5
Minimum		2	5	4	1.5	
Maximum		4	7	6	3.5	

Water Distribution (Millions of Acre-Feet)

		Berdoo	Los Devils	San Go	Hollyglass	Totals		Supply
		Destination (City)						
Source	Colombo	0	5	0	0	5	=	5
(River)	Sacron	2.5	2	0	1.5	6	=	6
	Calorie	1	0	4	0	5	=	5
Totals		3.5	7	4	1.5	2595	=	Total Cost
Minimum		2	5	4	1.5			($ Millions)
Maximum		4	7	6	3.5			

5.12

Unit Profit ($)

		1	2	3	4	Supply
		Destination (Customer)				
Source	1	800	700	500	200	60
(Plant)	2	500	200	100	300	80
	3	600	400	300	500	40
Minimum		40	60	20	0	
Maximum		40	60	180	180	

Shipments

		1	2	3	4	Totals		Supply
		Destination (Customer)						
Source	1	0	60	0	0	60	=	60
(Plant)	2	40	0	20	20	80	=	80
	3	0	0	0	40	40	=	40
Totals		40	60	20	60			
Minimum		40	60	20	0	Total Profit	=	$ 90,000
Maximum		40	60	180	180			

5.13

Unit Cost ($)

		Destination (Distribution Center)			
		1	2	3	Supply
Source	A	800	700	400	50
(Plant)	B	600	800	500	50
Demand		20	20	20	

Daily Production

		Destination (Distribution Center)			Totals		Supply
		1	2	3			
Source	A	0	20	20	40	≤	50
(Plant)	B	20	0	0	20	≤	50
Totals		20	20	20			
		=	=	=	Total Cost =		$ 34,000
Demand		20	20	20			

5.14

Unit Cost ($)

		Destination (Distribution Center)			
		1	2	3	Supply
Source	A	800	700	400	50
(Plant)	B	600	800	500	50
Minimum		10	10	10	
Maximum		30	30	30	

Daily Production

		Destination (Distribution Center)			Totals		Supply
		1	2	3			
Source	A	0	10	30	39.9999995	≤	50
(Plant)	B	20	0	0	20	≤	50
Totals		20	10	30	Total Shipped =		60
Minimum		10	10	10	Total Cost =		$ 31,000
Maximum		30	30	30			

5.15

Unit Cost (Thousands of Dollars)
Destination (Week Supplied)

		1	2	3	Supply
	start	0	50	100	2
	1 (RT)	300	350	400	2
	1 (OT)	400	450	500	2
Source	2 (RT)	-	500	550	3
(Week	2 (OT)	-	600	650	2
Produced)	3 (RT)	-	-	400	1
	3 (OT)	-	-	500	2
Demand		3	3	3	

Units Produced
Destination (Month Installed)

		1	2	3	Totals		Supply
	start	2	0	0	2	≤	2
	1(RT)	1	1	0	2	≤	2
	1 (OT)	0	2	0	2	≤	2
Source	2 (RT)	0	0	0	0	≤	3
(Week	2 (OT)	0	0	0	0	≤	2
Produced)	3 (RT)	0	0	1	1	≤	1
	3 (OT)	0	0	2	2	≤	2
Totals		3	3	3			
		=	=	=	Total Cost	=	$2,950
Demand		3	3	3			

5.16

Unit Cost (Thousands of Dollars)
Destination (Month Supplied (Product))

		1 (1)	1 (2)	2 (1)	2 (2)	3 (1)	3(2)	Supply
	1 (RT)	15	16	16	18	18	19	10
	1 (OT)	18	20	19	22	21	23	3
Source	2 (RT)	-	-	17	15	19	16	8
(Month	2 (OT)	-	-	20	18	22	19	2
Produced)	3 (RT)	-	-	-	-	19	17	10
	3 (OT)	-	-	-	-	22	22	3
Demand		5	3	3	5	4	4	

Unit Cost (Thousands of Dollars)
Destination (Month Supplied)

		1 (1)	1 (2)	2 (1)	2 (2)	3 (1)	3(2)	Totals		Supply
	1 (RT)	5	3	2	0	0	0	10	≤	10
	1 (OT)	0	0	0	0	0	0	0	≤	3
Source	2 (RT)	0	0	1	5	0	2	8	≤	8
(Month	2 (OT)	0	0	0	0	0	0	0	≤	2
Produced)	3 (RT)	0	0	0	0	4	2	6	≤	10
	3 (OT)	0	0	0	0	0	0	0	≤	3
Totals		5	3	3	5	4	4			
		=	=	=	=	=	=	Total Cost	=	$ 389
Demand		5	3	3	5	4	4			

5.17 a) The Feasible Solutions Property guarantees that, since the sum of the supplies and the sum of the demands are equal, the problem will have feasible solutions.

b) The Integer Solution Property guarantees that, since supplies and demands are integers, the resulting optimal solutions will be integers. Supplies and Demands are 1, so the only possible values of variables in an optimal solution are 0 or 1.

c) This can be interpreted as an assignment problem since all the supplies and demands are equal to 1.

d)

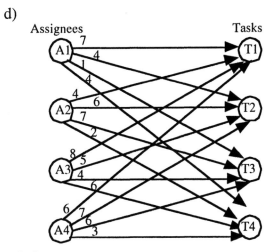

e & f)

Unit Cost ($)

		Task 1	2	3	4	Supply
	1	7	4	1	4	1
Assignee	2	4	6	7	2	1
	3	8	5	4	6	1
	4	6	7	6	3	1
Demand		1	1	1	1	

Assignments

		Task 1	2	3	4	Totals		Supply
	1	0	0	1	0	1	=	1
Assignee	2	1	0	0	0	1	=	1
	3	0	1	0	0	1	=	1
	4	0	0	0	1	1	=	1
Totals		1	1	1	1			
		=	=	=	=	Total Cost =	$ 13	
Demand		1	1	1	1			

5.18   a)

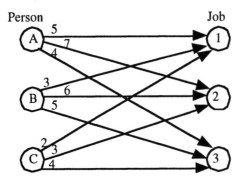

b & c)

| | | Unit Cost ($) Task (Job) | | | |
		1	2	3	Supply
Assignee	A	5	7	4	1
(Person)	B	3	6	5	1
	C	2	3	4	1
Demand		1	1	1	

| | | Assignments Task (Job) | | | | | |
		1	2	3	Totals		Supply
Assignee	A	0	0	1	1	=	1
(Person)	B	1	0	0	1	=	1
	C	0	1	0	1	=	1
Totals		1	1	1			
		=	=	=	Total Cost	=	$ 10
Demand		1	1	1			

5.19   a)

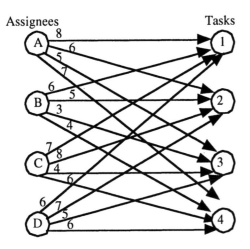

5-14

b & c)

		Unit Cost ($) Task				
		1	2	3	4	Supply
	A	8	6	5	7	1
Assignee	B	6	5	3	4	1
	C	7	8	4	6	1
	D	6	7	5	6	1
Demand		1	1	1	1	

		Assignments Task						
		1	2	3	4	Totals		Supply
	A	0	1	0	0	1	=	1
Assignee	B	0	0	0	1	1	=	1
	C	0	0	1	0	1	=	1
	D	1	0	0	0	1	=	1
Totals		1	1	1	1			
		=	=	=	=	Total Cost =		$ 20
Demand		1	1	1	1			

5.20 a) This problem fits as an assignment problem with ships as assignees and ports as assignments.

b)

		Unit Cost ($) Task (Port)				
		1	2	3	4	Supply
	1	500	400	600	700	1
Assignee	2	600	600	700	500	1
(Ship)	3	700	500	700	600	1
	4	500	400	600	600	1
Demand		1	1	1	1	

		Assignments Task (Port)						
		1	2	3	4	Totals		Supply
	1	1	0	0	0	1	=	1
Assignee	2	0	0	0	1	1	=	1
(Ship)	3	0	1	0	0	1	=	1
	4	0	0	1	0	1	=	1
Totals		1	1	1	1			
		=	=	=	=	Total Cost =		$ 2,100
Demand		1	1	1	1			

5.21

| | | Unit Cost ($) | | | |
| | | Task (Product) | | | |
		1	2	3	Supply
	1	7440	18000	12160	1
Assignee	2	6960	16400	11200	1
(Plant)	3	7680	18400	12800	1
	4	6720	16800	-	1
	5	6960	17200	-	1
Demand		1	1	1	

| | | Assignment | | | | | |
| | | Task (Product) | | | | | |
		1	2	3	Totals		Supply
	1	0	0	0	0	≤	1
Assignee	2	0	0	1	1	≤	1
(Plant)	3	0	0	0	0	≤	1
	4	0	1	0	1	≤	1
	5	1	0	0	1	≤	1
Totals		1	1	1			
		=	=	=	Total Cost =	$ 34,960	
Demand		1	1	1			

5.22 a) The problem fits into the format for an assignment problem with swimmers being assigned to strokes. The times of the swimmers replace the costs of a traditional problem.

b)

| | | Unit Cost (Seconds) | | | | | |
| | | Task (Swimmer) | | | | | |
		Carl	Chris	David	Tony	Ken	Supply
	Back	37.7	32.9	33.8	37	35.4	1
Assignee	Breast	43.4	33.1	42.2	34.7	41.8	1
(Stroke)	Fly	33.3	28.5	38.9	30.4	33.6	1
	Free	29.2	26.4	29.6	28.5	31.1	1
Demand		1	1	1	1	1	

| | | Assignment | | | | | | | |
| | | Task (Swimmer) | | | | | | | |
		Carl	Chris	David	Tony	Ken	Totals		Supply
	Back	0	0	1	0	0	1	=	1
Assignee	Breast	0	0	0	1	0	1	=	1
(Stroke)	Fly	0	1	0	0	0	1	=	1
	Free	1	0	0	0	0	1	=	1
Totals		1	1	1	1	0			
		≤	≤	≤	≤	≤	Total Cost =	126.20	
Demand		1	1	1	1	1			

5.23

Unit Cost ($)

		Task (Site) 1	2	3	Supply
Assignee	North	650	800	750	4
(Truck)	South	900	750	800	3
Demand		2	1	2	

Assignment

		Destination (Site) 1	2	3	Totals		Supply
Assignee	North	2	0	2	4	≤	4
(Truck)	South	0	1	0	1	≤	3
Totals		2	1	2			
		=	=	=	Total Cost =	$ 3,550	
Demand		2	1	2			

5.24

Unit Cost ($)

		Task (Distribution Center) 1	2	3	Supply
Assignee	A	8000	14000	12000	1
(Plant)	B	6000	16000	15000	1
Demand		1	1	1	

Assignment

		Task (Distribution Center) 1	2	3	Totals		Supply
Assignee	A	0	1	1	2	≤	2
(Plant)	B	1	0	0	1	≤	2
Totals		1	1	1			
		=	=	=	Total Cost =	$ 32,000	
Demand		1	1	1			

Cases

5.1   Option 1:

Unit Cost (1,000's)
Destination (Market)

		1	2	3	4	5	Supply
	1	61	72	45	55	66	15
Source 1	2	69	78	60	49	56	20
	3	59	66	63	61	47	15
Demand		11	12	9	10	8	

Unit Cost (1,000's)
Destination (Market)

		1	2	3	4	5	Totals		Supply
	1	6	0	9	0	0	15	=	15
Source 1	2	2	0	0	10	8	20	=	20
	3	3	12	0	0	0	15	=	15
Totals		11	12	9	10	8			
		=	=	=	=	=	Total Cost =		2,816.00
Demand		11	12	9	10	8			

Option 2:

Unit Cost (1,000's)
Destination (Market)

		1	2	3	4	5	Supply
	1	58.5	68.3	47.8	55	63.5	15
Source 1	2	65.3	74.8	55	49	57.5	20
	3	59	61.3	63.5	58.8	50	15
Demand		11	12	9	10	8	

Unit Cost (1,000's)
Destination (Market)

		1	2	3	4	5	Totals		Supply
	1	6	0	9	0	0	15	=	15
Source 1	2	5	0	0	10	5	20	=	20
	3	0	12	0	0	3	15	=	15
Totals		11	12	9	10	8			
		=	=	=	=	=	Total Cost =		2,770.80
Demand		11	12	9	10	8			

Option 3:

		1	2	3	4	5	Supply
		Unit Cost (1,000's)					
		Destination (Market)					
Source 1	1	58.5	68.3	45	55	63.5	15
	2	65.3	74.8	55	49	56	20
	3	59	61.3	63	58.8	47	15
Demand		11	12	9	10	8	

		1	2	3	4	5	Totals		Supply
		Unit Cost (1,000's)							
		Destination (Market)							
Source 1	1	6	0	9	0	0	15	=	15
	2	5	0	0	10	5	20	=	20
	3	0	12	0	0	3	15	=	15
Totals		11	12	9	10	8			
		=	=	=	=	=	Total Cost =		2,729.10
Demand		11	12	9	10	8			

When comparing the three options, it is best to use the combination plan, while shipping entirely by rail leads to the highest costs.

If costs of shipping by water are expected to rise considerably more than for shipping by rail, stay with rail and use Option 1. If the reverse is true, then use Option 2. If the cost comparisons will remain roughly the same, use Option 3. Option 3 is clearly the most feasible but may not be chosen if it is too logistically cumbersome. More knowledge of the situation is necessary to determine this.

5.2   The problem in this case can be solved using the assignment problem. Throughout this case we use the template for the assignment problem (see the Sellmore example in this chapter).

a) The projects are the tasks, and the scientists are the assignees in this assignment problem.

	A	B	C	D	E	F	G	H	I	J	K
1											
2						Points					
3						Task					
4				Up	Stable	Choice	Hope	Release	Supply		
5			Kvaal	100	400	200	200	100	1		
6		Assignee	Zuner	0	200	800	0	0	1		
7			Tsai	100	100	100	100	600	1		
8			Mickey	267	153	99	451	30	1		
9			Rollins	100	33	33	34	800	1		
10		Demand		1	1	1	1	1			
11											
12											
13						Assignments					
14						Task					
15				Up	Stable	Choice	Hope	Release	Totals		Supply
16			Kvaal	0	1	0	0	0	1	=	1
17		Assignee	Zuner	0	0	1	0	0	1	=	1
18			Tsai	1	0	0	0	0	1	=	1
19			Mickey	0	0	0	1	0	1	=	1
20			Rollins	0	0	0	0	1	1	=	1
21		Totals		1	1	1	1	1	2551	=	Total Points
22				=	=	=	=	=			
23		Demand		1	1	1	1	1			

The solver dialogue box appears as follows:

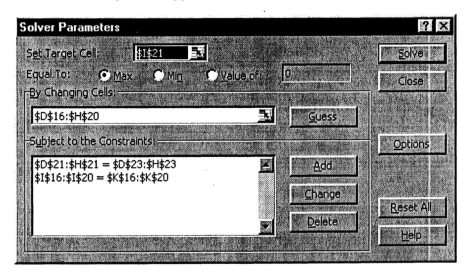

The solver options throughout this case are:

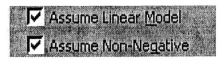

To maximize the scientists preferences you want to assign Dr. Tsai to lead project Up, Dr. Kvaal to lead project Stable, Dr. Zuner to lead project Choice, Dr. Mickey to lead project Hope, and Dr. Rollins to lead project Release.

b) Since there are only four assignees we introduce a dummy assignee with preferences of −1. The task that gets assigned the dummy assignee will not be done.

	A	B	C	D	E	F	G	H	I	J	K
1											
2						Points					
3						Task					
4				Up	Stable	Choice	Hope	Release	Supply		
5			Kvaal	100	400	200	200	100	1		
6		Assignee	Zuner	0	200	800	0	0	1		
7			Tsai	100	100	100	100	600	1		
8			Mickey	267	153	99	451	30	1		
9			dummy	-1	-1	-1	-1	-1	1		
10		Demand		1	1	1	1	1			
11											
12											
13						Assignments					
14						Task					
15				Up	Stable	Choice	Hope	Release	Totals		Supply
16			Kvaal	0	1	0	0	0	1	=	1
17		Assignee	Zuner	0	0	1	0	0	1	=	1
18			Tsai	0	0	0	0	1	1	=	1
19			Mickey	0	0	0	1	0	1	=	1
20			dummy	1	0	0	0	0	1	=	1
21		Totals		1	1	1	1	1	2250	=	Total Points
22				=	=	=	=	=			
23		Demand		1	1	1	1	1			

The solver dialogue box remains the same.

We give up on project Up.

c) Since two of the assignees can do two tasks we need to double them. We include assignees Zuner-1, Zuner-2, Mickey-1, and Mickey-2 into the problem. In order to have an equal number of assignees and tasks we also need to include one dummy task. In order to ensure that neither Dr. Kvaal nor Dr. Tsai can get assigned the dummy task and thus no project, we insert a large negative number as their point bid for the dummy project.

	A	B	C	D	E	F	G	H	I	J	K	L
1												
2						Points						
3						Task						
4				Up	Stable	Choice	Hope	Release	dummy	Supply		
5			Kvaal	100	400	200	200	100	-10000	1		
6			Zuner-1	0	200	800	0	0	-1	1		
7		Assignee	Zuner-2	0	200	800	0	0	-1	1		
8			Tsai	100	100	100	100	600	-10000	1		
9			Mickey-1	267	153	99	451	30	-1	1		
10			Mickey-2	267	153	99	451	30	-1	1		
11		Demand		1	1	1	1	1	1			
12												
13												
14						Assignments						
15						Task						
16				Up	Stable	Choice	Hope	Release	dummy	Totals		Supply
17			Kvaal	0	1	0	0	0	0	1	=	1
18			Zuner-1	0	0	0	0	0	1	1	=	1
19		Assignee	Zuner-2	0	0	1	0	0	0	1	=	1
20			Tsai	0	0	0	0	1	0	1	=	1
21			Mickey-1	0	0	0	1	0	0	1	=	1
22			Mickey-2	1	0	0	0	0	0	1	=	1
23		Totals		1	1	1	1	1	1	2517	=	Total Points
24				=	=	=	=	=	=			
25		Demand		1	1	1	1	1	1			

Dr. Kvaal leads project Stable, Dr. Zuner leads project Choice, Dr. Tsai leads project Release, and Dr. Mickey leads the projects Hope and Up.

d) Under the new bids of Dr. Zuner the assignment does not change:

	A	B	C	D	E	F	G	H	I	J	K	L
1												
2						Points						
3						Task						
4				Up	Stable	Choice	Hope	Release	dummy	Supply		
5			Kvaal	100	400	200	200	100	-10000	1		
6			Zuner-1	20	450	451	39	40	-1	1		
7		Assignee	Zuner-2	20	450	451	39	40	-1	1		
8			Tsai	100	100	100	100	600	-10000	1		
9			Mickey-1	267	153	99	451	30	-1	1		
10			Mickey-2	267	153	99	451	30	-1	1		
11		Demand		1	1	1	1	1	1			
12												
13												
14						Assignments						
15						Task						
16				Up	Stable	Choice	Hope	Release	dummy	Totals		Supply
17			Kvaal	0	1	0	0	0	0	1	=	1
18			Zuner-1	0	0	1	0	0	0	1	=	1
19		Assignee	Zuner-2	0	0	0	0	0	1	1	=	1
20			Tsai	0	0	0	0	1	0	1	=	1
21			Mickey-1	0	0	0	1	0	0	1	=	1
22			Mickey-2	1	0	0	0	0	0	1	=	1
23		Totals		1	1	1	1	1	1	2168	=	Total Points
24				=	=	=	=	=	=			
25		Demand		1	1	1	1	1	1			

5-22

e) Certainly Dr. Zuner could be disappointed that she is not assigned to project Stable, especially when she expressed a higher preference for that project than the scientist assigned. The optimal solution maximizes the preferences overall, but individual scientists may be disappointed. We should therefore make sure to communicate the reasoning behind the assignments to the scientists.

f) Whenever a scientist cannot lead a particular project we use a large negative number as the point bid.

	A	B	C	D	E	F	G	H	I	J	K
1											
2						Points					
3						Task					
4				Up	Stable	Choice	Hope	Release	Supply		
5			Kvaal	86	343	171	-10000	-10000	1		
6		Assignee	Zuner	0	200	800	0	0	1		
7			Tsai	100	100	100	100	600	1		
8			Mickey	300	-10000	125	-10000	175	1		
9			Rollins	-10000	50	50	100	600	1		
10		Demand		1	1	1	1	1			
11											
12											
13						Assignments					
14						Task					
15				Up	Stable	Choice	Hope	Release	Totals		Supply
16			Kvaal	0	1	0	0	0	1	=	1
17		Assignee	Zuner	0	0	1	0	0	1	=	1
18			Tsai	0	0	0	1	0	1	=	1
19			Mickey	1	0	0	0	0	1	=	1
20			Rollins	0	0	0	0	1	1	=	1
21		Totals		1	1	1	1	1	2143	=	Total Points
22				=	=	=	=	=			
23		Demand		1	1	1	1	1			

Dr. Kvaal leads project Stable, Dr. Zuner leads project Choice, Dr. Tsai leads project Hope, Dr. Mickey leads project Up, and Dr. Rollins leads project Release.

g) When we want to assign two assignees to the same task we need to duplicate that task.

	A	B	C	D	E	F	G	H	I	J	K	L	M
1													
2							Points						
3							Task						
4				Up	Stable	Choice	Hope-A	Hope-B	Release-A	Release-B	Supply		
5			Kvaal	86	343	171	-10000	-10000	-10000	-10000	1		
6		Assignee	Zuner	0	200	800	0	0	0	0	1		
7			Tsai	100	100	100	100	100	600	600	1		
8			Mickey	300	-10000	125	-10000	-10000	175	175	1		
9			Rollins	-10000	50	50	100	100	600	600	1		
10			Arriaga	250	250	-10000	250	250	250	250	1		
11			Santos	111	1	-10000	333	333	555	555	1		
12		Demand		1	1	1	1	1	1	1			
13													
14													
15							Assignments						
16							Task						
17				Up	Stable	Choice	Hope-A	Hope-B	Release-A	Release-B	Totals		Supply
18			Kvaal	0	1	0	0	0	0	0	1	=	1
19		Assignee	Zuner	0	0	1	0	0	0	0	1	=	1
20			Tsai	0	0	0	0	0	1	0	1	=	1
21			Mickey	1	0	0	0	0	0	0	1	=	1
22			Rollins	0	0	0	0	0	0	1	1	=	1
23			Arriaga	0	0	0	0	1	0	0	1	=	1
24			Santos	0	0	0	1	0	0	0	1	=	1
25		Totals		1	1	1	1	1	1	1	3226	=	Total Points
26				=	=	=	=	=	=	=			
27		Demand		1	1	1	1	1	1	1			

Project Up is led by Dr. Mickey, Stable by Dr. Kvaal, Choice by Dr. Zuner, Hope by Dr. Arriaga and Dr. Santos, and Release by Dr. Tsai and Dr. Rollins.

h) No. Maximizing overall preferences does not maximize individual preferences. Scientists who do not get their first choice may become resentful and therefore lack the motivation to lead their assigned project. For example, in the optimal solution of part (g), Dr. Santos clearly elected project Release as his first choice, but he was assigned to lead project Hope.

In addition, maximizing preferences ignores other considerations that should be factored into the assignment decision. For example, the scientist with the highest preference for a project may not be the scientist most qualified to lead the project.

CHAPTER 6
NETWORK OPTIMIZATION PROBLEMS

Review Questions

6.1-1 A supply node is a node where the net amount of flow generated is a fixed positive number. A demand node is a node where the net amount of flow generated is a fixed negative number. A transshipment node is a node where the net amount of flow generated is fixed at zero.

6.1-2 The maximum amount of flow allowed through an arc is referred to as the capacity of that arc.

6.1-3 The objective is to minimize the total cost of sending the available supply through the network to satisfy the given demand.

6.1-4 The feasible solutions property is necessary. It states that a minimum cost flow problem will have a feasible solution if and only if the sum of the supplies from its supply nodes equals the sum of the demands at its demand nodes.

6.1-5 As long as all its supplies and demands have integer values, any minimum cost flow problem with feasible solutions is guaranteed to have an optimal solution with integer values for all its flow quantities.

6.1-6 Network simplex method.

6.1-7 Minimum cost flow problems include operation of a distribution network, solid waste management, operation of a supply network, coordinating product mixes at plants, and cash flow management.

6.1-8 Transportation problems, assignment problems, transshipment problems, maximum flow problems, and shortest path problems are special types of minimum cost flow problems.

6.2-1 One of the company's most important distribution centers urgently needs an increased flow of shipments from the company.

6.2-2 Auto replacement parts are flowing through the network from the company's main factory in Europe to its distribution center in LA.

6.2-3 The objective is to maximize the flow of replacement parts from the factory to the LA distribution center.

6.3-1 Rather than minimizing the cost of the flow, the objective is to find a flow plan that maximizes the amount flowing through the network.

6.3-2 The source is the node at which all flow through the network originates. The sink is the node at which all flow through the network terminates. At the source, all arcs point away from the node. At the sink, all arcs point into the node.

6.3-3 The amount is measured by either the amount leaving the source or the amount entering the sink.

6.3-4 1. Whereas supply nodes have fixed supplies and demand nodes have fixed demands, the source and sink do not.

2. Whereas the number of supply nodes and the number of demand nodes in a minimum cost flow problem may be more than one, there can be only one source and only one sink in a maximum flow problem.

6.3-5 Maximum flow problems can maximize the flow through a distribution network, maximize the flow through a supply network, maximize the flow of oil through a system of pipelines, maximize the flow of water through a system of aqueducts, and maximize the flow of vehicles through a transportation network.

6.4-1 The origin is the fire station and the destination is the farm community.

6.4-2 Flow can go in either direction between the nodes connected by links as opposed to only one direction with an arc.

6.4-3 The origin now is the one supply node, with a supply of one. The destination now is the one demand node, with a demand of one.

6.4-4 The length of a link can measure distance, cost, or time.

6.4-5 Sarah wants to minimize her total cost of purchasing, operating, and maintaining the cars over her four years of college.

6.4-6 When "real travel" through a network can end at more that one node, a dummy destination needs to be added so that the network will have just a single destination.

6.4-7 Quick's management must consider trade-offs between time and cost in making its final decision.

6.5-1 The nodes are given, but the links need to be designed.

6.5-2 A state-of-the-art fiber-optic network is being designed.

6.5-3 A tree is a network that does not have any paths that begin and end at the same node without backtracking. A spanning tree is a tree that provides a path between every pair of nodes. A minimum spanning tree is the one spanning tree that minimizes total cost.

6.5-4 The number of links in a spanning tree always is one less than the number of nodes. Furthermore, each node is directly connected by a single link to at least one other node.

6.5-5 To design a network so that there is a path between every pair of nodes at the minimum possible cost.

6.5-6 No, it is not a special type of a minimum cost flow problem.

6.5-7 A greedy algorithm will solve a minimum spanning tree problem.

6.5-8 Minimum spanning tree problems include design of telecommunication networks, design of a lightly used transportation network, design of a network of high-voltage power lines, design of a network of wiring on electrical equipment, and design of a network of pipelines.

Problems

6.1 a) linear programming: 45 numbers

minimum cost flow: 14 numbers

b) The minimum cost flow formulation more clearly depicts the problem. It lays out the problem visually so that it is easily interpreted and only the necessary numbers are included.

c) The minimum cost flow model more clearly depicts the problem. It is a simpler spreadsheet model that is based directly on the network representation of the problem.

6.2   a)

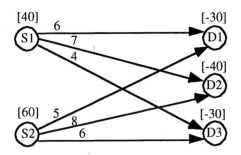

b)

Unit Cost ($)

		Destination			Supply
		1	2	3	
Source	1	6	7	4	40
	2	5	8	6	60
Demand		30	40	30	

Shipment Quantities

		Destination			Totals		Supply
		1	2	3			
Source	1	0	10	30	40	=	40
	2	30	30	0	60	=	60
Totals		30	40	30			
		=	=	=	Total Cost =		$ 580
Demand		30	40	30			

c)

From	To	Ship	Unit Cost
S1	D1	0	$6
S1	D2	10	$7
S1	D3	30	$4
S2	D1	30	$5
S2	D2	30	$8
S2	D3	0	$6

Nodes	Net Flow		Supply/Demand
S1	40	=	40
S2	60	=	60
D1	-30	=	-30
D2	-40	=	-40
D3	-30	=	-30

Total Cost = $ 580

6.3   a)

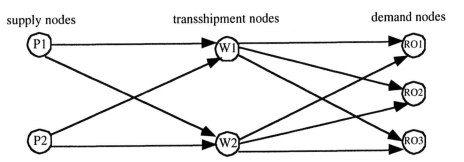

supply nodes   transshipment nodes   demand nodes

b)

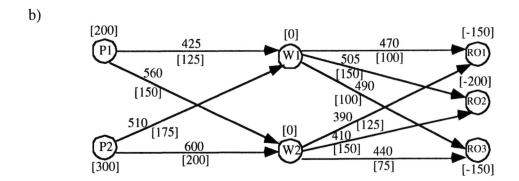

c)

From	To	Ship		Capacity	Unit Cost
P1	W1	125	≤	125	$425
P1	W2	75	≤	150	$560
P2	W1	125	≤	175	$510
P2	W2	175	≤	200	$600
W1	RO1	100	≤	100	$470
W1	RO2	50	≤	150	$505
W1	RO3	100	≤	100	$490
W2	RO1	50	≤	125	$390
W2	RO2	150	≤	150	$410
W2	RO3	50	≤	75	$440

Nodes	Net Flow		Output/Demand
P1	200	=	200
P2	300	=	300
W1	0	=	0
W2	0	=	0
RO1	-150	=	-150
RO2	-200	=	-200
RO3	-150	=	-150

Total Cost = $ 488,125

6.4   a)

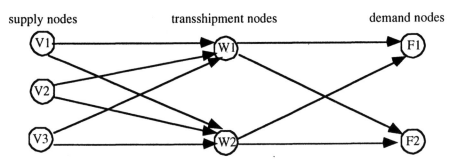

b)

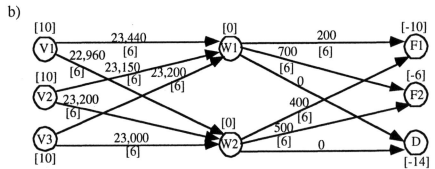

c)

From	To	Ship		Capacity	Unit Cost
V1	W1	4	≤	6	$23,440
V1	W2	6	≤	6	$22,960
V2	W1	6	≤	6	$23,150
V2	W2	4	≤	6	$23,200
V3	W1	4	≤	6	$23,200
V3	W2	6	≤	6	$23,000
W1	F1	6	≤	6	$200
W1	F2	0	≤	6	$700
W1	D	8	-		$0
W2	F1	4	≤	6	$400
W2	F2	6	≤	6	$500
W2	D	6	-		$0

Nodes	Net Flow		Output/Demand
V1	10	=	10
V2	10	=	10
V3	10	=	10
W1	0	=	0
W2	0	=	0
F1	-10	=	-10
F2	-6	=	-6
D	-14	=	-14

Total Cost = $ 699,820

6.5 a)

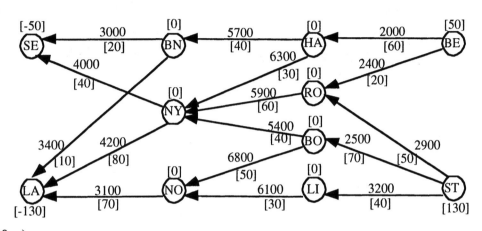

b & c)

From	To	Ship		Capacity	Unit Cost
Stuttgart	Rotterdam	30	≤	50	$2,900
Stuttgart	Bordeaux	70	≤	70	$2,500
Stuttgart	Lisbon	30	≤	40	$3,200
Berlin	Rotterdam	0	≤	20	$2,400
Berlin	Hamburg	50	≤	60	$2,000
Rotterdam	New York	30	≤	60	$5,900
Bordeaux	New York	40	≤	40	$5,400
Bordeaux	New Orleans	30	≤	50	$6,800
Lisbon	New Orleans	30	≤	30	$6,100
Hamburg	New York	20	≤	30	$6,300
Hamburg	Boston	30	≤	40	$5,700
New Orleans	Los Angeles	60	≤	70	$3,100
New York	Los Angeles	60	≤	80	$4,200
New York	Seattle	30	≤	40	$4,000
Boston	Los Angeles	10	≤	10	$3,400
Boston	Seattle	20	≤	20	$3,000

Nodes	Net Flow		Supply/Demand
Stuttgart	130	=	130
Berlin	50	=	50
Hamburg	0	=	0
Rotterdam	0	=	0
Bordeaux	0	=	0
Lisbon	0	=	0
Boston	0	=	0
New York	0	=	0
New Orleans	0	=	0
Los Angeles	-130	=	-130
Seattle	-50	=	-50

Total Cost= $2,187,000

6.6   a)

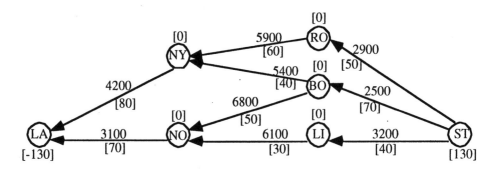

b)

From	To	Ship		Capacity	Unit Cost
Stuttgart	Rotterdam	30	≤	50	$2,900
Stuttgart	Bordeaux	70	≤	70	$2,500
Stuttgart	Lisbon	30	≤	40	$3,200
Rotterdam	New York	30	≤	60	$5,900
Bordeaux	New York	40	≤	40	$5,400
Bordeaux	New Orleans	30	≤	50	$6,800
Lisbon	New Orleans	30	≤	30	$6,100
New Orleans	Los Angeles	60	≤	70	$3,100
New York	Los Angeles	70	≤	80	$4,200

Nodes	Net Flow		Supply/Demand
Stuttgart	130	=	130
Rotterdam	0	=	0
Bordeaux	0	=	0
Lisbon	0	=	0
New York	0	=	0
New Orleans	0	=	0
Los Angeles	-130	=	-130

Total Cost= $1,618,000

c)

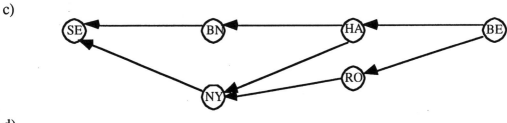

d)

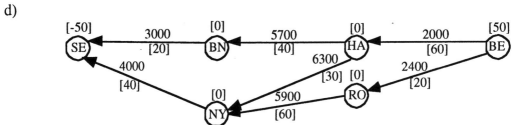

e)

From	To	Ship		Capacity	Unit Cost
Berlin	Rotterdam	0	≤	20	$2,400
Berlin	Hamburg	50	≤	60	$2,000
Rotterdam	New York	0	≤	60	$5,900
Hamburg	New York	30	≤	30	$6,300
Hamburg	Boston	20	≤	40	$5,700
New York	Seattle	30	≤	40	$4,000
Boston	Seattle	20	≤	20	$3,000

Nodes	Net Flow		Supply/Demand
Berlin	50	=	50
Hamburg	0	=	0
Rotterdam	0	=	0
Boston	0	=	0
New York	0	=	0
Seattle	-50	=	-50

Total Cost= $583,000

f) $1,618,000 + $583,000 = $2,201,000 which is higher than the total in Problem 7.5 ($2,187,000).

6.7

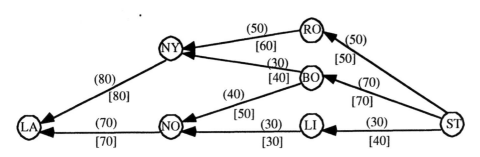

There are only two arcs into LA, with a combined capacity of 150 (80 + 70). Because of this bottleneck, it is not possible to ship any more than 150 from ST to LA. Since 150 actually are being shipped in this solution, it must be optimal.

6.8

From	To	Ship		Capacity
A	B	8	≤	9
A	C	7	≤	7
B	D	7	≤	7
B	E	1	≤	2
C	D	2	≤	4
C	E	5	≤	6
D	E	3	≤	3
D	F	6	≤	6
E	F	9	≤	9

Nodes	Net Flow		Supply/Demand
A	15		
B	0	=	0
C	0	=	0
D	0	=	0
E	0	=	0
F	-15		

Maximum Flow = 15

6.9   a)

Sources   Transshipment Nodes   Sink

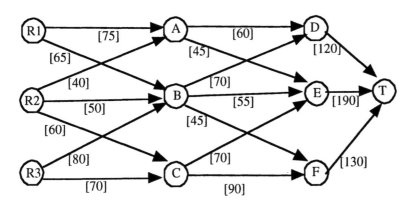

b)

From	To	Ship		Capacity
R1	A	75	≤	75
R1	B	65	≤	65
R2	A	30	≤	40
R2	B	50	≤	50
R2	C	60	≤	60
R3	B	45	≤	80
R3	C	70	≤	70
A	D	60	≤	60
A	E	45	≤	45
B	D	60	≤	70
B	E	55	≤	55
B	F	45	≤	45
C	E	45	≤	70
C	F	85	≤	90
D	T	120	≤	120
E	T	145	≤	190
F	T	130	≤	130

Nodes	Net Flow		Supply/Demand
R1	140		
R2	140		
R3	115		
A	0	=	0
B	0	=	0
C	0	=	0
D	0	=	0
E	0	=	0
F	0	=	0
T	-395		

Maximum Flow = 395

6.10 a)

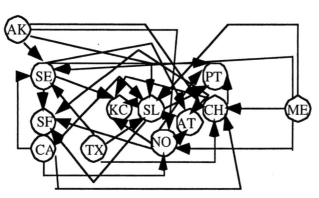

b)

Oil Fields   Refineries   Distribution
                                         Centers

c)

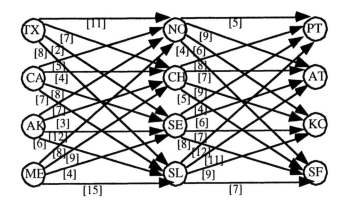

d)

From	To	Ship		Capacity
TX	NO	9	≤	11
TX	CH	7	≤	7
TX	SE	2	≤	2
TX	SL	8	≤	8
CA	NO	0	≤	5
CA	CH	4	≤	4
CA	SE	7	≤	8
CA	SL	7	≤	7
AK	NO	7	≤	7
AK	CH	5	≤	5
AK	SE	12	≤	12
AK	SL	6	≤	6
ME	NO	8	≤	8
ME	CH	9	≤	9
ME	SE	4	≤	4
ME	SL	15	≤	15
NO	PT	5	≤	5
NO	AT	9	≤	9
NO	KC	6	≤	6
NO	SF	4	≤	4
CH	PT	4	≤	8
CH	AT	7	≤	7
CH	KC	9	≤	9
CH	SF	5	≤	5
SE	PT	4	≤	4
SE	AT	6	≤	6
SE	KC	7	≤	7
SE	SF	8	≤	8
SL	PT	12	≤	12
SL	AT	11	≤	11
SL	KC	9	≤	9
SL	SF	4	≤	7

Nodes	Net Flow		Supply/Demand
TX	26		
CA	18		
AK	30		
ME	36		
NO	0	=	0
CH	0	=	0
SE	0	=	0
SL	0	=	0
PT	-25		
AT	-33		
KC	-31		
SF	-21		

Maximum Flow = 110

6.11

From	To	On Route	Distance
Fire St.	A	1	3
Fire St.	B	0	6
Fire St.	C	0	4
A	B	0	4
A	D	1	6
B	A	0	1
B	C	0	2
B	D	0	4
B	E	0	5
C	B	0	2
C	E	0	7
D	E	0	3
D	F	1	8
E	D	0	3
E	F	0	6
E	G	0	5
E	H	0	4
F	G	0	3
F	Farm Com.	1	4
G	F	0	3
G	H	0	2
G	Farm Com.	0	6
H	G	0	2
H	Farm Com.	0	7

Total Distance = 21

Nodes	Net Flow		Supply/Demand
Fire St.	1	=	1
A	0	=	0
B	0	=	0
C	0	=	0
D	0	=	0
E	0	=	0
F	0	=	0
G	0	=	0
H	0	=	0
Farm Com.	- 1	=	- 1

Shortest path: Fire Station – D – F – Farming Community

6.12   a)

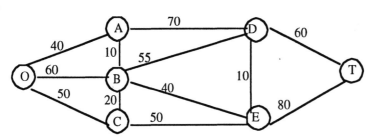

b)

From	To	On Route	Distance
Origin	A	1	40
Origin	B	0	60
Origin	C	0	50
A	B	1	10
A	D	0	70
B	C	0	20
B	D	1	55
B	E	0	40
C	E	0	50
D	E	0	10
D	Destination	1	60
E	Destination	0	80

Total Distance = 165

Nodes	Net Flow		Supply/Demand
Origin	1	=	1
A	0	=	0
B	0	=	0
C	0	=	0
D	0	=	0
E	0	=	0
Destination	-1	=	-1

c)   Shortest route: Origin – A – B – D - Destination

d) Yes

e) Yes

6.13 a)

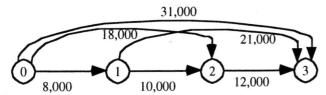

b)

From	To	On Route	Cost
Node 0	Node 1	1	$8,000
Node 0	Node 2	0	$18,000
Node 0	Node 3	0	$31,000
Node 1	Node 2	0	$10,000
Node 1	Node 3	1	$21,000
Node 2	Node 3	0	$12,000

Nodes	Net Flow		Supply/Demand
0	1	=	1
1	0	=	0
2	0	=	0
3	-1	=	-1

Total Cost = $29,000

6.14 a) Times play the role of distances.

b)

From	To	On Route	Time
SE	A	0	4.6
SE	B	0	4.7
SE	C	1	4.2
A	D	0	3.5
A	E	0	3.4
B	D	0	3.6
B	E	0	3.2
B	F	0	3.3
C	E	1	3.5
C	F	0	3.4
D	LN	0	3.4
E	LN	1	3.6
F	LN	0	3.8

Nodes	Net Flow		Supply/Demand
SE	1	=	1
A	0	=	0
B	0	=	0
C	0	=	0
D	0	=	0
E	0	=	0
F	0	=	0
LN	-1	=	-1

Total Time = 11.3

6.15

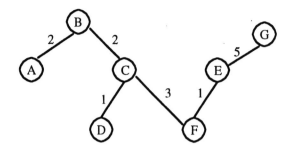

1.	C---D: Cost = 1		4.	E---G: Cost = 5	
	E---F: Cost = 1	*choose arbitrarily		D---A: Cost = 4	
2.	E---G: Cost = 5			E---B: Cost = 7	
	E---B: Cost = 7			F---G: Cost = 7	
	E---C: Cost = 4			C---A: Cost = 5	
	F---G: Cost = 7			C---B: Cost = 2	*lowest
	F---C: Cost = 3	*lowest	5.	E---G: Cost = 5	
	F---D: Cost = 4			D---A: Cost = 4	
3.	E---G: Cost = 5			B---A: Cost = 2	*lowest
	E---B: Cost = 7			F---G: Cost = 7	
	F---G: Cost = 7			C---A: Cost = 5	
	F---D: Cost = 4		6.	E---G: Cost = 5	*lowest
	C---D: Cost = 1	*lowest		F---G: Cost = 7	
	C---A: Cost = 5				
	C---B: Cost = 2				

Total = $14 million

6.16

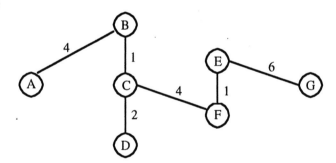

1.	B---C: Cost = 1	*lowest	4.	B---E: Cost = 7	
2.	B---A: Cost = 4			C---F: Cost = 4	*lowest
	B---E: Cost = 7			C---E: Cost = 5	
	C---A: Cost = 6			D---F: Cost = 5	
	C---D: Cost = 2	*lowest	5.	B---E: Cost = 7	
	C---F: Cost = 4			C---E: Cost = 5	
	C---E: Cost = 5			F---E: Cost = 1	*lowest
3.	B---A: Cost = 4	*lowest		F---G: Cost = 8	
	B---E: Cost = 7		6.	E---G: Cost = 6	*lowest
	C---A: Cost = 6			F---G: Cost = 8	
	C---F: Cost = 4				
	C---E: Cost = 5				
	D---A: Cost = 5				
	D---F: Cost = 5				

Total = $18,000

6.17

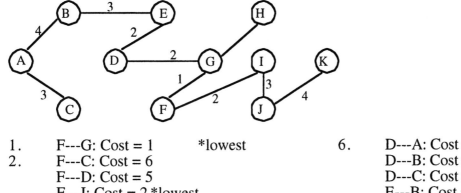

1.	F---G: Cost = 1	*lowest		6.	D---A: Cost = 6	

1.   F---G: Cost = 1   *lowest

2.   F---C: Cost = 6
        F---D: Cost = 5
        F---I: Cost = 2 *lowest
        F---J: Cost = 5
        G---D: Cost = 2
        G---E: Cost = 2
        G---H: Cost = 2
        G---I: Cost = 5

3.   F---C: Cost = 6
        F---D: Cost = 5
        F---J: Cost = 5
        G---D: Cost = 2   *lowest
        G---E: Cost = 2
        G---H: Cost = 2
        I---H: Cost = 2
        I---K: Cost = 8
        I---J: Cost = 3

4.   D---A: Cost = 6
        D---B: Cost = 5
        D---E: Cost = 2   *lowest
        D---C: Cost = 4
        F---C: Cost = 6
        F---J: Cost = 5
        G---E: Cost = 2
        G---H: Cost = 2
        I---H: Cost = 2
        I---K: Cost = 8
        I---J: Cost = 3

5.   D---A: Cost = 6
        D---B: Cost = 5
        D---C: Cost = 4
        E---B: Cost = 3
        E---H: Cost = 4
        F---C: Cost = 6
        F---J: Cost = 5
        G---H: Cost = 2   *lowest
        I---H: Cost = 2
        I---K: Cost = 8
        I---J: Cost = 3

6.   D---A: Cost = 6
        D---B: Cost = 5
        D---C: Cost = 4
        E---B: Cost = 3   *lowest
        F---C: Cost = 6
        F---J: Cost = 5
        H---K: Cost = 7
        I---K: Cost = 8
        I---J: Cost = 3

7.   B---A: Cost = 4
        D---A: Cost = 6
        D---C: Cost = 4
        F---C: Cost = 6
        F---J: Cost = 5
        H---K: Cost = 7
        I---K: Cost = 8
        I---J: Cost = 3   *lowest

8.   B---A: Cost = 4   *lowest
        D---A: Cost = 6
        D---C: Cost = 4
        F---C: Cost = 6
        H---K: Cost = 7
        I---K: Cost = 8
        J---K: Cost = 4

9.   A---C: Cost = 3   *lowest
        D---C: Cost = 4
        F---C: Cost = 6
        H---K: Cost = 7
        I---K: Cost = 8
        J---K: Cost = 4

10.   H---K: Cost = 7
        I---K: Cost = 8
        J---K: Cost = 4   *lowest

Total = $26 million

6.18   a)   The company wants a path between each pair of nodes (groves) that minimizes cost (length of road).

b) 7---8 : Distance = 0.5
    7---6 : Distance = 0.6
    6---5 : Distance = 0.9
    5---1 : Distance = 0.7
    5---4 : Distance = 0.7
    8---3 : Distance = 1.0
    3---2 : Distance = 0.9
    Total = 5.3 miles

6.19 a) The bank wants a path between each pair of nodes (offices) that minimizes cost (distance).

b) B1---B5 : Distance = 50
    B5---B3 : Distance = 80
    B1---B2 : Distance = 100
    B2---M : Distance = 70
    B2---B4 : Distance = 120
    Total = 420 miles

Cases

6.1 a) The network showing the different routes troops and supplies may follow to reach the Russian Federation appears below.

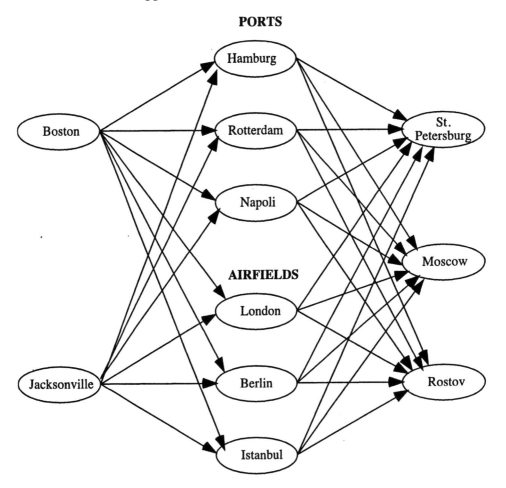

b) The President is only concerned about how to most quickly move troops and supplies from the United States to the three strategic Russian cities. Obviously, the best way to achieve this goal is to find the fastest connection between the US and the three cities. We therefore need to find the shortest path between the US and each of the three cities.

The President only cares about the time it takes to get the troops and supplies to Russia. It does not matter how great a distance the troops and supplies cover. Therefore we define the arc length between two nodes in the network to be the time it takes to travel between the respective cities. For example, the distance between Boston and London equals 6,200 km. The mode of transportation between the cities is a Starfighter traveling at a speed of 400 miles per hour * 1.609 km per mile = 643.6 km per hour. The time is takes to bring troops and supplies from Boston to London equals 6,200 km / 643.6 km per hour = 9.6333 hours. Using this approach we can compute the time of travel along all arcs in the network.

By simple inspection and common sense it is apparent that the fastest transportation involves using only airplanes. We therefore can restrict ourselves to only those arcs in the network where the mode of transportation is air travel. We can omit the three port cities and all arcs entering and leaving these nodes.

Finally, we define a new node ("dummy" node) in the network called "US," and we introduce two new arcs: one going from the US to Boston and the other going from the US to Jacksonville. The arc length on both new arcs equals 0. The objective is now to find the shortest path from the US to each of the three Russian cities. We define the US node to be a supply node with supply 3, and we define each of the three nodes representing Russian cities as demand nodes with a demand of -1. The nodes representing the three European airfields – London, Berlin, and Istanbul – are all transshipment nodes.

The following spreadsheet shows the entire linear programming model, which identifies the three shortest paths.

	A	B	C	D	E	F	G	H	I	J	K
1		From	To	On Route	Distance	Time (hr)		Nodes	Net Flow		Supply/Demand
2		US	Boston	3	0	0		US	3	=	3
3		US	Jacksonville	0	0	0		Boston	0	=	0
4		Boston	London	2	6200	9.63331		Jacksonville	0	=	0
5		Boston	Berlin	1	7250	11.2648		London	0	=	0
6		Boston	Istanbul	0	8300	12.8962		Berlin	0	=	0
7		Jacksonville	London	0	7900	12.2747		Istanbul	0	=	0
8		Jacksonville	Berlin	0	9200	14.2946		St. Petersburg	-1	=	-1
9		Jacksonville	Istanbul	0	10100	15.693		Moscow	-1	=	-1
10		London	St. Petersburg	1	1980	3.07644		Rostov	-1	=	-1
11		London	Moscow	1	2300	3.57365					
12		London	Rostov	0	2860	4.44375					
13		Berlin	St. Petersburg	0	1280	1.98881					
14		Berlin	Moscow	0	1600	2.48602					
15		Berlin	Rostov	1	1730	2.688					
16		Istanbul	St. Petersburg	0	2040	3.16967					
17		Istanbul	Moscow	0	1700	2.64139					
18		Istanbul	Rostov	0	990	1.53822					
19											
20			Total Time =	39.86948415							

The spreadsheet contains the following formulas:

	F
1	Time (hr)
2	0
3	0
4	=E4/(400*1.609)
5	=E5/(400*1.609)
6	=E6/(400*1.609)
7	=E7/(400*1.609)
8	=E8/(400*1.609)
9	=E9/(400*1.609)
10	=E10/(400*1.609)
11	=E11/(400*1.609)
12	=E12/(400*1.609)
13	=E13/(400*1.609)
14	=E14/(400*1.609)
15	=E15/(400*1.609)
16	=E16/(400*1.609)
17	=E17/(400*1.609)
18	=E18/(400*1.609)
19	
20	

	I
1	Net Flow
2	=SUM(D2:D3)
3	=-D2+SUM(D4:D6)
4	=-D3+SUM(D7:D9)
5	=-D4-D7+D10+D11+D12
6	=-D5-D8+D13+D14+D15
7	=-D6-D9+D16+D17+D18
8	=-D10-D13-D16
9	=-D11-D14-D17
10	=-D12-D15-D18
11	

	C	D
20	Total Time =	=SUMPRODUCT(D2:D18,F2:F18)

The solver dialogue box appears as follows.

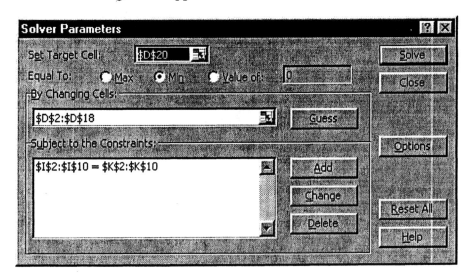

Throughout the analysis of this case we use the following solver options.

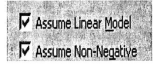

From the optimal solution to the linear programming model we see that the shortest path from the US to Saint Petersburg is Boston → London → Saint Petersburg with a total travel time of 12.710 hours. The shortest path from the US to Moscow is Boston → London → Moscow with a total travel time of 13.207 hours. The shortest path from the US to Rostov is Boston → Berlin → Rostov with a total travel time of 13.953 hours. The following network diagram highlights these shortest paths.

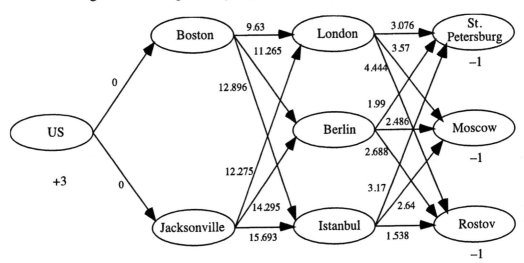

c) The President must satisfy each Russian city's military requirements at minimum cost. Therefore, this problem can be solved as a minimum-cost network flow problem. The two nodes representing US cities are supply nodes with a supply of 500 each (we measure all weights in 1000 tons). The three nodes representing Saint Petersburg, Moscow, and Rostov are demand nodes with demands of –320, -440, and –240, respectively. All nodes representing European airfields and ports are transshipment nodes. We measure the flow along the arcs in 1000 tons. For some arcs, capacity constraints are given. All arcs from the European ports into Saint Petersburg have zero capacity. All truck routes from the European ports into Rostov have a transportation limit of 2,500*16 = 40,000 tons. Since we measure the arc flows in 1000 tons, the corresponding arc capacities equal 40. An analogous computation yields arc capacities of 30 for both the arcs connecting the nodes London and Berlin to Rostov. For all other nodes we determine natural arc capacities based on the supplies and demands at the nodes. We define the unit costs along the arcs in the network in $1000 per 1000 tons. For example, the cost of transporting 1 ton of material from Boston to Hamburg equals $30,000 / 240 = $125, so the costs of transporting 1000 tons from Boston to Hamburg equals $125,000.

The objective is to satisfy all demands in the network at minimum cost. The following spreadsheet shows the entire linear programming model.

	A	B	C	D	E	F	G	H	I	J	K
1	From	To	Ship	Capacity (in 1000 tons)	Cost of Transport	Unit Cost (in $1000 per 1000 tons)		Nodes	Net Flow		Supply/Demand
2	Boston	Hamburg	440	500	30000	125		Boston	500	=	500
3	Boston	Rotterdam	0	500	30000	125		Jacksonville	500	=	500
4	Boston	Napoli	0	500	32000	133.3333333		Hamburg	0	=	0
5	Boston	London	0	500	45000	300		Rotterdam	0	=	0
6	Boston	Berlin	0	500	50000	333.3333333		Napoli	0	=	0
7	Boston	Istanbul	60	500	55000	366.6666667		London	0	=	0
8	Jacksonville	Hamburg	0	500	48000	200		Berlin	0	=	0
9	Jacksonville	Rotterdam	0	500	44000	183.3333333		Istanbul	0	=	0
10	Jacksonville	Napoli	0	500	56000	233.3333333		St. Petersburg	-320	=	-320
11	Jacksonville	London	350	500	49000	326.6666667		Moscow	-440	=	-440
12	Jacksonville	Berlin	0	500	57000	380		Rostov	-240	=	-240
13	Jacksonville	Istanbul	150	500	61000	406.6666667					
14	Hamburg	St. Petersburg	0	0	3000	187.5					
15	Rotterdam	St. Petersburg	0	0	3000	187.5					
16	Napoli	St. Petersburg	0	0	5000	312.5					
17	London	St. Petersburg	320	320	22000	146.6666667					
18	Berlin	St. Petersburg	0	320	24000	160					
19	Istanbul	St. Petersburg	0	320	28000	186.6666667					
20	Hamburg	Moscow	440	440	4000	250					
21	Rotterdam	Moscow	0	440	5000	312.5					
22	Napoli	Moscow	0	440	5000	312.5					
23	London	Moscow	0	440	19000	126.6666667					
24	Berlin	Moscow	0	440	22000	146.6666667					
25	Istanbul	Moscow	0	440	25000	166.6666667					
26	Hamburg	Rostov	0	40	7000	437.5					
27	Rotterdam	Rostov	0	40	8000	500					
28	Napoli	Rostov	0	40	9000	562.5					
29	London	Rostov	30	30	4000	26.66666667					
30	Berlin	Rostov	0	30	23000	153.3333333					
31	Istanbul	Rostov	210	240	2000	13.33333333					
32											
33		Total Cost =	412866.6667								

The following formulas appear in the spreadsheet.

	F
1	Unit Cost (in $1000 per 1000 tons)
2	=E2/240
3	=E3/240
4	=E4/240
5	=E5/150
6	=E6/150
7	=E7/150
8	=E8/240
9	=E9/240
10	=E10/240
11	=E11/150
12	=E12/150
13	=E13/150
14	=E14/16
15	=E15/16
16	=E16/16
17	=E17/150
18	=E18/150
19	=E19/150
20	=E20/16
21	=E21/16
22	=E22/16
23	=E23/150
24	=E24/150
25	=E25/150
26	=E26/16
27	=E27/16
28	=E28/16
29	=E29/150
30	=E30/150
31	=E31/150
32	

	I
1	Net Flow
2	=SUM(C2:C7)
3	=SUM(C8:C13)
4	=-C2-C8+C14+C20+C26
5	=-C3-C9+C15+C21+C27
6	=-C4-C10+C16+C22+C28
7	=-C5-C11+C17+C23+C29
8	=-C6-C12+C18+C24+C30
9	=-C7-C13+C19+C25+C31
10	=-SUM(C14:C19)
11	=-SUM(C20:C25)
12	=-SUM(C26:C31)
13	

	B	C
33	Total Cost =	=SUMPRODUCT(C2:C31,F2:F31)

We use the following solver dialogue box for this model.

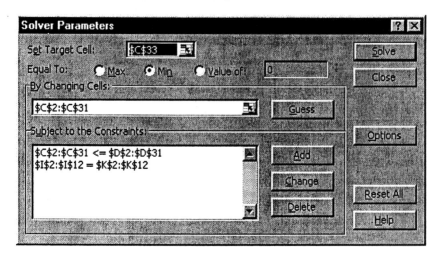

The total cost of the operation equals \$412,866,666.67. The entire supply for Saint Petersburg is supplied from Jacksonville via London. The entire supply for Moscow is supplied from Boston via Hamburg. Of the 240 (= 240,000 tons) demanded by Rostov, 60 are shipped from Boston via Istanbul, 150 are shipped from Jacksonville via Istanbul, and 30 are shipped from Jacksonville via London. The paths used to ship supplies to Saint Petersburg, Moscow, and Rostov are highlighted on the following network diagram.

PORTS

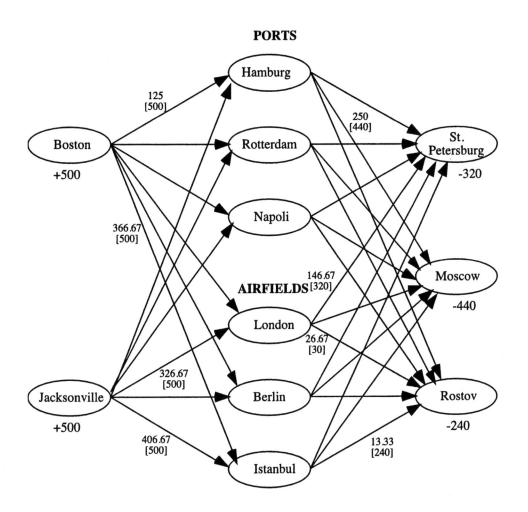

d) Now the President wants to maximize the amount of cargo transported from the US to the Russian cities. In other words, the President wants to maximize the flow from the two US cities to the three Russian cities. All the nodes representing the European ports and airfields are once again transshipment nodes. The flow along an arc is again measured in thousands of tons. The new restrictions can be transformed into arc capacities using the same approach that was used in part (c). The objective is now to maximize the combined flow into the three Russian cities.

The linear programming model describing the maximum flow problem appears as follows.

	A	B	C	D	E	F	G	H	I
1	From	To	Ship	Capacity (in 1000 tons)		Nodes	Net Flow		Supply/Demand
2	Boston	Hamburg	19.2	500		Boston	282.2		
3	Boston	Rotterdam	21.6	500		Jacksonville	240		
4	Boston	Napoli	46.4	500		Hamburg	0	=	0
5	Boston	London	75	75		Rotterdam	0	=	0
6	Boston	Berlin	45	45		Napoli	0	=	0
7	Boston	Istanbul	75	75		London	0	=	0
8	Jacksonville	Hamburg	0	500		Berlin	0	=	0
9	Jacksonville	Rotterdam	0	500		Istanbul	0	=	0
10	Jacksonville	Napoli	0	500		St. Petersburg	-225		
11	Jacksonville	London	90	90		Moscow	-104.8		
12	Jacksonville	Berlin	75	75		Rostov	-192.4		
13	Jacksonville	Istanbul	75	105					
14	Hamburg	St. Petersburg	0	0					
15	Rotterdam	St. Petersburg	0	0					
16	Napoli	St. Petersburg	0	0					
17	London	St. Petersburg	150	150					
18	Berlin	St. Petersburg	75	75					
19	Istanbul	St. Petersburg	0	0					
20	Hamburg	Moscow	11.2	11.2					
21	Rotterdam	Moscow	9.6	9.6					
22	Napoli	Moscow	24	24					
23	London	Moscow	0	30					
24	Berlin	Moscow	45	45					
25	Istanbul	Moscow	15	15					
26	Hamburg	Rostov	8	8					
27	Rotterdam	Rostov	12	12					
28	Napoli	Rostov	22.4	22.4					
29	London	Rostov	15	15					
30	Berlin	Rostov	0	0					
31	Istanbul	Rostov	135	135					
32									
33		Total Cost =	522.2						

6-22

The following formulas appear in the spreadsheet.

	G
1	Net Flow
2	=SUM(C2:C7)
3	=SUM(C8:C13)
4	=-C2-C8+C14+C20+C26
5	=-C3-C9+C15+C21+C27
6	=-C4-C10+C16+C22+C28
7	=-C5-C11+C17+C23+C29
8	=-C6-C12+C18+C24+C30
9	=-C7-C13+C19+C25+C31
10	=-SUM(C14:C19)
11	=-SUM(C20:C25)
12	=-SUM(C26:C31)
13	

	B	C
33	Total Cost =	=SUM(G2:G3)

We use the following solver dialogue box.

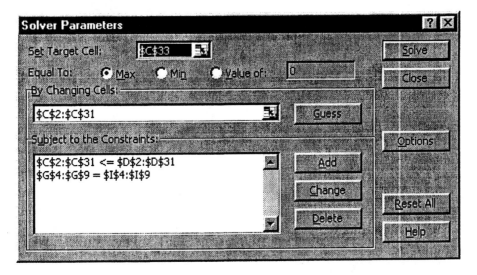

The worksheet shows all the amounts that are shipped between the various cities. The total supply for Saint Petersburg, Moscow, and Rostov equals 225,000 tons, 104,800 tons, and 192,400 tons, respectively. The following network diagram highlights the paths used to ship supplies between the US and the Russian Federation.

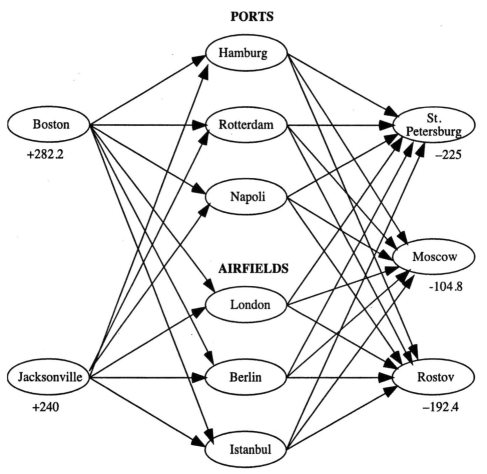

PORTS

Hamburg

Boston
+282.2

Rotterdam

St. Petersburg
−225

Napoli

AIRFIELDS

Moscow
-104.8

London

Jacksonville
+240

Berlin

Rostov
−192.4

Istanbul

e) The creation of the new communications network is a minimum spanning tree problem. As usual, a greedy algorithm solves this type of problem.

Arcs are added to the network in the following order (one of several optimal solutions):

Rostov - Orenburg	120
Ufa - Orenburg	75
Saratov - Orenburg	95
Saratov - Samara	100
Samara - Kazan	95
Ufa – Yekaterinburg	125
Perm – Yekaterinburg	85

The minimum cost of reestablishing the communication lines is $695,000.

6.2 a) There are three supply nodes – the Yen node, the Rupiah node, and the Ringgit node. There is one demand node – the US$ node. Below, we draw the network originating from only the Yen supply node to illustrate the overall design of the network. In this network, we exclude both the Rupiah and Ringgit nodes for simplicity.

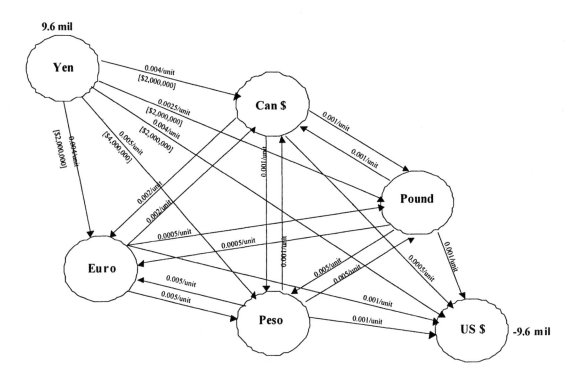

b) Since all transaction limits are given in the equivalent of 1000 dollars we define the flow variables as the amount in 1000's of dollars that Jake converts from one currency into another one. His total holdings in Yen, Rupiah, and Ringgit are equivalent to $9.6 million, $1.68 million, and $5.6 million, respectively. So, the supplies at the supply nodes Yen, Rupiah, and Ringgit are -$9.6 million, -$1.68 million, and -$5.6 million, respectively. The demand at the only demand node US$ equals $16.88 million. The transaction limits are capacity constraints for all arcs leaving from the nodes Yen, Rupiah, and Ringgit. The unit cost for every arc is given by the transaction cost for the currency conversion.

	A	B	C	D	E	F	G	H	I	J	K	L	M
1													
2		From	To	Ship		Capacity	Unit Cost		Nodes	Net Flow		Supply /Demand	
3		Yen	Rupiah	0	<=	5000	0.005		Yen	-9600	=	-9600	
4		Yen	Ringgit	0	<=	5000	0.005		Rupiah	-1680	=	-1680	
5		Yen	US$	2000	<=	2000	0.004		Ringgit	-5600	=	-5600	
6		Yen	Can$	2000	<=	2000	0.004		US$	16880	=	16880	
7		Yen	Euro	2000	<=	2000	0.004		Can$	0	=	0	
8		Yen	Pound	2000	<=	2000	0.0025		Euro	0	=	0	
9		Yen	Peso	1600	<=	4000	0.005		Pound	0	=	0	
10		Rupiah	Yen	0	<=	5000	0.005		Peso	0	=	0	
11		Rupiah	Ringgit	0	<=	2000	0.007						
12		Rupiah	US$	200	<=	200	0.005						
13		Rupiah	Can$	200	<=	200	0.003						
14		Rupiah	Euro	1000	<=	1000	0.003						
15		Rupiah	Pound	80	<=	500	0.0075						
16		Rupiah	Peso	200	<=	200	0.0075						
17		Ringgit	Yen	0	<=	3000	0.005						
18		Ringgit	Rupiah	0	<=	4500	0.007						
19		Ringgit	US$	1100	<=	1500	0.007						
20		Ringgit	Can$	0	<=	1500	0.007						
21		Ringgit	Euro	2500	<=	2500	0.004						
22		Ringgit	Pound	1000	<=	1000	0.0045						
23		Ringgit	Peso	1000	<=	1000	0.005						
24		Can$	US$	2200		-	0.0005						
25		Can$	Euro	0		-	0.002						
26		Can$	Pound	0		-	0.001						
27		Can$	Peso	0		-	0.001						
28		Euro	US$	5500		-	0.001						
29		Euro	Can$	0		-	0.002						
30		Euro	Pound	0		-	0.0005						
31		Euro	Peso	0		-	0.005						
32		Pound	US$	3080		-	0.001						
33		Pound	Can$	0		-	0.001						
34		Pound	Euro	0		-	0.0005						
35		Pound	Peso	0		-	0.005						
36		Peso	US$	2800		-	0.001						
37		Peso	Can$	0		-	0.001						
38		Peso	Euro	0		-	0.005						
39		Peso	Pound	0		-	0.005						
40													
41			Total Cost	$83,380.00									

	J
1	
2	Net Flow
3	=-SUM(D3:D9)+D10+D17
4	=-SUM(D10:D16)+D3+D18
5	=-SUM(D17:D23)+D4+D11
6	=D5+D12+D19+D24+D28+D32+D36
7	=D6+D13+D20-SUM(D24:D27)+D29+D33+D37
8	=D7+D14+D21+D25-SUM(D28:D31)+D34+D38
9	=D8+D15+D22+D26+D30-SUM(D32:D35)+D39
10	=D9+D16+D23+D27+D31+D35-SUM(D36:D39)
11	

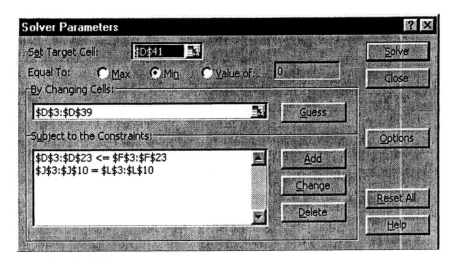

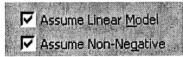

Jake should convert the equivalent of $2 million from Yen to each US$, Can$, Euro, and Pound. He should convert $1.6 million from Yen to Peso. Moreover, he should convert the equivalent of $200,000 from Rupiah to each US$, Can$, and Peso, $1 million from Rupiah to Euro, and $80,000 from Rupiah to Pound. Furthermore, Jake should convert the equivalent of $1.1 million from Ringgit to US$, $2.5 million from Ringgit to Euro, and $1 million from Ringgit to each Pound and Peso. Finally, he should convert all the money he converted into Can$, Euro, Pound, and Peso directly into US$. Specifically, he needs to convert into US$ the equivalent of $2.2 million, $5.5 million, $3.08 million, and $2.8 million Can$, Euro, Pound, and Peso, respectively. Assuming Jake pays for the total transaction costs of $83,380 directly from his American bank accounts he will have $16,880,000 dollars to invest in the US.

c) We eliminate all capacity restrictions on the arcs.

	From	To	Ship	Capacity	Unit Cost		Nodes	Net Flow		Supply /Demand	
3	Yen	Rupiah	0	-	0.005		Yen	-9600	=	-9600	
4	Yen	Ringgit	0	-	0.005		Rupiah	-1680	=	-1680	
5	Yen	US$	0	-	0.004		Ringgit	-5600	=	-5600	
6	Yen	Can$	0	-	0.004		US$	16880	=	16880	
7	Yen	Euro	0	-	0.004		Can$	0	=	0	
8	Yen	Pound	9600	-	0.0025		Euro	0	=	0	
9	Yen	Peso	0	-	0.005		Pound	0	=	0	
10	Rupiah	Yen	0	-	0.005		Peso	0	=	0	
11	Rupiah	Ringgit	0	-	0.007						
12	Rupiah	US$	0	-	0.005						
13	Rupiah	Can$	1680	-	0.003						
14	Rupiah	Euro	0	-	0.003						
15	Rupiah	Pound	0	-	0.0075						
16	Rupiah	Peso	0	-	0.0075						
17	Ringgit	Yen	0	-	0.005						
18	Ringgit	Rupiah	0	-	0.007						
19	Ringgit	US$	0	-	0.007						
20	Ringgit	Can$	0	-	0.007						
21	Ringgit	Euro	5600	-	0.004						
22	Ringgit	Pound	0	-	0.0045						
23	Ringgit	Peso	0	-	0.005						
24	Can$	US$	1680	-	0.0005						
25	Can$	Euro	0	-	0.002						
26	Can$	Pound	0	-	0.001						
27	Can$	Peso	0	-	0.001						
28	Euro	US$	5600	-	0.001						
29	Euro	Can$	0	-	0.002						
30	Euro	Pound	0	-	0.0005						
31	Euro	Peso	0	-	0.005						
32	Pound	US$	9600	-	0.001						
33	Pound	Can$	0	-	0.001						
34	Pound	Euro	0	-	0.0005						
35	Pound	Peso	0	-	0.005						
36	Peso	US$	0	-	0.001						
37	Peso	Can$	0	-	0.001						
38	Peso	Euro	0	-	0.005						
39	Peso	Pound	0	-	0.005						
41		Total Cost = $67,480.00									

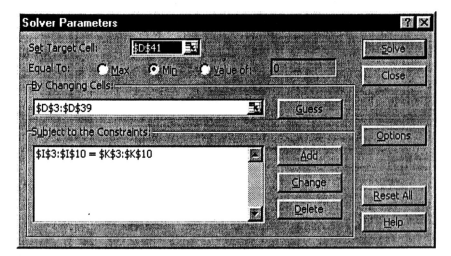

Solver Parameters

Set Target Cell: $D$41

Equal To: ○ Max ● Min ○ Value of: 0

By Changing Cells:

$D$3:$D$39

Subject to the Constraints:

$I$3:$I$10 = $K$3:$K$10

[Solve] [Close] [Options] [Add] [Change] [Delete] [Reset All] [Help]

Jake should convert the entire holdings in Japan from Yen into Pound and then into US$, the entire holdings in Indonesia from Rupiah into Can$ and then into US$, and the entire holdings in Malaysia from Ringgit into Euro and then into US$. Without the capacity limits the transaction costs are reduced to $67,480.00.

6-28

d) We multiply all unit cost for Rupiah by 6.

	A	B	C	D	E	F	G	H	I	J	K	L
1												
2		From	To	Ship	Capacity	Unit Cost		Nodes	Net Flow		Supply/ Demand	
3		Yen	Rupiah	0	-	0.005		Yen	-9600	=	-9600	
4		Yen	Ringgit	0	-	0.005		Rupiah	-1680	=	-1680	
5		Yen	US$	0	-	0.004		Ringgit	-5600	=	-5600	
6		Yen	Can$	0	-	0.004		US$	16880	=	16880	
7		Yen	Euro	0	-	0.004		Can$	0	=	0	
8		Yen	Pound	9600	-	0.0025		Euro	0	=	0	
9		Yen	Peso	0	-	0.005		Pound	0	=	0	
10		Rupiah	Yen	0	-	0.03		Peso	0	=	0	
11		Rupiah	Ringgit	0	-	0.042						
12		Rupiah	US$	0	-	0.03						
13		Rupiah	Can$	1680	-	0.018						
14		Rupiah	Euro	0	-	0.018						
15		Rupiah	Pound	0	-	0.045						
16		Rupiah	Peso	0	-	0.045						
17		Ringgit	Yen	0	-	0.005						
18		Ringgit	Rupiah	0	-	0.007						
19		Ringgit	US$	0	-	0.007						
20		Ringgit	Can$	0	-	0.007						
21		Ringgit	Euro	5600	-	0.004						
22		Ringgit	Pound	0	-	0.0045						
23		Ringgit	Peso	0	-	0.005						
24		Can$	US$	1680	-	0.0005						
25		Can$	Euro	0	-	0.002						
26		Can$	Pound	0	-	0.001						
27		Can$	Peso	0	-	0.001						
28		Euro	US$	5600	-	0.001						
29		Euro	Can$	0	-	0.002						
30		Euro	Pound	0	-	0.0005						
31		Euro	Peso	0	-	0.005						
32		Pound	US$	9600	-	0.001						
33		Pound	Can$	0	-	0.001						
34		Pound	Euro	0	-	0.0005						
35		Pound	Peso	0	-	0.005						
36		Peso	US$	0	-	0.001						
37		Peso	Can$	0	-	0.001						
38		Peso	Euro	0	-	0.005						
39		Peso	Pound	0	-	0.005						
40												
41			Total Cost	$92,680.00								
42												

The optimal routing for the money doesn't change, but the total transaction costs are now increased to $92,680.

e) In the described crisis situation the currency exchange rates might change every minute. Jake should carefully check the exchange rates again when he performs the transactions.

The European economies might be more insulated from the Asian financial collapse than the US economy. To impress his boss Jake might want to explore other investment opportunities in safer European economies that provide higher rates of return than US bonds.

CHAPTER 7
PROJECT MANAGEMENT WITH PERT/CPM

Review Questions

7.1-1 The bid is for $5.4 million with a penalty of $300,000 if the deadline of 47 weeks is not met. In addition, a bonus of $150,000 will be paid if the plant is completed within 40 weeks.

7.1-2 He has decided to focus on meeting the deadline of 47 weeks.

7.1-3 An immediate predecessor is an activity that must be completed just prior to starting the given activity. Given the immediate predecessors of an activity, this activity then becomes the immediate successor of each of these immediate predecessors.

7.1-4 1. the activities of the project
2. the immediate predecessors of the activities
3. the estimated duration of the activities

7.2-1 1. activity information
2. precedence relationships
3. time information (duration)

7.2-2 In an AOA network, each activity is represented by an arc, while in an AON network, each activity is represented by a node. AON networks are being used here.

7.2-3 The bars in a Gantt chart show the scheduled start and finish times for activities in a project.

7.3-1 A path through a project network is one of the routes following the arrows (arcs) from the start node to the finish node. The length of a path is the sum of the estimated durations of the activities on the path. The longest path is called the critical path.

7.3-2 1. The actual duration of each activity must be the same as its estimated duration.
2. Each activity must begin as soon as all its immediate predecessors are finished.

7.3-3 The earliest start time of an activity is equal to the largest of the earliest finish times of its immediate predecessors.

7.3-4 A forward pass is the process of starting with the initial activities and working forward in time toward the final activities.

7.3-5 It is a last chance schedule because anything later will delay the completion of the project.

7.3-6 The latest finish time of an activity is equal to the smallest of the latest start times of its immediate successors.

7.3-7 A backward pass starts with the final activities and works backward in time toward the initial activities instead of starting with the initial activities.

7.3-8 Any delay along the critical path will delay project completion.

7.3-9 1. Identify the longest path through the project network.
2. Identify the activities with zero slack - they are on the critical path.

7.4-1 The three estimates are the most likely estimate, optimistic estimate, and pessimistic estimate.

7.4-2 The optimistic and pessimistic estimates are meant to lie at the extremes of what is possible, whereas the most likely estimate provides the highest point of the probability distribution.

7.4-3 Assume that the mean critical path will turn out to be the longest path through the project network.

7.4-4 Assume that the durations of the activities on the mean critical path are statistically independent.

7.4-5 μ_p=sum of the means of the durations for the activities on the mean critical path.

7.4-6 σ_p^2=sum of the variances of the durations for the activities on the mean critical path.

7.4-7 Assume that the form of the probability distribution of project duration is the normal distribution.

7.4-8 It is usually higher than the true probability.

7.5-1 Using overtime, hiring additional labor, and using special materials or equipment are all ways of crashing an activity.

7.5-2 The two key points are labeled normal and crash. The normal point shows the time and cost of the activity when it is performed in the normal way. The crash point shows the time and cost when the activity is fully crashed.

7.5-3 No, only crashing activities on the critical path will reduce the duration of the project.

7.5-4 Crash costs per week saved are being examined.

7.5-5 The decisions to be made are the start time of each activity, the reduction in the duration of each activity due to crashing, and the finish time of the project.

7.5-6 An activity cannot start until its immediate predecessor starts and then completes its duration.

7.5-7 Because of uncertainty, the plan for crashing the project only provides a 50% chance of actually finishing within 40 weeks, so the extra cost of the plan is not justified.

7.6-1 PERT/Cost is a systematic procedure to help the manager plan, schedule, and control project costs.

7.6-2 It begins by developing an estimate of the cost of each activity when it is performed in the planned way.

7.6-3 A common assumption is that the costs of performing an activity are incurred at a constant rate throughout its duration.

7.6-4 A work package is a group of related activities.

7.6-5 PERT/Cost uses earliest start time and latest start time schedules as a basis for developing cost schedules.

7.6-6 A PERT/Cost schedule of costs shows the weekly project cost and cumulative project cost for each time period.

7.6-7 A PERT/Cost report shows the budgeted value of the work completed of each activity and the cost overruns to date.

7.6-8 Since deviations from the planned work schedule may occur, a PERT/Cost report is needed to evaluate the cost performance of individual activities.

7.7-1 Planning, scheduling, dealing with uncertainty, time-cost trade-offs, and controlling costs are addressed by PERT/CPM.

7.7-2 Computer implementation has allowed for application to larger projects, faster revisions in project plans and effortless updates and changes in schedules.

7.7-3 The accuracy and reliability of end-point estimates are not as good for points that are not at the extremes of the probability distribution.

7.7-4 The technique of computer simulation to approximate the probability that the project will meet its deadline is an alternative for improving on PERT/CPM.

7.7-5 The Precedence Diagramming Method has been developed as an extension of PERT/CPM to deal with overlapping activities.

7.7-6 PERT/CPM assumes that each activity has available all the resources needed to perform the activity in a normal way.

7.7-7 It encourages effective interaction between the project manager and subordinates that leads to setting mutual goals for the project.

7.7-8 New improvements and extensions are still being developed but have not been incorporated much into practice yet.

Problems

7.1 a)

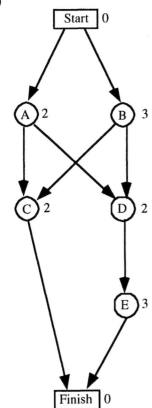

b) Start → A → C → Finish   Length = 4 weeks
Start → A → D → E → Finish   Length = 7 weeks
Start → B → C → Finish   Length = 5 weeks
Start → B → D → E → Finish   Length = 8 weeks   *critical path

7-3

c)

Activity	ES	EF	LS	LF	Slack	Critical Path
Start	0	0	0	0	0	Yes
A	0	2	1	3	1	No
B	0	3	0	3	0	Yes
C	3	5	6	8	3	No
D	3	5	3	5	0	Yes
E	5	8	5	8	0	Yes
Finish	8	8	8	8	0	Yes

Critical Path: Start $\rightarrow$ B $\rightarrow$ D $\rightarrow$ E $\rightarrow$ Finish

d) No, this will not shorten the length of the project because the activity is not on the critical path.

7.2   a)

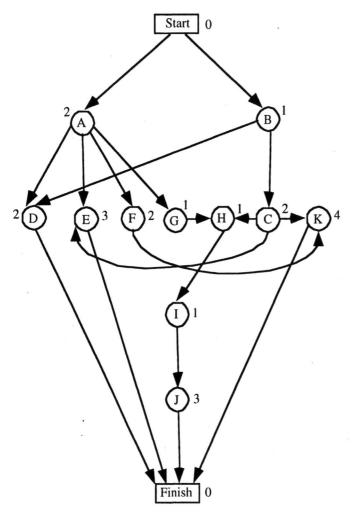

b) Start → A → D → Finish   Length = 4 weeks
    Start → A → E → Finish   Length = 5 weeks
    Start → A → F → K → Finish   Length = 8 weeks   *critical path
    Start → A → G → H → I →J → Finish   Length = 8 weeks   *critical path
    Start → B → D → Finish   Length = 3 weeks
    Start → B → C → E → Finish   Length = 6 weeks
    Start → B → C → H → I →J → Finish   Length = 8 weeks   *critical path
    Start → B → C → K → Finish   Length = 7 weeks

c)

Activity	ES	EF	LS	LF	Slack	Critical Path
Start	0	0	0	0	0	Yes
A	0	2	0	2	0	Yes
B	0	1	0	1	0	Yes
C	1	3	1	3	0	Yes
D	2	4	6	8	4	No
E	3	6	5	8	2	No
F	2	4	2	4	0	Yes
G	2	3	2	3	0	Yes
H	3	4	3	4	0	Yes
I	4	5	4	5	0	Yes
J	5	8	5	8	0	Yes
K	4	8	4	8	0	Yes
Finish	8	8	8	8	0	Yes

Critical Paths: Start → A → F → K → Finish
                 Start → A → G → H → I →J → Finish
                 Start → B → C → H → I →J → Finish

d) No, this will not shorten the length of the project because A is not on all of the critical paths.

7.3   a)

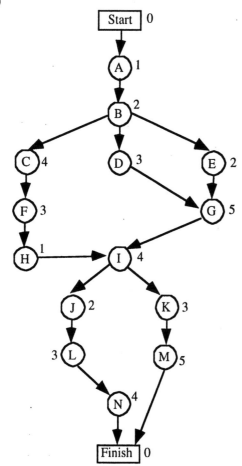

b, c, & d)

Activity	ES	EF	LS	LF	Slack	Critical Path
Start	0	0	0	0	0	Yes
A	0	1	0	1	0	Yes
B	1	3	1	3	0	Yes
C	3	7	3	7	0	Yes
D	3	6	3	6	0	Yes
E	3	5	4	6	1	No
F	7	10	7	10	0	Yes
G	6	11	6	11	0	Yes
H	10	11	10	11	0	Yes
I	11	15	11	15	0	Yes
J	15	17	15	17	0	Yes
K	15	18	16	19	1	No
L	17	20	17	20	0	Yes
M	18	23	19	24	1	No
N	20	24	20	24	0	Yes
Finish	24	24	24	24	0	Yes

Critical Paths: Start $\rightarrow$ A $\rightarrow$ B $\rightarrow$ C $\rightarrow$ F $\rightarrow$ H $\rightarrow$ I $\rightarrow$ J $\rightarrow$ L $\rightarrow$ N $\rightarrow$ Finish

Start $\rightarrow$ A $\rightarrow$ B $\rightarrow$ D $\rightarrow$ G $\rightarrow$ I $\rightarrow$ J $\rightarrow$ L $\rightarrow$ N $\rightarrow$ Finish

7.4   a)

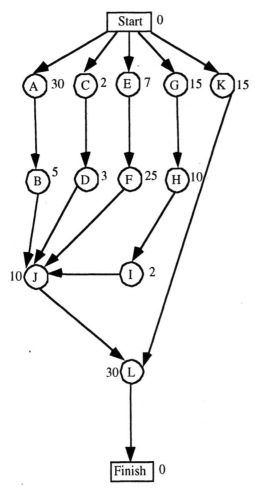

b)   Start → A → B → J → L → Finish   Length = 75 minutes   *critical path
       Start → C → D → J → L → Finish   Length = 45 minutes
       Start → E → F → J → L → Finish   Length = 72 minutes
       Start → G → H → I → J → L → Finish   Length = 67 minutes
       Start → K → L → Finish   Length = 45 minutes

c, d & e)

Activity	ES	EF	LS	LF	Slack	Critical Path
Start	0	0	0	0	0	Yes
A	0	30	0	30	0	Yes
B	30	35	30	35	0	Yes
C	0	2	30	32	30	No
D	2	5	32	35	30	No
E	0	7	3	10	3	No
F	7	32	10	35	3	No
G	0	15	8	23	8	No
H	15	25	23	33	8	No
I	25	27	33	35	8	No
J	35	45	35	45	0	Yes
K	0	15	30	45	30	No
L	45	75	45	75	0	Yes
Finish	75	75	75	75	0	Yes

Critical Path: Start → A → B → J → L → Finish

f) Dinner will be delayed 3 minutes because of the phone call. If the food processor is used then dinner will not be delayed because there was 3 minutes of slack and 5 minutes of cutting time saved and the call only used 6 minutes of the 8 total.

7.5 a)

Start → A → D → H → M → Finish   Length = 19 weeks

Start → B → E → J → M → Finish   Length = 20 weeks   *critical path

Start → C → F → K → N → Finish   Length = 16 weeks

Start → A → I → M → Finish   Length = 17 weeks

Start → C → G → L → N → Finish   Length = 20 weeks   *critical path

b)

Activity	ES	EF	LS	LF	Slack	Critical Path
Start	0	0	0	0	0	Yes
A	0	6	1	7	1	No
B	0	3	0	3	0	Yes
C	0	4	0	4	0	Yes
D	6	10	7	11	1	No
E	3	10	3	10	0	Yes
F	4	8	8	12	4	No
G	4	10	4	10	0	Yes
H	10	13	11	14	1	No
I	6	11	9	14	3	No
J	10	14	10	14	0	Yes
K	8	11	12	15	4	No
L	10	15	10	15	0	Yes
M	14	20	14	20	0	Yes
N	15	20	15	20	0	Yes
Finish	20	20	20	20	0	Yes

Ken will be able to meet his deadline if no delays occur.

c) Critical Paths: Start → B → E → J → M → Finish

Start → C → G → L → N → Finish

Focus attention on activities with 0 slack.

d) If activity I takes 2 extra weeks there will be no delay because its slack is 3. If activity H takes 2 extra weeks then there will be a delay of 1 week because its slack is 1. If activity J takes 2 extra weeks there will be a delay of 2 weeks because it has no slack.

7.6 a)

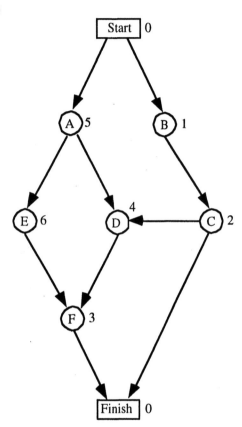

b)

Activity	ES	EF	LS	LF	Slack	Critical Path
Start	0	0	0	0	0	Yes
A	0	5	0	5	0	Yes
B	0	1	11	12	11	No
C	1	3	12	14	11	No
D	5	9	7	11	2	No
E	5	11	5	11	0	Yes
F	11	14	11	14	0	Yes
Finish	14	14	14	14	0	Yes

Critical Path: Start → A → E → F → Finish Length = 14 months

c) 6 months

7.7

Activity	ES	EF	LS	LF	Slack	Critical Path
Start	0	0	0	0	0	Yes
A	0	3	0	3	0	Yes
B	3	11	3	11	0	Yes
C	11	29	11	29	0	Yes
D	29	39	29	39	0	Yes
E	29	34	30	35	1	No
F	34	44	35	45	1	No
G	39	50	39	50	0	Yes
H	50	67	50	67	0	Yes
I	29	38	36	45	7	No
J	44	53	45	54	1	No
K	53	57	57	61	4	No
L	53	60	54	61	1	No
M	67	70	67	70	0	Yes
N	60	69	61	70	1	No
Finish	70	70	70	70	0	Yes

Critical Path: Start $\rightarrow$ A $\rightarrow$ B $\rightarrow$ C $\rightarrow$ D $\rightarrow$ G $\rightarrow$ H $\rightarrow$ M $\rightarrow$ Finish
Total duration = 70 weeks

7.8

Activity	ES	EF	LS	LF	Slack	Critical Path
Start	0	0	0	0	0	Yes
A	0	1	0	1	0	Yes
B	1	3	1	3	0	Yes
C	3	9	3	9	0	Yes
D	9	13	11	15	2	No
E	9	10	9	10	0	Yes
F	10	14	10	14	0	Yes
G	13	18	15	20	2	No
H	18	23	20	25	2	No
I	9	12	11	14	2	No
J	14	17	14	17	0	Yes
K	17	21	17	21	0	Yes
L	17	18	20	21	3	No
M	23	24	25	26	2	No
N	21	26	21	26	0	Yes
Finish	26	26	26	26	0	Yes

Critical Path: Start $\rightarrow$ A $\rightarrow$ B $\rightarrow$ C $\rightarrow$ E $\rightarrow$ F $\rightarrow$ J $\rightarrow$ K $\rightarrow$ N $\rightarrow$ Finish
Total duration = 26 weeks

7.9

Activity	ES	EF	LS	LF	Slack	Critical Path
Start	0	0	0	0	0	Yes
A	0	1	0	1	0	Yes
B	1	3	1	3	0	Yes
C	3	10	3	10	0	Yes
D	10	14	13	17	3	No
E	10	13	10	13	0	Yes
F	13	16	13	16	0	Yes
G	14	18	17	21	3	No
H	18	24	21	27	3	No
I	10	15	11	16	1	No
J	16	22	16	22	0	Yes
K	22	25	22	25	0	Yes
L	22	25	22	25	0	Yes
M	24	25	27	28	3	No
N	25	28	25	28	0	Yes
Finish	28	28	28	28	0	Yes

Critical Paths: Start $\to$ A $\to$ B $\to$ C $\to$ E $\to$ F $\to$ J $\to$ K $\to$ N$\to$ Finish

Start $\to$ A $\to$ B $\to$ C $\to$ E $\to$ F $\to$ J $\to$ L $\to$ N$\to$ Finish

Total duration = 28 weeks

7.10

$$\mu = \frac{o + 4m + p}{6} = \frac{30 + (4)(36) + 48}{6} = 37$$

$$\sigma^2 = \left(\frac{p - o}{6}\right)^2 = \left(\frac{48 - 30}{6}\right)^2 = 9$$

7.11   a)   Start $\to$ A $\to$ E $\to$ I $\to$ Finish   Length = 17 months

Start $\to$ A $\to$ C $\to$ F $\to$ I $\to$ Finish   Length = 17 months

Start $\to$ B $\to$ D $\to$ G $\to$ J $\to$ Finish   Length = 17 months

Start $\to$ B $\to$ H $\to$ J $\to$ Finish   Length = 18 months   *critical path

b) $\dfrac{d - \mu_p}{\sqrt{\sigma_p^2}} = \dfrac{22 - 18}{\sqrt{31}} = 0.718$ $\Rightarrow$ $P(T \le 22) \approx 0.77$

c) Start $\to$ A $\to$ E $\to$ I $\to$ Finish

$$\frac{d-\mu_p}{\sqrt{\sigma_p^2}} = \frac{22-17}{\sqrt{25}} = 1 \quad \Rightarrow \quad P(T \le 22) \approx 0.84$$

Start $\to$ A $\to$ C $\to$ F $\to$ I $\to$ Finish

$$\frac{d-\mu_p}{\sqrt{\sigma_p^2}} = \frac{22-17}{\sqrt{27}} = 0.962 \quad \Rightarrow \quad P(T \le 22) \approx 0.84$$

Start $\to$ B $\to$ D $\to$ G $\to$ J $\to$ Finish

$$\frac{d-\mu_p}{\sqrt{\sigma_p^2}} = \frac{22-17}{\sqrt{28}} = 0.945 \quad \Rightarrow \quad P(T \le 22) \approx 0.84$$

d) There is approximately a 77% chance that the drug will be ready in 22 weeks.

7.12   Start $\to$ B $\to$ H $\to$ J $\to$ Finish   Start $\to$ A $\to$ E $\to$ I $\to$ Finish

Mean Critical Path	
$\mu =$	18.4166667
$\sigma^2 =$	31.2013889
P(T≤d)=	0.73940284
where	
d =	22

Mean Critical Path	
$\mu =$	17.0833333
$\sigma^2 =$	25.3402778
P(T≤d)=	0.83564332
where	
d =	22

Start $\to$ A $\to$ C $\to$ F $\to$ I $\to$ Finish   Start $\to$ B $\to$ D $\to$ G $\to$ J $\to$ Finish

Mean Critical Path	
$\mu =$	17.5833333
$\sigma^2 =$	27.3680556
P(T≤d)=	0.80073605
where	
d =	22

Mean Critical Path	
$\mu =$	17.8333333
$\sigma^2 =$	28.0416667
P(T≤d)=	0.78431252
where	
d =	22

There is approximately a 73% chance that the drug will be ready in 22 weeks.

7.13   a)

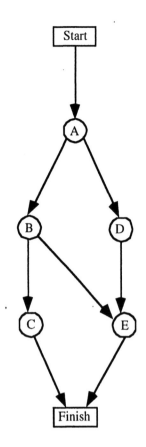

b)

Activity	μ	σ^2
A	4	0.111
B	2	0
C	4.83	0.25
D	3	0.444
E	3.17	0.25

c)   Start $\rightarrow$ A $\rightarrow$ B $\rightarrow$ C $\rightarrow$ Finish   Length = 10.83 weeks   *critical path
     Start $\rightarrow$ A $\rightarrow$ B $\rightarrow$ E $\rightarrow$ Finish   Length = 9.17 weeks
     Start $\rightarrow$ A $\rightarrow$ D $\rightarrow$ E $\rightarrow$ Finish   Length = 10.17 weeks

d) $\dfrac{d - \mu_p}{\sqrt{\sigma_p^2}} = \dfrac{11 - 10.83}{\sqrt{.361}} = 0.028$ $\Rightarrow$ $P(T \leq 11) = 0.6$

e)   Make the bid since there is approximately a 60% chance that the project will be completed
     in 11 weeks or less.

7.14 a)

Activity	μ	σ^2
A	12	0
B	23	16
C	15	1
D	27	9
E	18	4
F	6	4

b) Start $\to$ A $\to$ C $\to$ E $\to$ F $\to$ Finish   Length = 51 days   *critical path

    Start $\to$ B $\to$ D $\to$ Finish   Length = 50 days

c) $\dfrac{d - \mu_p}{\sqrt{\sigma_p^2}} = \dfrac{57 - 51}{\sqrt{9}} = 2$ $\Rightarrow$ $P(T \leq 57) = 0.9772$ (from the Normal table)

d) $\dfrac{d - \mu_p}{\sqrt{\sigma_p^2}} = \dfrac{57 - 50}{\sqrt{25}} = 1.4$ $\Rightarrow$ $P(T \leq 57) = 0.9192$ (from the Normal table)

e) $(0.9772)(0.9192) = 0.8982$ This answer tells us that the procedure used in part c) overestimates the probability of completing within 57 days.

7.15 a)

Activity	μ	σ^2
A	32	1.78
B	27.7	2.78
C	36	11.1
D	16	0.444
E	32	0
F	53.7	32.1
G	16.7	4
H	20.3	2.78
I	34	7.11
J	17.7	9

b) Start $\to$ A $\to$ C $\to$ J $\to$ Finish   Length = 85.7 weeks

    Start $\to$ B $\to$ F $\to$ J $\to$ Finish   Length = 99.1 weeks   *critical path

    Start $\to$ B $\to$ E $\to$ H $\to$ Finish   Length = 80 weeks

    Start $\to$ B $\to$ E $\to$ I $\to$ Finish   Length = 93.7 weeks

    Start $\to$ B $\to$ D $\to$ G $\to$ H $\to$ Finish   Length = 80.7 weeks

    Start $\to$ B $\to$ D $\to$ G $\to$ I $\to$ Finish   Length = 94.4 weeks

c) $\dfrac{d - \mu_p}{\sqrt{\sigma_p^2}} = \dfrac{100 - 99.1}{\sqrt{43.89}} = 0.136$ $\Rightarrow$ $P(T \leq 100) = 0.4443$ (from the Normal table)

d) Higher

7.16 a) True. The optimistic and pessimistic estimates are meant to lie at the extremes of what is possible. (Pg. 33)

b) False. The form of the probability distribution is a beta distribution. (Pg. 33)

c) False. The mean critical path will turn out to be the longest path through the project network. (Pg. 40)

7.17

Activity to Crash	Crash Cost	Length of Path	
		A – C	B - D
		14	16
B	$5,000	14	15
B	$5,000	14	15
D	$6,000	14	14
C	$4,000	13	14
D	$6,000	13	13
C	$4,000	12	13
D	$6,000	12	12

7.18 a)

Let x_A = reduction in A due to crashing

Let x_C = reduction in C due to crashing

Minimize $C = 5,000x_A + 4,000x_c$,

subject to $\quad x_A \leq 3$

$\qquad\qquad x_C \leq 2$

$\qquad\qquad x_A + x_C \geq 2$

and $\qquad\quad x_A \geq 0, \ x_C \geq 0.$

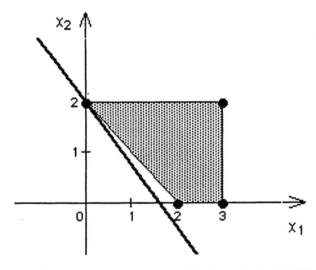

Optimal solution $(x_A, x_C) = (0, 2)$ and $C = 8,000.$

b)

Let x_B = reduction in B due to crashing
Let x_D = reduction in D due to crashing

Minimize $C = 5,000x_B + 6,000x_D$,
subject to $\quad x_B \leq 2$
$\qquad\qquad x_D \leq 3$
$\qquad\qquad x_B + x_D \geq 4$
and $\qquad\quad x_B \geq 0, \ x_D \geq 0.$

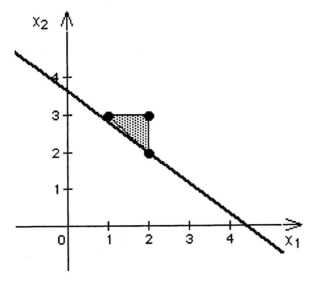

Optimal solution $(x_B, x_D) = (2, 2)$ and $C = 22,000.$

c)

Let x_A = reduction in A due to crashing
Let x_B = reduction in B due to crashing
Let x_C = reduction in C due to crashing
Let x_D = reduction in D due to crashing

Minimize $C = 5,000x_A + 5,000x_B + 4,000x_C + 6,000x_D$,
subject to $\quad x_A \leq 3$
$\qquad\qquad x_B \leq 2$
$\qquad\qquad x_C \leq 2$
$\qquad\qquad x_D \leq 3$
$\qquad\qquad x_A + x_C \geq 2$
$\qquad\qquad x_B + x_D \geq 4$
and $\qquad\quad x_A \geq 0, \ x_B \geq 0, \ x_c \geq 0, \ x_D \geq 0.$

Optimal solution $(x_A, x_B, x_{c,} x_D) = (0, 2, 2, 2)$ and $C = 30,000.$

d)

Activity	Time Normal	Time Crash	Cost Normal	Cost Crash	Maximum Time Reduction	Crash Cost per Week saved	Start Time	Time Reduction	Finish Time
A	8	5	$25000	$40000	3	$5000	0	0	8
B	9	7	$20000	$30000	2	$5000	0	2	7
C	6	4	$16000	$24000	2	$4000	8	2	12
D	7	4	$27000	$45000	3	$6000	7	2	12

Finish Time = 12
Total Cost = $118000

e) <u>Deadline of 11 months:</u>

Activity	Time Normal	Time Crash	Cost Normal	Cost Crash	Maximum Time Reduction	Crash Cost per Week saved	Start Time	Time Reduction	Finish Time
A	8	5	$25000	$40000	3	$5000	0	1	7
B	9	7	$20000	$30000	2	$5000	0	2	7
C	6	4	$16000	$24000	2	$4000	7	2	11
D	7	4	$27000	$45000	3	$6000	7	3	11

Finish Time = 11
Total Cost = $129000

<u>Deadline of 13 months:</u>

Activity	Time Normal	Time Crash	Cost Normal	Cost Crash	Maximum Time Reduction	Crash Cost per Week saved	Start Time	Time Reduction	Finish Time
A	8	5	$25000	$40000	3	$5000	0	0	8
B	9	7	$20000	$30000	2	$5000	0	2	7
C	6	4	$16000	$24000	2	$4000	8	1	13
D	7	4	$27000	$45000	3	$6000	7	1	13

Finish Time = 13
Total Cost = $108000

7.19 a)

Activity to Crash	Crash Cost	Length of Path B – D
		50
B	$10,000	49
B	$10,000	48
B	$10,000	47

b)

Activity to Crash	Crash Cost	Length of Path A – C – E – F
		51
C	$10,000	50
C	$10,000	49
C	$10,000	48
E	$15,000	47

c)

Activity	Time		Cost		Maximum Time Reduction	Crash Cost per Week saved	Start Time	Time Reduction	Finish Time
	Normal	Crash	Normal	Crash					
A	12	9	$210000	$270000	3	$20000	0	0	12
B	23	18	$410000	$460000	5	$10000	0	3	20
C	15	12	$290000	$320000	3	$10000	12	3	24
D	27	21	$440000	$500000	6	$10000	20	0	47
E	18	14	$350000	$410000	4	$15000	24	1	41
F	6	4	$160000	$210000	2	$25000	41	0	47

Finish Time = 47
Total Cost = $1935000

7.20   a)

Activity	ES	EF	LS	LF	Slack	Critical Path
Start	0	0	0	0	0	Yes
A	0	3	0	3	0	Yes
B	3	7	4	8	1	No
C	3	8	3	8	0	Yes
D	7	10	9	12	2	No
E	8	12	8	12	0	Yes
Finish	12	12	12	12	0	Yes

Critical Path: Start → A → C → E → Finish
Total duration = 12 weeks

b)

Activity to Crash	Crash Cost	Length of Path		
		A – B – D	A – B – E	A – C - E
		10	11	12
C	$1,333	10	11	11
E	$2,500	10	10	10
D & E	$4,000	9	9	9
B & C	$4,333	8	8	8

New Plan:

Activity	Duration	Cost
A	3 weeks	$54,000
B	3 weeks	$65,000
C	3 weeks	$68,666
D	2 weeks	$41,500
E	2 weeks	$80,000

$7834 is saved by this crashing schedule.

c)

Activity	Time Normal	Time Crash	Cost Normal	Cost Crash	Maximum Time Reduction	Crash Cost per Week saved	Start Time	Time Reduction	Finish Time
A	3	2	$54000	$60000	1	$6000	0	0	3
B	4	3	$62000	$65000	1	$3000	4	0	8
C	5	2	$66000	$70000	3	$1333	3	0	8
D	3	1	$40000	$43000	2	$1500	9	0	12
E	4	2	$75000	$80000	2	$2500	8	0	12

Finish Time = 12
Total Cost = $297000

Activity	Time Normal	Time Crash	Cost Normal	Cost Crash	Maximum Time Reduction	Crash Cost per Week saved	Start Time	Time Reduction	Finish Time
A	3	2	$54000	$60000	1	$6000	0	0	3
B	4	3	$62000	$65000	1	$3000	3	0	7
C	5	2	$66000	$70000	3	$1333	3	1	7
D	3	1	$40000	$43000	2	$1500	8	0	11
E	4	2	$75000	$80000	2	$2500	7	0	11

Finish Time = 11
Total Cost = $298333

Activity	Time Normal	Time Crash	Cost Normal	Cost Crash	Maximum Time Reduction	Crash Cost per Week saved	Start Time	Time Reduction	Finish Time
A	3	2	$54000	$60000	1	$6000	0	0	3
B	4	3	$62000	$65000	1	$3000	3	0	7
C	5	2	$66000	$70000	3	$1333	3	1	7
D	3	1	$40000	$43000	2	$1500	7	$1.22E-15$	10
E	4	2	$75000	$80000	2	$2500	7	1	10

Finish Time = 10
Total Cost = $300833

Activity	Time Normal	Time Crash	Cost Normal	Cost Crash	Maximum Time Reduction	Crash Cost per Week saved	Start Time	Time Reduction	Finish Time
A	3	2	$54000	$60000	1	$6000	0	0	3
B	4	3	$62000	$65000	1	$3000	3	$4.66E-12$	7
C	5	2	$66000	$70000	3	$1333	3	1	7
D	3	1	$40000	$43000	2	$1500	7	1	9
E	4	2	$75000	$80000	2	$2500	7	2	9

Finish Time = 9
Total Cost = $304833

Activity	Time Normal	Time Crash	Cost Normal	Cost Crash	Maximum Time Reduction	Crash Cost per Week saved	Start Time	Time Reduction	Finish Time
A	3	2	$54000	$60000	1	$6000	0	$3.66E-11$	3
B	4	3	$62000	$65000	1	$3000	3	1	6
C	5	2	$66000	$70000	3	$1333	3	2	6
D	3	1	$40000	$43000	2	$1500	6	1	8
E	4	2	$75000	$80000	2	$2500	6	2	8

Finish Time = 8
Total Cost = $309167

Activity	Time Normal	Time Crash	Cost Normal	Cost Crash	Maximum Time Reduction	Crash Cost per Week saved	Start Time	Time Reduction	Finish Time
A	3	2	$54000	$60000	1	$6000	0	1	2
B	4	3	$62000	$65000	1	$3000	2	1	5
C	5	2	$66000	$70000	3	$1333	2	2	5
D	3	1	$40000	$43000	2	$1500	5	1	7
E	4	2	$75000	$80000	2	$2500	5	2	7

Finish Time = 7
Total Cost = $315167

Crash to 8 weeks.

7.21

Activity	Time Normal	Time Crash	Cost Normal	Cost Crash	Maximum Time Reduction	Crash Cost per Week saved	Start Time	Time Reduction	Finish Time
A	5	3	$20	$30	2	$5	0	2	3
B	3	2	$10	$20	1	$10	0	1	2
C	4	2	$16	$24	2	$4	3	0	7
D	6	3	$25	$43	3	$6	3	0	9
E	5	4	$22	$30	1	$8	2	0	7
F	7	4	$30	$48	3	$6	2	0	9
G	9	5	$25	$45	4	$5	7	1	15
H	8	6	$30	$44	2	$7	9	2	15

Finish Time = 15
Total Cost = $217

7.22

Activity	Time Normal	Time Crash	Cost Normal	Cost Crash	Maximum Time Reduction	Crash Cost per Week saved	Start Time	Time Reduction	Finish Time
A	32	28	$160	$180	4	$5	8	0	40
B	28	25	$125	$146	3	$7	0	3	25
C	36	31	$170	$210	5	$8	40	0	76
D	16	13	$60	$72	3	$4	25	0	41
E	32	27	$135	$160	5	$5	25	0	57
F	54	47	$215	$257	7	$6	25	3	76
G	17	15	$90	$96	2	$3	41	0	58
H	20	17	$120	$132	3	$4	58	0	78
I	34	30	$190	$226	4	$9	58	0	92
J	18	16	$80	$84	2	$2	76	2	92

Finish Time = 92
Total Cost = $1388

7.23 a)

Activity	ES	EF
Start	0	0
A	0	3
B	3	6
C	3	6
D	6	8
E	6	8
Finish	8	8

Total duration = 8 weeks

b, c & d)

Activity	Estimated Duration (weeks)	Estimated Cost	Start Time	Cost Per Week of Its Duration	Week 1	Week 2	Week 3	Week 4	Week 5	Week 6	Week 7	Week 8
A	3	$54,000	0	$18,000	18000	18000	18000	0	0	0	0	0
B	3	$65,000	3	$21,667	0	0	0	21667	21667	21667	0	0
C	3	$68,666	3	$22,889	0	0	0	22889	22889	22889	0	0
D	2	$41,500	6	$20,750	0	0	0	0	0	0	20750	20750
E	2	$80,000	6	$40,000	0	0	0	0	0	0	40000	40000
					0	0	0	0	0	0	0	0

	Week 1	Week 2	Week 3	Week 4	Week 5	Week 6	Week 7	Week 8
Weekly Project Cost	18000	18000	18000	44555	44555	44555	60750	60750
Cumulative Project Cost	18000	36000	54000	98555	143111	187666	248416	309166

e)

Activity	Budgeted Cost	Percent Completed	Value Completed	Actual Cost To Date	Cost Overrun To Date
A	$54,000	100%	$54,000	$65,000	$11,000
B	$65,000	100%	$65,000	$55,000	-$10,000
C	$68,666	33%	$22,660	$44,000	$21,340
Total	$187,666		$141,660	$164,000	$22,340

Michael should concentrate his efforts on activity C since it is not yet completed.

7.24   a)

Activity	ES	EF	LS	LF	Slack
Start	0	0	0	0	0
A	0	6	0	6	0
B	0	2	4	6	4
C	6	10	9	13	3
D	6	11	6	11	0
E	10	17	13	20	3
F	11	20	11	20	0
Finish	20	20	20	20	0

The earliest finish time for the project is 20 weeks.

b)

Activity	Estimated Duration (weeks)	Estimated Cost	Start Time	Cost Per Week of Its Duration	Week 1	Week 2	Week 3	Week 4	Week 5	Week 6	Week 7	Week 8
A	6	$420,000	0	$70,000	70000	70000	70000	70000	70000	70000	0	0
B	2	$180,000	0	$90,000	90000	90000	0	0	0	0	0	0
C	4	$540,000	6	$135,000	0	0	0	0	0	0	135000	135000
D	5	$360,000	6	$72,000	0	0	0	0	0	0	72000	72000
E	7	$590,000	10	$84,286	0	0	0	0	0	0	0	0
F	9	$630,000	11	$70,000	0	0	0	0	0	0	0	0
					0	0	0	0	0	0	0	0

	Week 1	Week 2	Week 3	Week 4	Week 5	Week 6	Week 7	Week 8
Weekly Project Cost	160000	160000	70000	70000	70000	70000	207000	207000
Cumulative Project Cost	160000	320000	390000	460000	530000	600000	807000	1014000

Week 9	Week 10	Week 11	Week 12	Week 13	Week 14	Week 15	Week 16	Week 17	Week 18	Week 19	Week 20
0	0	0	0	0	0	0	0	0	0	0	0
0	0	0	0	0	0	0	0	0	0	0	0
135000	135000	0	0	0	0	0	0	0	0	0	0
72000	72000	72000	0	0	0	0	0	0	0	0	0
0	0	84286	84285.7	84285.7	84285.7	84285.7	84285.7	84285.7	0	0	0
0	0	0	70000	70000	70000	70000	70000	70000	70000	70000	70000
0	0	0	0	0	0	0	0	0	0	0	0
207000	207000	156285.7	154286	154286	154286	154286	154286	154286	70000	70000	70000
1221000	1428000	1584286	1738571	1892857	2047143	2201429	2355714	2510000	2580000	2650000	2720000

c)

Activity	Estimated Duration (weeks)	Estimated Cost	Start Time	Cost Per Week of Its Duration	Week 1	Week 2	Week 3	Week 4	Week 5	Week 6	Week 7	Week 8
A	6	$420,000	0	$70,000	70000	70000	70000	70000	70000	70000	0	0
B	2	$180,000	4	$90,000	0	0	0	0	90000	90000	0	0
C	4	$540,000	9	$135,000	0	0	0	0	0	0	0	0
D	5	$360,000	6	$72,000	0	0	0	0	0	0	72000	72000
E	7	$590,000	13	$84,286	0	0	0	0	0	0	0	0
F	9	$630,000	11	$70,000	0	0	0	0	0	0	0	0
					0	0	0	0	0	0	0	0

Week 9	Week 10	Week 11	Week 12	Week 13	Week 14	Week 15	Week 16	Week 17	Week 18	Week 19	Week 20
0	0	0	0	0	0	0	0	0	0	0	0
0	0	0	0	0	0	0	0	0	0	0	0
0	135000	135000	135000	135000	0	0	0	0	0	0	0
72000	72000	72000	0	0	0	0	0	0	0	0	0
0	0	0	0	0	84285.7	84285.7	84285.7	84285.7	84285.7	84285.7	84285.7
0	0	0	70000	70000	70000	70000	70000	70000	70000	70000	70000
0	0	0	0	0	0	0	0	0	0	0	0
72000	207000	207000	205000	205000	154286	154286	154286	154286	154286	154286	154286
816000	1023000	1230000	1435000	1640000	1794286	1948571	2102857	2257143	2411429	2565714	2720000

d)

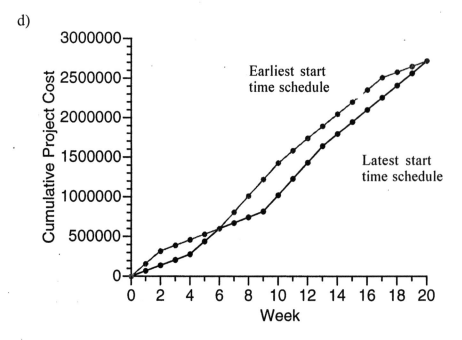

	Budgeted Cost	Percent Completed	Value Completed	Actual Cost To Date	Cost Overrun To Date
A	$420,000	50%	$210,000	$200,000	-$10,000
B	$180,000	100%	$180,000	$200,000	$20,000
D	$360,000	50%	$180,000	$210,000	$30,000
Total	$960,000		$570,000	$610,000	$40,000

The project manager should focus attention on activity D since it is not yet finished and is running over budget.

7.25 a)

Activity	Estimated Duration (weeks)	Estimated Cost	Start Time	Cost Per Week of Its Duration	Week 1	Week 2	Week 3	Week 4	Week 5	Week 6	Week 7	Week 8
A	6	$180,000	0	$30,000	30000	30000	30000	30000	30000	30000	0	0
B	3	$75,000	0	$25,000	25000	25000	25000	0	0	0	0	0
C	4	$120,000	0	$30,000	30000	30000	30000	30000	0	0	0	0
D	4	$140,000	6	$35,000	0	0	0	0	0	0	35000	35000
E	7	$175,000	3	$25,000	0	0	0	25000	25000	25000	25000	25000
F	4	$80,000	4	$20,000	0	0	0	0	20000	20000	20000	20000
G	6	$210,000	4	$35,000	0	0	0	0	35000	35000	35000	35000
H	3	$45,000	10	$15,000	0	0	0	0	0	0	0	0
I	5	$125,000	6	$25,000	0	0	0	0	0	0	25000	25000
J	4	$100,000	10	$25,000	0	0	0	0	0	0	0	0
K	3	$60,000	8	$20,000	0	0	0	0	0	0	0	0
L	5	$50,000	10	$10,000	0	0	0	0	0	0	0	0
M	6	$90,000	14	$15,000	0	0	0	0	0	0	0	0
N	5	$150,000	15	$30,000	0	0	0	0	0	0	0	0
					0	0	0	0	0	0	0	0

	Week 1	Week 2	Week 3	Week 4	Week 5	Week 6	Week 7	Week 8
Weekly Project Cost	85000	85000	85000	85000	110000	110000	140000	140000
Cumulative Project Cost	85000	170000	255000	340000	450000	560000	700000	840000

Week 9	Week 10	Week 11	Week 12	Week 13	Week 14	Week 15	Week 16	Week 17	Week 18	Week 19	Week 20
0	0	0	0	0	0	0	0	0	0	0	0
0	0	0	0	0	0	0	0	0	0	0	0
0	0	0	0	0	0	0	0	0	0	0	0
35000	35000	0	0	0	0	0	0	0	0	0	0
25000	25000	0	0	0	0	0	0	0	0	0	0
0	0	0	0	0	0	0	0	0	0	0	0
35000	35000	0	0	0	0	0	0	0	0	0	0
0	0	15000	15000	15000	0	0	0	0	0	0	0
25000	25000	25000	0	0	0	0	0	0	0	0	0
0	0	25000	25000	25000	25000	0	0	0	0	0	0
20000	20000	20000	0	0	0	0	0	0	0	0	0
0	0	10000	10000	10000	10000	10000	0	0	0	0	0
0	0	0	0	0	0	15000	15000	15000	15000	15000	15000
0	0	0	0	0	0	0	30000	30000	30000	30000	30000
0	0	0	0	0	0	0	0	0	0	0	0

140000	140000	95000	50000	50000	35000	25000	45000	45000	45000	45000	45000
980000	1120000	1215000	1265000	1315000	1350000	1375000	1420000	1465000	1510000	1555000	1600000

b)

Activity	Estimated Duration (weeks)	Estimated Cost	Start Time	Cost Per Week of Its Duration	Week 1	Week 2	Week 3	Week 4	Week 5	Week 6	Week 7	Week 8	Week 9	Week 10	Week 11	Week 12	Week 13	Week 14	Week 15	Week 16	Week 17	Week 18	Week 19	Week 20
A	6	$180,000	1	$30,000	0	30000	30000	30000	30000	30000	30000	0	0	0	0	0	0	0	0	0	0	0	0	0
B	3	$75,000	0	$25,000	25000	25000	25000	0	0	0	0	0	0	0	0	0	0	0	0	0	0	0	0	0
C	4	$120,000	0	$30,000	30000	30000	30000	30000	0	0	0	0	0	0	0	0	0	0	0	0	0	0	0	0
D	4	$140,000	7	$35,000	0	0	0	0	0	0	0	35000	35000	35000	35000	0	0	0	0	0	0	0	0	0
E	7	$175,000	3	$25,000	0	0	0	25000	25000	25000	25000	25000	25000	25000	0	0	0	0	0	0	0	0	0	0
F	4	$80,000	8	$20,000	0	0	0	0	0	0	0	0	20000	20000	20000	20000	0	0	0	0	0	0	0	0
G	6	$210,000	4	$35,000	0	0	0	0	35000	35000	35000	35000	35000	35000	0	0	0	0	0	0	0	0	0	0
H	3	$45,000	11	$15,000	0	0	0	0	0	0	0	0	0	0	0	15000	15000	15000	0	0	0	0	0	0
I	5	$125,000	9	$25,000	0	0	0	0	0	0	0	0	0	25000	25000	25000	25000	25000	0	0	0	0	0	0
J	4	$100,000	10	$25,000	0	0	0	0	0	0	0	0	0	0	25000	25000	25000	25000	0	0	0	0	0	0
K	3	$60,000	12	$20,000	0	0	0	0	0	0	0	0	0	0	0	0	20000	20000	20000	0	0	0	0	0
L	5	$50,000	10	$10,000	0	0	0	0	0	0	0	0	0	0	10000	10000	10000	10000	10000	0	0	0	0	0
M	6	$90,000	14	$15,000	0	0	0	0	0	0	0	0	0	0	0	0	0	0	15000	15000	15000	15000	15000	15000
N	5	$150,000	15	$30,000	0	0	0	0	0	0	0	0	0	0	0	0	0	0	0	30000	30000	30000	30000	30000
Weekly Project Cost					55000	85000	85000	85000	90000	90000	90000	95000	115000	140000	115000	95000	95000	95000	45000	45000	45000	45000	45000	45000
Cumulative Project Cost					55000	140000	225000	310000	400000	490000	580000	675000	790000	930000	1045000	1140000	1235000	1330000	1375000	1420000	1465000	1510000	1555000	1600000

c)

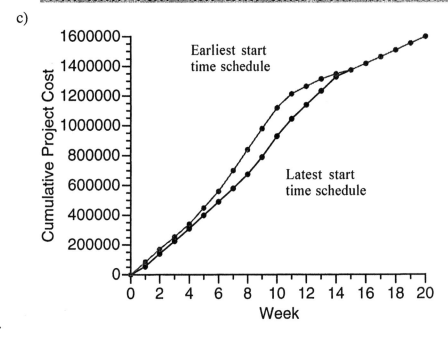

d)

Activity	Budgeted Cost	Percent Completed	Value Completed	Actual Cost To Date	Cost Overrun To Date
A	$180,000	100%	$180,000	$190,000	$10,000
B	$75,000	100%	$75,000	$70,000	-$5,000
C	$120,000	100%	$120,000	$150,000	$30,000
D	$140,000	40%	$56,000	$70,000	$14,000
E	$175,000	50%	$87,500	$100,000	$12,500
F	$80,000	60%	$48,000	$45,000	-$3,000
G	$210,000	25%	$52,500	$50,000	-$2,500
I	$125,000	20%	$25,000	$35,000	$10,000
Total	$1,105,000		$644,000	$710,000	$66,000

The project manager should investigate activities D, E and I since they are not yet finished and running over budget.

Cases

7.1 a) A diagram of the project network appears below.

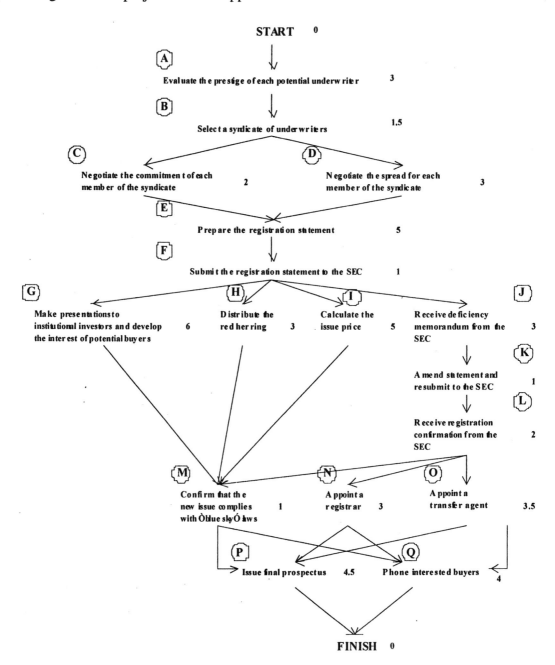

The estimated project duration equals the length of the longest path through the project network. To calculate the length of the longest path, we use the layout of the worksheet titled "Reliable" in the "Ch. 7 – Project Management" workbook. We need to modify the spreadsheet to reflect the precedents unique to this case. The formulas in the new spreadsheet appear below.

	A	B	C	D	E	F	G	H	I	J
3		Activity	Description	Time	ES	EF	LS	LF	Slack	Critical?
4		A	Evaluate prestige	3	0	=E4+D4	=H4-D4	=G5	=H4-F4	=IF(I4=0,"Yes","No")
5		B	Select syndicate	1.5	=MAX(F4)	=E5+D5	=H5-D5	=MIN(G6,G7)	=H5-F5	=IF(I5=0,"Yes","No")
6		C	Negotiate commitment	2	=MAX(F5)	=E6+D6	=H6-D6	=G8	=H6-F6	=IF(I6=0,"Yes","No")
7		D	Negotiate spread	3	=MAX(F5)	=E7+D7	=H7-D7	=G8	=H7-F7	=IF(I7=0,"Yes","No")
8		E	Prepare registration	5	=MAX(F6,F7)	=E8+D8	=H8-D8	=G9	=H8-F8	=IF(I8=0,"Yes","No")
9		F	Submit registration	1	=MAX(F8)	=E9+D9	=H9-D9	=MIN(G10,G11,G12,G13)	=H9-F9	=IF(I9=0,"Yes","No")
10		G	Present	6	=MAX(F9)	=E10+D10	=H10-D10	=G16	=H10-F10	=IF(I10=0,"Yes","No")
11		H	Distribute red herring	3	=MAX(F9)	=E11+D11	=H11-D11	=G16	=H11-F11	=IF(I11=0,"Yes","No")
12		I	Calculate price	5	=MAX(F9)	=E12+D12	=H12-D12	=G16	=H12-F12	=IF(I12=0,"Yes","No")
13		J	Receive deficiency	3	=MAX(F9)	=E13+D13	=H13-D13	=G14	=H13-F13	=IF(I13=0,"Yes","No")
14		K	Amend statement	1	=MAX(F13)	=E14+D14	=H14-D14	=G15	=H14-F14	=IF(I14=0,"Yes","No")
15		L	Receive registration	2	=MAX(F14)	=E15+D15	=H15-D15	=MIN(G18,G17,G16)	=H15-F15	=IF(I15=0,"Yes","No")
16		M	Confirm blue sky	1	=MAX(F10,F11,F12,F15)	=E16+D16	=H16-D16	=MIN(G19,G20)	=H16-F16	=IF(I16=0,"Yes","No")
17		N	Appoint registrar	3	=MAX(F15)	=E17+D17	=H17-D17	=MIN(G19,G20)	=H17-F17	=IF(I17=0,"Yes","No")
18		O	Appoint transfer	3.5	=MAX(F15)	=E18+D18	=H18-D18	=MIN(G19,G20)	=H18-F18	=IF(I18=0,"Yes","No")
19		P	Issue prospectus	4.5	=MAX(F16,F17,F18)	=E19+D19	=H19-D19	=F22	=H19-F19	=IF(I19=0,"Yes","No")
20		Q	Phone buyers	4	=MAX(F16,F17,F18)	=E20+D20	=H20-D20	=F22	=H20-F20	=IF(I20=0,"Yes","No")
21										
22						Project Duration	=MAX(F19,F20)			

The values in the new spreadsheet appear below.

	A	B	C	D	E	F	G	H	I	J
3		Activity	Description	Time	ES	EF	LS	LF	Slack	Critical?
4		A	Evaluate prestige	3	0	3	0	3	0	Yes
5		B	Select syndicate	1.5	3	4.5	3	4.5	0	Yes
6		C	Negotiate commitment	2	4.5	6.5	5.5	7.5	1	No
7		D	Negotiate spread	3	4.5	7.5	4.5	7.5	0	Yes
8		E	Prepare registration	5	7.5	12.5	7.5	12.5	0	Yes
9		F	Submit registration	1	12.5	13.5	12.5	13.5	0	Yes
10		G	Present	6	13.5	19.5	16	22	2.5	No
11		H	Distribute red herring	3	13.5	16.5	19	22	5.5	No
12		I	Calculate price	5	13.5	18.5	17	22	3.5	No
13		J	Receive deficiency	3	13.5	16.5	13.5	16.5	0	Yes
14		K	Amend statement	1	16.5	17.5	16.5	17.5	0	Yes
15		L	Receive registration	2	17.5	19.5	17.5	19.5	0	Yes
16		M	Confirm blue sky	1	19.5	20.5	22	23	2.5	No
17		N	Appoint registrar	3	19.5	22.5	20	23	0.5	No
18		O	Appoint transfer	3.5	19.5	23	19.5	23	0	Yes
19		P	Issue prospectus	4.5	23	27.5	23	27.5	0	Yes
20		Q	Phone buyers	4	23	27	23.5	27.5	0.5	No
21										
22					Project Duration	= 27.5				

The initial public offering process is 27.5 weeks long. The critical path is:
START → A → B → D → E → F → J → K → L → O → P → FINISH

b) We explore each change independently.

i) Negotiating the commitment (step C) is performed parallel to negotiating the spread (step D). In part (a) above, negotiating the spread is on the critical path since it takes three days to complete while negotiating the commitment takes only two days to complete. We now increase the time to negotiate the commitment from two days to three days, and negotiating the commitment now takes as much time as negotiating the spread. Thus, there are now two critical paths through the network:

$$START \rightarrow A \rightarrow B \rightarrow C \rightarrow E \rightarrow F \rightarrow J \rightarrow K \rightarrow L \rightarrow O \rightarrow P \rightarrow FINISH$$
$$START \rightarrow A \rightarrow B \rightarrow D \rightarrow E \rightarrow F \rightarrow J \rightarrow K \rightarrow L \rightarrow O \rightarrow P \rightarrow FINISH$$

The project duration is still 27.5 weeks.

ii) In part (a) above, calculating the issue price is not on the critical path. Thus, decreasing the time to calculate the price does not change the solution found in part (a). The critical path remains the same, and the project duration is still 27.5 weeks.

iii) In part (a) above, the step to amend the statement and resubmit it to the SEC (step K) is on the critical path. Therefore, increasing the time for the step increases the project duration. The project duration increases to 29 weeks, and the critical path remains the same.

iv) In part (a) above, the step to confirm that the new issue complies with "blue sky" laws (step M) occurs in parallel to appointing a registrar (step N) and to appointing a transfer agent (step O). Step M is not on the critical path since it only takes one week while step O takes 3.5 weeks. When we increase the time to complete step M from one week to four weeks, we change the critical path since step M now takes longer than step O. We also change the project duration. The project duration is now 28 weeks. Two new critical paths appear:

$$START \rightarrow A \rightarrow B \rightarrow D \rightarrow E \rightarrow F \rightarrow G \rightarrow M \rightarrow P \rightarrow FINISH$$
$$START \rightarrow A \rightarrow B \rightarrow D \rightarrow E \rightarrow F \rightarrow J \rightarrow K \rightarrow L \rightarrow M \rightarrow P \rightarrow FINISH$$

c) We formulate a linear programming problem to make the crashing decisions. We use a worksheet similar to the worksheet titled "Reliable's Time Cost" in the "Ch. 7 – Project Management" workbook. The formulas we use for the worksheet appear below.

	A	B	C	D	E	F	G	H	I	J	K
3							Maximum	Crash Cost			
4			Time		Cost		Time	per Week	Start	Time	Finish
5		Activity	Normal	Crash	Normal	Crash	Reduction	saved	Time	Reduction	Time
6		A	3	1.5	8000	14000	=C6-D6	=(F6-E6)/G6	0	1.5	=I6+C6-J6
7		B	1.5	0.5	4500	8000	=C7-D7	=(F7-E7)/G7	1.5	1	=I7+C7-J7
8		C	2	2	9000	0	=C8-D8	0	2	0	=I8+C8-J8
9		D	3	3	12000	0	=C9-D9	0	2	0	=I9+C9-J9
10		E	5	4	50000	95000	=C10-D10	=(F10-E10)/G10	5	0	=I10+C10-J10
11		F	1	1	1000	0	=C11-D11	0	10	0	=I11+C11-J11
12		G	6	4	25000	60000	=C12-D12	=(F12-E12)/G12	11	0	=I12+C12-J12
13		H	3	2	15000	22000	=C13-D13	=(F13-E13)/G13	14	0	=I13+C13-J13
14		I	5	3.5	12000	31000	=C14-D14	=(F14-E14)/G14	11	0	=I14+C14-J14
15		J	3	3	0	0	=C15-D15	0	11	0	=I15+C15-J15
16		K	1	0.5	6000	9000	=C16-D16	=(F16-E16)/G16	14	0.5	=I16+C16-J16
17		L	2	2	0	0	=C17-D17	0	14.5	0	=I17+C17-J17
18		M	1	0.5	5000	8300	=C18-D18	=(F18-E18)/G18	17	0	=I18+C18-J18
19		N	3	1.5	12000	19000	=C19-D19	=(F19-E19)/G19	16.5	1.5	=I19+C19-J19
20		O	3.5	1.5	13000	21000	=C20-D20	=(F20-E20)/G20	16.5	2	=I20+C20-J20
21		P	4.5	2	40000	99000	=C21-D21	=(F21-E21)/G21	18	0.5	=I21+C21-J21
22		Q	4	1.5	9000	20000	=C22-D22	=(F22-E22)/G22	18	0	=I22+C22-J22
23											
24									Desired Finish	22	
25									Finish Time =	22	
26									Total Cost =	=SUM(E6:E22)+SUMPRODUCT(H6:H22,J6:J22)	

The values used in the spreadsheet appear below.

	A	B	C	D	E	F	G	H	I	J	K
3							Maximum	Crash Cost			
4			Time		Cost		Time	per Week	Start	Time	Finish
5		Activity	Normal	Crash	Normal	Crash	Reduction	saved	Time	Reduction	Time
6		A	3	1.5	$8000	$14000	1.5	$4000	0.0	1.5	1.5
7		B	1.5	0.5	$4500	$8000	1	$3500	1.5	1	2
8		C	2	2	$9000	$0	0	$0	2.0	0	4
9		D	3	3	$12000	$0	0	$0	2.0	0	5
10		E	5	4	$50000	$95000	1	$45000	5.0	0	10
11		F	1	1	$1000	$0	0	$0	10.0	0	11
12		G	6	4	$25000	$60000	2	$17500	11.0	0	17
13		H	3	2	$15000	$22000	1	$7000	14.0	0	17
14		I	5	3.5	$12000	$31000	1.5	$12667	11.0	0	16
15		J	3	3	$0	$0	0	$0	11.0	0	14
16		K	1	0.5	$6000	$9000	0.5	$6000	14.0	0.5	14.5
17		L	2	2	$0	$0	0	$0	14.5	0	16.5
18		M	1	0.5	$5000	$8300	0.5	$6600	17.0	0	18
19		N	3	1.5	$12000	$19000	1.5	$4667	16.5	1.5	18
20		O	3.5	1.5	$13000	$21000	2	$4000	16.5	2.0	18
21		P	4.5	2	$40000	$99000	2.5	$23600	18.0	0.5	22
22		Q	4	1.5	$9000	$20000	2.5	$4400	18.0	0	22
23											
24									Desired Finish	22	
25									Finish Time =	22	
26									Total Cost =	$260800	

The Solver settings for the linear programming appear below.

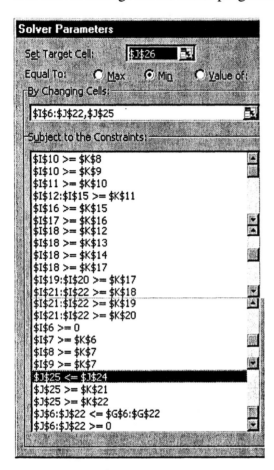

Solver Parameters

Set Target Cell: $J$26

Equal To: ○ Max ◉ Min ○ Value of:

By Changing Cells:

$I$6:$J$22,$J$25

Subject to the Constraints:

```
$I$10 >= $K$8
$I$10 >= $K$9
$I$11 >= $K$10
$I$12:$I$15 >= $K$11
$I$16 >= $K$15
$I$17 >= $K$16
$I$18 >= $K$12
$I$18 >= $K$13
$I$18 >= $K$14
$I$18 >= $K$17
$I$19:$I$20 >= $K$17
$I$21:$I$22 >= $K$18
$I$21:$I$22 >= $K$19
$I$21:$I$22 >= $K$20
$I$6 >= 0
$I$7 >= $K$6
$I$8 >= $K$7
$I$9 >= $K$7
$J$25 <= $J$24
$J$25 >= $K$21
$J$25 >= $K$22
$J$6:$J$22 <= $G$6:$G$22
$J$6:$J$22 >= 0
```

Janet and Gilbert should reduce the time for step A (evaluating the prestige of each potential underwriter) by 1.5 weeks, the time for step B (selecting a syndicate of underwriters) by one week, the time for step K (amending statement and resubmitting it to the SEC) by 0.5 weeks, the time for step N (appointing a registrar) by 1.5 weeks, the time for step O (appointing a transfer agent) by two weeks, and the time for step P (issuing final prospectus) by 0.5 weeks. Janet and Gilbert can now meet the new deadline of 22 weeks at a total cost of $260,800.

d) We use the same model formulation that was used in part (c). We change one constraint, however. The project duration now has to be greater than or equal to 24 weeks instead of 22 weeks. We obtain the following solution in Excel.

	A	B	C	D	E	F	G	H	I	J	K
							Maximum	Crash Cost			
3							Time	per Week	Start	Time	Finish
4			Time		Cost		Reduction	saved	Time	Reduction	Time
5		Activity	Normal	Crash	Normal	Crash					
6		A	3	1.5	$8000	$14000	1.5	$4000	0.0	1.5	1.5
7		B	1.5	0.5	$4500	$8000	1	$3500	1.5	1	2
8		C	2	2	$9000	$0	0	$0	2.0	0	4
9		D	3	3	$12000	$0	0	$0	2.0	0	5
10		E	5	4	$50000	$95000	1	$45000	5.0	0	10
11		F	1	1	$1000	$0	0	$0	10.0	0	11
12		G	6	4	$25000	$60000	2	$17500	12.5	0	18.5
13		H	3	2	$15000	$22000	1	$7000	15.5	0	18.5
14		I	5	3.5	$12000	$31000	1.5	$12667	11.0	0	16
15		J	3	3	$0	$0	0	$0	11.0	0	14
16		K	1	0.5	$6000	$9000	0.5	$6000	14.0	0.5	14.5
17		L	2	2	$0	$0	0	$0	14.5	0	16.5
18		M	1	0.5	$5000	$8300	0.5	$6600	18.5	0	19.5
19		N	3	1.5	$12000	$19000	1.5	$4667	16.5	0	19.5
20		O	3.5	1.5	$13000	$21000	2	$4000	16.5	0.5	19.5
21		P	4.5	2	$40000	$99000	2.5	$23600	19.5	0	24
22		Q	4	1.5	$9000	$20000	2.5	$4400	19.5	0	23.5
23											
24									Desired Finish	24	
25									Finish Time =	24	
26									Total Cost =	$236000	

Janet and Gilbert should reduce the time for step A (evaluating the prestige of each potential underwriter) by 1.5 weeks, the time for step B (selecting a syndicate of underwriters) by one week, the time for step K (amending statement and resubmitting it to the SEC) by 0.5 weeks, and the time for step O (appointing a transfer agent) by 0.5 weeks. Janet and Gilbert can now meet the new deadline of 24 weeks at a total cost of $236,000.

7.2 a) The project network appears below.

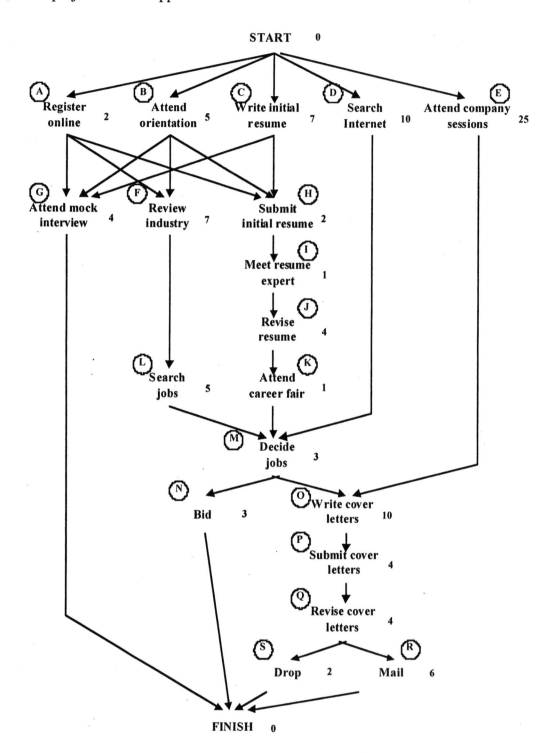

The estimated project duration equals the length of the longest path through the project network. To calculate the length of the longest path, we use the layout of the worksheet titled "Reliable" in the "Ch. 7 – Project Management" workbook. We need to modify the spreadsheet to reflect the network unique to this case. The formulas in the new spreadsheet appear below.

	A	B	C	D	E	F	G	H	I	J
3		Activity	Description	Time	ES	EF	LS	LF	Slack	Critical?
4		A	Register online	2	0	=E4+D4	=H4-D4	=MIN(G9,G10,G11)	=H4-F4	=F(I4=0,"Yes","No")
5		B	Attend orientation	5	0	=E5+D5	=H5-D5	=MIN(G9,G10,G11)	=H5-F5	=F(I5=0,"Yes","No")
6		C	Write initial resume	7	0	=E6+D6	=H6-D6	=MIN(G11,G10)	=H6-F6	=F(I6=0,"Yes","No")
7		D	Search Internet	10	0	=E7+D7	=H7-D7	=G16	=H7-F7	=F(I7=0,"Yes","No")
8		E	Attend company sessions	25	0	=E8+D8	=H8-D8	=G18	=H8-F8	=F(I8=0,"Yes","No")
9		F	Review industry, etc.	7	=MAX(F4,F5)	=E9+D9	=H9-D9	=G15	=H9-F9	=F(I9=0,"Yes","No")
10		G	Attend mock interview	4	=MAX(F4,F5,F6)	=E10+D10	=H10-D10	=F25	=H10-F10	=F(I10=0,"Yes","No")
11		H	Submit initial resume	2	=MAX(F4,F5,F6)	=E11+D11	=H11-D11	=G12	=H11-F11	=F(I11=0,"Yes","No")
12		I	Meet resume expert	1	=F11	=E12+D12	=H12-D12	=G13	=H12-F12	=F(I12=0,"Yes","No")
13		J	Revise resume	4	=F12	=E13+D13	=H13-D13	=G14	=H13-F13	=F(I13=0,"Yes","No")
14		K	Attend career fair	1	=F13	=E14+D14	=H14-D14	=G16	=H14-F14	=F(I14=0,"Yes","No")
15		L	Search jobs	5	=F9	=E15+D15	=H15-D15	=G16	=H15-F15	=F(I15=0,"Yes","No")
16		M	Decide jobs	3	=MAX(F15,F14,F7)	=E16+D16	=H16-D16	=MIN(G17,G18)	=H16-F16	=F(I16=0,"Yes","No")
17		N	Bid	3	=F16	=E17+D17	=H17-D17	=F25	=H17-F17	=F(I17=0,"Yes","No")
18		O	Write cover letters	10	=MAX(F16,F8)	=E18+D18	=H18-D18	=G19	=H18-F18	=F(I18=0,"Yes","No")
19		P	Submit cover letters	4	=F18	=E19+D19	=H19-D19	=G20	=H19-F19	=F(I19=0,"Yes","No")
20		Q	Revise cover letters	4	=F19	=E20+D20	=H20-D20	=MIN(G21,G22)	=H20-F20	=F(I20=0,"Yes","No")
21		R	Mail	6	=F20	=E21+D21	=H21-D21	=F25	=H21-F21	=F(I21=0,"Yes","No")
22		S	Drop	2	=F20	=E22+D22	=H22-D22	=F25	=H22-F22	=F(I22=0,"Yes","No")
23										
24										
25					Project Duration =	=MAX(F22,F21,F17,F10)				

The values in the new spreadsheet appear below.

	A	B	C	D	E	F	G	H	I	J
3		Activity	Description	Time	ES	EF	LS	LF	Slack	Critical?
4		A	Register online	2	0	2	8	10	8	No
5		B	Attend orientation	5	0	5	5	10	5	No
6		C	Write initial resume	7	0	7	7	14	7	No
7		D	Search Internet	10	0	10	12	22	12	No
8		E	Attend company sessions	25	0	25	0	25	0	Yes
9		F	Review industry, etc.	7	5	12	10	17	5	No
10		G	Attend mock interview	4	7	11	45	49	38	No
11		H	Submit initial resume	2	7	9	14	16	7	No
12		I	Meet resume expert	1	9	10	16	17	7	No
13		J	Revise resume	4	10	14	17	21	7	No
14		K	Attend career fair	1	14	15	21	22	7	No
15		L	Search jobs	5	12	17	17	22	5	No
16		M	Decide jobs	3	17	20	22	25	5	No
17		N	Bid	3	20	23	46	49	26	No
18		O	Write cover letters	10	25	35	25	35	0	Yes
19		P	Submit cover letters	4	35	39	35	39	0	Yes
20		Q	Revise cover letters	4	39	43	39	43	0	Yes
21		R	Mail	6	43	49	43	49	0	Yes
22		S	Drop	2	43	45	47	49	4	No
23										
24										
25				Project Duration = 49						

Brent can start the interviews in 49 days. The critical steps in the process are:

$$\text{START} \rightarrow E \rightarrow O \rightarrow P \rightarrow Q \rightarrow R \rightarrow \text{FINISH}$$

b) We substitute first the pessimistic and then the optimistic estimates for the time values used in the part (a) spreadsheet.

The spreadsheet estimating the longest path for the pessimistic values appears below.

	A	B	C	D	E	F	G	H	I	J
3		Activity	Description	Time	ES	EF	LS	LF	Slack	Critical?
4		A	Register online	4	0	4	6	10	6	No
5		B	Attend orientation	10	0	10	0	10	0	Yes
6		C	Write initial resume	14	0	14	4	18	4	No
7		D	Search Internet	12	0	12	20	32	20	No
8		E	Attend company sessions	30	0	30	6	36	6	No
9		F	Review industry, etc.	12	10	22	10	22	0	Yes
10		G	Attend mock interview	8	14	22	66	74	52	No
11		H	Submit initial resume	6	14	20	18	24	4	No
12		I	Meet resume expert	1	20	21	24	25	4	No
13		J	Revise resume	6	21	27	25	31	4	No
14		K	Attend career fair	1	27	28	31	32	4	No
15		L	Search jobs	10	22	32	22	32	0	Yes
16		M	Decide jobs	4	32	36	32	36	0	Yes
17		N	Bid	8	36	44	66	74	30	No
18		O	Write cover letters	12	36	48	36	48	0	Yes
19		P	Submit cover letters	7	48	55	48	55	0	Yes
20		Q	Revise cover letters	9	55	64	55	64	0	Yes
21		R	Mail	10	64	74	64	74	0	Yes
22		S	Drop	3	64	67	71	74	7	No
23										
24										
25					Project Duration =74					

Under the worst-case scenario, Brent will require 74 days before he is ready to begin interviewing. The critical path changes to:

START → B → F → L → M → O → P → Q → R → FINISH

The spreadsheet estimating the longest path for the optimistic values appears below.

	A	B	C	D	E	F	G	H	I	J
3		Activity	Description	Time	ES	EF	LS	LF	Slack	Critical?
4		A	Register online	1	0	1	9	10	9	No
5		B	Attend orientation	3	0	3	7	10	7	No
6		C	Write initial resume	5	0	5	7	12	7	No
7		D	Search Internet	7	0	7	11	18	11	No
8		E	Attend company sessions	20	0	20	0	20	0	Yes
9		F	Review industry, etc.	5	3	8	10	15	7	No
10		G	Attend mock interview	3	5	8	29	32	24	No
11		H	Submit initial resume	1	5	6	12	13	7	No
12		I	Meet resume expert	1	6	7	13	14	7	No
13		J	Revise resume	3	7	10	14	17	7	No
14		K	Attend career fair	1	10	11	17	18	7	No
15		L	Search jobs	3	8	11	15	18	7	No
16		M	Decide jobs	2	11	13	18	20	7	No
17		N	Bid	2	13	15	30	32	17	No
18		O	Write cover letters	3	20	23	20	23	0	Yes
19		P	Submit cover letters	2	23	25	23	25	0	Yes
20		Q	Revise cover letters	3	25	28	25	28	0	Yes
21		R	Mail	4	28	32	28	32	0	Yes
22		S	Drop	1	28	29	31	32	3	No
23										
24										
25					Project Duration = 32					

Under the best-case scenario, Brent will require 32 days before he is ready to begin interviewing. The critical path remains the same as that in part (a).

c) The mean critical is the path through the project network that would be the critical path if the duration of each activity equals its mean. We therefore first need to determine the mean duration of each activity given the optimistic, most likely, and pessimistic length estimates. To calculate the mean duration of each activity, we use the PERT template in the "Ch. 7 – Project Management" workbook.

The formulas for the calculation of the mean duration of each activity appear below.

	A	B	C	D	E	F	G
3			Time Estimates				
4		Activity	o	m	p	μ	σ^2
5		A	1	2	4	=IF(C5="","",(C5+4*D5+E5)/6)	=IF(C5="","",((E5-C5)/6)^2)
6		B	3	5	10	=IF(C6="","",(C6+4*D6+E6)/6)	=IF(C6="","",((E6-C6)/6)^2)
7		C	5	7	14	=IF(C7="","",(C7+4*D7+E7)/6)	=IF(C7="","",((E7-C7)/6)^2)
8		D	7	10	12	=IF(C8="","",(C8+4*D8+E8)/6)	=IF(C8="","",((E8-C8)/6)^2)
9		E	20	25	30	=IF(C9="","",(C9+4*D9+E9)/6)	=IF(C9="","",((E9-C9)/6)^2)
10		F	5	7	12	=IF(C10="","",(C10+4*D10+E10)/6)	=IF(C10="","",((E10-C10)/6)^2)
11		G	3	4	8	=IF(C11="","",(C11+4*D11+E11)/6)	=IF(C11="","",((E11-C11)/6)^2)
12		H	1	2	6	=IF(C12="","",(C12+4*D12+E12)/6)	=IF(C12="","",((E12-C12)/6)^2)
13		I	1	1	1	=IF(C13="","",(C13+4*D13+E13)/6)	=IF(C13="","",((E13-C13)/6)^2)
14		J	3	4	6	=IF(C14="","",(C14+4*D14+E14)/6)	=IF(C14="","",((E14-C14)/6)^2)
15		K	1	1	1	=IF(C15="","",(C15+4*D15+E15)/6)	=IF(C15="","",((E15-C15)/6)^2)
16		L	3	5	10	=IF(C16="","",(C16+4*D16+E16)/6)	=IF(C16="","",((E16-C16)/6)^2)
17		M	2	3	4	=IF(C17="","",(C17+4*D17+E17)/6)	=IF(C17="","",((E17-C17)/6)^2)
18		N	2	3	8	=IF(C18="","",(C18+4*D18+E18)/6)	=IF(C18="","",((E18-C18)/6)^2)
19		O	3	10	12	=IF(C19="","",(C19+4*D19+E19)/6)	=IF(C19="","",((E19-C19)/6)^2)
20		P	2	4	7	=IF(C20="","",(C20+4*D20+E20)/6)	=IF(C20="","",((E20-C20)/6)^2)
21		Q	3	4	9	=IF(C21="","",(C21+4*D21+E21)/6)	=IF(C21="","",((E21-C21)/6)^2)
22		R	4	6	10	=IF(C22="","",(C22+4*D22+E22)/6)	=IF(C22="","",((E22-C22)/6)^2)
23		S	1	2	3	=IF(C23="","",(C23+4*D23+E23)/6)	=IF(C23="","",((E23-C23)/6)^2)

The values for the mean duration of each activity appear below.

	A	B	C	D	E	F	G
3			Time Estimates				
4		Activity	o	m	p	μ	σ^2
5		A	1	2	4	2.167	0.25
6		B	3	5	10	5.5	1.361
7		C	5	7	14	7.833	2.25
8		D	7	10	12	9.833	0.694
9		E	20	25	30	25	2.778
10		F	5	7	12	7.5	1.361
11		G	3	4	8	4.5	0.694
12		H	1	2	6	2.5	0.694
13		I	1	1	1	1	0
14		J	3	4	6	4.167	0.25
15		K	1	1	1	1	0
16		L	3	5	10	5.5	1.361
17		M	2	3	4	3	0.111
18		N	2	3	8	3.667	1
19		O	3	10	12	9.167	2.25
20		P	2	4	7	4.167	0.694
21		Q	3	4	9	4.667	1
22		R	4	6	10	6.333	1
23		S	1	2	3	2	0.111

We now substitute the mean duration for each activity for the time values used in the part (a) spreadsheet. We obtain the following values:

	A	B	C	D	E	F	G	H	I	J
3		Activity	Description	Time	ES	EF	LS	LF	Slack	Critical?
4		A	Register online	2.17	0.00	2.17	6.83	9.00	6.833	No
5		B	Attend orientation	5.5	0.00	5.50	3.50	9.00	3.5	No
6		C	Write initial resume	7.83	0.00	7.83	5.50	13.33	5.5	No
7		D	Search Internet	9.83	0.00	9.83	12.17	22.00	12.17	No
8		E	Attend company sessions	25	0.00	25.00	0.00	25.00	0	Yes
9		F	Review industry, etc.	7.5	5.50	13.00	9.00	16.50	3.5	No
10		G	Attend mock interview	4.5	7.83	12.33	44.83	49.33	37	No
11		H	Submit initial resume	2.5	7.83	10.33	13.33	15.83	5.5	No
12		I	Meet resume expert	1	10.33	11.33	15.83	16.83	5.5	No
13		J	Revise resume	4.17	11.33	15.50	16.83	21.00	5.5	No
14		K	Attend career fair	1	15.50	16.50	21.00	22.00	5.5	No
15		L	Search jobs	5.5	13.00	18.50	16.50	22.00	3.5	No
16		M	Decide jobs	3	18.50	21.50	22.00	25.00	3.5	No
17		N	Bid	3.67	21.50	25.17	45.67	49.33	24.17	No
18		O	Write cover letters	9.17	25.00	34.17	25.00	34.17	0	Yes
19		P	Submit cover letters	4.17	34.17	38.33	34.17	38.33	0	Yes
20		Q	Revise cover letters	4.67	38.33	43.00	38.33	43.00	0	Yes
21		R	Mail	6.33	43.00	49.33	43.00	49.33	0	Yes
22		S	Drop	2	43.00	45.00	47.33	49.33	4.333	No
23										
24										
25					Project Duration = 49.33					

The mean critical path is the same as that in part (a).

To calculate the variance of the project duration, we again use the PERT template. The formulas for the mean and variance calculations are shown below.

	J	K
5		Mean Critical
6		Path
7	$\mu =$	=SUMIF(H5:H23,"*",F5:F23)
8	$\sigma^2 =$	=SUMIF(H5:H23,"*",G5:G23)

The mean and variance of the mean critical path are:

	J	K
5	Mean Critical	
6	Path	
7	$\mu =$	49.3333
8	$\sigma^2 =$	7.72222

d) We use the PERT template used in part (c). We substitute the value 60 for d in cell K12. The formulas to calculate the probability that Brent will be ready to interview within 60 days are shown below.

	J	K
5		Mean Critical
6		Path
7	$\mu =$	=SUMIF(H5:H23,"*",F5:F23)
8	$\sigma^2 =$	=SUMIF(H5:H23,"*",G5:G23)
9		
10	P(T=d) =	=NORMDIST(K12,K7,SQRT(K8),1)
11	where	
12	d =	60

The values obtained from the above calculations are shown below.

	J	K
5	Mean Critical	
6	Path	
7	$\mu =$	49.3333
8	$\sigma^2 =$	7.72222
9		
10	P(T=d) =	0.99994
11	where	
12	d =	60

Brent will be ready for his interviews within 60 days with 99.994 percent probability. Good for him!

e) Now the earliest start time for the career fair is day 24, and the career fair itself still lasts one day. To ensure that the earliest start time for the career fair is day 24, we add a dummy node T to the project network that has a duration of 24 days, directly follows the START node, and directly precedes the career fair node K. The updated project network appears below.

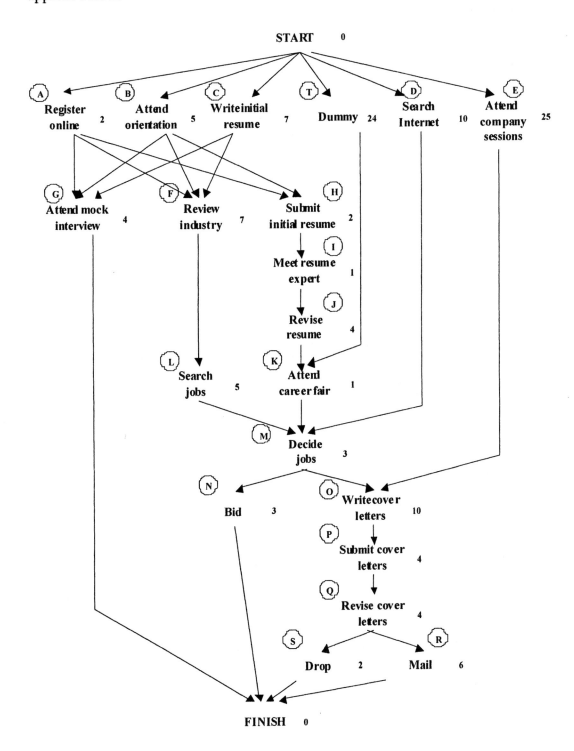

f) To obtain the mean critical path for the new network and the probability that Brent will complete his project within 60 days, we first use the PERT template to calculate the mean duration for each activity. We add the new node T to the list of activities, and the values of the mean duration for each activity appear below.

	A	B	C	D	E	F	G
3		Time Estimates					
4		Activity	o	m	p	μ	σ^2
5		A	1	2	4	2.17	0.25
6		B	3	5	10	5.50	1.3611111
7		C	5	7	14	7.83	2.25
8		D	7	10	12	9.83	0.6944444
9		E	20	25	30	25.00	2.7777777
10		T	24	24	24	24.00	0
11		F	5	7	12	7.50	1.3611111
12		G	3	4	8	4.50	0.6944444
13		H	1	2	6	2.50	0.6944444
14		I	1	1	1	1.00	0
15		J	3	4	6	4.17	0.25
16		K	1	1	1	1.00	0
17		L	3	5	10	5.50	1.3611111
18		M	2	3	4	3.00	0.1111111
19		N	2	3	8	3.67	1
20		O	3	10	12	9.17	2.25
21		P	2	4	7	4.17	0.6944444
22		Q	3	4	9	4.67	1
23		R	4	6	10	6.33	1
24		S	1	2	3	2.00	0.1111111

We next substitute these mean duration values for the time values used to calculate the critical path. We need to alter our spreadsheet used to calculate the critical path in part (a) to reflect the addition of the new node T. The formulas used in the new critical path spreadsheet appear below.

	A	B	C	D	E	F	G	H	I	J
3		Activity	Description	Time	ES	EF	LS	LF	Slack	Critical?
4		A	Register online	2.166	0	=E4+D4	=H4-D4	=MIN(G10,G11,G12)	=H4-F4	=IF(I4=0,"Yes","No")
5		B	Attend orientation	5.5	0	=E5+D5	=H5-D5	=MIN(G10,G11,G12)	=H5-F5	=IF(I5=0,"Yes","No")
6		C	Write initial resume	7.833	0	=E6+D6	=H6-D6	=MIN(G12,G11)	=H6-F6	=IF(I6=0,"Yes","No")
7		D	Search Internet	9.833	0	=E7+D7	=H7-D7	=G17	=H7-F7	=IF(I7=0,"Yes","No")
8		E	Attend company sessions	25	0	=E8+D8	=H8-D8	=G19	=H8-F8	=IF(I8=0,"Yes","No")
9		T	Dummy for career fair	24	0	=E9+D9	=H9-D9	=G15	=H9-F9	=IF(I9=0,"Yes","No")
10		F	Review industry, etc.	7.5	=MAX(F4,F5)	=E10+D10	=H10-D10	=G16	=H10-F10	=IF(I10=0,"Yes","No")
11		G	Attend mock interview	4.5	=MAX(F4,F5,F6)	=E11+D11	=H11-D11	=F26	=H11-F11	=IF(I11=0,"Yes","No")
12		H	Submit initial resume	2.5	=MAX(F4,F5,F6)	=E12+D12	=H12-D12	=G13	=H12-F12	=IF(I12=0,"Yes","No")
13		I	Meet resume expert	1	=F12	=E13+D13	=H13-D13	=G14	=H13-F13	=IF(I13=0,"Yes","No")
14		J	Revise resume	4.166	=F13	=E14+D14	=H14-D14	=G15	=H14-F14	=IF(I14=0,"Yes","No")
15		K	Attend career fair	1	=MAX(F14,F9)	=E15+D15	=H15-D15	=G17	=H15-F15	=IF(I15=0,"Yes","No")
16		L	Search jobs	5.5	=F10	=E16+D16	=H16-D16	=G17	=H16-F16	=IF(I16=0,"Yes","No")
17		M	Decide jobs	3	=MAX(F16,F15,F7)	=E17+D17	=H17-D17	=MIN(G18,G19)	=H17-F17	=IF(I17=0,"Yes","No")
18		N	Bid	3.666	=F17	=E18+D18	=H18-D18	=F26	=H18-F18	=IF(I18=0,"Yes","No")
19		O	Write cover letters	9.166	=MAX(F17,F8)	=E19+D19	=H19-D19	=G20	=H19-F19	=IF(I19=0,"Yes","No")
20		P	Submit cover letters	4.166	=F19	=E20+D20	=H20-D20	=G21	=H20-F20	=IF(I20=0,"Yes","No")
21		Q	Revise cover letters	4.666	=F20	=E21+D21	=H21-D21	=MIN(G22,G23)	=H21-F21	=IF(I21=0,"Yes","No")
22		R	Mail	6.333	=F21	=E22+D22	=H22-D22	=F26	=H22-F22	=IF(I22=0,"Yes","No")
23		S	Drop	2	=F21	=E23+D23	=H23-D23	=F26	=H23-F23	=IF(I23=0,"Yes","No")
24										
25										
26						Project Duration =	=MAX(F23,F22,F18,F11)			

The values used in the calculation of the new critical path appear below.

	A	B	C	D	E	F	G	H	I	J
3		Activity	Description	Time	ES	EF	LS	LF	Slack	Critical?
4		A	Register online	2.17	0.00	2.17	9.83	12.00	9.833	No
5		B	Attend orientation	5.50	0.00	5.50	6.50	12.00	6.5	No
6		C	Write initial resume	7.83	0.00	7.83	8.50	16.33	8.5	No
7		D	Search Internet	9.83	0.00	9.83	15.17	25.00	15.17	No
8		E	Attend company sessions	25.00	0.00	25.00	3.00	28.00	3	No
9		T	Dummy for career fair	24.00	0.00	24.00	0.00	24.00	0	Yes
10		F	Review industry, etc.	7.50	5.50	13.00	12.00	19.50	6.5	No
11		G	Attend mock interview	4.50	7.83	12.33	47.83	52.33	40	No
12		H	Submit initial resume	2.50	7.83	10.33	16.33	18.83	8.5	No
13		I	Meet resume expert	1.00	10.33	11.33	18.83	19.83	8.5	No
14		J	Revise resume	4.17	11.33	15.50	19.83	24.00	8.5	No
15		K	Attend career fair	1.00	24.00	25.00	24.00	25.00	0	Yes
16		L	Search jobs	5.50	13.00	18.50	19.50	25.00	6.5	No
17		M	Decide jobs	3.00	25.00	28.00	25.00	28.00	0	Yes
18		N	Bid	3.67	28.00	31.67	48.67	52.33	20.67	No
19		O	Write cover letters	9.17	28.00	37.17	28.00	37.17	0	Yes
20		P	Submit cover letters	4.17	37.17	41.33	37.17	41.33	0	Yes
21		Q	Revise cover letters	4.67	41.33	46.00	41.33	46.00	0	Yes
22		R	Mail	6.33	46.00	52.33	46.00	52.33	0	Yes
23		S	Drop	2.00	46.00	48.00	50.33	52.33	4.333	No
24										
25										
26					Project Duration = 52.33					

The mean project duration is now 52.33 days, and the new mean critical path is START $\rightarrow$ T $\rightarrow$ K $\rightarrow$ M $\rightarrow$ O $\rightarrow$ P $\rightarrow$ Q $\rightarrow$ R $\rightarrow$ FINISH. We specify this new critical path in the PERT spreadsheet to obtain the probability that Brent will complete his project within 60 days.

	J	K
5	Mean Critical	
6	Path	
7	$\mu =$	52.3333
8	$\sigma^2 =$	5.05556
9		
10	$P(T \leq d) =$	0.99967
11	where	
12	$d =$	60

Brent will be ready for his interviews within 60 days with 99.967 percent probability. The probability that Brent will complete his project decreases slightly over the probability obtained in part (d). The probability decreases because this new network has a longer mean project duration than the network in part (d). The probability decreases only slightly, however, since the variance of the project duration for the new network is smaller than the variance in part (d).

Review Questions

8.1-1   In some applications, such as assigning people, machines, or vehicles, decision variables will make sense only if they have integer values.

8.1-2   Constraints are added to the model that restrict the values of the decision variables to integer values.

8.1-3   The divisibility assumption of linear programming is a basic assumption that allows the decision variables to have any values, including fractional values, that satisfy the functional and nonnegativity constraints.

8.1-4   The LP relaxation of an integer programming problem is the linear programming problem obtained by deleting from the current integer programming problem the constraints that require the decision variables to have integer values.

8.1-5   Rather than stopping at the last instant that the straight edge still passes through the feasible region, we now stop at the last instant that the straight edge passes through an integer point that lies within the feasible region.

8.1-6   No, rounding cannot be relied on to find an optimal solution, or even a good feasible integer solution.

8.1-7   Pure integer programming problems are those where all the decision variables must be integers. Mixed integer programming problems only require some of the variables to have integer values.

8.1-8   Binary integer programming problems are those where all the decision variables are limited to values of 0 and 1. These problems arise when dealing with yes or no decisions.

8.2-1   The contribution of each activity to the value of the objective function is proportional to the level of the activity.

8.2-2   An activity has decreasing marginal returns if the slope of its profit graph never increases but sometimes decreases as the level of the activity increases.

8.2-3   The profit graph must have a kink where the slope changes (decreases) in order to apply separable programming.

8.2-4   A linear programming model is eventually formulated.

8.3-1   The objective function is a nonlinear function.

8.3-2   A simple nonlinear programming problem that has the same constraints as a linear programming model, a nonlinear function for the objective function, and decreasing marginal returns for each activity that violates the proportionality assumption of linear programming can be readily solved by the Excel Solver.

8.3-3 Instead of having objective function lines, there are objective function curves.

8.3-4 The additivity assumption of linear programming is a basic assumption that requires that each term in the objective function only contain a single variable. It might be violated by a nonlinear programming problem because of cross-product terms involving the product of two variables.

8.3-5 In portfolio selection, a trade-off is being sought between expected return and risk.

8.4-1 The management science team has been asked to analyze what the new product mix should be for the company.

8.4-2 1. Achieve a total profit of at least $125 million.
2. Maintain the current employment level of 4,000 employees.
3. Keep capital investment below $55 million.

8.4-3 When using a goal programming approach, the total number of penalty points incurred by missing goals is to be minimized.

8.5-1 Goal programming does not possess the characteristic of a single objective function.

8.5-2 The basic approach of goal programming is to establish a specific number goal for each of the objectives and then to seek a solution that balances how close this solution comes to each of these goals.

8.5-3 The objective function represents the weighted sum of deviations of the individual objective functions from their respective goals.

8.5-4 The changing cells show the amounts over or under the respective goals.

8.5-5 A goal programming model can be reformulated into a linear programming model.

Problems

8.1 a)

Let $T =$ the number of tow bars produced

Let $S =$ the number of stabilizer bars produced

Maximize $P = 130T + 150S$,

subject to $\quad 3.2T + 2.4S \leq 16$

$\qquad 2T + 3S \leq 15$

and $\qquad T \geq 0, \ S \geq 0$

$\qquad T, \ S$ are integers.

b) Optimal solution: $(T,S) = (0,5)$, $P = \$750$.

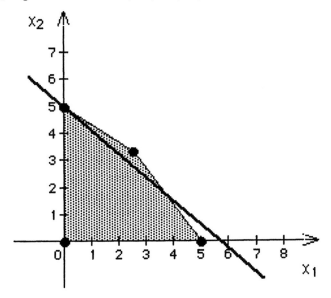

c & d)

	Resource Usage Per Unit of Each Activity				Resource
Resource	Tow Bars	Stabilizer Bars	Totals		Available
Machine 1	3.2	2.4	12	≤	16
Machine 2	2	3	15	≤	15
Unit Profit	$ 130.00	$ 150.00	$750		
Solution	0	5			

8.2 a)

	Requirement Per Unit of Each Activity				Required
Requirements	Model A	Model B	Totals		Amount
Total Need	1	1	6	≥	6
High-Sped Need	1	0	2	≥	1
Capacity	20000	10000	80000	≥	75000
Cost	$ 6,000.00	$ 4,000.00	$28000		
Solution	2	4			

b)

Let $A =$ the number of Model A copiers to buy

Let $B =$ the number of Model B copiers to buy

Minimize $C = 6000A + 4000B$,

subject to $A + B \geq 6$

$A \geq 1$

$20,000A + 10,000B \geq 75,000$

and $A \geq 0, \; B \geq 0$

$A, \; B$ are integers.

c) Optimal solution: $(A,B) = (2,4)$, $C = \$28,000$.

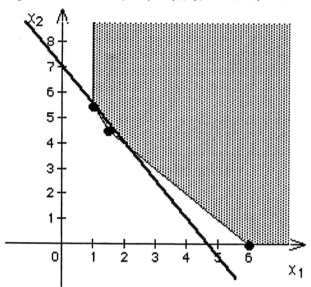

8.3   a) Optimal solution: $(x_1, x_2) = (2,3)$, $P = 13$.

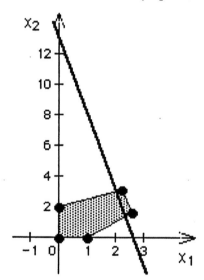

b) Optimal solution: $(x_1, x_2) = (2.6, 1.6)$, $P = 14.6$.

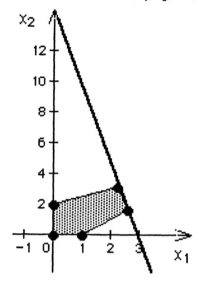

Rounded Solution	Feasible?	Constraint Violated	P
(3,2)	No	3rd	-
(3,1)	No	2nd & 3rd	-
(2,2)	Yes	-	12
(2,1)	Yes	-	11

None of these is optimal for the integer programming model. Two are not feasible and the other two have lower values of Profit.

8.4   a) Optimal solution: $(x_1, x_2) = (2, 3)$, $P = 680$.

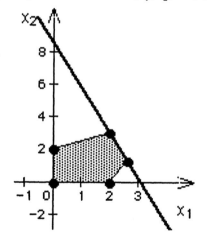

b) Optimal solution: $(x_1, x_2) = (2.667, 1.333)$, $P = 693.33$.

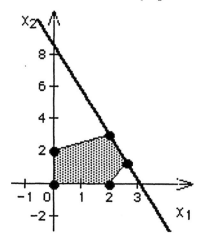

Rounded Solution	Feasible?	Constraint Violated	P
(3,1)	No	2nd & 3rd	-
(3,2)	No	2nd	-
(2,2)	Yes	-	600
(2,1)	Yes	-	520

None of these is optimal for the integer programming model. Two are not feasible and the other two have lower values of Profit.

8.5   a)

| | Resource Usage Per Unit of Each Activity | | | | | Resource |
Resource	Long-range	Medium-range	Short-range	Totals		Available
Money	67	50	35	1498	≤	1500
Pilots	1	1	1	30	≤	30
Maintenance	1.667	1.333	1	39.338	≤	40
Profit	$ 4.20	$ 3.00	$ 2.30	$95.6		
Solution	14	0	16			

b)

Let $L =$ the number of long-range jets to buy

Let $M =$ the number of medium-range jets to buy

Let $S =$ the number of short-range jets to buy.

Maximize $P = 4.2L + 3M + 2.3S$,

subject to $\quad 67L + 50M + 35S \le 1500$

$$L + M + S \le 30$$

$$\frac{5}{3}L + \frac{4}{3}M + S \le 40$$

and $\quad L \ge 0,\ M \ge 0,\ S \ge 0$

$L,\ M,\ S$ are integers.

8.6 a)

Let $\quad x_{ij} =$ the number of trucks hauling from pit i to site j (for i = N,S; j = 1,2,3)

$y_{ij} =$ tons of gravel hauled from pit i to site j (for i = N,S; j = 1,2,3).

Minimize $C = 130y_{N1} + 160y_{N2} + 150y_{N3} + 180y_{S1} + 150y_{S2} + 160y_{S3} +$

$$50x_{N1} + 50x_{N2} + 50x_{N3} + 50x_{S1} + 50x_{S2} + 50x_{S3}$$

subject to $\quad y_{N1} + y_{N2} + y_{N3} \le 18$

$$y_{S1} + y_{S2} + y_{S3} \le 14$$

$$y_{ij} \le 5x_{ij} \qquad \text{(for i = N,S; j = 1,2,3)}$$

$$y_{N1} + y_{S1} \ge 10$$

$$y_{N2} + y_{S2} \ge 5$$

$$y_{N3} + y_{S3} \ge 10$$

and $\quad y_{ij} \ge 0,\ x_{ij} \ge 0,$

x_{ij} are integers (for i = N,S; j = 1,2,3).

b & c)

Resource Usage Per Unit of Each Activity

| | Truck | | | | | | Gravel | | | | | | | Resource |
Resource	N1	N2	N3	S1	S2	S3	N1	N2	N3	S1	S2	S3	Totals		Available
No. supply	0	0	0	0	0	0	1	1	1	0	0	0	15	≤	18
So. supply	0	0	0	0	0	0	0	0	0	1	1	1	10	≤	14
cap. N1	5	0	0	0	0	0	-1	0	0	0	0	0	0	≥	0
cap. N2	0	5	0	0	0	0	0	-1	0	0	0	0	0	≥	0
cap. N3	0	0	5	0	0	0	0	0	-1	0	0	0	0	≥	0
cap. S1	0	0	0	5	0	0	0	0	0	-1	0	0	0	≥	0
cap. S2	0	0	0	0	5	0	0	0	0	0	-1	0	0	≥	0
cap. S3	0	0	0	0	0	5	0	0	0	0	0	-1	0	≥	0
Site 1 need	0	0	0	0	0	0	1	0	0	1	0	0	10	≥	10
Site 2 need	0	0	0	0	0	0	0	1	0	0	1	0	5	≥	5
Site 3 need	0	0	0	0	0	0	0	0	1	0	0	1	10	≥	10
Cost	$ 50	$ 50	$ 50	$ 50	$ 50	$ 50	$ 130	$ 160	$ 150	$ 180	$ 150	$ 160	$3850		
Solution	2	0	1	0	1	1	10	0	5	0	5	5			

8.7   a) The profit graph for power saws is shown below:

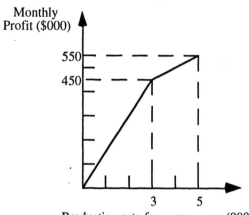

Production rate for power saws (000s)

The profit graph for power drills is shown below:

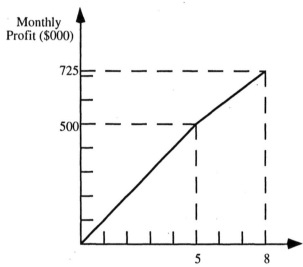

Production rate for power drills (000s)

b & c)

| | Resource Usage Per Unit of Each Activity | | | | | | |
Resource	Power Saws Regular	Power Saws Overtime	Power Drills Regular	Power Drills Overtime	Totals		Resource Available
power supplies	1	1	1	1	10000	≤	10000
gear assemblies	2	2	1	1	13000	≤	15000
Unit Profit	150	50	100	75	$ 1,100,000		
Solution	3000	0	5000	2000			
Maximum	3000	2000	5000	3000			

3,000 power saws and 7,000 power drills should be produced in November.

8.8 a) Profit data for doors when marketing costs are considered:

Production Rate	Gross Profit	Marketing Cost	Net Profit	Incremental Net Profit
0	0	0	0	—
1	$400	$100	$300	$300
2	$800	$800	$0	-$300
3	$1200	$2700	-$1900	-$1900
D	4D	D^3	$4D - D^3$	

Profit data for windows when marketing costs are considered:

Production Rate	Gross Profit	Marketing Cost	Net Profit	Incremental Net Profit
0	0	0	0	—
1	$600	$200	$400	$400
2	$1200	$800	$400	$0
3	$1800	$1800	0	-$400
W	6W	$2W^2$	$6W - 2W^2$	

b) The profit graphs for doors and windows are shown below:

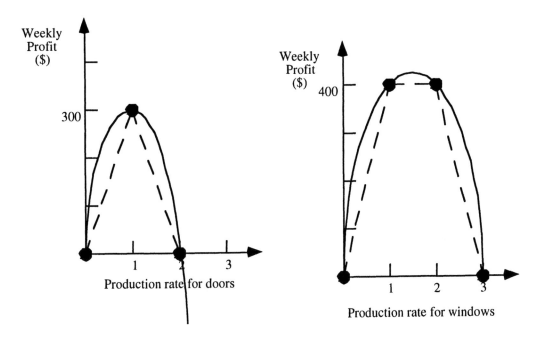

8-9

c & d)

Resource Usage Per Unit of Each Activity									
	Doors			Windows					Resource
Resource	1	2	3	1	2	3	Totals		Available
A	1	1	1	3	3	3	4	$\leq$	8
B	5	5	5	2	2	2	7	$\leq$	14
Unit Profit	3	-3	-19	4	0	-4	$ 7.00		
Solution	1	0	0	1	0	0			
Maximum	1	1	1	1	1	1			

Dorwyn should produce 1 door and 1 window.

8.9   a)   The profit graph for product 1 is shown below:

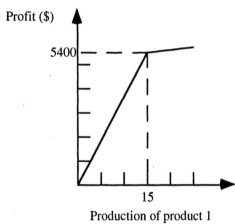

Production of product 1

The profit graph for product 2 is shown below:

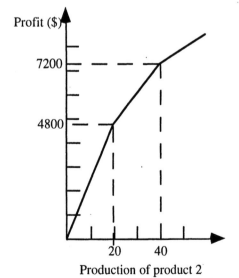

Production of product 2

The profit graph for product 3 is shown below:

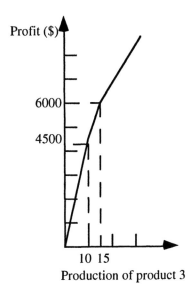

Profit ($)

6000

4500

10 15

Production of product 3

b & c)

Resource	Resource Usage Per Unit of Each Activity								Totals		Resource Available
	x11	x12	x21	x22	x23	x31	x32	x33			
A	1	1	1	1	1	1	1	1	60	≤	60
B	3	3	2	2	2				85	≤	200
C	1	1				2	2	2	65	≤	70
Unit Profit	360	30	240	120	90	450	300	180	$ 18,000		
Solution	15	0	20	0	0	10	5	10			
Maximum	15		20	20		10	5				

Recommend to management 15 units of x_1, 20 units of x_2, and 25 units of x_3.

8.10   The unit profit on overtime is less than on regular time. To maximize the total profit, an optimal solution automatically will use up all regular time for a product before starting on overtime.

8.11   The profit graph for product 1 is shown below:

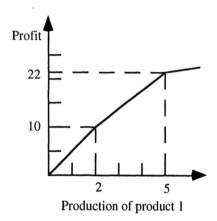

Production of product 1

The profit graph for product 2 is shown below:

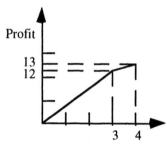

Production of product 2

The unit profit for product 1 is $5 for the first 2 units, $4 for the next 3 units, and $2 for any remaining units. The unit profit for product 2 is $4 for the first 3 units, and $1 for the fourth unit (the maximum allowed). The constraints for the original problem would be:

$$3x_1 + 2x_2 \leq 25$$
$$2x_1 - x_2 \leq 10$$
and
$$x_1 \geq 0, \ 0 \leq x_2 \leq 4.$$

8.12   a) Profit data for product 1:

Production Rate	Net Profit ($millions)	Incremental Net Profit ($millions)
0	-1	—
1	3	4
2	5	2
2.5	5.25	.25
3	5	-.25
4	3	-2
5	-1	-4
x_1	$3x_1 - (x_1 - 1)^2$	

Profit data for product 2:

Production Rate	Net Profit ($millions)	Incremental Net Profit ($millions)
0	-4	—
1	2	6
2	6	4
3	8	2
3.5	8.25	.25
4	8	-.25
5	6	-2
x_2	$3x_2 - (x_2 - 2)^2$	

b & c)   The profit graph for product 1 is shown below.

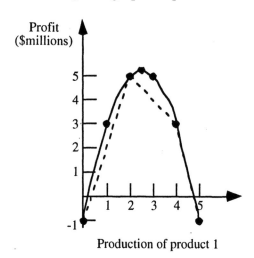

The profit graph for product 2 is shown below.

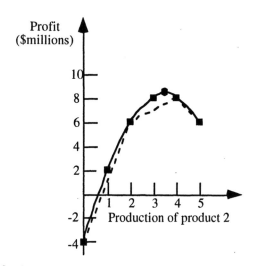

d & e)

Resource	Resource Usage Per Unit of Each Activity						Totals		Resource Available
	x11	x12	x13	x21	x22	x23			
A	4	4	4	1	1	1	12	≤	20
B	1	1	1	4	4	4	18	≤	20
Unit Profit	3	-1	-4	5	1	-2	$ 18		
Solution	2	0	0	2	2	0			
Maximum	2	2	1	2	2	1			

Advertising campaign 1 should be at 2 units and advertising campaign 2 should be at 4 units. The total net profit will be $13 million ($18 million plus the negative $5 million at $x_1 = 0$ and $x_2 = 0$).

f) The revised approximated profit graph for product 1 is shown below.

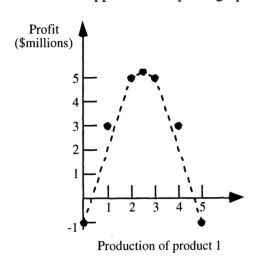

Production of product 1

The profit graph for product 2 is shown below.

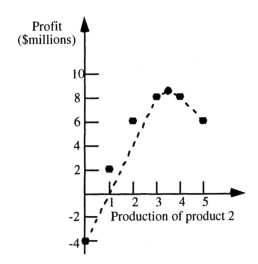

Production of product 2

The linear programming model is then as follows:

Resource	x11	x12	x13	x14	x21	x22	x23	x24	Totals		Resource Available
			Resource Usage Per Unit of Each Activity								
A	4	4	4	4	1	1	4	1	13.5	≤	20
B	1	1	1	1	4	4	4	4	16.5	≤	20
Unit Profit	3	0.5	-0.5	-3	4	0.5	-0.5	-2	$ 18.5		
Solution	2	0.5	0	0	3	0.5	0	0			
Maximum	2	0.5	0.5	2	3	0.5	0.5	1			

Advertising campaign 1 should be at 2.5 units and advertising campaign 2 should be at 3.5 units. The total net profit will be $13.5 million ($18.5 million plus the negative $5 million at $x_1 = 0$ and $x_2 = 0$).

g)

Resource	Resource Usage Per Unit of Each Activity				Resource
	x1	x2	Totals		Available
A	4	1	13.5	≤	20
B	1	4	16.5	≤	20
Solution	2.5	3.5	Profit =		13.5

This solution is the same as the one in part (f).

h) The derivatives of the functions equal zero at their maximum value.

The derivative of $3x_1 - (x_1 - 1)^2$ is $3 - 2(x_1 - 1)$ which equals zero when $x_1 = 2.5$.

The derivative of $3x_2 - (x_2 - 2)^2$ is $3 - 2(x_2 - 2)$ which equals zero when $x_2 = 3.5$.

These values also satisfy the constraints:
$4x_1 + x_2 = 4(2.5) + 3.5 = 13.5 \leq 20$,

$x_1 + 4x_2 = 2.5 + 4(3.5) = 16.5 \leq 20$.

This is the same solution that was found in parts (f) and (g).

8.13　a)

Factor	Amount Per Block			Totals		Right-Hand Side
	Stock 1	Stock 2	Stock 3			
Budget	60	40	50	725	≤	1000
Expected Return	25	20	9	250.54	≥	300
Risk	4	9	1	215.47		
Solution	6.416	2.257	5.000			

Joint Risk	Stock 1	Stock 2	Stock 3
Stock 1		2	-1
Stock 2			-1.5
Stock 3			

The expected return decreases by almost $50,000 and the risk decreases by about 30.

b)

Factor	Amount Per Block			Totals		Right-Hand Side
	Stock 1	Stock 2	Stock 3			
Budget	60	40	50	475	≤	1000
Expected Return	25	20	9	205.54	≥	300
Risk	4	9	1	239.48		
Solution	6.416	2.257	0.000			

Joint Risk	Stock 1	Stock 2	Stock 3
Stock 1		2	-1
Stock 2			-1.5
Stock 3			

The expected return decreases by almost $95,000 and the risk decreases by about 7.

c)

Stock1	Stock 2	Stock 3	Expected Return	Risk
6.416	2.257	10.495	300	246.76
6.416	4.757	8.495	331.99	386.4
6.416	7.257	6.495	363.99	661.56
6.416	9.757	4.495	395.99	1072.22
6.416	12.257	2.495	427.99	1618.38
6.416	14.757	0.495	459.99	2300.04

8.14   a)

Let S_1 = number of blocks of stock 1 to purchase

        S_2 = number of blocks of stock 2 to purchase.

Minimize Risk = $4S_1^2 + 100S_2^2 + 5S_1S_2$,

subject to $20S_1 + 30S_2 \leq 50$

              $5S_1 + 10S_2 \geq$ minimum acceptable expected return

and $S_1 \geq 0, \; S_2 \geq 0.$

b & c) <u>Minimum acceptable expected return = 13</u>

Factor	Amount Per Block		Totals		Right-Hand Side
	Stock 1	Stock 2			
Budget	20	30	50	≤	50
Expected Return	5	10	13.00	≥	13
Risk	4	100	25.56		
Solution	2.2	0.2			

Joint Risk	Stock 1	Stock 2
Stock 1		5
Stock 2		

Minimum acceptable expected return = 14

Factor	Amount Per Block		Totals		Right-Hand Side
	Stock 1	Stock 2			
Budget	20	30	50	≤	50
Expected Return	5	10	14.00	≥	14
Risk	4	100	51.04		
Solution	1.6	0.6			

Joint Risk	Stock 1	Stock 2
Stock 1		5
Stock 2		

Minimum acceptable expected return = 15

Factor	Amount Per Block		Totals		Right-Hand Side
	Stock 1	Stock 2			
Budget	20	30	50	≤	50
Expected Return	5	10	15.00	≥	15
Risk	4	100	109.00		
Solution	1.0	1.0			

Joint Risk	Stock 1	Stock 2
Stock 1		5
Stock 2		

<u>Minimum acceptable expected return = 16</u>

Factor	Amount Per Block		Totals		Right-Hand Side
	Stock 1	Stock 2			
Budget	20	30	50	$\leq$	50
Expected Return	5	10	16.00	$\geq$	16
Risk	4	100	199.44		
Solution	0.4	1.4			

Joint Risk	Stock 1	Stock 2
Stock 1		5
Stock 2		

d)

μ	σ	$\mu - \sigma$	$\mu - 3\sigma$
13	5.06	7.94	-2.18
14	7.14	6.86	-7.42
15	10.44	4.56	-16.32
16	14.12	1.88	-26.36

The portfolio of 0.4 blocks of stock 1 and1.4 blocks of stock 2 with gives the highest μ.

8.15 a)

Let S_1 = number of blocks of stock 1 to purchase

S_2 = number of blocks of stock 2 to purchase

S_3 = number of blocks of stock 3 to purchase

S_4 = nymber of blocks of stock 4 to purchase.

Minimize Risk = $25S_1 + 20S_2 + 9S_3 + 18S_4 - .4(4S_1^2 + 9S_2^2 + S_3^2 + 3S_4^2$

$+2S_1S_2 - S_1S_3 - 1.5S_2S_3 - S_1S_4 - 2S_2S_4 + .5S_3S_4)$,

subject to $\quad 25S_1 + 20S_2 + 9S_3 + 18S_4 \geq 300$

$60S_1 + 40S_2 + 50S_3 + 45S_4 \leq 1000$

and $\quad S_1 \geq 0, \ S_2 \geq 0, \ S_3 \geq 0, \ S_4 \geq 0.$

b & c)

Factor	Amount Per Block				Totals		Right-Hand Side
	Stock 1	Stock 2	Stock 3	Stock 4			
Budget	60	40	50	45	936	≤	1000
Expected Return	25	20	9	18	300.00	≥	300
Risk	4	9	1	3	172.73		
Solution	4.635	1.887	7.864	4.201			

Joint Risk	Stock 1	Stock 2	Stock 3	Stock 4
Stock 1		2	-1	-1
Stock 2			-1.5	-2
Stock 3				0.5

d)

Expected Return ($000)	Blocks of Shares to Purchase				Risk
	Stock 1	Stock 2	Stock 3	Stock 4	
0	0.000	0.000	0.000	0.000	0.00
50	0.773	0.314	1.311	0.700	4.80
100	1.545	0.629	2.621	1.400	19.19
150	2.318	0.943	3.932	2.100	43.18
200	3.090	1.258	5.243	2.800	76.77
250	3.863	1.572	6.554	3.501	119.95
300	4.635	1.887	7.864	4.201	172.73
350	5.756	2.373	5.932	5.847	248.96
400	7.121	2.979	1.731	8.156	408.04
450	4.993	11.252	0.000	5.563	1291.38
500	no feasible solution possible				

8.16 a) This equation fits the profit for all of the production rates except for R = 2 where it is off by $4.

b) This equation fits the profit for the production rates of R = 0, 2, and 4 but is off by $3 for the production rates of 1 and 3.

c) The quadratic function $100R - 5R^2$ provides the better fit to all the data.

8.17 a)

Let R_1 = number of Product 1 to produce

R_2 = number of Product 2 to produce.

Maximize $P = 200R_1 - 100R_1^2 + 300R_2 - 100R_2^2$,

subject to $R_1 + R_2 \leq 2$

and $R_1 \geq 0, \ R_2 \geq 0.$

b)

Resource	Resource Usage Per Unit of Each Activity			Resource Available
	R1	R2	Totals	
capacity	1	1	2 ≤	2
Solution	0.75	1.25	Profit =	312.5

8.18 The coefficient for L7 is three times as large as the coefficient for K7.

8.19 a) Goal 1: Market share for Product 1 $0.5x_1 + 0.2\,x_3 \geq 15\%$
        Goal 2: Market share for Product 2 $0.3x_2 + 0.2\,x_3 \geq 10\%$

Overall objective is to minimize W = amount under Goal 1 + amount under Goal 2

b)

Goals	Unit Contribution Per Unit of Each Activity			Level Achieved		Goal	Amount Over	Amount Under	Totals		Right-Hand Side
	Campaign 1	Campaign 2	Campaign 3								
Market Share 1	0.5	0	0.2	15	≥	15	0	0	15	=	15
Market Share 2	0	0.3	0.2	8.33333	≥	10	0	1.667	10	=	10
Budget	1	1	1	55	≤	55			55	≤	55
Campaign 3 budget	0	0	1	41.6667	≥	10			41.667	≥	10
Solution	13.333	0	41.667								

Weighted Sum of Deviations = 1.667

c) Both goals of market share cannot be met with an advertising budget of $55 million. With this budget, spending $13.33 million on campaign 1 and $41.67 million on campaign 3, market shares of 15% and 8.33% can be achieved. Additional advertising budget will be necessary to achieve the desired market share.

8.20 a)

Goals	Unit Contribution Per Unit of Each Activity			Level Achieved		Goal	Amount Over	Amount Under	Totals		Right-Hand Side
	Product 1	Product 2	Product 3								
Profit	20	15	25	375							
Employment	6	4	5	75	=	50	25	0	50	=	50
Earnings	8	7	5	75	≥	75	0	0	75	=	75
Solution	0	0	15								

Weighted Sum of Deviations = 225

b) Emax should produce 15 units of product 3. While this does increase the present level of employment by 25, it does not decrease earnings and does maximize profit over the life of the new product.

8.21 a) No, we would not expect the optimal solution to change. Goal 1 is already met, so increasing the weight on that goal would not change anything. We already exceed goal 2, so decreasing the penalty weight for goal 2 would only decrease our desire to avoid exceeding this goal.

b)

Goals	Product 1	Product 2	Product 3	Achieved	Goal		Over	Under	Totals		Side
Profit	12	9	15	140	≥	140	0	0	140	=	140
Employment	5	3	4	58.3333	=	40	18.3333	0	40	=	40
Investment	5	7	8	58.3333	≤	55	3.33333	0	55	=	55
Solution	11.667	0	0								

Weighted Sum of Deviations = 46.6667

c)

Goals	Unit Contribution Per Unit of Each Act			Level Achieved		Goal	Amount Over	Amount Under	Totals		Right-Hand Side
	Product 1	Product 2	Product 3								
Profit	12	9	15	140	≥	140	0	0	140	=	140
Employment	5	3	4	58.3333	=	40	18.3333	0	40	=	40
Investment	5	7	8	58.3333	≤	55	3.33333	0	55	=	55
Solution	11.667	0	0								

Weighted Sum of Deviations = 28.3333

8.22 a) Goal 1: Foreign Capital $3000x_1 + 5000x_2 + 4000x_3 \geq 70{,}000{,}000$
Goal 2: Citizens Fed $150x_1 + 75x_2 + 100x_3 \geq 1{,}750{,}000$
Goal 3: Citizens Employed $10x_1 + 15x_2 + 12x_3 = 200{,}000$

Overall objective is to minimize W = (amount under Goal 1)/100 + amount under Goal 2 + amount under Goal 3 + amount over Goal 3.

b)

Goals	Unit Contribution Per Unit of Each Activity			Level Achieved		Goal	Amount Over	Amount Under	Totals		Right-Hand Side
	Product 1	Product 2	Product 3								
Foreign Capital	3000	5000	4000	58333333	≥	70000000	0	11666666.7	70000000	=	70000000
Citizens Fed	150	75	100	1750000	≥	1750000	0	0	1750000	=	1750000
Citizens Employed	10	15	12	183333.3	=	200000	0	16666.7	200000	=	200000
Acres	1000	1000	1000	15000000	≤	15000000					
Solution	8333.333	6666.667	0								

Weighted Sum of Deviations = 133333.3

c) Montega should plant 8.333 million acres of crop 1 and 6.667 million acres of crop 2. This will meet the goal of citizens fed, but fall short of the foreign capital goal by $11.667 million and the employment goal by 16,667.

Cases

8.1 a) With this approach, we need to formulate an integer program for each month and optimize each month individually.

In the first month, Emily does not buy any servers since none of the departments implement the intranet in the first month. In the second month she must buy computers to ensure that the Sales Department can start the intranet. Emily can formulate her decision problem as an integer problem. Her objective is to minimize the purchase cost. She has to satisfy to constraints. She cannot spend more than $9500 (she still has her entire budget for the first two months since she didn't buy any computers in the first month) and the computer(s) must support at least 60 employees. She solves her integer programming problem using the Excel solver.

	A	B	C	D	E	F	G	H
1								
2	Server	Std. PC	Enh. PC	SGI	Sun	Totals		
3	Support	30	80	200	2000	80	>=	60
4	Capital m2	$2500	$5000	$9000	$18750	$5000	<=	$9500
5	Capital	$2500	$5000	$9000	$18750	$5000		
6	Solution	0	1	0	0			
7								
8		Formula in cell F3:	"=SUMPRODUCT(B3:E3,B6:E6)"					
9		Formula in cell F4:	"=SUMPRODUCT(B4:E4,B6:E6)"					
10		Formula in cell F5:	"=SUMPRODUCT(B5:E5,B6:E6)"					

The solver dialogue box looks as follows:

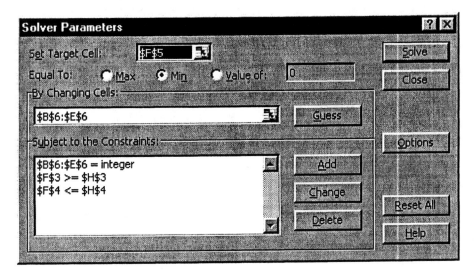

Emily uses the following options throughout her entire analysis of this case:

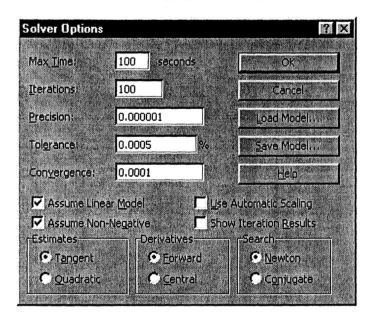

Notice that the price of the SGI server is 10 percent less than the actual price and the price of the Sun server is 25 percent less than the actual price because these two manufacturers offer discounts in the second month. Emily decides to buy one enhanced PC in the second month.

Note, that there is a second optimal solution to this integer programming problem. For the same amount of money Emily could buy two standard PC's that would also support 60 employees. However, since Emily knows that she needs to support more employees in the near future, she decides to buy the enhanced PC since it supports more users.

For the third month Emily needs to support 260 users. Since she has already computing power to support 80 users, she now needs to figure out how to support additional 180 users at minimum cost. She can disregard the constraint that the Manufacturing Department needs one of the three larger servers, since she already bought such a server in the previous month. Her task leads her to the following integer programming problem:

	A	B	C	D	E	F	G	H
1								Support
2	Server	Std. PC	Enh. PC	SGI	Sun	Totals		Needed
3	Support	30	80	200	2000	200	>=	180
4	Capital	$2,500	$5,000	$10,000	$25,000	$10,000		
5	Solution	0	0	1	0			
6								
7								
8		Formula in cell F3:		"=SUMPRODUCT(B3:E3,B6:E6)"				
9		Formula in cell F4:		"=SUMPRODUCT(B4:E4,B6:E6)"				

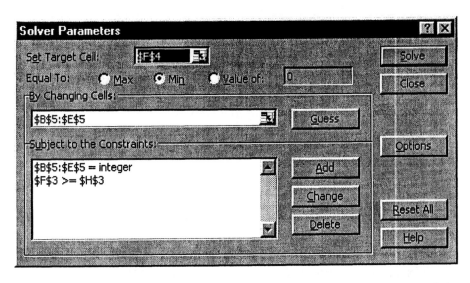

Emily decides to buy one SGI Workstation in month 3. The network is now able to support 280 users.

In the fourth month Emily needs to support a total of 290 users. Since she has already computing power to support 280 users, she now needs to figure out how to support additional 10 users at minimum cost. This task leads her to the following integer programming problem:

	A	B	C	D	E	F	G	H
1								Support
2	Server	Std. PC	Enh. PC	SGI	Sun	Totals		Needed
3	Support	30	80	200	2000	30	>=	10
4	Capital	$2,500	$5,000	$10,000	$25,000	$2,500		
5	Solution	1	0	0	0			
6								
7								
8		Formula in cell F3:		"=SUMPRODUCT(B3:E3,B6:E6)"				
9		Formula in cell F4:		"=SUMPRODUCT(B4:E4,B6:E6)"				

The solver dialogue box appears just as in her previous problem. Emily decides to buy a standard PC in the fourth month. The network is now able to support 310 users.

Finally, in the fifth and last month Emily needs to support the entire company with a total of 365 users. Since she has already computing power to support 310 users, she now needs to figure out how to support additional 55 users at minimum cost. This task leads her to the following integer programming problem:

	A	B	C	D	E	F	G	H
1								Support
2	Server	Std. PC	Enh. PC	SGI	Sun	Totals		Needed
3	Support	30	80	200	2000	80	>=	55
4	Capital	$2,500	$5,000	$10,000	$25,000	$5,000		
5	Solution	0	1	0	0			
6								
7								
8		Formula in cell F3:		"=SUMPRODUCT(B3:E3,B6:E6)"				
9		Formula in cell F4:		"=SUMPRODUCT(B4:E4,B6:E6)"				

Again, the solver dialogue box has not changed. Emily decides to buy another enhanced PC in the fifth month. (Note that again she could have also bought two standard PC's, but clearly the enhanced PC provides more room for the workload of the system to grow.) The entire network of CommuniCorp consists now of 1 standard PC, 2 enhanced PC's and 1 SGI workstation and it is able to support 390 users. The total purchase cost for this network is $22,500.

b) Emily realizes that she will not be able to buy a Sun workstation during the first and second month, since the cost of such a server exceeds her budget even after the 25% discount. However, she could buy any one of the other three servers during the first two months. Due to the budget restriction she faces in the first two months she needs to distinguish between the computers she buys in those early months and in the later months. Therefore, Emily introduces two variables for each of the first three servers but only one for the Sun workstation:

Std. PC m2 = number of standard PCs bought during the first two months
Std. PC = number of standard PCs bought during the later three months
Enh. PC m2 = number of enhanced PCs bought during the first two months
Enh. PC = number of enhanced PCs bought during the later three months
SGI m2 = number of SGI workstations bought during the first two months
SGI = number of SGI workstations bought during the later three months
Sun = number of Sun workstations bought during the later three months

Emily essentially faces four constraints. First, she must support the 60 users in the sales department in the second month. She realizes that, since she no longer buys the computers sequentially after the second month, that it suffices to include only the constraint on the network to support the all users in the entire company. This second constraint requires her to support a total of 365 users. The third constraint requires her to buy at least one of the three large servers. Finally, Emily has to make sure that she stays within her budget during the second month.

	A	B	C	D	E	F	G	H	I	J	K
1											
2	Server	Stdd. PC m2	Stdd. PC	Enh. PC m2	Enh. PC	SGI m2	SGI	Sun	Totals		
3	Support m2	30	0	80	0	200	0	0	200	>=	60
4	Support	30	30	80	80	200	200	2000	400	>=	365
5	Large Comp.	0	0	1	1	1	1	1	2	>=	1
6	Capital m2	$2500	$0	$5,000	$0	$9,000	$0	$0	$9000	<=	$9500
7	Capital	$2,500	$2,500	$5,000	$5,000	$9,000	$10,000	$25,000	$19,000		
8	Solution	0	0	0	0	1	1	0			
9											
10											
11		Formula for cell I3:		"=SUMPRODUCT(B3:H3,B8:H8)"							
12		Formula for cell I4:		"=SUMPRODUCT(B4:H4,B8:H8)"							
13		Formula for cell I5:		"=SUMPRODUCT(B5:H5,B8:H8)"							
14		Formula for cell I6:		"=SUMPRODUCT(B6:H6,B8:H8)"							
15		Formula for cell I7:		"=SUMPRODUCT(B7:H7,B8:H8)"							

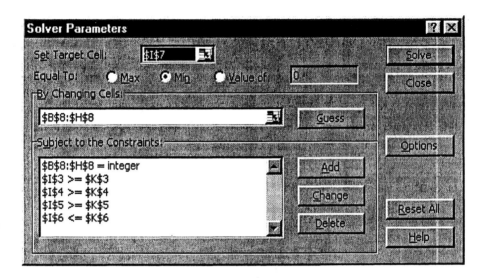

Emily should purchase a discounted SGI workstation in the second month, and another regular priced one in the third month. The total purchase cost is $19,000.

c) Emily's second method in part (b) finds the cost for the best overall purchase policy. The method in part (a) only finds the best purchase policy for the given month, ignoring the fact that the decision in a particular month has an impact on later decisions. The method in (a) is very short-sighted and thus yields a worse result that the method in part (b).

d) Installing the intranet will incur a number of other costs. These costs include:

Training cost,
Labor cost for network installation,
Additional hardware cost for cabling, network interface cards, necessary hubs, etc.,
Salary and benefits for a network administrator and web master,
Cost for establishing or outsourcing help desk support.

e) The intranet and the local area network are complete departures from the way business has been done in the past. The departments may therefore be concerned that the new technology will eliminate jobs. For example, in the past the manufacturing department has produced a greater number of pagers than customers have ordered. Fewer employees may be needed when the manufacturing department begins producing only enough pagers to meet orders. The departments may also become territorial about data and procedures, fearing that another department will encroach on their business. Finally, the departments may be concerned about the security of their data when sending it over the network.

8.2 a) When Charles sells a portion of his B-Bonds in a given year, the first DM 6100 of interest are tax-free, but the interest earnings exceeding DM 6100 are levied a 30 percent tax. Therefore, Charles encounters decreasing marginal returns, and we can use separable programming to solve this problem.

Define the following variables:

$NoTax5$ = The base amount of B-Bonds Charles sells in the fifth year that yield untaxed interest

$Tax5$ = The base amount of B-Bonds Charles sells in the fifth year that yield taxed interest

Similarly, $NoTax6$, $Tax6$, $NoTax7$, and $Tax7$ are defined.

The sum of these six variables must equal the total of DM 30,000 that Charles invested at the beginning of year 1. When Charles sells B-Bonds with the base amount $NoTax5$, he earns $0.5001*NoTax5$ in interest. In order for him not to pay any taxes on this amount, the interest must be less than or equal DM 6100. We have to include this constraint. Any additional base amount of B-bonds sold in year 5 yields Charles only $0.7*0.5001=0.35007$. A similar reasoning applies to the variables for the other years. The objective is to maximize Charles' interest income.

	A	B	C	D	E	F	G	H	I	J
1										
2	Server	NoTax5	Tax5	NoTax6	Tax6	NoTax7	Tax7	Totals		
3	Selling	1	1	1	1	1	1	30000	=	30000
4	Untaxed5	0.5001	0	0	0	0	0	0	<=	6100
5	Untaxed6	0	0	0.6351	0	0	0	6100	<=	6100
6	Untaxed7	0	0	0	0	0.7823	0	6100	<=	6100
7	Interest	0.5001	0.35007	0.6351	0.44457	0.7823	0.54761	19098.62		
8	Solution	0	0	9604.79	0	7797.52	12597.69			
9										
10		Formula in cell H3:			"=SUMPRODUCT(B3:G3,B8:G8)"					
11		Formula in cell H4:			"=SUMPRODUCT(B4:G4,B8:G8)"					
12		Formula in cell H5:			"=SUMPRODUCT(B5:G5,B8:G8)"					
13		Formula in cell H6:			"=SUMPRODUCT(B6:G6,B8:G8)"					
14		Formula in cell H7:			"=SUMPRODUCT(B7:G7,B8:G8)"					

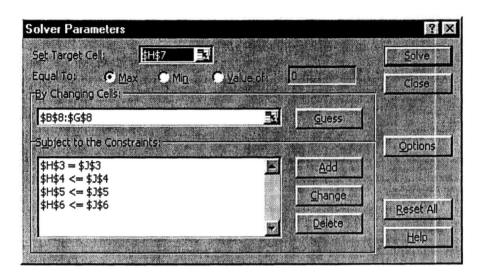

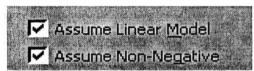

b) The optimal investment strategy for Charles is to sell a base amount of DM 9604.79 at the end of year 6 and the remaining DM 20395.21 at the end of year 7. His total after-tax interest income equals DM 19098.62.

c) When Charles sells all B-Bonds in the seventh year, then he must pay 30% of taxes on the amount of interest income exceeding DM 6100. This amount is earned interest not only from the last year, but it includes interest from all the previous years. So Charles does not pay 30% tax on the 9 percent interest he earned in the last year, but he effectively pays tax on the total interest of all the years. This tax payment decreases his after-tax interest so much that it pays for him to sell some of his bonds in the sixth year in order to take advantage of the yearly tax-free income of DM 6100. Compare the total amount of interest Charles earns if he sells tax-free after year 6 and taxed after year 7: In the former case his total interest equals 63.51% while in the latter case it is only 54.761%. Therefore, it is better to sell some bonds at the end of the sixth year than to keep them until the end of the last year.

d) The following observation greatly simplifies the analysis of this problem: The interest rate on the CD is much lower than the yearly interest rates on the B-Bonds. Therefore, it can never be optimal for Charles to sell B-Bonds in year 5 in order to buy a CD for year 6 if he does not take advantage of the maximal tax-free amount of selling B-Bonds in year 6. Put differently, Charles will only buy a CD for year 6 if he already plans to sell B-Bonds in year 6 to obtain at least the maximal tax-free amount of interest. The same argument applies to year 7. This observation implies that Charles will never earn untaxed interest on a CD. Therefore, his yearly interest on the CD will always be $0.7*0.04 = 0.028 = 2.8\%$.

Define
CD6 =   Amount invested in a CD in year 6
CD7 =   Amount invested in a CD in year 7

The amount of money Charles can invest in a CD in year 6 equals the base amount of B-Bonds sold in year 5 plus the total after-tax interest earned on the base amount. This condition results in the constraint $CD6 = 1.5001*NoTax5 + 1.35007*Tax5$. The corresponding constraint for CD7 is $CD7 = 1.6351*NoTax6 + 1.44457*Tax6 + 1.028*CD6$.

	A	B	C	D	E	F	G	H	I	J	K	L
1												
2	Server	NoTax5	Tax5	CD6	NoTax6	Tax6	CD7	NoTax7	Tax7	Totals		
3	Selling	1	1	0	1	1	0	1	1	30000	=	30000
4	Untaxed5	0.5001	0	0	0	0	0	0	0	6100	<=	6100
5	Untaxed6	0	0	0	0.6351	0	0	0	0	6100	<=	6100
6	Untaxed7	0	0	0	0	0	0	0.7823	0	6100	<=	6100
7	CDInvest5	1.5001	1.35007	-1	0	0	0	0	0	0	=	0
8	CDInvest6	0	0	1.028	1.6351	1.44457	-1	0	0	0	=	0
9	Interest	0.5001	0.35007	0.028	0.6351	0.44457	0.028	0.7823	0.5476	19997.86		
10	Solution	12197.56	0	18297.56	9604.79	0	34514.68	7797.52	400.13			
11												
12		Formula in cell J3:			"=SUMPRODUCT(B3:I3,B10:I10)"							
13		Formula in cell J4:			"=SUMPRODUCT(B4:I4,B10:I10)"							
14		Formula in cell J5:			"=SUMPRODUCT(B5:I5,B10:I10)"							
15		Formula in cell J6:			"=SUMPRODUCT(B6:I6,B10:I10)"							
16		Formula in cell J7:			"=SUMPRODUCT(B7:I7,B10:I10)"							
17		Formula in cell J8:			"=SUMPRODUCT(B8:I8,B10:I10)"							
18		Formula in cell J9:			"=SUMPRODUCT(B9:I9,B10:I10)"							

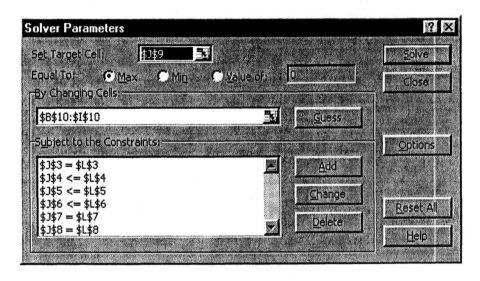

The options for the solver are the same as before.

Charles should sell the maximal base amount of B-bonds in year 5 that yields tax-free interest and then invest this money (base amount + interest) into a one-year CD for year 6. In year 6 he should sell again the maximal base amount of B-bonds that yields tax-free interest and then invest this money (base amount + interest) and the money from his CD into a one-year CD for year 7. In year 7 he should sell the remainder of the base amount of B-bonds. He again takes advantage of the maximum tax-free amount, but he also sells a base amount of DM 400.13 for which he must pay taxes on the interest earnings.

e) The right-hand side of the selling constraint needs to be changed:

	A	B	C	D	E	F	G	H	I	J	K	L
1												
2	Server	NoTax5	Tax5	CD6	NoTax6	Tax6	CD7	NoTax7	Tax7	Totals		
3	Selling	1	1	0	1	1	0	1	1	50000	=	50000
4	Untaxed5	0.5001	0	0	0	0	0	0	0	6100	<=	6100
5	Untaxed6	0	0	0	0.6351	0	0	0	0	6100	<=	6100
6	Untaxed7	0	0	0	0	0	0	0.7823	0	6100	<=	6100
7	CDInvest5	1.5001	1.35007	-1	0	0	0	0	0	0	=	0
8	CDInvest6	0	0	1.028	1.6351	1.44457	-1	0	0	0	=	0
9	Interest	0.5001	0.35007	0.028	0.6351	0.44457	0.028	0.7823	0.54761	30950.06		
10	Solution	12197.56	0	18297.56	9604.79	0	34514.68	7797.52	20400.13			
11												
12		Formula in cell J3:		"=SUMPRODUCT(B3:I3,B10:I10)"								
13		Formula in cell J4:		"=SUMPRODUCT(B4:I4,B10:I10)"								
14		Formula in cell J5:		"=SUMPRODUCT(B5:I5,B10:I10)"								
15		Formula in cell J6:		"=SUMPRODUCT(B6:I6,B10:I10)"								
16		Formula in cell J7:		"=SUMPRODUCT(B7:I7,B10:I10)"								
17		Formula in cell J8:		"=SUMPRODUCT(B8:I8,B10:I10)"								
18		Formula in cell J9:		"=SUMPRODUCT(B9:I9,B10:I10)"								

The optimal investment strategy is similar to the previous one, except that Charles must now pay taxes on the interest earned from selling a base amount of DM 20400.13 in year 7.

f) The right-hand sides of the Untaxed5, Untaxed6, and Untaxed7 constraints need to be changed.

	A	B	C	D	E	F	G	H	I	J	K	L
1												
2	Server	NoTax5	Tax5	CD6	NoTax6	Tax6	CD7	NoTax7	Tax7	Totals		
3	Selling	1	1	0	1	1	0	1	1	30000	=	30000
4	Untaxed5	0.5001	0	0	0	0	0	0	0	0	<=	12200
5	Untaxed6	0	0	0	0.6351	0	0	0	0	9148.59	<=	12200
6	Untaxed7	0	0	0	0	0	0	0.7823	0	12200	<=	12200
7	CDInvest 5	1.5001	1.35007	-1	0	0	0	0	0	0	=	0
8	CDInvest 6	0	0	1.028	1.6351	1.44457	-1	0	0	0	=	0
9	Interest	0.5001	0.35007	0.028	0.6351	0.44457	0.028	0.7823	0.54761	22008.09		
10	Solution	0	0	0	14404.96	0	23553.55	15595.04	0			
11												
12		Formula in cell J3:			"=SUMPRODUCT(B3:I3,B10:I10)"							
13		Formula in cell J4:			"=SUMPRODUCT(B4:I4,B10:I10)"							
14		Formula in cell J5:			"=SUMPRODUCT(B5:I5,B10:I10)"							
15		Formula in cell J6:			"=SUMPRODUCT(B6:I6,B10:I10)"							
16		Formula in cell J7:			"=SUMPRODUCT(B7:I7,B10:I10)"							
17		Formula in cell J8:			"=SUMPRODUCT(B8:I8,B10:I10)"							
18		Formula in cell J9:			"=SUMPRODUCT(B9:I9,B10:I10)"							

By getting married in the fifth year, Charles can increase his interest income by (22008.09 - 19997.86) = 2010.23 German marks. He should sell the maximal base amount of B-Bonds earning tax-free interest in year 7 (DM 15595.04). The remainder of DM 14404.96 he should sell at the end of year 6. His entire interest income on this base amount will be tax-free. He then should invest the total amount (base amount + interest) in a CD for the seventh year.

g) Instead of maximizing his interest income Charles now wants to maximize the expected dollar amount he will have at the end of the seventh year. He considers exchanging marks for dollars either at the end of year 5 or at the end of year 7. We define

CD-US = The amount of money (in dollars) Charles invests in a two-year CD at the end of year 5

US = The amount of dollars Charles converts at the end of year 7

The total amount of money in dollars Charles has at the end of year 7 equals $(1.036)^2 *$CD-US + US; this function is the new objective. At the end of year 5, 1 US\$ is assumed to equal DM 1.50, so Charles can exchange marks for dollars at this rate in year 5; this condition must be included as a constraint. Similarly, we include a constraint for the currency conversion at the end of the last year.

	A	B	C	D	E	F	G	H	I	J	K	L	M	N
1														
2	Server	NoTax5	Tax5	CD6	CD-US	NoTax6	Tax6	CD7	NoTax7	Tax7	US	Totals		
3	Selling	1	1	0	0	1	1	0	1	1	0	30000	=	30000
4	Untaxed5	0.5001	0	0	0	0	0	0	0	0	0	6100	<=	6100
5	Untaxed6	0	0	0	0	0.6351	0	0	0	0	0	0	<=	6100
6	Untaxed7	0	0	0	0	0	0	0	0.7823	0	0	6100	<=	6100
7	CDInvest5	1.5001	1.35007	-1	-1.5	0	0	0	0	0	0	0	=	0
8	CDInvest6	0	0	1.028	0	1.6351	1.44457	-1	0	0	0	0	=	0
9	Conversion	0	0	0	0	0	0	1.028	1.7823	1.5461	-1.8	0	=	0
10	Dollars	0	0	0	1.073296	0	0	0	0	0	1	30478.23		
11	Solution	12197.56	10004.92	0	21203.27	0	0	0	7797.52	0	7720.84			
12														
13														
14			Formula in cell L3:			"=SUMPRODUCT(B3:K3,B11:K11)"								
15			Formula in cell L4:			"=SUMPRODUCT(B4:K4,B11:K11)"								
16			Formula in cell L5:			"=SUMPRODUCT(B5:K5,B11:K11)"								
17			Formula in cell L6:			"=SUMPRODUCT(B6:K6,B11:K11)"								
18			Formula in cell L7:			"=SUMPRODUCT(B7:K7,B11:K11)"								
19			Formula in cell L8:			"=SUMPRODUCT(B8:K8,B11:K11)"								
20			Formula in cell L9:			"=SUMPRODUCT(B9:K9,B11:K11)"								
21			Formula in cell L10			"=SUMPRODUCT(B10:K10,B11:K11)"								

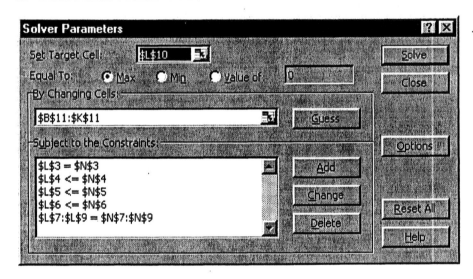

Charles converts DM (1.5001*12197.56 + 1.35007*10004.92) to dollars at the end of year 5. With the exchange rate of DM 1.50 for $1, he is able to invest $21203.27 in the American CD. At the end of the seventh year he converts the remaining DM (1.7823*7797.52) to dollars. The total amount of his investments at the end of year 7 will be $30478.23.

8.3   a)   If Lydia wants to ignore the risk of her investment she should invest all her money into the stock that promises the highest expected return. According to the predictions of the investment advisors the expected returns equal 0.2 (=20%) for Bigbell, 0.42 for Lotsofplace, 1 for Internetlife, 0.5 for Healthtomorrow, 0.46 for Quicky, and 0.3 for Automobile Alliance. Therefore, she should invest 100% of her money into Internetlife. The risk of this portfolio equals 0.333.

b) Lydia should put 40% of her money into the stock with the highest expected returns, 40% into the stock with the second highest expected returns, and 20% into the stock with the third highest expected returns.

We can also find this intuitive solution by solving a simple linear programming problem. We define the variables as follows:

BB = proportion (in percentage points) of Lydia's money invested in the stock Bigbell.

All other variables are defined correspondingly. The sum of all variables must equal 1 and no variable can exceed 0.4.

	A	B	C	D	E	F	G	H	I	J
1										
2	Server	BB	LOP	ILI	HEAL	QUI	AUA	Totals		
3	budget	1	1	1	1	1	1	1	=	1
4	objective	0.2	0.42	1	0.5	0.46	0.3	0.692		
5	Solution	0	0	0.4	0.4	0.2	0			
6	Maximum	0.40	0.40	0.40	0.40	0.40	0.40	0.04548		risk
7										
8		Formula in cell H3:		"=SUMPRODUCT(B3:G3,B5:G5)"						
9		Formula in cell H4:		"=SUMPRODUCT(B4:G4,B5:G5)"						
10										
11		Formula in cell H6:		"=SUMPRODUCT(B22:G22,B5:G5)"						
12										
13										
14		BB	LOP	ILI	HEAL	QUI	AUA			
15	BB	0.032	0.005	0.03	-0.031	-0.027	0.01			
16	LOP	0.005	0.1	0.085	-0.07	-0.05	0.02			
17	ILI	0.03	0.085	0.333	-0.11	-0.02	0.042			
18	HEAL	-0.031	-0.07	-0.11	0.125	0.05	-0.06			
19	QUI	-0.027	-0.05	-0.02	0.05	0.065	-0.02			
20	AUA	0.01	0.02	0.042	-0.06	-0.02	0.08			
21										
22		-0.0058	-0.004	0.0852	0.016	0.025	-0.0112			
23										
24		Formula in cell B22:		"=MMULT($B$5:$G$5,B$15:B$20)"						
25		Formula in cell C22:		"=MMULT($B$5:$G$5,C$15:C$20)"						
26		Formula in cell D22:		"=MMULT($B$5:$G$5,D$15:D$20)"						
27		Formula in cell E22:		"=MMULT($B$5:$G$5,E$15:E$20)"						
28		Formula in cell F22:		"=MMULT($B$5:$G$5,F$15:F$20)"						
29		Formula in cell G22:		"=MMULT($B$5:$G$5,G$15:G$20)"						

The solver dialogue box for this problem appears as follows:

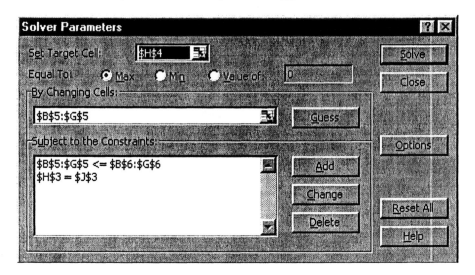

Throughout this case we use the following solver options:

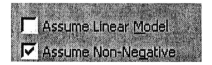

The total expected return of her portfolio is 69.2% with a total variance of 0.04548.

c) The risk of Lydia's portfolio is a quadratic function of her decision variables. We, therefore, apply quadratic programming to her decision problem.

d) Lydia's objective is now to maximize return – beta*risk. The constraints are the same as in part (b).

	A	B	C	D	E	F	G	H	I	J
1										
2	Server	BB	LOP	ILI	HEAL	QUI	AUA	Totals		
3	budget	1	1	1	1	1	1	1	=	1
4	objective	0.2	0.42	1	0.5	0.46	0.3	0.68063		
5	Solution	0	0	0.4	0.4	0.2	0	0.692		Return
6	Maximum	0.40	0.40	0.40	0.40	0.40	0.40	0.04548		Risk
7								0.25		beta
8		Formula in cell H3:	"=SUMPRODUCT(B3:G3,B5:G5)"							
9		Formula in cell H4:	"=H5-H7*H6"							
10		Formula in cell H5:	"=SUMPRODUCT(B4:G4,B5:G5)"							
11		Formula in cell H6:	"=SUMPRODUCT(B22:G22,B5:G5)"							
12										
13										
14		BB	LOP	ILI	HEAL	QUI	AUA			
15	BB	0.032	0.005	0.03	-0.031	-0.027	0.01			
16	LOP	0.005	0.1	0.085	-0.07	-0.05	0.02			
17	ILI	0.03	0.085	0.333	-0.11	-0.02	0.042			
18	HEAL	-0.031	-0.07	-0.11	0.125	0.05	-0.06			
19	QUI	-0.027	-0.05	-0.02	0.05	0.065	-0.02			
20	AUA	0.01	0.02	0.042	-0.06	-0.02	0.08			
21										
22		-0.0058	-0.004	0.0852	0.016	0.025	-0.0112			
23										
24		Formula in cell B22:	"=MMULT($B$5:$G$5,B$15:B$20)"							
25		Formula in cell C22:	"=MMULT($B$5:$G$5,C$15:C$20)"							
26		Formula in cell D22:	"=MMULT($B$5:$G$5,D$15:D$20)"							
27		Formula in cell E22:	"=MMULT($B$5:$G$5,E$15:E$20)"							
28		Formula in cell F22:	"=MMULT($B$5:$G$5,F$15:F$20)"							
29		Formula in cell G22:	"=MMULT($B$5:$G$5,G$15:G$20)"							

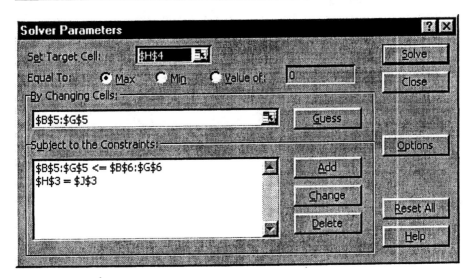

Due to the small emphasis (beta = 0.25) Lydia puts on risk her investment portfolio is the same as in part (b).

e) For the investment policy of part (d) Lydia invests $6000 in ILI (1500 shares at $4), $6000 in HEAL (120 shares at $50), and $3000 in QUI (20 shares at $150).

f) For beta = 0.5 the optimal portfolio does not change (we only display the relevant output of the spreadsheet):

	A	B	C	D	E	F	G	H	I	J
1										
2	Server	BB	LOP	ILI	HEAL	QUI	AUA	Totals		
3	budget	1	1	1	1	1	1	1	=	1
4	objective	0.2	0.42	1	0.5	0.46	0.3	0.66926		
5	Solution	0	0	0.4	0.4	0.2	0	0.692		Return
6	Maximum	0.40	0.40	0.40	0.40	0.40	0.40	0.04548		Risk
7								0.5		beta

For beta = 1 we obtain the following result:

	A	B	C	D	E	F	G	H	I	J
1										
2	Server	BB	LOP	ILI	HEAL	QUI	AUA	Totals		
3	budget	1	1	1	1	1	1	1	=	1
4	objective	0.2	0.42	1	0.5	0.46	0.3	0.6468257		
5	Solution	0	0.033962	0.4	0.4	0.16604	0	0.6906415		Return
6	Maximum	0.40	0.40	0.40	0.40	0.40	0.40	0.0438158		Risk
7								1		beta

Lydia invests 40% of her money in ILI and HEAL respectively, 16.604% in QUI, and 3.396% in LOP.

When beta = 2 the portfolio changes again:

	A	B	C	D	E	F	G	H	I	J
1										
2	Server	BB	LOP	ILI	HEAL	QUI	AUA	Totals		
3	budget	1	1	1	1	1	1	1	=	1
4	objective	0.2	0.42	1	0.5	0.46	0.3	0.6037645		
5	Solution	0	0.071698	0.4	0.4	0.1283	0	0.6891321		Return
6	Maximum	0.40	0.40	0.40	0.40	0.40	0.40	0.0426838		Risk
7								2		beta

Lydia invests 40% of her money in ILI and HEAL respectively, 12.83% in QUI, and 7.17% in LOP.

g) The general rule is that as we include more and more different stocks into Lydia's portfolio, the total variance (risk) decreases - or gets "diversified away". LOP has a negative covariance with respect to QUI and HEAL. Including LOP into the portfolio thus reduces total variance. The benefit of this lower variance outweighs the fact that LOP offers a slightly lower expected return than QUI (42% vs. 46%). However, low variance becomes more and more important as beta increases. That explains why LOP is being substituted for QUI.

h) The return of Lydia's portfolio is no longer a part of the objective but now becomes part of a new constraint: return >= 0.35. The objective is now to minimize the risk.

	A	B	C	D	E	F	G	H	I	J
1										
2	Server	BB	LOP	ILI	HEAL	QUI	AUA	Totals		
3	budget	1	1	1	1	1	1	1	=	1
4	return	0.2	0.42	1	0.5	0.46	0.3	0.3591996	>=	0.35
5	Solution	0.317717	0.198843	0	0.168351	0.209	0.10609	0.0013602		Risk
6	Maximum	0.40	0.40	0.40	0.40	0.40	0.40			
7										
8										
9		Formula in cell H3:			"=SUMPRODUCT(B3:G3,B5:G5)"					
10		Formula in cell H4:			"=SUMPRODUCT(B4:G4,B5:G5)"					
11		Formula in cell H5:			"=SUMPRODUCT(B22:G22,B5:G5)"					
12										
13										
14		BB	LOP	ILI	HEAL	QUI	AUA			
15	BB	0.032	0.005	0.03	-0.031	-0.027	0.01			
16	LOP	0.005	0.1	0.085	-0.07	-0.05	0.02			
17	ILI	0.03	0.085	0.333	-0.11	-0.02	0.042			
18	HEAL	-0.031	-0.07	-0.11	0.125	0.05	-0.06			
19	QUI	-0.027	-0.05	-0.02	0.05	0.065	-0.02			
20	AUA	0.01	0.02	0.042	-0.06	-0.02	0.08			
21										
22		0.00136	0.00136	0.00819	0.00136	0.00136	0.00136			
23										
24		Formula in cell B22:			"=MMULT($B$5:$G$5,B15:B20)"					
25		Formula in cell C22:			"=MMULT($B$5:$G$5,C15:C20)"					
26		Formula in cell D22:			"=MMULT($B$5:$G$5,D15:D20)"					
27		Formula in cell E22:			"=MMULT($B$5:$G$5,E15:E20)"					
28		Formula in cell F22:			"=MMULT($B$5:$G$5,F15:F20)"					
29		Formula in cell G22:			"=MMULT($B$5:$G$5,G15:G20)"					

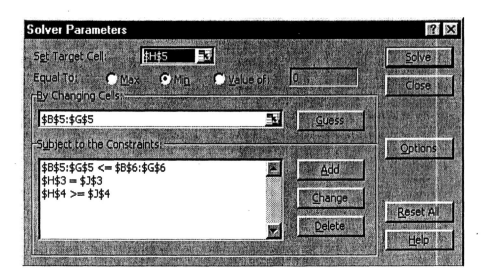

Lydia's optimal portfolio consists of 31.77% BB, 19.88% LOP, 16.84% HEAL, 20.90% QUI, and 10.61% AUA. Her expected return equals 35.92% with a risk of 0.00136.

i) Since the return constraint in not binding in part (h), decreasing the right-hand-side will not change the optimal solution. The minimum risk for a minimum expected return of 25% is the same as for a minimum expected return of 35%.

For a minimum expected return of 40% we obtain a new portfolio:

	A	B	C	D	E	F	G	H	I	J
1										
2	Server	BB	LOP	ILI	HEAL	QUI	AUA	Totals		
3	budget	1	1	1	1	1	1	1	=	1
4	return	0.2	0.42	1	0.5	0.46	0.3	0.4	>=	0.4
5	Solution	0.229309	0.21032	0.03392	0.219701	0.18757	0.11919	0.0023269		Risk
6	Maximum	0.40	0.40	0.40	0.40	0.40	0.40			

Lydia's optimal portfolio consists of 22.93% BB, 21.03% LOP, 3.39% ILI, 21.97% HEAL, 18.76% QUI, and 11.92% AUA. Her expected return equals 40% with a risk of 0.00233.

j) Lydia's approach is very risky. She puts a lot of confidence in the advice of the two investment experts. Of course, Lydia cannot expect to find an optimal investment strategy with her model if the estimates she uses for the input parameters are wrong.

8.4   a)   We can apply goal programming to Mr. Baker's problem.

b) We need to develop a goal programming problem whose solution characterizes Mr. Baker's shipping policy. We define the following variables:

Basic = Number (in 1000's) of basic packages sent
Advanced = Number (in 1000's) of advanced packages sent
Supreme = Number (in 1000's) of supreme packages sent
Doctors = Number of doctors sent

For Mr. Baker's goals we define the following variables:

V-cost = Amount (in 1000's of dollars) over the cost goal
U-cost = Amount (in 1000's of dollars) under the cost goal
V-people = Number (in 1000's) of people over the people goal
U-people = Number (in 1000's) of people under the people goal
V-sup = Number (in 1000's) of supreme packages over the supreme goal
U-sup = Number (in 1000's) of supreme packages under the supreme goal

Note: Measuring most variables in 1000's greatly improves the reliability of the Excel Solver.

Mr. Baker faces three hard constraints. First, the sum of the package variables (Basic + Advanced + Supreme) must not exceed 40 (Note, packages are measured in 1000's). Second, the weight of all packages combined (120*Basic + 180*Advanced + 220*Supreme) must be less than or equal to 6000 (since packages are measured in 1000's, we divide also the total weight by 1000). Third, we need to incorporate the safety restriction Supreme <= 0.1*Doctors.

In addition, we need to include three constraints for Mr. Baker's goals. For example, for his cost goal the constraint equals

300*Basic + 350*Advanced + 720*Supreme + U-cost − V-cost = 20000.

Three deviations from Mr. Baker's goals are penalized resulting in an objective function of 0.001*V-cost + 0.07*U-people + U-sup

	A	B	C	D	E	F	G	H	I	J	K	L	M	N
1														
2	Server	Basic	Advanced	Supreme	Doctors	U-cost	V-cost	U-people	V-people	U-sup	V-sup	Totals		
3	packets	1	1	1	0	0	0	0	0	0	0	40	<=	40
4	weight	120	180	220	0	0	0	0	0	0	0	6000	<=	6000
5	safety	0	0	1	-0.1	0	0	0	0	0	0	0	<=	0
6	cost	300	350	720	33	1	-1	0	0	0	0	20000	=	20000
7	people	30	35	54	0	0	0	1	-1	0	0	2200	=	2200
8	supreme	0	0	1	0	0	0	0	0	1	-1	3	=	3
9	Points	0	0	0	0	0	0.001	0.07	0	1	0	50.84		
10	Solution	28	0	12	120	0	1000	712	0	0	9			
11														
12														
13			Formula in cell L3:			"=SUMPRODUCT(B3:K3,B10:K10)"								
14			Formula in cell L4:			"=SUMPRODUCT(B4:K4,B10:K10)"								
15			Formula in cell L5:			"=SUMPRODUCT(B5:K5,B10:K10)"								
16			Formula in cell L6:			"=SUMPRODUCT(B6:K6,B10:K10)"								
17			Formula in cell L7:			"=SUMPRODUCT(B7:K7,B10:K10)"								
18			Formula in cell L8:			"=SUMPRODUCT(B8:K8,B10:K10)"								
19			Formula in cell L9:			"=SUMPRODUCT(B9:K9,B10:K10)"								

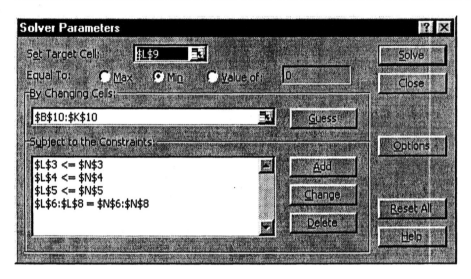

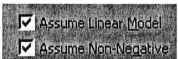

Mr. Baker should send 28,000 basic packages and 12,000 supreme packages along with 120 doctors to Cuba.

c) The coefficient of U-people in the objective function changes. The new penalty weight for being below the people goal equals 10/55.

	A	B	C	D	E	F	G	H	I	J	K	L	M	N
1														
2	Server	Basic	Advanced	Supreme	Doctors	U-cost	V-cost	U-people	V-people	U-sup	V-sup	Totals		
3	packets	1	1	1	0	0	0	0	0	0	0	40	<=	40
4	weight	120	180	220	0	0	0	0	0	0	0	6000	<=	6000
5	safety	0	0	1	-0.1	0	0	0	0	0	0	0	<=	0
6	cost	300	350	720	33	1	-1	0	0	0	0	20000	=	20000
7	people	30	35	54	0	0	0	1	-1	0	0	2200	=	2200
8	supreme	0	0	1	0	0	0	0	0	1	-1	3	=	3
9	Points	0	0	0	0	0	0.001	0.18182	0	1	0	130.4545		
10	Solution	28	0	12	120	0	1000	712	0	0	9			
11														
12														
13			Formula in cell L3:			"=SUMPRODUCT(B3:K3,B10:K10)"								
14			Formula in cell L4:			"=SUMPRODUCT(B4:K4,B10:K10)"								
15			Formula in cell L5:			"=SUMPRODUCT(B5:K5,B10:K10)"								
16			Formula in cell L6:			"=SUMPRODUCT(B6:K6,B10:K10)"								
17			Formula in cell L7:			"=SUMPRODUCT(B7:K7,B10:K10)"								
18			Formula in cell L8:			"=SUMPRODUCT(B8:K8,B10:K10)"								
19			Formula in cell L9:			"=SUMPRODUCT(B9:K9,B10:K10)"								

The optimal shipping policy did not change. The plan appears to be very insensitive to drastic increases in the penalty weight for violating the goal to reach at least 20% of the Cuban population.

d) The coefficient of Doctors in the safety constraint changes from –0.1 to –0.075.

	A	B	C	D	E	F	G	H	I	J	K	L	M	N
1														
2	Server	Basic	Advanced	Supreme	Doctors	U-cost	V-cost	U-people	V-people	U-sup	V-sup	Totals		
3	packets	1	1	1	0	0	0	0	0	0	0	40	<=	40
4	weight	120	180	220	0	0	0	0	0	0	0	6000	<=	6000
5	safety	0	0	1	-0.075	0	0	0	0	0	0	0	<=	0
6	cost	300	350	720	33	1	-1	0	0	0	0	20000	=	20000
7	people	30	35	54	0	0	0	1	-1	0	0	2200	=	2200
8	supreme	0	0	1	0	0	0	0	0	1	-1	3	=	3
9	Points	0	0	0	0	0	0.001	0.18182	0	1	0	131.7745		
10	Solution	28	0	12	160	0	2320	712	0	0	9			
11														
12														
13			Formula in cell L3:			"=SUMPRODUCT(B3:K3,B10:K10)"								
14			Formula in cell L4:			"=SUMPRODUCT(B4:K4,B10:K10)"								
15			Formula in cell L5:			"=SUMPRODUCT(B5:K5,B10:K10)"								
16			Formula in cell L6:			"=SUMPRODUCT(B6:K6,B10:K10)"								
17			Formula in cell L7:			"=SUMPRODUCT(B7:K7,B10:K10)"								
18			Formula in cell L8:			"=SUMPRODUCT(B8:K8,B10:K10)"								
19			Formula in cell L9:			"=SUMPRODUCT(B9:K9,B10:K10)"								

While the number of packages Mr. Baker should ship has not changed, the number of doctors is now 160.

e) The budget restriction is now a hard constraint and the penalty variables for the cost goal can be eliminated.

	A	B	C	D	E	F	G	H	I	J	K	L
1												
2	Server	Basic	Advanced	Supreme	Doctors	U-people	V-people	U-sup	V-sup	Totals		
3	packets	1	1	1	0	0	0	0	0	40	<=	40
4	weight	120	180	220	0	0	0	0	0	6000	<=	6000
5	safety	0	0	1	-0.1	0	0	0	0	0	<=	0
6	cost	300	350	720	33	0	0	0	0	20000	<=	20000
7	people	30	35	54	0	1	-1	0	0	2200	=	2200
8	supreme	0	0	1	0	0	0	1	-1	3	=	3
9	Points	0	0	0	0	0.07	0	1	0	51.485		
10	Solution	27	2.5	10.5	105	735.5	0	0	7.5			
11												
12												
13			Formula in cell L3:			"=SUMPRODUCT(B3:I3,B10:I10)"						
14			Formula in cell L4:			"=SUMPRODUCT(B4:I4,B10:I10)"						
15			Formula in cell L5:			"=SUMPRODUCT(B5:I5,B10:I10)"						
16			Formula in cell L6:			"=SUMPRODUCT(B6:I6,B10:I10)"						
17			Formula in cell L7:			"=SUMPRODUCT(B7:I7,B10:I10)"						
18			Formula in cell L8:			"=SUMPRODUCT(B8:I8,B10:I10)"						
19			Formula in cell L9:			"=SUMPRODUCT(B9:I9,B10:I10)"						

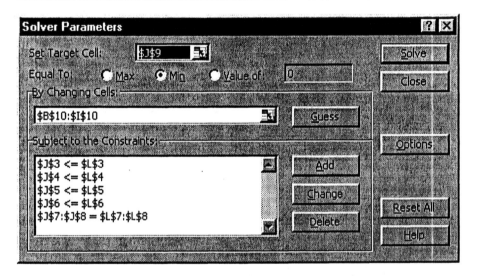

Mr. Baker should send 27,000 basic packages, 2,500 advanced packages, and 10,500 supreme packages along with 105 doctors to Cuba.

CHAPTER 9
USING BINARY INTEGER PROGRAMMING TO DEAL WITH YES-OR-NO DECISIONS

Review Questions

9.1-1   The decisions are 1) whether to build a factory in Los Angeles, 2) whether to build a factory in San Francisco, 3) whether to build a warehouse in Los Angeles, and 4) whether to build a warehouse in San Francisco.

9.1-2   Binary decision variables are appropriate because there are only two alternatives, choose yes or choose no.

9.1-3   The objective is to find the feasible combination of investments that maximizes the total net present value.

9.1-4   The mutually exclusive alternatives are to build a warehouse in Los Angeles or build a warehouse in San Francisco. The form of the resulting constraint is that the sum of these variables must be less than or equal to 1 ($x_3 + x_4 \leq 1$).

9.1-5   The contingent decisions are the decisions to build a warehouse. The forms of these constraints are $-x_1 + x_3 \leq 0$ and $-x_2 + x_4 \leq 0$.

9.2-1   A value of 1 is assigned for choosing yes and a value of 0 is assigned for choosing no.

9.2-2   Yes-or-no decisions for capital budgeting with fixed investments are whether or not to make a certain fixed investment.

9.2-3   Yes-or-no decisions for site selections are whether or not a certain site should be selected for the location of a certain new facility.

9.2-4   When designing a production and distribution network, yes-or-no decisions like should a certain plant remain open, should a certain site be selected for a new plant, should a certain distribution center remain open, should a certain site be selected for a new distribution center, and should a certain distribution center be assigned to serve a certain market area might arise.

9.2-5   Should a certain route be selected for one of the trucks.

9.2-6   It is estimated that China is saving about $6.4 billion over the 15 years.

9.2-7   The form of each yes-or-no decision is should a certain asset be sold in a certain time period.

9.2-8   The airline industry uses BIP for fleet assignment problems and crew scheduling problems.

9.3-1   A binary decision variable is a binary variable that represents a yes-or-no decision. An auxiliary binary variable is an additional binary variable that is introduced into the model, not to represent a yes-or-no decision, but simply to help formulate the model as a BIP problem.

9.3-2   The net profit is no longer directly proportional to the number of units produced so a linear programming formulation is no longer valid.

9.3-3   An auxiliary binary variable can be introduced for a setup cost and can be defined as 1 if the setup is performed to initiate the production of a certain product and defined as 0 if setup is not performed.

9.3-4 Mutually exclusive products exist when at most one product can be chosen for production due to competition for the same customers.

9.3-5 An auxiliary binary variable can be defined as 1 if the product can be produced and defined as 0 if the product cannot be produced.

9.3-6 An either-or constraint arises because the products are to be produced at either Plant 3 or Plant 4, not both.

9.3-7 An auxiliary binary variable can be defined as 1 if the first constraint must hold and defined as 0 if the second constraint must hold.

9.4-1 Restriction 1 is similar to the restriction imposed in Variation 2 except that it involves more products and choices.

9.4-2 The constraint $y_1 + y_2 + y_3 \leq 2$ forces choosing at most two of the possible new products.

9.4-3 It is not possible to write a legitimate objective function because profit is not proportional to the number of TV spots allocated to that product.

9.4-4 The groups of mutually exclusive alternative in Example 2 are $x_1 = 0,1,2,$ or 3, $x_2 = 0,1,2,$ or 3, and $x_3 = 0,1,2,$ or 3.

9.4-5 The mathematical form of the constraint is $x_1 + x_4 + x_7 + x_{10} \geq 1$. This constraint says that sequence 1,4,7, and 10 include a necessary flight and that one of the sequences must be chosen to ensure that a crew covers the flight.

Problems

9.1   a)

Let F_{LA} = 1 if build a factory in LA; 0 otherwise

F_{SF} = 1 if build a factory in SF; 0 otherwise

F_{SD} = 1 if build a factory in SD; 0 otherwise

W_{LA} = 1 if build a warehouse in LA; 0 otherwise

W_{SF} = 1 if build a warehouse in SF; 0 otherwise

W_{SD} = 1 if build a warehouse in SD; 0 otherwise

Maximize $NPV = 9F_{LA} + 5F_{SF} + 7F_{SD} + 6W_{LA} + 4W_{SF} + 5W_{SD}$

subject to $6F_{LA} + 3F_{SF} + 4F_{SD} + 5W_{LA} + 2W_{SF} + 3W_{SD} \leq 10$

$W_{LA} + W_{SF} + W_{SD} \leq 1$

$-F_{LA} + W_{LA} \leq 0$

$-F_{SF} + W_{SF} \leq 0$

$-F_{SD} + W_{SD} \leq 0$

and $F_{LA}, F_{SF}, F_{SD}, W_{LA}, W_{SF}, W_{SD}$ are binary variables.

b)

Constraint	Warehouse in LA?	Factory in LA?	Warehouse in SD?	Factory in SD?	Warehouse in SF?	Factory in SF?	Totals		Right-Hand Side
				Yes-or-No Question					
Capital ($millions)	5	6	3	4	2	3	10	≤	10
≤ 1 Warehouse	1	0	1	0	1	0	1	≤	1
NPV ($millions)	6	9	5	7	4	5	17		
Solution	0	≤	0	1	≤	1	0	≤	1

9.2   See the articles in Interfaces.

9.3   a)

Let M_E = 1 if Eve does marketing; 0 if not

M_S = 1 if Steven does marketing; 0 if not

C_E = 1 if Eve does cooking; 0 if not

C_S = 1 if Steven does cooking; 0 if not

D_E = 1 if Eve does dishwashing; 0 if not

D_S = 1 if Steven does dishwashing; 0 if not

L_E = 1 if Eve does laundry; 0 if not

L_S = 1 if Steven does laundry; 0 if not.

Minimize $T = 4.5M_E + 7.8C_E + 3.6D_E + 2.9L_E$

$+4.9M_S + 7.2C_S + 4.3D_S + 3.1L_S,$

subject to $M_E + C_E + D_E + L_E = 2$

$M_S + C_S + D_S + L_S = 2$

$M_E + M_S = 1$

$C_E + C_S = 1$

$D_E + D_S = 1$

$L_E + L_S = 1,$

and $M_E, M_S, C_E, C_S, D_E, D_S, L_E, L_S$ are binary variables.

b)

Constraint	Marketing by Eve	Marketing by Steven	Cooking by Eve	Cooking by Steven	Dishes by Eve	Dishes by Steven	Laundry by Eve	Laundry by Steven	Total		Right-Hand Side
					Yes-or-No Question						
Eve's Chores	1	0	1	0	1	0	1	0	2	=	2
Steven's Chores	0	1	0	1	0	1	0	1	2	=	2
Marketing	1	1	0	0	0	0	0	0	1	=	1
Cooking	0	0	1	1	0	0	0	0	1	=	1
Dishwashing	0	0	0	0	1	1	0	0	1	=	1
Laundry	0	0	0	0	0	0	1	1	1	=	1
Time Needed	4.5	4.9	7.8	7.2	3.6	4.3	2.9	3.1	18.4 hours		
Solution	1	0	0	1	1	0	0	1			

9.4 a)

Let $\quad x_1 =$ 1 if invest in project 1; 0 if not

$\quad x_2 =$ 1 if invest in project 2; 0 if not

$\quad x_3 =$ 1 if invest in project 3; 0 if not

$\quad x_4 =$ 1 if invest in project 4; 0 if not

$\quad x_5 =$ 1 if invest in project 5; 0 if not

Maximize $NPV = x_1 + 1.8x_2 + 1.6x_3 + 0.8x_4 + 1.4x_5$

subject to $\quad 6x_1 + 12x_2 + 10x_3 + 4x_4 + 8x_5 \leq 20$

and $\quad x_1,\ x_2,\ x_3,\ x_4,\ x_5,$ are binary variables.

b)

Constraint	Project 1	Project 2	Project 3	Project 4	Project 5	Total		Right-Hand Side
			Yes-or-No Question					
Capital	6	12	10	4	8	20	$\leq$	20
Net Present Value	1	1.8	1.6	0.8	1.4	$3.4 million		
Solution	1	0	1	1	0			

9.5

Constraint	Opp. 1	Opp. 2	Opp. 3	Opp. 4	Opp. 5	Opp. 6	Opp. 7	Totals		Right-Hand Side
			Yes-or-No Question							
Capital ($millions)	43	28	34	48	17	32	23	100	$\leq$	100
1 & 2 Exclusive	1	1	0	0	0	0	0	1	$\leq$	1
3 & 4 Exclusive	0	0	1	1	0	0	0	1	$\leq$	1
NPV ($millions)	17	10	15	19	7	13	9	41		
Solution	1	0	1	0	0	0	1			
			$\leq$	$\leq$						
3 & 4 only if 1 or 2			1	1						

9.6

		Carl	Chris	David	Tony	Ken	Supply
		Unit Cost (Seconds) Task (Swimmer)					
Assignee (Stroke)	Back	37.7	32.9	33.8	37	35.4	1
	Breast	43.4	33.1	42.2	34.7	41.8	1
	Fly	33.3	28.5	38.9	30.4	33.6	1
	Free	29.2	26.4	29.6	28.5	31.1	1
Demand		1	1	1	1	1	

Assignment

		Carl	Chris	David	Tony	Ken	Totals		Supply
		Task (Swimmer)							
Assignee (Stroke)	Back	0	0	1	0	0	1	=	1
	Breast	0	0	0	1	0	1	=	1
	Fly	0	1	0	0	0	1	=	1
	Free	1	0	0	0	0	1	=	1
Totals		1	1	1	1	0			
		≤	≤	≤	≤	≤	Total Cost =		126.20
Demand		1	1	1	1	1			

Each swimmer can only swim one stroke. Each stroke can only be swum by one swimmer.

9.7

Constraint	Product 1	Product 2	Product 3	Product 4	Totals		Modified Right-Hand Side	Original Right-Hand Side
First	5	3	6	4	6000	≤	6000	6000
Second	4	6	3	5	12000	≤	105999	6000
Marginal revenue	$70	$60	$90	$80	$80000			
Solution	0	2000	0	0				
	≤	≤	≤	≤				
	0	9999	0	0				
Set Up?	0	1	0	0	1	≤	2	
Start-up Cost	$50,000	$40,000	$70,000	$60,000				

Contingency Constraints:

Product 3:	0	≤	1	:Product 1 or 2
Product 4:	0	≤	1	:Product 1 or 2

Which Constraint (0 = First, 1 = Second):	0

9.8

Constraint	Toy 1	Toy 2	Totals		Modified Right-Hand Side	Original Right-Hand Side
Factory 1	0.02	0.025	560	≤	10499	500
Factory 2	0.025	0.04	700	≤	700	700
Unit Profit	$10	$15	$230000			
Solution	28000	0				
	≤	≤				
	99999	0				
Set Up?	1	0				
Setup Cost	$50,000	$80,000				

Which factory? (0=Factory 1, 1=Factory 2)	1

9.9

Constraint	Amt. For Customer 1	Amt. For Customer 2	Amt. For Customer 3	Totals		Right-Hand Side
Capacity	0.2	0.4	0.2	1	≤	1
Max. Sales - Customer 1	1	0	0	0	≤	3
Max. Sales - Customer 2	0	1	0	2	≤	2
Max. Sales - Customer 3	0	0	1	1	≤	5
Marginal Net Revenue	$2	$3	$1	$4.8 million		
Solution	0	2	1			
	≤	≤	≤			
	0	99	99			
Set Up?	0	1	1			
Setup Cost(millions)	$3	$2	$0			

9.10

Constraint	Customer 1 1 Plane	2 Planes	3 Planes	Customer 2 1 Plane	2 Planes	Customer 3 1 Plane	2 Planes	3 Planes	4 Planes	5 Planes	Total		Right-Hand Side
Capacity	0.2	0.4	0.6	0.4	0.8	0.2	0.4	0.6	0.8	1	1	≤	1
Customer 1	1	1	1	0	0	0	0	0	0	0	1	≤	1
Customer 2	0	0	0	1	1	0	0	0	0	0	0	≤	1
Customer 3	0	0	0	0	0	1	1	1	1	1	1	≤	1
Profit	-1	2	4	1	5	1	3	5	6	7	$7.0 million		
Solution	0	0	1	0	0	0	1	0	0	0			

An alternative optimal solution is to produce 5 planes for customer 3.

9.11

Constraint	Product 1	Product 2	Product 3	Total		Right-Hand Side
Milling	9	3	5	498	≤	500
Lathe	5	4	0	349	≤	350
Grinder	3	0	2	135	≤	150
Sales Potential	0	0	1	0	≤	20
Unit Profit	50	20	25	$2870		
Solution	45	31	0			
	≤	≤	≤			
	999	999	0			
Produce?	1	1	0	2	≤	2

9.12 a)

Let $y_{ij} = 1$ if $x_i = j$; 0 if not (for $i = 1, 2$ and $j = 1, 2, 3$).

Maximize Profit $= 3y_{11} + 8y_{12} + 9y_{13} + 9y_{21} + 24y_{22} + 9y_{23}$,

subject to $\quad y_{11} + y_{12} + y_{13} \le 1$

$$y_{21} + y_{22} + y_{23} \le 1$$

$$(y_{11} + 2y_{12} + 3y_{13}) + (y_{21} + 2y_{22} + 3y_{23}) \le 3,$$

and $\quad y_{ij}$ are binary variables.

b)

Constraint	X1=1	X1=2	X1=3	X2=1	X2=2	X2=3	Total		Right-Hand Side
X1	1	1	1	0	0	0	1	$\le$	1
X2	0	0	0	1	1	1	1	$\le$	1
No more than 3	1	2	3	1	2	3	3	$\le$	3
Profit	3	8	9	9	24	9	$27.0		
Solution	1	0	0	0	1	0			

c) Optimal Solution $(x_1, x_2) = (1, 2)$. Profit $= \$27$.

9.13

			Yes-or-No?								
			Arc Between Nodes								Right-Hand
Constraint	OA	OB	AC	AD	BC	BD	CT	DT	Total		Side
Stage 1	1	1	0	0	0	0	0	0	1	=	1
Stage 2	0	0	1	1	1	1	0	0	1	=	1
Stage 3	0	0	0	0	0	0	1	1	1	=	1
OA chosen	-1	0	1	1	0	0	0	0	0	$\le$	0
OB chosen	0	-1	0	0	1	1	0	0	0	$\le$	0
CT chosen	0	0	-1	0	-1	0	1	0	0	$\le$	0
DT chosen	0	0	0	-1	0	-1	0	1	0	$\le$	0
Cost	3	6	6	5	4	3	3	2	10		
Solution	1	0	0	1	0	0	0	1			

The first three constraints are for mutually exclusive alternative (at each stage, exactly one arc is used). The last four constraints are for contingent decisions (a route leaves a node only if a route enters the node).

9.14

Delivery Location	1	2	3	4	5	6	7	8	9	10	Total		Right-Hand Side
					Yes-or-No? Possible Routes								
A	1	0	0	0	1	0	0	0	1	0	1	≥	1
B	0	1	0	1	0	1	0	0	1	1	1	≥	1
C	0	0	1	1	0	0	1	0	1	0	1	≥	1
D	1	0	0	0	0	1	0	1	0	0	1	≥	1
E	0	0	1	1	0	1	0	0	0	0	1	≥	1
F	0	1	0	0	1	0	0	0	0	0	1	≥	1
G	1	0	0	0	0	0	1	1	0	1	1	≥	1
H	0	0	1	0	1	0	0	0	0	1	1	≥	1
I	0	1	0	1	0	0	1	0	0	0	1	≥	1
3 routes	1	1	1	1	1	1	1	1	1	1	3	=	3
Cost	6	4	7	5	4	6	5	3	7	6	12		
Solution	0	0	0	1	1	0	0	1	0	0			

9.15

Station Location	Station?	Tract 1	Tract 2	Tract 3	Tract 4	Tract 5
		Tract Assigned to Station?				
1	1	1	0	0	0	1
2	1	0	1	1	1	0
3	0	0	0	0	0	0
4	0	0	0	0	0	0
5	0	0	0	0	0	0
Total	2	1	1	1	1	1
	=	=	=	=	=	=
	2	1	1	1	1	1

Station Location	Tract 1	Tract 2	Tract 3	Tract 4	Tract 5
	Average Total Response Time Per Day				
1	10	12	90	20	45
2	40	4	45	10	75
3	30	20	18	15	36
4	50	15	75	4	30
5	20	25	45	12	15

Average Response Time (minutes) = 11.4

The six equality constraints (total stations = 2; one station assigned to each tract) correspond to mutually exclusive alternatives. In addition, there are the following contingent decision constraints: each tract can only be assigned to a station location if there is a station at that location.

9.16 a)

Let $x_i = 1$ if a station is located in tract i; 0 if not

(for $i = 1, 2, 3, 4, 5$).

Minimize Cost $= 200,000x_1 + 250,000x_2 + 400,000x_3 + 300,000x_4 + 500,000x_5$

subject to $\quad x_1 + x_3 + x_5 \geq 1$

$\qquad\qquad x_1 + x_2 + x_4 \geq 1$

$\qquad\qquad x_2 + x_3 + x_5 \geq 1$

$\qquad\qquad x_2 + x_3 + x_4 + x_5 \geq 1$

$\qquad\qquad x_1 + x_3 + x_4 + x_5 \geq 1,$

and $\quad x_i$ are binary variables (for $i = 1, 2, 3, 4, 5$).

b)

Delivery Location	Yes-or-No? Locate a station in Tract					Total		Right-Hand Side
	1	2	3	4	5			
1	1	0	1	0	1	1	≥	1
2	1	1	0	1	0	2	≥	1
3	0	1	1	0	1	1	≥	1
4	0	1	1	1	1	1	≥	1
5	1	0	1	1	1	1	≥	1
Cost	200	250	400	300	500	450	thousand	
Solution	1	1	0	0	0			

Cases

9.1   a) We want to maximize the number of pieces displayed in the exhibit. For each piece, we therefore need to decide whether or not we should display the piece. Each piece becomes a binary decision variable. The decision variable is assigned 1 if we want to display the piece and assigned 0 if we do not want to display the piece.

We group our constraints into four categories – the artistic constraints imposed by Ash, the personal constraints imposed by Ash, the constraints imposed by Celeste, and the cost constraint. We now step through each of these constraint categories.

Artistic Constraints Imposed by Ash

Ash imposes the following constraints that depend upon the type of art that is displayed. The constraints are as follows:

1. Ash wants to include only one collage. We have four collages available: "Wasted Resources" by Norm Marson, "Consumerism" by Angie Oldman, "My Namesake" by Ziggy Lite, and "Narcissism" by Ziggy Lite. This constraint forces us to include only one of these four pieces.

2. Ash wants at least one wire-mesh sculpture displayed if a computer-generated drawing is displayed. We have three wire-mesh sculptures available and two computer-generated drawings available. Thus, if we include either one or two computer-generated drawings, we have to include at least one wire-mesh sculpture.

3. Ash wants at least one computer-generated drawing displayed if a wire-mesh sculpture is displayed. We have two computer-generated drawings available and three wire-mesh sculptures available. Thus, if we include one, two, or three wire-mesh sculptures, we have to include either one or two computer-generated drawings.

4. Ash wants at least one photo-realistic painting displayed. We have three photo-realistic paintings available: "Storefront Window" by David Lyman, "Harley" by David Lyman, and "Rick" by Rick Rawls. At least one of these three paintings has to be displayed.

5. Ash wants at least one cubist painting displayed. We have three cubist paintings available: "Rick II" by Rick Rawls, "Study of a Violin" by Helen Row, and "Study of a Fruit Bowl" by Helen Row. At least one of these three paintings has to be displayed.

6. Ash wants at least one expressionist painting displayed. We have only one expressionist painting available: "Rick III" by Rick Rawls. This painting has to be displayed.

7. Ash wants at least one watercolor painting displayed. We have six watercolor paintings available: "Serenity" by Candy Tate, "Calm Before the Storm" by Candy Tate, "All That Glitters" by Ash Briggs, "The Rock" by Ash Briggs, "Winding Road" by Ash Briggs, and "Dreams Come True" by Ash Briggs. At least one of these six paintings has to be displayed.

8. Ash wants at least one oil painting displayed. We have five oil paintings available: "Void" by Robert Bayer, "Sun" by Robert Bayer, "Beyond" by Bill Reynolds, "Pioneers" by Bill Reynolds, and "Living Land" by Bear Canton. At least one of these five paintings has to be displayed.

9. Finally, Ash wants the number of paintings to be no greater than twice the number of other art forms. We have 18 paintings available and 16 other art forms available. We classify the following pieces as paintings: "Serenity," "Calm Before the Storm," "Void," "Sun," "Storefront Window," "Harley," "Rick," "Rick II," "Rick III," "Beyond," "Pioneers," "Living Land," "Study of a Violin," "Study of a Fruit Bowl," "All That Glitters," "The Rock," "Winding Road," and "Dreams Come True." The maximum number of these paintings that we display has to be less than or equal to twice the number of other art forms we display.

Personal Constraints Imposed by Ash

1. Ash wants all of his own paintings included in the exhibit, so we must include "All That Glitters," "The Rock," "Winding Road," and "Dreams Come True."

2. Ash wants all of Candy Tate's work included in the exhibit, so we must include "Serenity" and "Calm Before the Storm."

3. Ash wants to include at least one piece from David Lyman, so we have to include one or more of the following pieces: "Storefront Window" and "Harley."

4. Ash wants to include at least one piece from Rick Rawls, so we have to include one or more of the following pieces: "Rick," "Rick II," and "Rick III."

5. Ash wants to display as many pieces from David Lyman as from Rick Rawls. Because the number of displayed pieces from David Lyman has to equal the number of displayed pieces from Rick Rawls and because David Lyman only has two pieces available, we can only display a maximum of two pieces from each of these artists.

6. Finally, Ash wants at most one piece from Ziggy Lite displayed. We can therefore include either none or one of the following pieces: "My Namesake" and "Narcissism."

Constraints Imposed by Celeste

1. Celeste wants to include at least one piece from a female artist for every two pieces included from a male artist. We have 11 pieces by female artists available: "Chaos Reigns" by Rita Losky, "Who Has Control?" by Rita Losky, "Domestication" by Rita Losky, "Innocence" by Rita Losky, "Serenity" by Candy Tate, "Calm Before the Storm" by Candy Tate, "Consumerism" by Angie Oldman, "Reflection" by Angie Oldman, "Trojan Victory" by Angie Oldman, "Study of a Violin" by Helen Row, and "Study of a Fruit Bowl" by Helen Row. One or more of these pieces has to be displayed for every two pieces by male artists displayed.

2. Celeste wants either one or both of the pieces "Aging Earth" and "Wasted Resources" displayed.

3. Celeste wants to include at least one piece by Bear Canton, so we must include one or more of the following pieces: "Wisdom," "Superior Powers," and "Living Land."

4. Celeste wants to include one or more of the following pieces: "Chaos Reigns," "Who Has Control," "Beyond," and "Pioneers."

5. Celeste knows that the museum only has enough floor space for four sculptures. We have six sculptures available: "Perfection" by Colin Zweibell, "Burden" by Colin Zweibell, "The Great Equalizer" by Colin Zweibell, "Aging Earth" by Norm Marson, "Reflection" by Angie Oldman, and "Trojan Victory" by Angie Oldman. We can only include a maximum of four of these six sculptures.

6. Celeste also knows that the museum only has enough wall space for 20 paintings, collages, and drawings. We have 28 paintings, collages, and drawings available: "Chaos Reigns," "Who Has Control," "Domestication," "Innocence," "Wasted Resources," "Serenity," "Calm Before the Storm," "Void," "Sun," "Storefront Window," "Harley," "Consumerism," "Rick," "Rick II," "Rick III," "Beyond," "Pioneers," "Wisdom," "Superior Powers," "Living Land," "Study of a Violin," "Study of a Fruit Bowl," "My Namesake," "Narcissism," "All That Glitters," "The Rock," "Winding Road," and "Dreams Come True." We can only include a maximum of 20 of these 28 wall pieces.

7. Finally, Celeste wants "Narcissism" displayed if "Reflection" is displayed. So if the decision variable for "Reflection" is 1, the decision variable for "Narcissism" must also be 1. However, the decision variable for "Narcissism" can still be 1 even if the decision variable for "Reflection" is 0.

Cost Constraint

The cost of all of the pieces displayed has to be less than or equal to $4 million.

The problem formulation in an Excel spreadsheet follows.

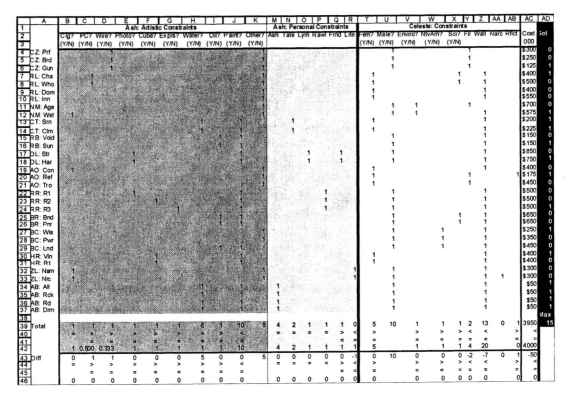

The Solver settings used in the problem are shown below.

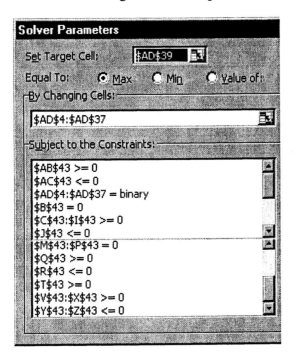

Solver Parameters

Set Target Cell: $AD$39

Equal To: ● Max ○ Min ○ Value of:

By Changing Cells:

$AD$4:$AD$37

Subject to the Constraints:

```
$AB$43 >= 0
$AC$43 <= 0
$AD$4:$AD$37 = binary
$B$43 = 0
$C$43:$I$43 >= 0
$J$43 <= 0
$M$43:$P$43 = 0
$Q$43 >= 0
$R$43 <= 0
$T$43 >= 0
$V$43:$X$43 >= 0
$Y$43:$Z$43 <= 0
```

In the optimal solution, 15 pieces are displayed at a cost of $3.95 million. The following pieces are displayed:

1. "The Great Equalizer" by Colin Zweibell
2. "Chaos Reigns" by Rita Losky
3. "Wasted Resources" by Norm Marson
4. "Serenity" by Candy Tate
5. "Calm Before the Storm" by Candy Tate
6. "Sun" by Robert Bayer
7. "Harley" by David Lyman
8. "Reflection" by Angie Oldman
9. "Rick III" by Rick Rawls
10. "Wisdom" by Bear Canton
11. "Study of a Violin" by Helen Row
12. "All That Glitters" by Ash Briggs
13. "The Rock" by Ash Briggs
14. "Winding Road" by Ash Briggs
15. "Dreams Come True" by Ash Briggs

b) The formulation of this problem is the same as the formulation in part (a) except that the objective function from part (a) now becomes a constraint and the cost constraint from part (a) now becomes the objective function. Thus, we have the new constraint that we need to select 20 or more pieces to display in the exhibit. We also have the new objective to minimize the cost of the exhibit.

The new formulation of the problem in an Excel spreadsheet appears below.

The Solver settings used in the problem appear below.

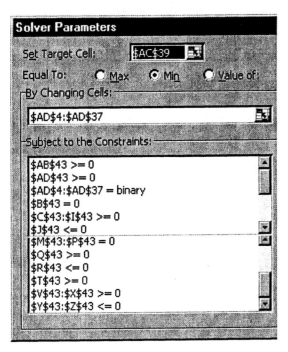

In the optimal solution, exactly 20 pieces are displayed at a cost of $5.5 million – $1.5 million more than Ash decided to allocate in part (a). All pieces from part (a) are displayed in addition to the following five new pieces:

1. "Burden" by Colin Zweibell
2. "Domestication" by Rita Losky
3. "Void" by Robert Bayer
4. "Superior Powers" by Bear Canton
5. "Study of a Fruit Bowl" by Helen Row

c) This problem is also a cost minimization problem. The problem formulation is the same as that used in part (b). A new constraint is added, however. The patron wants all of Rita's pieces displayed. Rita has four pieces: "Chaos Reigns," "Who Has Control?," "Domestication," and "Innocence." All of these four pieces must be displayed.

The problem formulation in Excel appears below.

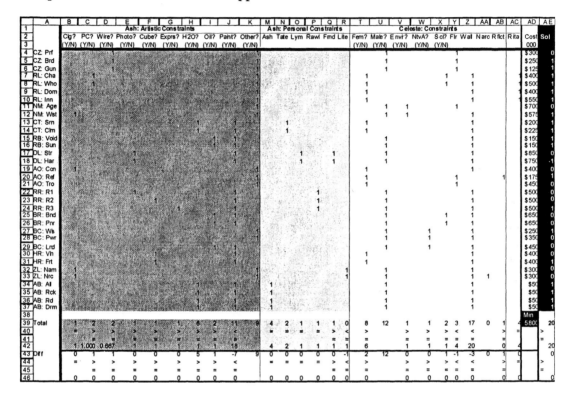

The Solver settings used in this problem appear below.

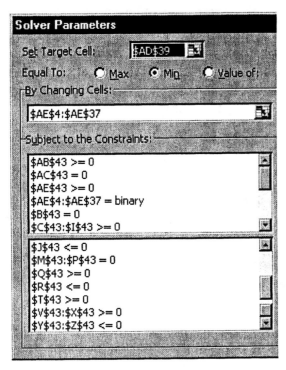

In the optimal solution, exactly 20 pieces are displayed at a total cost of $5.8 million. The patron has to pay $1.8 million. The following pieces are displayed:

1. "Burden" by Colin Zweibell
2. "The Great Equalizer" by Colin Zweibell
3. "Chaos Reigns" by Rita Losky
4. "Who Has Control?" by Rita Losky
5. "Domestication" by Rita Losky
6. "Innocence" by Rita Losky
7. "Wasted Resources" by Norm Marson
8. "Serenity" by Candy Tate
9. "Calm Before the Storm" by Candy Tate
10. "Void" by Robert Bayer
11. "Sun" by Robert Bayer
12. "Harley" by David Lyman
13. "Reflection" by Angie Oldman
14. "Rick III" by Rick Rawls
15. "Wisdom" by Bear Canton
16. "Study of a Fruit Bowl" by Helen Row
17. "All That Glitters" by Ash Briggs
18. "The Rock" by Ash Briggs
19. "Winding Road" by Ash Briggs
20. "Dreams Come True" by Ash Briggs

9.2 a) We want to maximize the total number of kitchen sets, so each of the 20 kitchen sets becomes a decision variable. But the kitchen sets are not our only decision variables. Because we assume that any particular item composing a kitchen set is replenished immediately, we only need to stock one of each item. A particular item may compose multiple kitchen sets. For example, tile T1 is part of kitchen sets 3, 7, 10, and 17. So a kitchen set exists when all of the items composing that kitchen set are in stock. Therefore, each of 30 items also becomes a decision variable. These decision variables are binary decision variables. If a kitchen set or item is in stock, the decision variable is 1. If a kitchen set or item is not in stock, the decision variable is 0.

A handful of constraints exist in this problem.
1. We cannot indicate that a kitchen set is in stock unless all the items composing that kitchen set are also in stock. Thus, a kitchen set decision variable is 1 only if all the decision variables for the items composing that kitchen set are also 1. For example, for set 1 this constraint equals 8*(Set 1) <= T2+W2+L4+C2+O4+S2+D2+R2
2. Each kitchen set requires 20 square feet of tile. Thus, if a particular tile is in stock, 20 square feet of that tile are in stock. The warehouse can only hold 50 square feet of tile, so only a maximum of two different styles of tile can be in stock.
3. Each kitchen set requires five rolls of wallpaper. Thus, if a particular style of wallpaper is in stock, five rolls of that wallpaper are in stock. The warehouse can only hold 12 rolls of wallpaper, so only a maximum of two different styles of wallpaper can be in stock.
4. A maximum of two different styles of light fixtures can be in stock.
5. A maximum of two different styles of cabinets can be in stock.
6. A maximum of three different styles of countertops can be in stock.
7. A maximum of two different sinks can be in stock.
8. A combination of four different styles of dishwashers and ranges can be held in stock.

The problem formulated in an Excel spreadsheet follows.

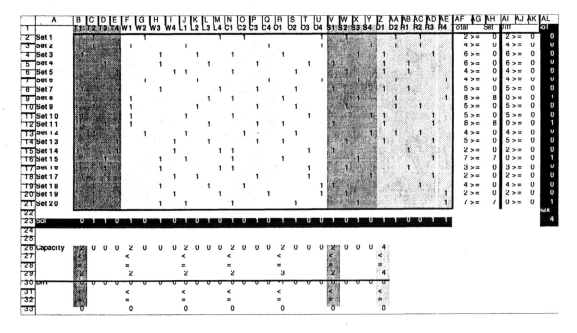

The solver settings are the following:

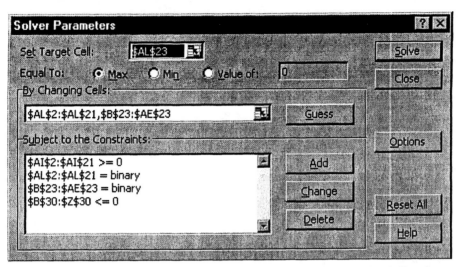

b) Four different kitchen sets are in stock. We should stock the following number of items:

Item	Quantity
T1	0
T2	1
T3	1
T4	0
W1	1
W2	0
W3	1
W4	0
L1	1
L2	0
L3	1
L4	0
C1	1
C2	0
C3	1
C4	0
O1	1
O2	1
O3	0
O4	0
S1	1
S2	0
S3	1
S4	0
D1	1
D2	1
R1	0
R2	0
R3	1
R4	1

Note that the above optimal solution is not a unique solution. The value of the objective function is always four complete kitchen sets, but the specific items and kitchen sets stocked may be different. Throughout this solution, we will refer to the optimal solution shown above, but because other optimal solutions exist, student answers may differ from the solution somewhat.

c) We model this new problem by changing the capacity constraint for the dishwashers and ranges. Now, instead of being able to stock a combination of only four different styles of dishwashers and ranges, we can stock a maximum of two different styles of dishwashers and a maximum of three different styles of ranges. Because we only have two different styles of dishwashers available, we now effectively do not have a constraint on the number of dishwashers we can carry.

The formulation of the problem in Excel follows:

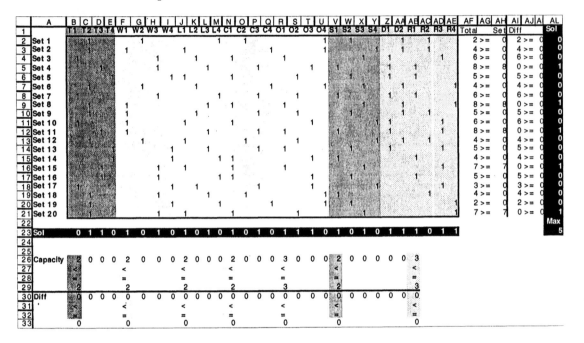

The Solver settings for this problem follow.

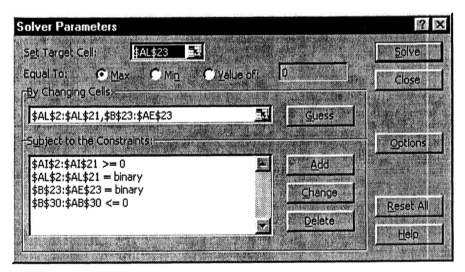

With the extra space, the number of kitchen sets we can stock increases from four to five. In part (a), the constraint on the number of different styles of dishwashers and ranges was binding, and we could only stock four different kitchen sets – sets 8, 11, 15, and 20. With the extra space, we can add set 4 to our stock. Set 4 requires two items that are not required by sets 8, 11, 15, and 20 – a different countertop O3 and a different range R1. In part (a), the constraint limiting the maximum number of different styles of countertops was non-binding, so we can add a new countertop style to our stock. The new space vacated by the nursery department provides us with the space to stock the new range.

d) With the additional space, our constraints change. We eliminate the constraints limiting the maximum number of different styles of sinks and countertops we can stock. Instead of stocking two of the four styles of light fixtures, we can now stock three of the four styles of light fixtures. Finally, instead of stocking only two of the four cabinet styles, we can now stock three of the four cabinet styles.

The problem formulated in Excel follows.

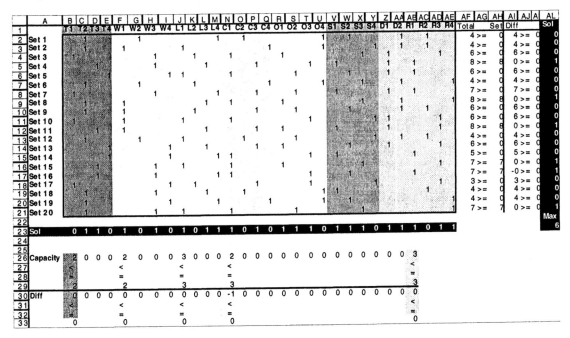

The Solver settings are the same settings used in part (c).

With the extra space, we are now able to stock six complete kitchen kits. In part (c), we stocked five sets – sets 4, 8, 11, 15, and 20. Now we add set 16 to the inventory. All of the extra space does not increase the number of complete sets we can stock significantly because the capacity constraints on the countertops, and cabinets were not binding in part (c). Only the capacity constraints on the sinks and light fixtures were binding. Set 16 requires both a sink and a light fixture that sets 4, 8, 11, 15, and 20 do not require. We therefore add an additional style of sink and light fixture to our stock. We still have space for one additional sink, so the constraint is not binding in this problem.

e) If the items composing a kitchen set could not be replenished immediately, we could not formulate this problem as a binary integer program. We would have to formulate the problem as an integer program since we may have to store more than one kitchen component or kitchen set to ensure that we meet demand.

The assumption of immediate replenishment is justified if the average time to replenish the component is less than the average time between demands for that component.

9.3 a)

Let $x_{ij} = 1$ if students from area i are assigned to school j; 0 if not

C_{ij} = bussing cost

S_i = student population of area i

K_j = capacity of school j

P_{ik} = % of students in area i in grade k

(for $i = 1, 2, 3, 4, 5, 6$ $j = 1, 2, 3$ and $k = 6, 7, 8$).

Minimize Cost = $\sum_{i=1}^{6} \sum_{j=1}^{3} (C_{ij})(S_i)(x_{ij})$

subject to $\sum_i S_i x_{ij} \leq K_j$

$\sum_j x_{ij} = 1$

$\sum_i P_{ik} S_i x_{ij} \leq 0.35 \sum_i S_i x_{ij}$, $(k = 6, 7, 8)$

and x_{ij} are binary variables (for $i = 1, 2, 3, 4, 5, 6$ and $j = 1, 2, 3$).

Note $x_{21} = x_{43} = x_{52} = 0$ due to infeasibility.

b) The models really aren't too different. x_{ij} are binary here, which amounts to forcing their value in the LP of Case 4-2 to be either 0 or S_i. We can leave out the three variables known to be 0, and also 9 redundant constraints. The LP-relaxation of this model, with $0 \leq x_{ij} \leq 1$ would allow us to interpret x_{ij} as the fraction of students from area i to be assigned to school j. This obviously would be a more general model, equivalent to that in Case 4-2.

c)

Data:

Area	Number of Students	Percentage in 6th Grade	Percentage in 7th Grade	Percentage in 8th Grade	Bussing Cost ($/Student) School 1	School 2	School 3
1	450	0.32	0.38	0.3	300	0	700
2	600	0.37	0.28	0.35	9999	400	500
3	550	0.3	0.32	0.38	600	300	200
4	350	0.28	0.4	0.32	200	500	9999
5	500	0.39	0.34	0.27	0	9999	400
6	450	0.34	0.28	0.38	500	300	0
				Capacity:	950	1150	1050

Solution:

	Area Assignments School 1	School 2	School 3	Total		
Area 1	1	0	0	1	=	1
Area 2	0	1	0	1	=	1
Area 3	0	0	1	1	=	1
Area 4	0	1	0	1	=	1
Area 5	0	0	1	1	=	1
Area 6	1	0	0	1	=	1

	Number of Students School 1	School 2	School 3
Area 1	450	0	0
Area 2	0	600	0
Area 3	0	0	550
Area 4	0	350	0
Area 5	0	0	500
Area 6	450	0	0
Total	900	950	1050
	≤	≤	≤
Capacity	950	1150	1050

Total Bussing Cost = $ 1,085,000.00

Grade Constraints:

	School 1	School 2	School 3
6th Graders	297	320	360
7th Graders	297	308	346
8th Graders	306	322	344
35% of Total	315	332.5	367.5

d) Without prohibiting the splitting of residential areas, the total cost was $644,444. Thus, adding this restriction increases the cost by $1,085,000 - $644,444 = $440,556.

e) As shown in the spreadsheet, the solution remains the same, but the bussing costs are reduced to $975,000.

Data:

Area	Number of Students	Percentage in 6th Grade	Percentage in 7th Grade	Percentage in 8th Grade	Bussing Cost ($/Student) School 1	School 2	School 3
1	450	0.32	0.38	0.3	300	0	700
2	600	0.37	0.28	0.35	9999	400	500
3	550	0.3	0.32	0.38	600	300	0
4	350	0.28	0.4	0.32	0	500	9999
5	500	0.39	0.34	0.27	0	9999	400
6	450	0.34	0.28	0.38	500	300	0
				Capacity:	950	1150	1050

Solution:

	Area Assignments School 1	School 2	School 3	Total		
Area 1	1	0	0	1	=	1
Area 2	0	1	0	1	=	1
Area 3	0	0	1	1	=	1
Area 4	0	1	0	1	=	1
Area 5	0	0	1	1	=	1
Area 6	1	0	0	1	=	1

Total Bussing Cost = $ 975,000.00

	Number of Students School 1	School 2	School 3
Area 1	450	0	0
Area 2	0	600	0
Area 3	0	0	550
Area 4	0	350	0
Area 5	0	0	500
Area 6	450	0	0
Total	900	950	1050
	≤	≤	≤
Capacity	950	1150	1050

Grade Constraints:

	School 1	School 2	School 3
6th Graders	297	320	360
7th Graders	297	308	346
8th Graders	306	322	344
35% of Total	315	332.5	367.5

9-24

f) Again, as shown in the spreadsheet below, the solution remains the same, but the bussing costs are reduced to $840,000.

Data:

Area	Number of Students	Percentage in 6th Grade	Percentage in 7th Grade	Percentage in 8th Grade	Bussing Cost ($/Student) School 1	School 2	School 3
1	450	0.32	0.38	0.3	0	0	700
2	600	0.37	0.28	0.35	9999	400	500
3	550	0.3	0.32	0.38	600	0	0
4	350	0.28	0.4	0.32	0	500	9999
5	500	0.39	0.34	0.27	0	9999	400
6	450	0.34	0.28	0.38	500	0	0
				Capacity:	950	1150	1050

Solution:

	Area Assignments School 1	School 2	School 3	Total		
Area 1	1	0	0	1	=	1
Area 2	0	1	0	1	=	1
Area 3	0	0	1	1	=	1
Area 4	0	1	0	1	=	1
Area 5	0	0	1	1	=	1
Area 6	1	0	0	1	=	1

Total Bussing Cost = $ 840,000.00

	Number of Students School 1	School 2	School 3
Area 1	450	0	0
Area 2	0	600	0
Area 3	0	0	550
Area 4	0	350	0
Area 5	0	0	500
Area 6	450	0	0
Total	900	950	1050
	≤	≤	≤
Capacity	950	1150	1050

Grade Constraints:

	School 1	School 2	School 3
6th Graders	297	320	360
7th Graders	297	308	346
8th Graders	306	322	344
35% of Total	315	332.5	367.5

g) For all three options, the assignments of areas to schools are identical. For the current alternative, the bussing costs are $1,085,000. For option 1, the bussing costs are $975,000 (a reduction of $110,000). This savings results from the fact that students from area 3 would no longer be bussed to school 3. For option 2, the bussing costs are $840,000 (a reduction of $135,000 over option 1, and $245,000 over the current alternative). This additional savings results from the fact that students would no longer be bussed from area 1 to school 1.

h) Arguments can be made for all three alternatives. Answers will vary.

Review Questions

CD9-1 Push the objective function line in the direction of improving values of the objective function. Stop at the last instant when the objective function line passes through a feasible integer point (a binary solution).

CD9-2 The exhaustive enumeration method can be used for larger problems while the graphical method is limited to problems with just two variables.

CD9-3 The exhaustive enumeration method quickly becomes unwieldy if the number of variable is increased very much.

CD9-4 For problems with more than a few variables, it is generally easier to solve linear programming problems than BIP problems of the same size.

CD9-5 The LP relaxation of a BIP problem replaces the constraint on each binary variable that the variable is binary by the constraint that it is between 0 and 1.

CD9-6 The LP relaxation is relevant for helping to solve a BIP problem because the solution may end up being the solution for the BIP problem, and if not it at least gives a good place to begin the search for an optimal solution.

CD9-7 A BIP problem containing mutually exclusive alternative is an example of a problem with special structure.

CD9-8 The two primary determinants of computational difficulty for a BIP problem are the number of binary variables and any special structure in the problem.

CD9-9 One major pitfall with the rounding procedure is that it may produce a solution that is infeasible for the BIP problem. The other pitfall is that there is no guarantee that a feasible solution will be optimal, or even nearly optimal, for the BIP problem.

Problems

CD9-1 a)

Solution	Feasible?	$P = 2x_1 + 5x_2$	Optimal?
(0,0)	Yes	0	
(1,0)	No		
(0,1)	Yes	5	***
(1,1)	No		

b) Optimal solution: $(x_1, x_2) = (0,1)$.

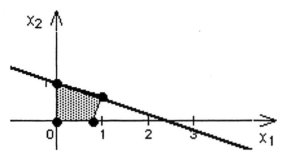

c) Solving the LP relaxation graphically, the optimal solution is $(x_1, x_2) = (1, 0.667)$. This rounds to $(1,1)$ which is not a feasible solution.

d) Rounding down results in a solution of $(1,0)$ which is also not a feasible solution.

CD9-2 a)

Solution	Feasible?	$P = -5x_1 + 25x_2$	Optimal?
(0,0)	Yes	0	
(1,0)	Yes	-5	
(0,1)	No		
(1,1)	Yes	20	***

b) Optimal solution: $(x_1, x_2) = (1,1)$.

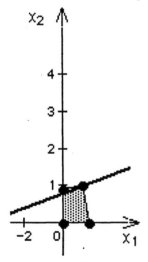

c) Solving the LP relaxation graphically, the optimal solution is $(x_1, x_2) = (0, 0.9)$. This rounds to $(0,1)$ which is not a feasible solution.

d) Rounding down results in a solution of $(0,0)$ which is a feasible solution but yields Z=0 which in not an optimal solution.

Solution	Feasible?	$P = 9x_1 + 5x_2 + 6x_3 + 4x_4$	Optimal?
(0,0,0,0)	Yes	0	
(1,0,0,0)	Yes	9	
(0,1,0,0)	Yes	5	
(0,0,1,0)	No		
(0,0,0,1)	No		
(1,1,0,0)	Yes	14	***
(0,1,1,0)	No		
(0,0,1,1)	No		
(1,0,0,1)	No		
(1,0,1,0)	No		
(0,1,0,1)	Yes	9	
(1,1,1,0)	No		
(0,1,1,1)	No		
(1,0,1,1)	No		
(1,1,0,1)	No		
(1,1,1,1)	No		

CD9-4 a) True. The current algorithms for solving BIP problems still are not nearly as efficient as those for solving linear programming problems.

  b) True. The two primary determinants of computational difficulty for a BIP problem are (1) the number of binary variables and (2) any special structure in the problem. This situation is in contrast to linear programming, where the number of (functional) constraints is much more important that the number of variables.

  c) False. One major pitfall with the rounding procedure is that it may produce a solution that in infeasible for the BIP problem.

CHAPTER 10
DECISION ANALYSIS

Teaching notes for this chapter are available in the Teaching Notes section near the front of this Instructor's Manual.

Review Questions

10.1-1 The decision alternatives are to drill for oil or to sell the land.

10.1-2 The consulting geologist believes that there is 1 chance in 4 of oil on the tract of land.

10.1-3 Max does not put much faith in the assessment.

10.1-4 A detailed seismic survey of the land could be done to obtain more information.

10.2-1 The possible states of nature are the possible outcomes of the random factors that affect the payoff that would be obtained from a decision alternative.

10.2-2 Prior probabilities are the estimated probabilities of the states of nature prior to obtaining additional information through a test or survey.

10.2-3 The payoffs are quantitative measures of the outcomes from a decision alternative and a state of nature. Payoffs are generally expressed in monetary terms.

10.2-4 A decision tree is a graphical display of the progression of decisions and random events to be considered.

10.2-5 A decision node indicates that a decision needs to be made at that point in the process. A chance node indicates that a random event occurs at that point.

10.2-6 Decision nodes are represented by squares while circles represent chance nodes.

10.3-1 The maximum likelihood criterion focuses on the most likely state of nature, the one with the largest prior probability.

10.3-2 Criticisms of the maximum likelihood criterion include: 1) this criterion chooses an alternative without considering its payoffs for states of nature other than the most likely one, 2) for alternatives that are not chosen, this criterion ignores their payoffs for states of nature other than the most likely one, 3) if the differences in the payoffs for the most likely state of nature are much less than for another somewhat likely state of nature, then it might make sense to focus on this latter state of nature instead, and 4) if there are many states of nature and they are nearly equally likely, then the probability that the most likely state of nature will be the true one is fairly low.

10.3-3 The equally likely criterion assumes that all states of nature are equally likely to occur.

10.3-4 Criticisms of the equally likely criterion include: 1) assigning equally likely values to each prior probability is just as arbitrary as assigning any other values to these probabilities, 2) in some situations, there is good evidence that certain states of nature are more likely than others, and 3) it is undesirable to have the decision depend on the arbitrary way in which the possible states of nature are itemized.

10.3-5 Bayes' decision rule says to choose the alternative with the largest expected payoff.

10.3-6 The expected payoff is calculated by multiplying each payoff by the prior probability of the corresponding state of nature and then summing these products.

10.3-7 Criticisms of Bayes' decision rule include: 1) there usually is considerable uncertainty involved in assigning values to prior probabilities, 2) prior probabilities inherently are at least largely subjective in nature, whereas sound decision making should be based on objective data and procedures, and 3) by focusing on average outcomes, expected payoffs ignore the effect that the amount of variability in the possible outcomes should have on the decision making.

10.3-8 Sensitivity analysis might be helpful to study the effect if some of the numbers included in the model are not correct.

10.3-9 The crossover point represents the point at which the decision shifts from one alternative to the other as the prior probability increases.

10.4-1 Perfect information means knowing for sure which state of nature is the true state of nature.

10.4-2 The expected payoff with perfect information is calculated by multiplying the maximum payoff for each alternative by the prior probability of the corresponding state of nature.

10.4-3 The decision tree should be started with a chance node whose branches are the various states of nature.

10.4-4 EVPI = EP (with perfect information) − EP (without more information)

10.4-5 If the cost of obtaining more information is more than the expected value of perfect information then it is not worthwhile to obtain more information.

10.4-6 If the cost of obtaining more information is less than the expected value of perfect information then it might be worthwhile to obtain more information.

10.4-7 In the Goferbroke problem the EVPI >C so it might be worthwhile to do the seismic survey.

10.5-1 Posterior probabilities are revised probabilities of the states of nature after doing a test or survey to improve the prior probabilities.

10.5-2 The possible findings are favorable with oil being fairly likely, or unfavorable with oil being quite unlikely.

10.5-3 Conditional probabilities need to be estimated.

10.5-4 The five kinds of probabilities considered are prior, conditional, joint, unconditional, and posterior.

10.5-5 P(state and finding) = P(state)P(finding/state).

10.5-6 P(finding) = P(Oil and finding) + P(Dry and finding).

10.5-7 $P(\text{state}|\text{finding}) = \dfrac{P(\text{state and finding})}{P(\text{finding})}$.

10.5-8 Bayes' theorem is used to calculate posterior probabilities.

10.6-1 A decision tree provides a graphical display of the progression of decisions and random events for a problem.

10.6-2 A decision needs to be made at a decision node.

10.6-3 A random event will occur at a chance node.

10.6-4 The probabilities of random events and the payoffs need to be inserted before beginning analysis.

10.6-5 When performing the analysis, start at the right side of the decision tree and move left one column at a time.

10.6-6 For each chance node, calculate its expected payoff by multiplying the payoff of each branch by the probability of that branch and then summing these products.

10.6-7 For each decision node, compare the expected payoffs of its branches and choose the alternative whose branch has the largest expected payoff.

10.6-8 Spider graphs, tornado diagrams, as well as plots of sensitivity graphs can help with sensitivity analysis.

10.7-1 Utilities are intended to reflect the true value of an outcome to the decision-maker.

10.7-2

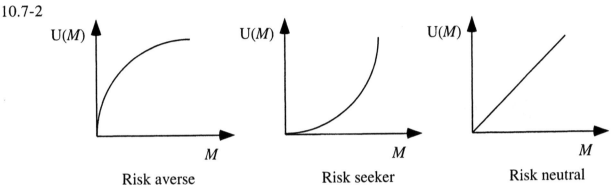

Risk averse   Risk seeker   Risk neutral

10.7-3 Under the assumptions of utility theory, the decision-maker's utility function for money has the property that the decision-maker is indifferent between two alternative courses of action if the two alternatives have the same expected utility.

10.7-4 The decision-maker is offered two hypothetical alternatives and asked to identify the point of indifference between the two.

10.7-5 The point of indifference is the value of p where the decision-maker is indifferent between the two hypothetical alternatives.

10.7-6 The value obtained to evaluate each node of the tree is the expected utility.

10.7-7 Max decided to do the seismic survey and to sell if the result is unfavorable or drill if the result is favorable.

10.8-1 The Goferbroke problem contained the same elements as typical applications of decision analysis but is oversimplified.

10.8-2 An influence diagram complements the decision tree for representing and analyzing decision analysis problems.

10.8-3 Typical participants include management, an analyst, and a group facilitator.

10.8-4 A manager can go to a management consulting firm that specializes in decision analysis.

10.8-5 Decision analysis is widely used around the world.

Problems

10.1   a)

| | State of Nature | |
Alternative	Sell 10,000	Sell 100,000
Build Computers	0	54
Sell Rights	15	15

b)

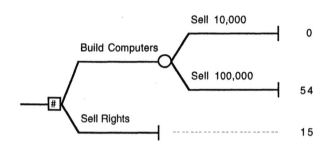

c)

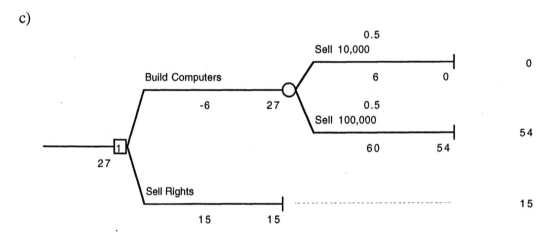

Choose to build computers (expected payoff is $27 million).

d)

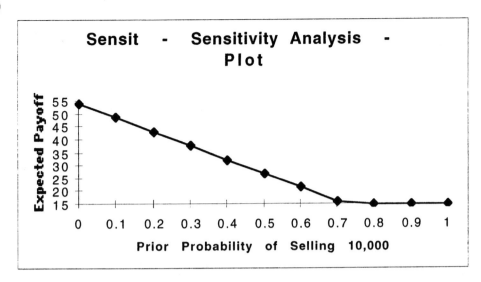

e)

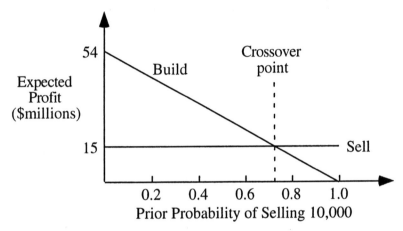

f) Let p = prior probability of selling 10,000.

For Build:

$$EP = p(0) + (1-p)(54)$$
$$= -54p + 54$$

For Sell:

$$EP = p(15) + (1-p)(15)$$
$$= 15$$

Build and Sell cross when $-54p + 54 = 15$ or $54p = 39$ or $p = 0.722$

They should build when $p \leq 0.722$, and sell when $p > 0.722$.

10.2 a)

	State of Nature			
Alternative	Sell 10 cases	Sell 11 cases	Sell 12 cases	Sell 13 cases
Buy 10 cases	50	50	50	50
Buy 11 cases	47	55	55	55
Buy 12 cases	44	52	60	60
Buy 13 cases	41	49	57	65
Prior Probability	0.2	0.4	0.3	0.1

b)

	State of Nature				
Alternative	Sell 10 cases	Sell 11 cases	Sell 12 cases	Sell 13 cases	
Buy 10 cases	50	50	50	50	
Buy 11 cases	47	55	55	55	Maximum
Buy 12 cases	44	52	60	60	
Buy 13 cases	41	49	57	65	
Prior Probability	0.2	0.4	0.3	0.1	
	Maximum				

Jean should purchase 11 cases.

c)

	State of Nature				Row
Alternative	Sell 10 cases	Sell 11 cases	Sell 12 cases	Sell 13 cases	Average
Buy 10 cases	50	50	50	50	50
Buy 11 cases	47	55	55	55	53
Buy 12 cases	44	52	60	60	54 Maximum
Buy 13 cases	41	49	57	65	53
Prior Probability	0.2	0.4	0.3	0.1	

Jean should purchase 12 cases.

d)

	State of Nature				Expected
Alternative	Sell 10 cases	Sell 11 cases	Sell 12 cases	Sell 13 cases	Payoff
Buy 10 cases	50	50	50	50	50
Buy 11 cases	47	55	55	55	53.4
Buy 12 cases	44	52	60	60	53.6 Maximum
Buy 13 cases	41	49	57	65	51.4
Prior Probability	0.2	0.4	0.3	0.1	

Jean should purchase 12 cases.

e) 0.2 and 0.5

Alternative	State of Nature				Expected Payoff	
	Sell 10 cases	Sell 11 cases	Sell 12 cases	Sell 13 cases		
Buy 10 cases	50	50	50	50	50	
Buy 11 cases	47	55	55	55	53.4	
Buy 12 cases	44	52	60	60	55.2	Maximum
Buy 13 cases	41	49	57	65	53	
Prior Probability	0.2	0.2	0.5	0.1		

Jean should purchase 12 cases.

0.3 and 0.4

Alternative	State of Nature				Expected Payoff	
	Sell 10 cases	Sell 11 cases	Sell 12 cases	Sell 13 cases		
Buy 10 cases	50	50	50	50	50	
Buy 11 cases	47	55	55	55	53.4	
Buy 12 cases	44	52	60	60	54.4	Maximum
Buy 13 cases	41	49	57	65	52.2	
Prior Probability	0.2	0.3	0.4	0.1		

Jean should purchase 12 cases.

0.5 and 0.2

Alternative	State of Nature				Expected Payoff	
	Sell 10 cases	Sell 11 cases	Sell 12 cases	Sell 13 cases		
Buy 10 cases	50	50	50	50	50	
Buy 11 cases	47	55	55	55	53.4	Maximum
Buy 12 cases	44	52	60	60	52.8	
Buy 13 cases	41	49	57	65	50.6	
Prior Probability	0.2	0.5	0.2	0.1		

Jean should purchase 11 cases.

10.3   a)

Alternative	State of Nature			
	Improving	Stable	Worsening	
Conservative	30	5	-10	
Speculative	40	10	-30	Maximum
Counter-cyclical	-10	0	15	
Prior Probability	0.1	0.5	0.4	
	Maximum			

Warren should make the speculative investment.

b)

Alternative	State of Nature			Row Average
	Improving	Stable	Worsening	
Conservative	30	5	-10	8.3333 Maximum
Speculative	40	10	-30	6.6667
Counter-cyclical	-10	0	15	1.6667
Prior Probability	0.1	0.5	0.4	

Warren should make the conservative investment.

c)

Alternative	State of Nature			Expected Payoff
	Improving	Stable	Worsening	
Conservative	30	5	-10	1.5
Speculative	40	10	-30	-3
Counter-cyclical	-10	0	15	5 Maximum
Prior Probability	0.1	0.5	0.4	

Warren should make the counter-cyclical investment.

10.4   a)

Alternative	State of Nature			Expected Payoff
	Improving	Stable	Worsening	
Conservative	30	5	-10	-1.5
Speculative	40	10	-30	-11
Counter-cyclical	-10	0	15	8 Maximum
Prior Probability	0.1	0.3	0.6	

Warren should make the counter-cyclical investment.

b)

Alternative	State of Nature			Expected Payoff
	Improving	Stable	Worsening	
Conservative	30	5	-10	4.5
Speculative	40	10	-30	5 Maximum
Counter-cyclical	-10	0	15	2
Prior Probability	0.1	0.7	0.2	

Warren should make the speculative investment.

c)

Counter-cyclical and conservative cross at approximately $p=0.62$.
Conservative and speculative cross at approximately $p = 0.68$.

d) Let p = prior probability of stable economy

For the conservative option:

$$\begin{aligned} EP &= (0.1)(30) + p(5) + (1\text{-}0.1\text{-}p)(\text{-}10) \\ &= 3 + 5p - 9 + 10p \\ &= 15p - 6 \end{aligned}$$

For the speculative option:

$$\begin{aligned} EP &= (0.1)(40) + p(10) + (1\text{-}0.1\text{-}p)(\text{-}30) \\ &= 4 + 10p - 27 + 30p \\ &= 40p - 23 \end{aligned}$$

For the counter-cyclical option:

$$\begin{aligned} EP &= (0.1)(\text{-}10) + p(0) + (1\text{-}0.1\text{-}p)(15) \\ &= \text{-}1 + 0 + 13.5 - 15p \\ &= \text{-}15p + 12.5 \end{aligned}$$

Counter-cyclical and conservative cross when
$-15p + 12.5 = 15p - 6$ or $30p = 18.5$ or $p=0.617$

Conservative and speculative cross when
$15p - 6 = 40p - 23$ or $25p = 17$ or $p = 0.68$

They should choose the counter-cyclical option when $p<0.617$, the conservative option when $0.617 \leq p < 0.68$, and the speculative option when $p \geq 0.68$.

e)

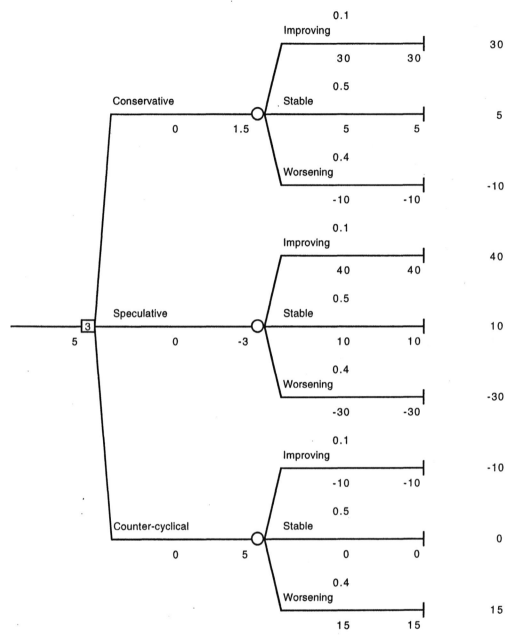

f) Part a)

	Improving	Stable	Worsening
Conservative	30	5	-10
Speculative	40	10	-30
Counter-cyclical	-10	0	15
Prior Probability	0.1	0.3	0.6

Results

Investment	Counter-cyclical
Expected Payoff	8

Part b)

	Improving	Stable	Worsening
Conservative	30	5	-10
Speculative	40	10	-30
Counter-cyclical	-10	0	15
Prior Probability	0.1	0.7	0.2

Results

Investment	Speculative
Expected Payoff	5

g)

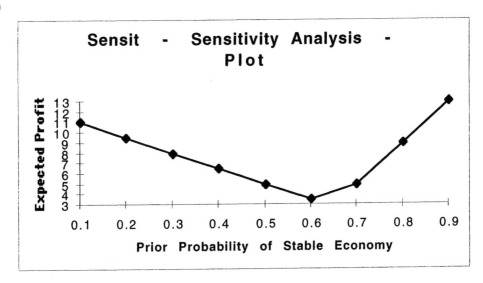

h & i)

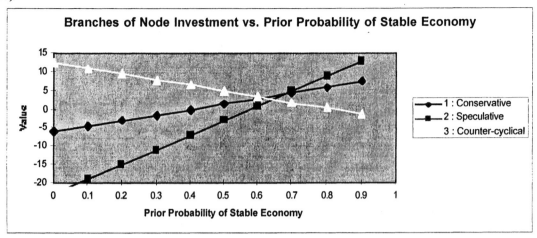

If the prior probability for a stable economy is less than 0.61, then counter-cyclical is the best strateger; between 0.62 and 0.68, conservative is best; greater than 0.69, and speculative is best.

10.5   a)

	State of Nature		
Alternative	S1	S2	
A1	80	25	
A2	30	50	Maximum
A3	60	40	
Prior Probability	0.4	0.6	
	Maximum		

Alternative 2 should be chosen.

b)

	State of Nature		Row Average	
Alternative	S1	S2		
A1	80	25	52.5	Maximum
A2	30	50	40	
A3	60	40	50	
Prior Probability	0.4	0.6		

Alternative 1 should be chosen.

c)

Alternative	State of Nature		Expected Payoff	
	S1	S2		
A1	80	25	47	
A2	30	50	42	
A3	60	40	48	Maximum
Prior Probability	0.4	0.6		

Alternative 3 should be chosen.

d)

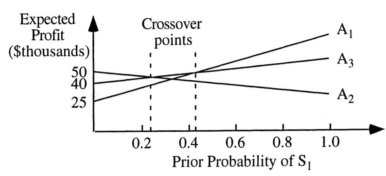

A_2 and A_3 cross at approximately $p=0.25$.
A_1 and A_3 cross at approximately $p = 0.43$.

e) Let p = prior probability of S_1.

For A_1:
$$EP = p(80) + (1\text{-}p)(25)$$
$$= 80p + 25 - 25p$$
$$= 55p + 25$$

For A_2:
$$EP = p(30) + (1\text{-}p)(50)$$
$$= 30p + 50 - 50p$$
$$= -20p + 50$$

For A_3:
$$EP = p(60) + (1\text{-}p)(40)$$
$$= 60p + 40 - 40p$$
$$= 20p + 40$$

A_2 and A_3 cross when $-20p + 50 = 20p + 40$ or $40p = 10$ or $p=0.250$.
A_1 and A_3 cross when $55p + 25 = 20p + 40$ or $35p = 15$ or $p = 0.429$

They should choose A_2 when $p<0.250$, A_3 when $0.250 \leq p<0.429$, and A_1 when $p \geq 0.429$.

10.6 a)

Alternative	State of Nature				
	S1	S2	S3		
A1	220	170	110		Maximum
A2	200	180	150		
Prior Probability	0.6	0.3	0.1		
	Maximum				

Alternative 1 should be chosen.

b)

Alternative	State of Nature			Row Average	
	S1	S2	S3		
A1	220	170	110	166.67	
A2	200	180	150	176.67	Maximum
Prior Probability	0.6	0.3	0.1		

Alternative 2 should be chosen.

c)

Alternative	State of Nature			Expected Payoff	
	S1	S2	S3		
A1	220	170	110	194	Maximum
A2	200	180	150	189	
Prior Probability	0.6	0.3	0.1		

Alternative 1 should be chosen.

d)

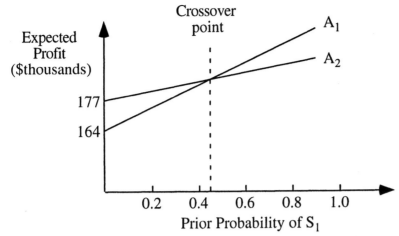

Let p = prior probability of S_1.
For A_1:

$$\begin{aligned} EP &= p(220) + (1-0.1-p)(170) + (0.1)(110) \\ &= 220p + 153 - 170p + 11 \\ &= 50p + 164 \end{aligned}$$

For A_2:

$$\begin{aligned} EP &= p(200) + (1-0.1-p)(180) + (0.1)(150) \\ &= 200p + 162 - 180p + 15 \\ &= 20p + 177 \end{aligned}$$

A1 and *A2* cross when $50p + 164 = 20p + 177$ or $30p = 13$ or $p=0.433$.

They should choose *A2* when $p \leq 0.433$, A_1 when $p>0.433$.

e)

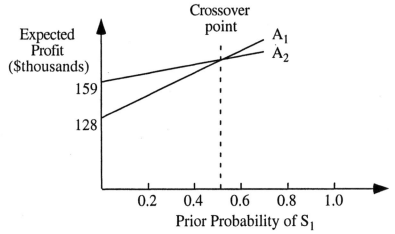

Crossover point

Expected Profit ($thousands)

A_1
A_2

159

128

0.2   0.4   0.6   0.8   1.0

Prior Probability of S_1

Let p = prior probability of S_1.

For A_1:

$$EP = p(220) + (0.3)(170) + (1-0.3-p)(110)$$
$$= 220p + 51 + 77 - 110p$$
$$= 110p + 128$$

For A_2:

$$EP = p(200) + (0.3)(180) + (1-0.3-p)(150)$$
$$= 200p + 54 + 105 - 150p$$
$$= 50p + 159$$

A_1 and A_2 cross when $110p + 128 = 50p + 159$ or $60p = 31$ or $p=0.517$.

They should choose A_2 when $p \leq 0.517$, A_1 when $p > 0.517$.

f)

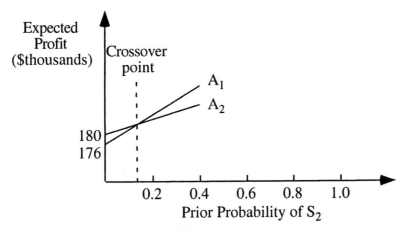

Let p = prior probability of S_2.

For A_1:

$$\begin{aligned}
EP &= (0.6)(220) + p(170) + (1\text{-}0.6\text{-}p)(110) \\
&= 132 + 170p + 44 - 110p \\
&= 60p + 176
\end{aligned}$$

For A_2:

$$\begin{aligned}
EP &= (0.6)(200) + p(180) + (1\text{-}0.6\text{-}p)(150) \\
&= 120 + 180p + 60 - 150p \\
&= 30p + 180
\end{aligned}$$

A_1 and A_2 cross when $60p + 176 = 30p + 180$ or $30p = 4$ or $p=0.133$.

They should choose A_2 when $p \leq 0.133$, A_1 when $p>0.133$.

g) Alternative A_1 should be chosen.

10.7   a)

Alternative	State of Nature		
	Dry	Moderate	Damp
Crop 1	20	35	40
Crop 2	22.5	30	45
Crop 3	30	25	25
Crop 4	20	20	20
Prior Probability	0.3	0.5	0.2

b)

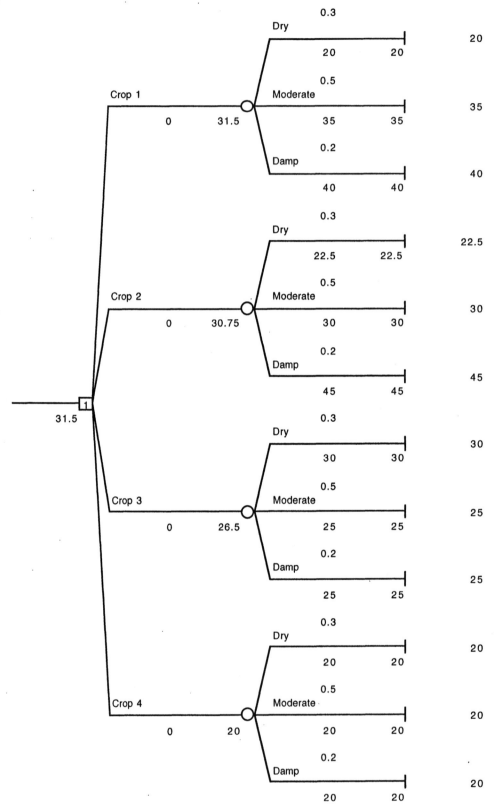

c)

Alternative	State of Nature			Expected Payoff	
	Dry	Moderate	Damp		
Crop 1	20	35	40	31.5	Maximum
Crop 2	22.5	30	45	30.75	
Crop 3	30	25	25	26.5	
Crop 4	20	20	20	20	
Prior Probability	0.3	0.5	0.2		

Grow crop 1.

d) Prior Probability of moderate weather = 0.2

Alternative	State of Nature			Expected Payoff	
	Dry	Moderate	Damp		
Crop 1	20	35	40	33	
Crop 2	22.5	30	45	35.25	Maximum
Crop 3	30	25	25	26.5	
Crop 4	20	20	20	20	
Prior Probability	0.3	0.2	0.5		

Grow crop 2.

Prior Probability of moderate weather = 0.3

Alternative	State of Nature			Expected Payoff	
	Dry	Moderate	Damp		
Crop 1	20	35	40	32.5	
Crop 2	22.5	30	45	33.75	Maximum
Crop 3	30	25	25	26.5	
Crop 4	20	20	20	20	
Prior Probability	0.3	0.3	0.4		

Grow crop 2.

Prior Probability of moderate weather = 0.4

Alternative	State of Nature			Expected Payoff	
	Dry	Moderate	Damp		
Crop 1	20	35	40	32	
Crop 2	22.5	30	45	32.25	Maximum
Crop 3	30	25	25	26.5	
Crop 4	20	20	20	20	
Prior Probability	0.3	0.4	0.3		

Grow crop 2.

Prior Probability of moderate weather = 0.6

Alternative	State of Nature			Expected Payoff	
	Dry	Moderate	Damp		
Crop 1	20	35	40	31	Maximum
Crop 2	22.5	30	45	29.25	
Crop 3	30	25	25	26.5	
Crop 4	20	20	20	20	
Prior Probability	0.3	0.6	0.1		

Grow crop 1.

10.8 A1: $(0.4)(2x) + (0.2)(50) + (0.4)(10) = 0.8x + 14$
A2: $(0.4)(25) + (0.2)(40) + (0.4)(90) = 54$
A3: $(0.4)(35) + (0.2)(3x) + (0.4)(30) = 0.6x + 26$

When $x = 50$, choose alternative 3 with an expected payoff of $5,600.
When $x = 75$, choose alternative 1 with an expected payoff of $7,400.

Barbara Miller should pay a maximum of $1,800 to increase x to 75.

10.9 a)

Alternative	State of Nature	
	Sell 10,000	Sell 100,000
Build Computers	0	5 4
Sell Rights	1 5	1 5
Prior Probability	0.5	0.5
Maximum Payoff	1 5	5 4

Expected Payoff with Perfect Information =	34.5

EVPI = EP (with perfect info) – EP (without more info) = 34.5 – 27 = $7.5 million

b) Since the market research will cost $1 million it might be worthwhile to perform it.

c)

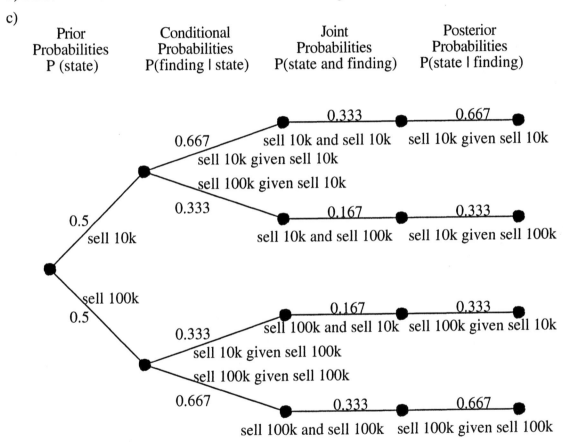

d)

Data:		P(Finding | State)	
		Finding	
State of Nature	Prior Probability	Sell 10,000	Sell 100,000
Sell 10,000	0.5	0.666666667	0.333333333
Sell 100,000	0.5	0.333333333	0.666666667

Posterior Probabilities:		P(State | Finding)	
		State of Nature	
Finding	P(Finding)	Sell 10,000	Sell 100,000
Sell 10,000	0.5	0.666666667	0.333333333
Sell 100,000	0.5	0.333333333	0.666666667

10.10 a)

	State of Nature			Expected
Alternative	S1	S2	S3	Payoff
A1	4	0	0	0.8
A2	0	2	0	1 Maximum
A3	3	0	1	0.9
Prior Probability	0.2	0.5	0.3	

Choose alternative 2 (expected payoff is $1,000).

b)

	State of Nature		
Alternative	S1	S2	S3
A1	4	0	0
A2	0	2	0
A3	3	0	1
Prior Probability	0.2	0.5	0.3
Maximum Payoff	4	2	1

Expected Payoff with Perfect Information =	2.1

EVPI = EP (with perfect info) – EP (without more info) = 2.1 – 1 = $1,100

c)

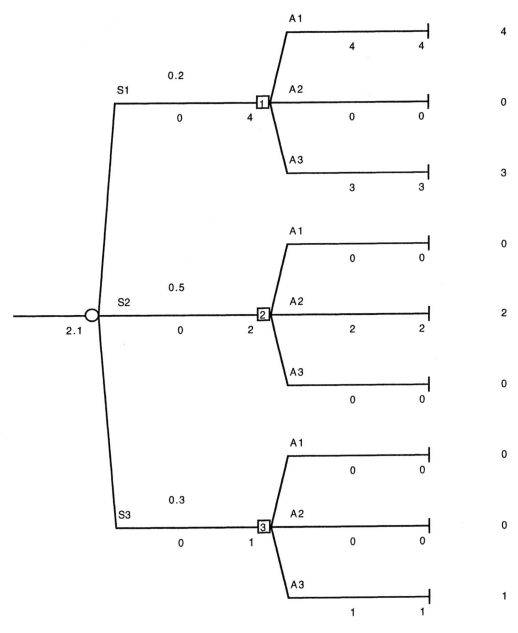

EVPI = EP (with perfect info) − EP (without more info) = 2.1 − 1 = $1,100

d) Since the information will cost $1,000 and the value is $1,100, it might be worthwhile to spend the money.

10.11 a)

Alternative	State of Nature			Expected Payoff	
	S1	S2	S3		
A1	50	100	-100	35	Maximum
A2	0	10	-10	1	
A3	20	40	-40	1 4	
Prior Probability	0.5	0.3	0.2		

Choose alternative 1 (expected payoff is $35).

b)

Alternative	State of Nature		
	S1	S2	S3
A1	50	100	-100
A2	0	10	-10
A3	20	40	-40
Prior Probability	0.5	0.3	0.2
Maximum Payoff	50	100	-10

Expected Payoff with Perfect Information =	53

EVPI = EP (with perfect info) – EP (without more info) = 53 – 35 = $18

c)

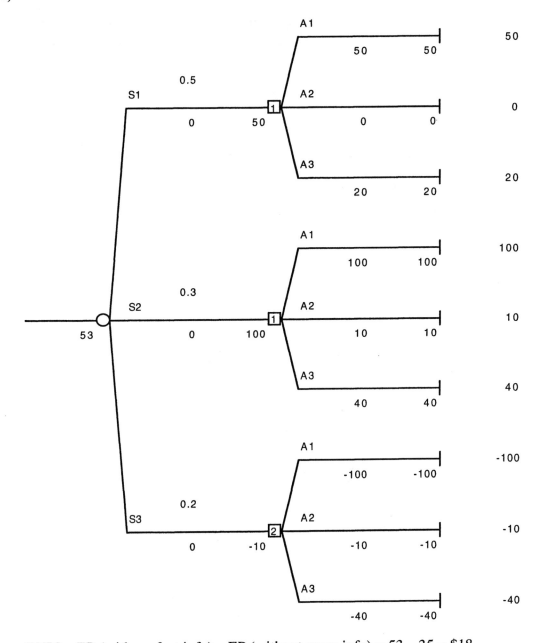

EVPI = EP (with perfect info) – EP (without more info) = 53 – 35 = $18

d) Betsy should consider spending up to $18 to obtain more information.

10.12 a)

	State of Nature			Expected
Alternative	S1	S2	S3	Payoff
A1	-100	10	100	33
A2	-10	20	50	29
A3	10	10	60	35 Maximum
Prior Probability	0.2	0.3	0.5	

Choose alternative 3 (expected payoff is $35,000).

b) If S1 occurs for certain then choose A3 (expected payoff is $10,000).

If S1 does not occur for certain then the chance of S2 occurring is 3/8 and the chance of S3 occurring is 5/8. So choose A1 (expected payoff is $66,250).

A1: $(3/8)(10) + (5/8)(100) = 66.25$
A2: $(3/8)(20) + (5/8)(50) = 38.75$
A3: $(3/8)(10) + (5/8)(60) = 41.25$

EVPI = EP (with perfect info) – EP (without more info)
$= [(0.2)(10) + (0.8)(66.25)] – 35 = \$20,000$

The maximum amount you should pay for the information is $20,000. The decision with this information would be to choose A1 with an expected payoff of $66,250.

c) If S2 occurs for certain then choose A2 (expected payoff is $20,000).

If S2 does not occur for certain then the chance of S1 occurring is 2/7 and the chance of S3 occurring is 5/7. So choose A3 (expected payoff is $45,714).

A1: $(2/7)(-100) + (5/7)(100) = 42.857$
A2: $(2/7)(-10) + (5/7)(50) = 32.857$
A3: $(2/7)(10) + (5/7)(60) = 45.714$

EVPI = EP (with perfect info) – EP (without more info)
$= [(0.3)(20) + (0.7)(45.714)] – 35 = \$3,000$

The maximum amount you should pay for the information is $3,000. The decision with this information would be to choose A3 with an expected payoff of $45,714.

d) If S3 occurs for certain then choose A1 (expected payoff is $100,000).

If S3 does not occur for certain then the chance of S1 occurring is 2/5 and the chance of S2 occurring is 3/5. So choose A3 (expected payoff is $10,000).

A1:   (2/5)(-100) + (3/5)(100) = -34
A2:   (2/5)(-10) + (3/5)(20) = 8
A3:   (2/5)(10) + (3/5)(10) = 10

EVPI = EP (with perfect info) – EP (without more info)
= [(0.5)(100) + (0.5)(10)] – 35 = 20

The maximum amount you should pay for the information is $20,000. The decision with this information would be to choose A1 with an expected payoff of $100,000.

e) EVPI = EP (with perfect info) – EP (without more info)
= [(0.2)(10) + (0.3)(20) + (0.5)(100)] – 35 = 23

A maximum of $23,000 should be paid for the information.

Choose the alternative that maximizes the payoff given the known state of nature. For S1 choose A3, for S2 choose A2, and for S3 choose A1.

The resulting expected payoff is $58,000
(0.2)(10) + (0.3)(20) + (0.5)(100) = 58

f) The maximum amount you should pay for testing is $23,000.

10.13 a)

Prior Probabilities P (state)	Conditional Probabilities P(finding | state)	Joint Probabilities P(state and finding)	Posterior Probabilities P(state | finding)

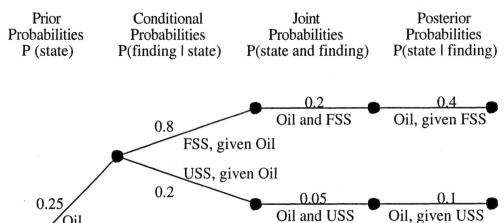

		0.2 Oil and FSS	0.4 Oil, given FSS
	0.8 FSS, given Oil		
0.25 Oil	USS, given Oil 0.2	0.05 Oil and USS	0.1 Oil, given USS
0.75 Dry	0.4 FSS, given Dry	0.3 Dry and FSS	0.6 Dry, given FSS
	USS, given Dry 0.6	0.45 Dry and USS	0.9 Dry, given USS

b)

Data:		P(Finding | State) Finding	
State of Nature	Prior Probability	FSS	USS
Oil	0.25	0.8	0.2
Dry	0.75	0.4	0.6

Posterior Probabilities:		P(State | Finding) State of Nature	
Finding	P(Finding)	Oil	Dry
FSS	0.5	0.4	0.6
USS	0.5	0.1	0.9

c & d)   The optimal policy is to do a seismic survey and sell if it is unfavorable or drill if it is favorable.

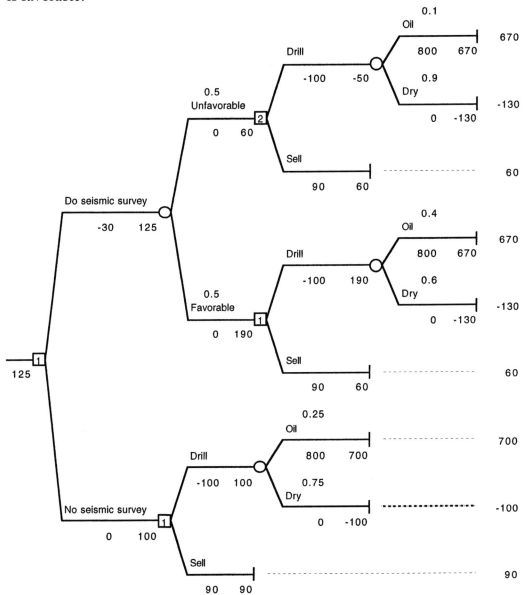

10.14 a&b)

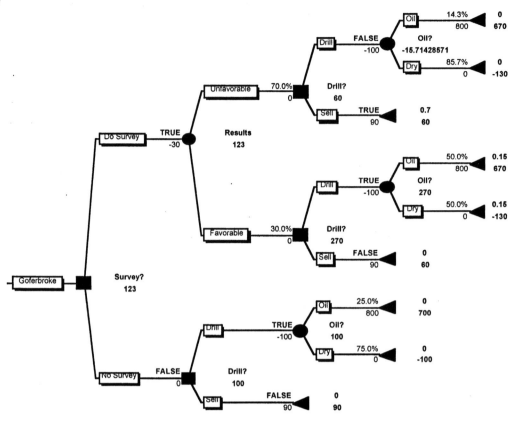

c)

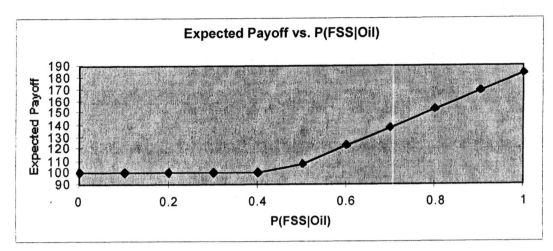

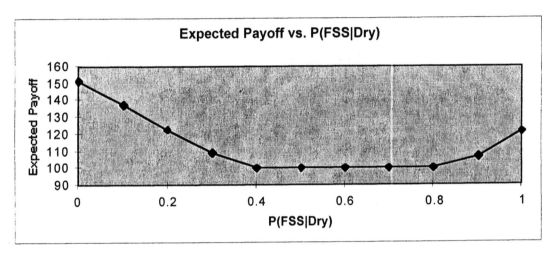

d)

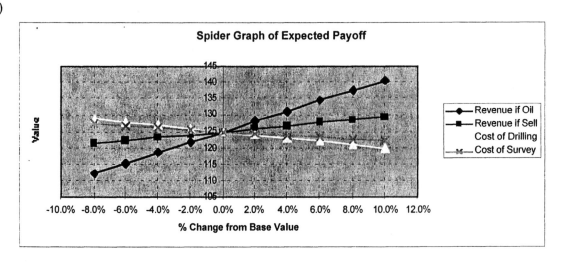

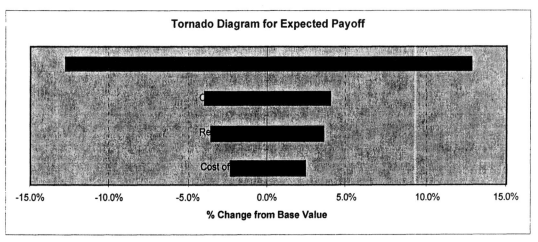

10.15 a)

		State of Nature	
Alternative	Poor Risk	Average Risk	Good Risk
Extend Credit	-15,000	10,000	20,000
Don't Extend Credit	0	0	0
Prior Probabilities	0.2	0.5	0.3

b)

		State of Nature		Expected Payoff	
Alternative	Poor Risk	Average Risk	Good Risk		
Extend Credit	-15000	10000	20000	8000	Maximum
Don't Extend Credit	0	0	0	0	
Prior Probability	0.2	0.5	0.3		

Choose to extend credit (expected payoff is $8,000).

c)

Alternative	State of Nature		
	Poor Risk	Average Risk	Good Risk
Extend Credit	-15000	10000	20000
Don't Extend Credit	0	0	0
Prior Probability	0.2	0.5	0.3
Maximum Payoff	0	10000	20000

Expected Payoff with Perfect Information =	11000

EVPI = EP (with perfect info) – EP (without more info) = 11,000 – 8,000 = \$3,000

This indicates that the credit-rating organization should not be used.

d) PF = Poor Finding   AF = Average Finding   GF = Good Finding
    PS = Poor State   AS = Average State   GS = Good State

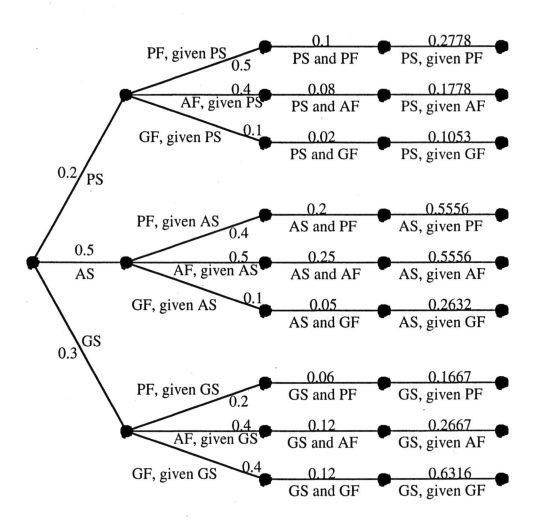

e)

Data:		P(Finding | State) Finding		
State of Nature	Prior Probability	Poor	Average	Good
Poor	0.2	0.5	0.4	0.1
Average	0.5	0.4	0.5	0.1
Good	0.3	0.2	0.4	0.4

Posterior Probabilities:		P(State | Finding) State of Nature		
Finding	P(Finding)	Poor	Average	Good
Poor	0.36	0.2778	0.5556	0.1667
Average	0.45	0.1778	0.5556	0.2667
Good	0.19	0.1053	0.2632	0.6316

f & g)   Vincent should not get the credit rating and extend credit. (Note: This decision tree
continues on the next page.)

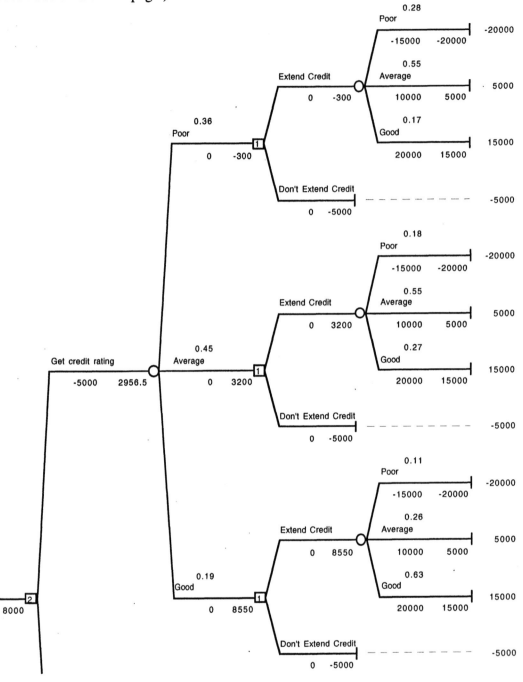

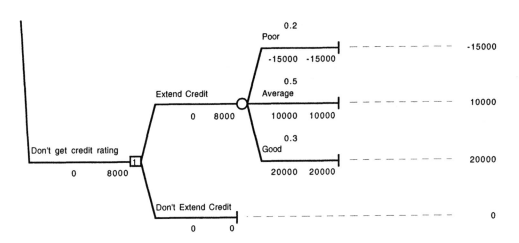

10.16 a)

Alternative	State of Nature			Expected Payoff	
	S1	S2			
A1	400	-100		100	Maximum
A2	0	100		60	
Prior Probability	0.4	0.6			

Choose A1 (expected payoff is $100).

b)

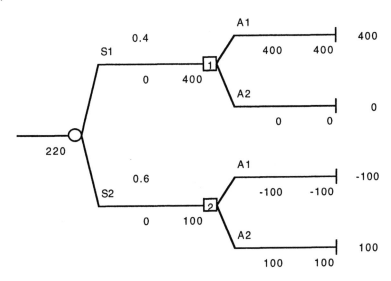

EVPI = EP (with perfect info) – EP (without more info) = 220 – 100 = $120

This indicates that it might be worthwhile to do the research.

c) P(state and finding) = P(state) P(finding/state)

    i)   P(S1 and S1) = (0.4)(0.6) = 0.24
    ii)   P(S1 and S2) = (0.4)(0.4) = 0.16
    iii)   P(S2 and S1) = (0.6)(0.2) = 0.12
    iv)   P(S2 and S2) = (0.6)(0.8) = 0.48

d) P(S1) = 0.24 + 0.12 = 0.36
     P(S2) = 0.16 + 0.48 = 0.64

e)

$$P(state \mid finding) = \frac{P(state \text{ and } finding)}{P(finding)}$$

$$P(S1|S1) = \frac{0.24}{0.36} = 0.667$$

$$P(S1|S2) = \frac{0.16}{0.64} = 0.25$$

$$P(S2|S1) = \frac{0.12}{0.36} = 0.333$$

$$P(S2|S2) = \frac{0.48}{0.64} = 0.75$$

f)

Data:		P(Finding I State)		
State of Nature	Prior Probability	Finding		
		S1	S2	
S1	0.4	0.6	0.4	
S2	0.6	0.2	0.8	

Posterior Probabilities:		P(State I Finding)		
Finding	P(Finding)	State of Nature		
		S1	S2	
S1	0.36	0.6667	0.3333	
S2	0.64	0.25	0.75	

g)

Alternative	State of Nature		Expected Payoff	
	S1	S2		
A1	400	-100	233.5	Maximum
A2	0	100	33.3	
Prior Probability	0.667	0.333		

If S1 is predicted then the choose A1 (expected payoff is $233.33)

10-38

h)

	State of Nature		Expected
Alternative	S1	S2	Payoff
A1	400	-100	25
A2	0	100	75 Maximum
Prior Probability	0.25	0.75	

If S2 is predicted then the choose A2 (expected payoff is $75)

i) Expected payoff given research is $(0.36)(233.33) + (0.64)(75) - 100 = \$32$

j) The optimal policy is to do no research and choose A1.

k)

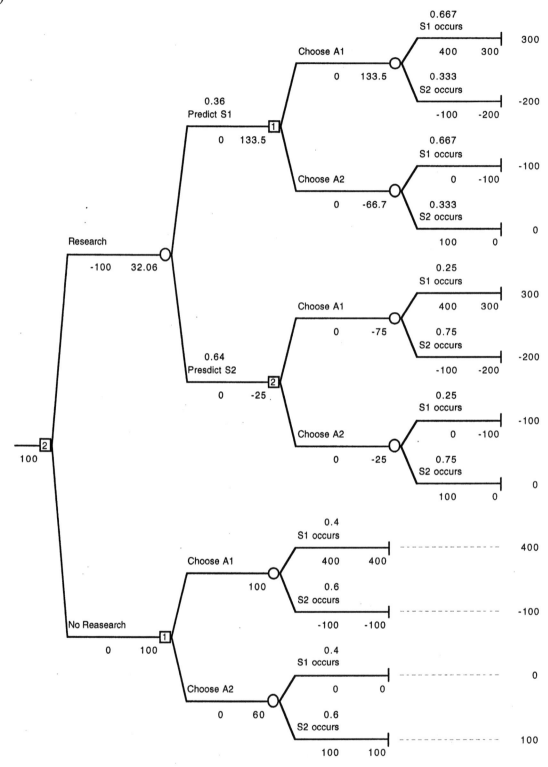

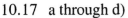

10.17 a through d)

| Prior Probabilities P (state) | Conditional Probabilities P(finding | state) | Joint Probabilities P(state and finding) | Posterior Probabilities P(state | finding) |

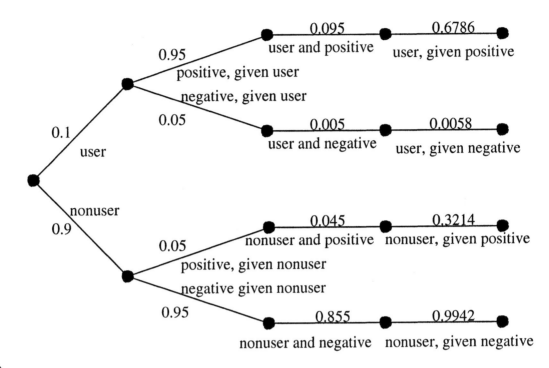

e)

Data:		P(Finding | State) Finding		
State of Nature	Prior Probability	Positive	Negative	
Positive	0.1	0.95	0.05	
Negative	0.9	0.05	0.95	

Posterior Probabilities:		P(State | Finding) State of Nature		
Finding	P(Finding)	Positive	Negative	
Positive	0.14	0.67857	0.32143	
Negative	0.86	0.00581	0.99419	

10.18 a)

	State of Nature	
Alternative	Successful	Unsuccessful
Develop new product	1,500,000	-1,800,000
Don't develop new product	0	0
Prior Probabilities	0.667	0.333

b)

	State of Nature		Expected	
Alternative	Successful	Unsuccessful	Payoff	
Develop product	1500000	-1800000	400000	Maximum
Don't develop product	0	0	0	
Prior Probability	0.666667	0.3333333		

Choose to develop new product (expected payoff is $400,000).

c)

	State of Nature	
Alternative	Successful	Jnsuccessful
Develop product	1500000	-1800000
Don't develop product	0	0
Prior Probability	0.666667	0.333333
Maximum Payoff	1500000	0

Expected Payoff with Perfect Information =	1000000

EVPI = EP (with perfect info) – EP (without more info)
= 1,000,000 – 400,000 = $600,000

This indicates that consideration should be given to conducting the market survey.

d)

Data:		P(Finding | State)		
State of	Prior		Finding	
Nature	Probability	Successful	Unsuccessful	
Successful	0.6666667	0.8	0.2	
Unsuccessful	0.3333333	0.3	0.7	

Posterior		P(State | Finding)		
Probabilities:		State of Nature		
Finding	P(Finding)	Successful	Unsuccessful	
Successful	0.6333333	0.842105	0.157894737	
Unsuccessful	0.3666667	0.363636	0.636363636	

e)

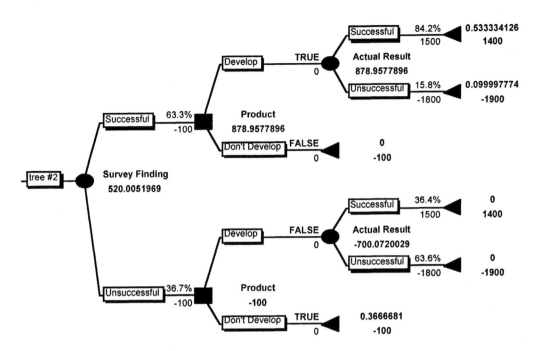

This tree assumes that they are doing the survey. The answer obtained is better than the answer obtained in part b) without doing the survey so they should do the survey.

f) Policy Suggestion:

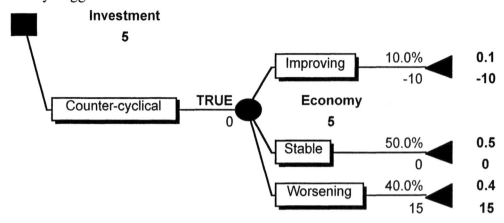

STATISTICS

Mean	5
Minimum	-10
Maximum	15
Mode	0
Std Dev	8.660254
Skewness	0
Kurtosis	1.666667

PROFILE:

#	X	P
1	-10	0.1
2	0	0.5
3	15	0.4

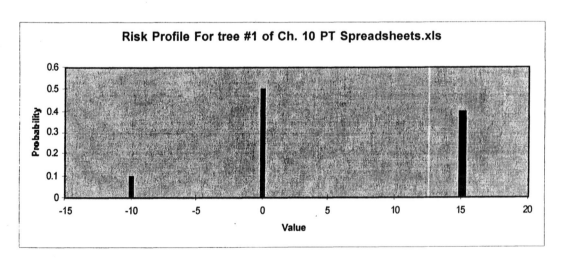

g)

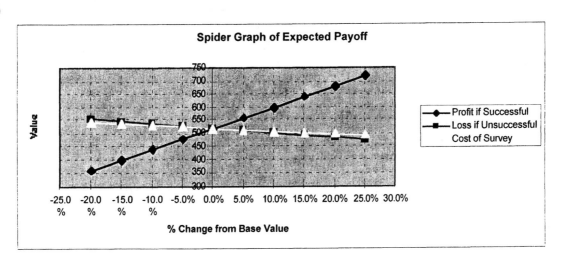

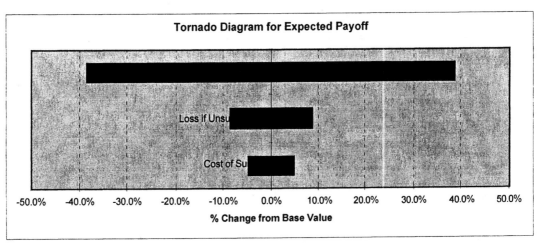

10.19 a)

| | State of Nature | |
Alternative	p=0.05	p=0.25
Screen	-1500	-1500
Don't screen	-750	-3750
Prior Probabilities	0.8	0.2

b)

| | State of Nature | | Expected Payoff |
Alternative	p=0.05	p=0.25	
Screen	-1500	-1500	-1500
Don't screen	-750	-3750	-1350 Maximum
Prior Probability	0.8	0.2	

Choose to not screen (expected loss is $1,350).

c)

Alternative	State of Nature	
	p=0.05	p=0.25
Screen	-1500	-1500
Don't screen	-750	-3750
Prior Probability	0.8	0.2
Maximum Payoff	-750	-1500

Expected Payoff with Perfect Information =	-900

EVPI = EP (with perfect info) – EP (without more info) = -900 + 1350 = $450

This indicates that consideration should be given to inspecting the single item.

d)

Data:		P(Finding | State)	
State of Nature	Prior Probability	Finding	
		defective	nondefective
p=0.05	0.8	0.05	0.95
p=0.25	0.2	0.25	0.75

Posterior Probabilities:		P(State | Finding)	
		State of Nature	
Finding	P(Finding)	p=0.05	p=0.25
defective	0.09	0.444444	0.555555556
nondefective	0.91	0.835165	0.164835165

e) The optimal policy is not to pre-screen or screen.

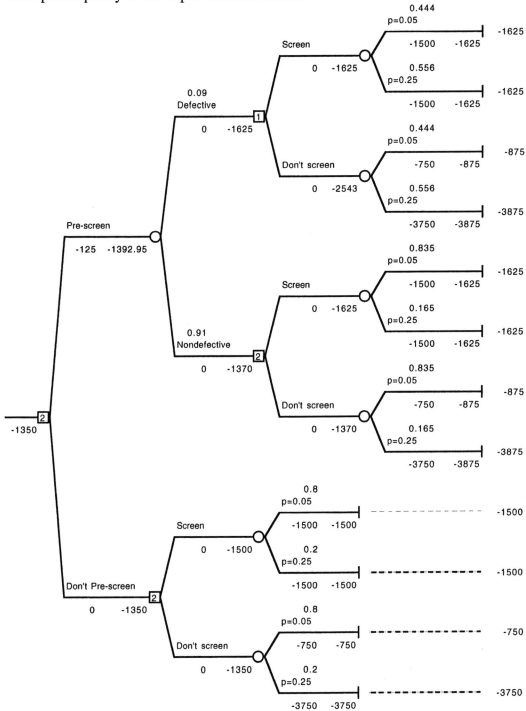

10.20 a)

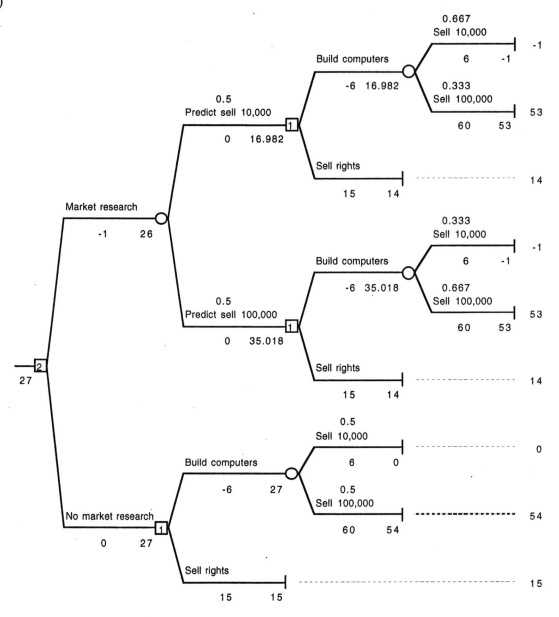

The optimal policy is to do no market research and build the computers.

b)

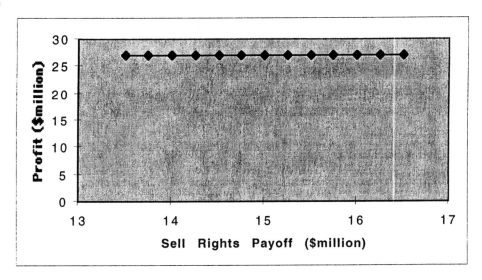

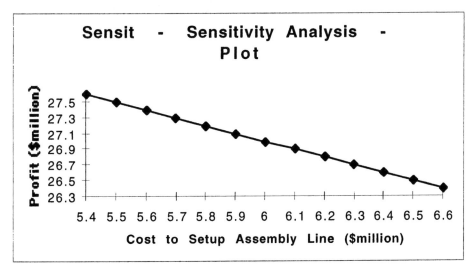

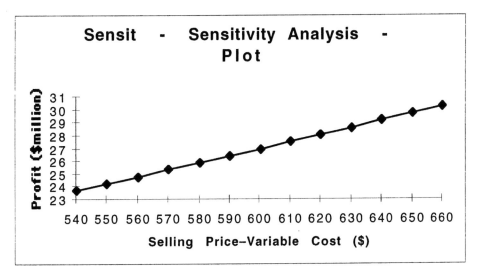

c)

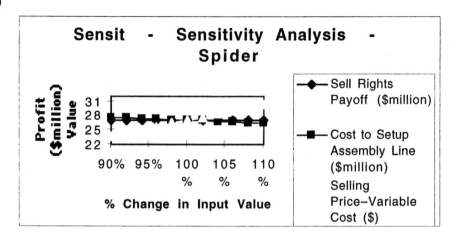

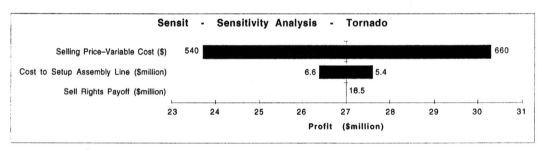

10.21 a)

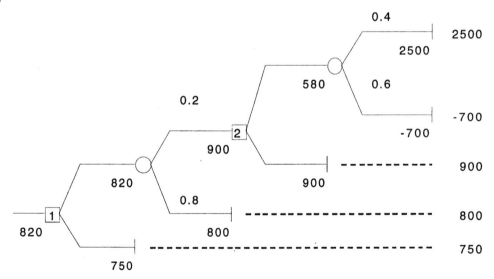

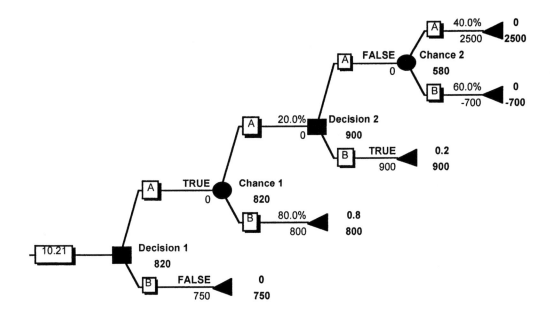

c) Policy Suggestion:

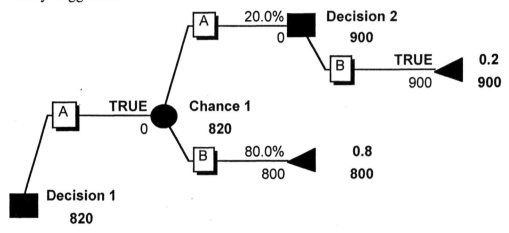

STATISTICS

Mean	820
Minimum	800
Maximum	900
Mode	800
Std Dev	40
Skewness	1.5
Kurtosis	3.25

PROFILE:

#	X	P
1	800	0.8
2	900	0.2

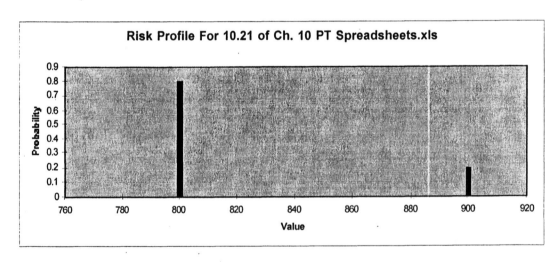

10.22

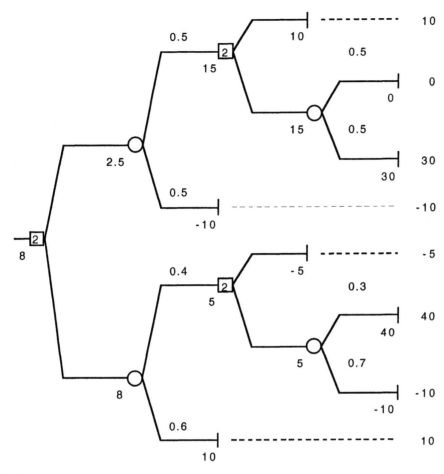

10.23 a)

| Alternative | State of Nature | |
	W	L
Hold campaign	3	-2
Don't hold campaign	0	0
Prior Probabilities	0.6	0.4

b)

| Alternative | State of Nature | | Expected Payoff | |
	W	L		
Hold campaign	3	-2	1	Maximum
Don't hold campaign	0	0	0	
Prior Probability	0.6	0.4		

Choose to hold the campaign (expected payoff is $1 million).

c)

Alternative	State of Nature	
	W	L
Hold campaign	3	-2
Don't hold campaign	0	0
Prior Probability	0.6	0.4
Maximum Payoff	3	0

Expected Payoff with Perfect Information =	1.8

EVPI = EP (with perfect info) – EP (without more info) = 1.8 - 1 = $800,000

d)

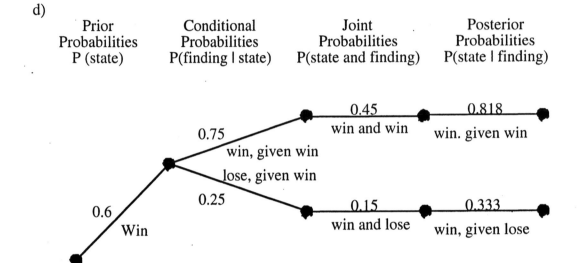

Prior Probabilities P (state)	Conditional Probabilities P(finding | state)	Joint Probabilities P(state and finding)	Posterior Probabilities P(state | finding)

0.75 win, given win
0.25 lose, given win

0.6 Win

0.45 win and win   0.818 win. given win
0.15 win and lose   0.333 win, given lose

0.4 Lose

0.25 win, given lose
0.75 lose, given lose

0.1 lose and win   0.182 lose, given win
0.3 lose and lose   0.667 lose, given lose

e)

Data:		P(Finding | State) Finding			
State of Nature	Prior Probability	Win	Lose		
Win	0.6	0.75	0.25		
Lose	0.4	0.25	0.75		

Posterior Probabilities:		P(State | Finding) State of Nature		
Finding	P(Finding)	Win	Lose	
Win	0.55	0.8182	0.1818	
Lose	0.45	0.3333	0.6667	

f & g)   Leland University should hire William. If he predicts a winning season then they
should hold the campaign, if he predicts a losing season then they should not hold the
campaign.

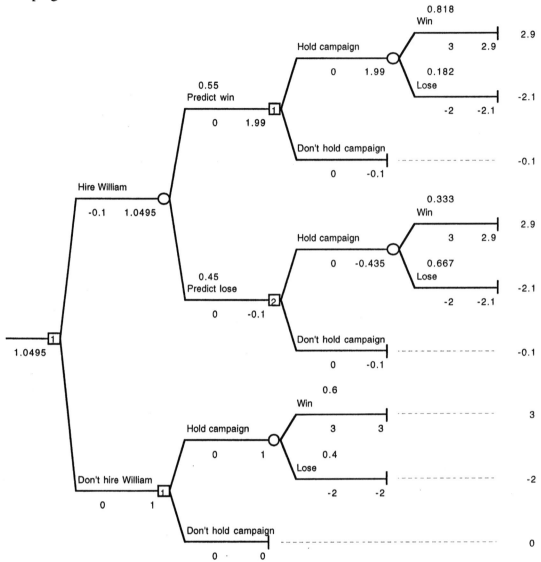

10.24 a & c)   (Note: this decision tree continues on the next page.)

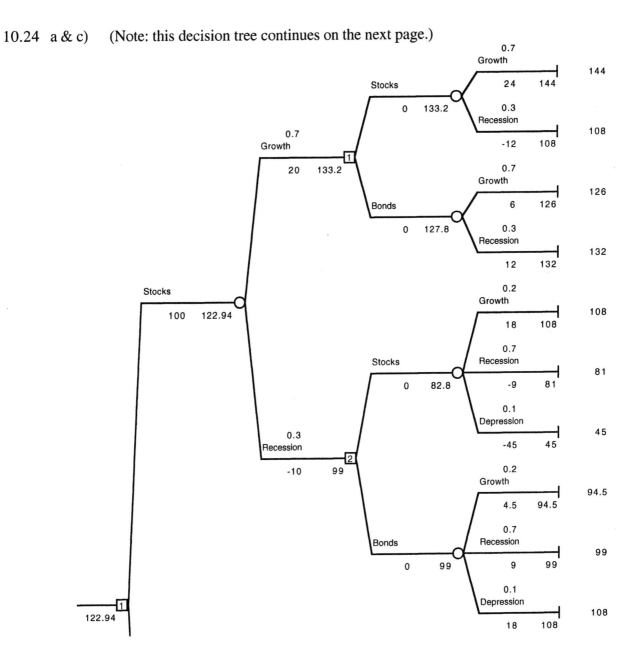

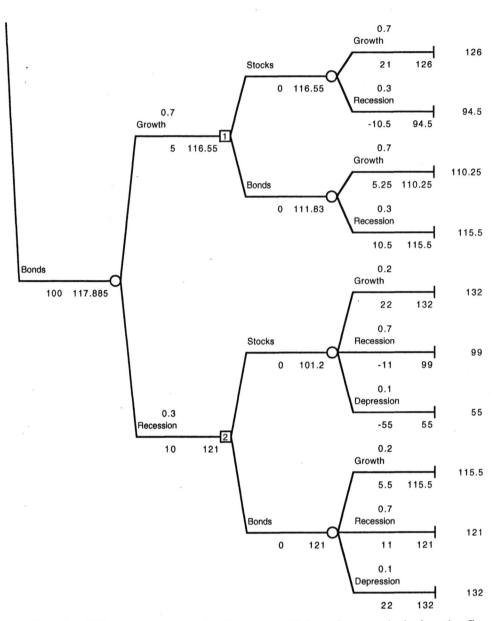

b) The comptroller should invest in stocks the first year. If there is growth during the first year then she should invest in stocks again the second year. If there is a recession during the first year then she should invest in bonds for the second year.

10.25 a & b)   The optimal policy is to wait until Wednesday to buy if the price is $9 on Tuesday. If the price is $10 or $11 on Tuesday then buy on Tuesday.

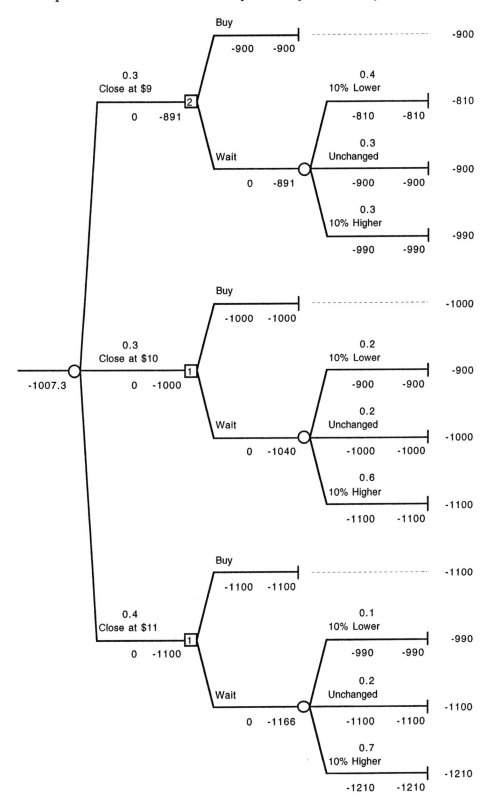

10.26 The optimal policy is to sample the fruit and buy if it is excellent and reject if it is unsatisfactory.

Data:		P(Finding | State)		
State of Nature	Prior Probability	Finding		
		Excellent	Unsatisfactory	
Excellent	0.9	0.8	0.2	
Unsatisfactory	0.1	0.3	0.7	

Posterior Probabilities:		P(State | Finding)		
		State of Nature		
Finding	P(Finding)	Excellent	Unsatisfactory	
Excellent	0.75	0.96	0.04	
Unsatisfactory	0.25	0.72	0.28	

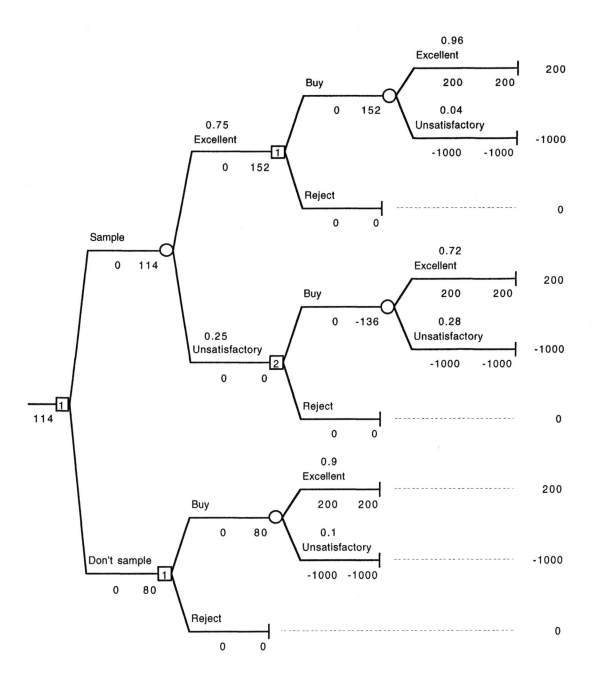

10.27 a)

Alternative	State of Nature	
	Successful	Unsuccessful
Introduce new product	40	-15
Don't introduce new product	0	0
Prior Probabilities	0.5	0.5

Alternative	State of Nature		Expected Payoff	
	Successful	Unsuccessful		
Introduce product	40	-15	12.5	Maximum
Don't introduce product	0	0	0	
Prior Probability	0.5	0.5		

Choose to introduce the new product (expected payoff is $12.5 million).

b)

Alternative	State of Nature	
	Successful	Unsuccessful
Introduce product	40	-15
Don't introduce product	0	0
Prior Probability	0.5	0.5
Maximum Payoff	40	0

Expected Payoff with Perfect Information =	20

EVPI = EP (with perfect info) – EP (without more info) = 20 – 12.5 = $7.5 million

c) The optimal policy is not to test but to introduce the new product.

Data:		P(Finding | State)		
State of Nature	Prior Probability	Finding		
		FSS	USS	
Successful	0.5	0.8	0.2	
Unsuccessful	0.5	0.25	0.75	

Posterior Probabilities:		P(State | Finding)		
		State of Nature		
Finding	P(Finding)	Successf	unsuccessf	
FSS	0.525	0.7619	0.2381	
USS	0.475	0.2105	0.7895	

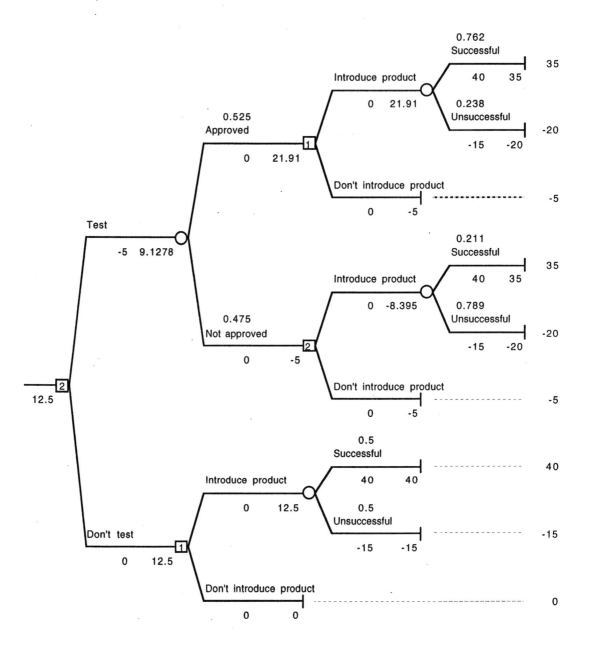

d)

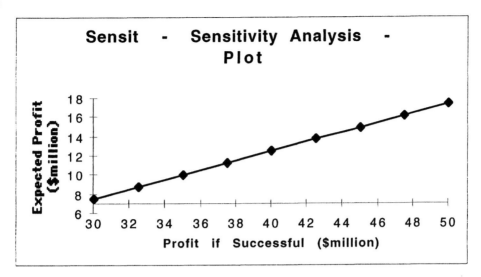

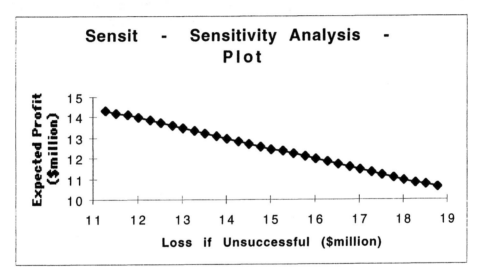

e)

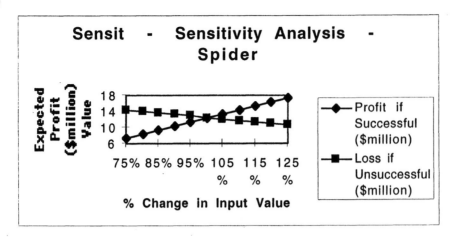

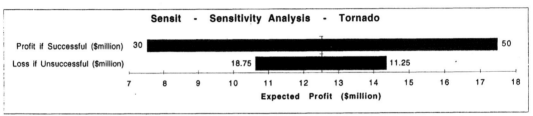

Both charts indicate that the expected profit is sensitive to both parameters, but is somewhat more sensitive to changes in the profit if successful than to changes in the loss if unsuccessful.

10.28 a) Chelsea should run in the NH primary. If she does well then she should run in the ST primaries. If she does poorly then she should not run in the ST primaries.

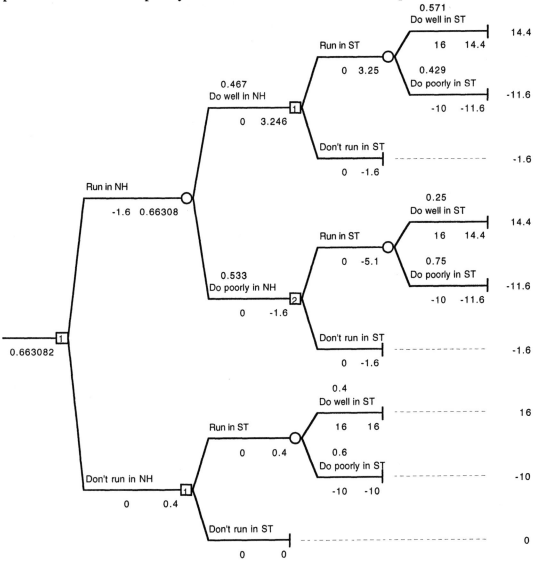

b)

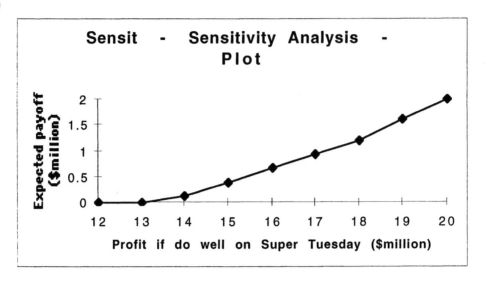

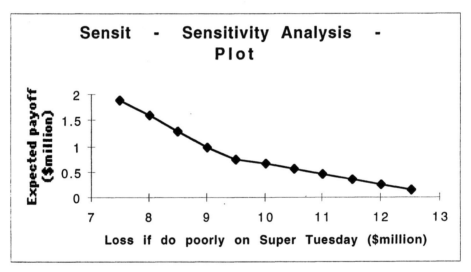

c)

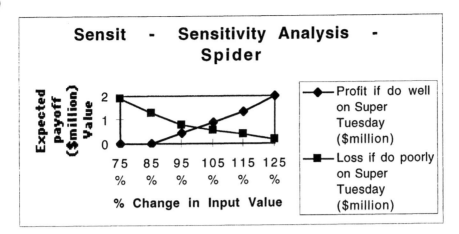

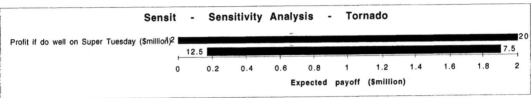

Both charts indicate that the expected payoff is sensitive to both parameters, although it is *slightly* more sensitive to changes in the profit if she does well than to changes in the loss if she does poorly.

10.29   a)

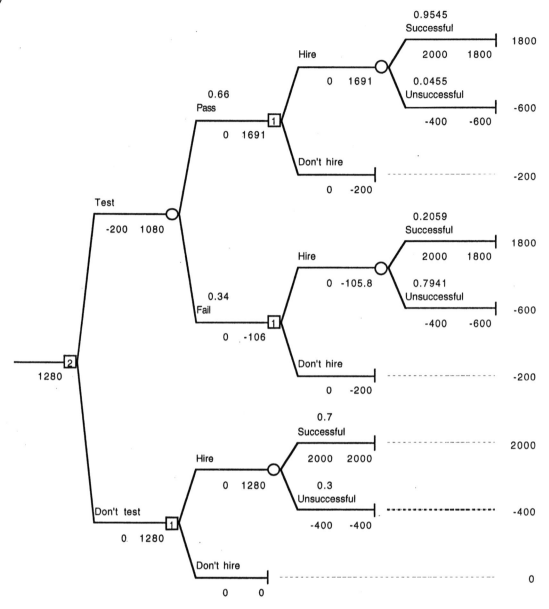

b)

Data:							
		P(Finding | State)					
		Finding					
State of Nature	Prior Probability	Pass	Fail				
Successful	0.7	0.9	0.1				
Unsuccessful	0.3	0.1	0.9				

Posterior Probabilities:		P(State | Finding)	
		State of Nature	
Finding	P(Finding)	Successf	unsuccessf
Pass	0.66	0.9545	0.0455
Fail	0.34	0.2059	0.7941

c) The optimal policy is not to pay for testing and to hire Matthew.

d) If the fee is 0 then the company is still has the same policy so they should not be willing to pay anything for the detailed report.

10.30 a & b)

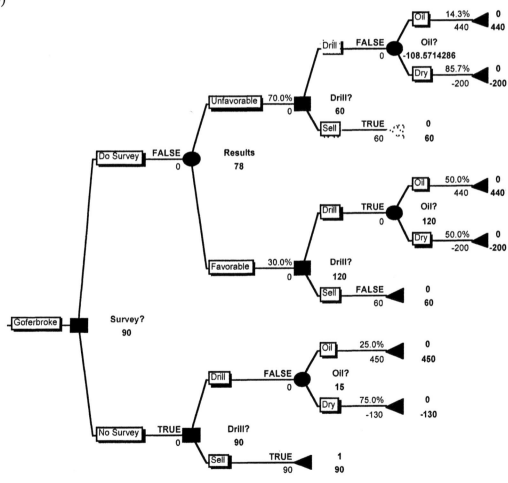

10.31 a)

Alternative	State of Nature			Expected Payoff
	Earthquake	No earthquake		
Buy insurance	249820	249820		249820
Don't buy insurance	90000	250000		249840 Maximum
Prior Probability	0.001	0.999		

Choose not to buy insurance (expected payoff is $249,840).

b) $U(\text{insurance}) = U(250,000\text{-}180) = \sqrt{249,820} = 499.82$
$U(\text{no insurance}) = (0.999)U(250,000) + (0.001)U(90,000) = 499.8$

Optimal policy is to buy insurance.

10.32 $E(\text{utility})$ of $19,000 = U(19) = \sqrt{25} = 5$
$E(\text{utility})$ of investment $= (0.3)U(10) + (0.7)U(30) = (0.3)\sqrt{16} + (0.7)\sqrt{36} = 5.4$

Choose the investment to maximize expected utility.

10.33 $E(\text{utility for } A_1) = E(\text{utility for } A_2)$
$pU(10) + (1\text{-}p)U(30) = U(19)$
$(0.3)U(10) + (0.7)(20) = 16.7$
$U(10) = 9$

10.34 a) $E(\text{utility for } A_1) = E(\text{utility for } A_2)$
$pU(10) + (1\text{-}p)U(0) = U(1)$
$(0.125)U(10) + (1\text{-}0.125)(0) = 1$
$U(10) = 8$

b) $E(\text{utility for } A_1) = E(\text{utility for } A_2)$
$pU(10) + (1\text{-}p)U(0) = U(5)$
$(0.5625)(8) + (1\text{-}0.5625)(0) = U(5)$
$U(5) = 4.5$

c) Answers will vary.

10.35 a) Expected utility of $A_1 = pU(25) + (1-p)(36) = 5p + 6(1-p) = 6 - p$.
Expected utility of $A_2 = pU(100) + (1-p)U(0) = 10p + 0 = 10p$.
Expected utility of $A_3 = pU(0) + (1-p)U(49) = 7(1-p) = 7 - 7p$.

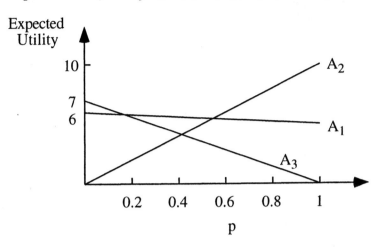

A_1 and A_3 cross when $6-p = 7-7p$, or $p=1/6$.
A_1 and A_2 cross when $6-p=10p$, or $p=2/3$.
Thus, A_3 is best when $p \leq 1/6$, A_1 is best when $1/6 < p \leq 2/3$, and A_2 is best when $p > 2/3$.

b)

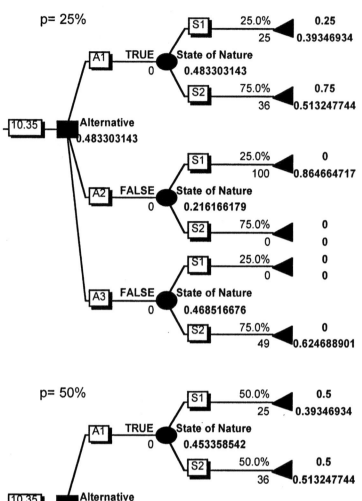

p= 25%

```
                              S1  25.0%  ◀  0.25
                   TRUE              25     0.39346934
         A1 ─────────●  State of Nature
                   0   0.483303143
                              S2  75.0%  ◀  0.75
                                    36     0.513247744

                              S1  25.0%  ◀  0
                  FALSE             100    0.864664717
         A2 ─────────●  State of Nature
10.35 ─■  0   0.216166179
  Alternative                 S2  75.0%  ◀  0
  0.483303143                        0      0

                              S1  25.0%  ◀  0
                  FALSE              0      0
         A3 ─────────●  State of Nature
                   0   0.468516676
                              S2  75.0%  ◀  0
                                    49     0.624688901
```

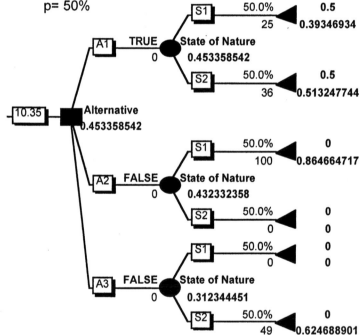

p= 50%

```
                              S1  50.0%  ◀  0.5
                   TRUE             25     0.39346934
         A1 ─────────●  State of Nature
                   0   0.453358542
                              S2  50.0%  ◀  0.5
                                    36     0.513247744

                              S1  50.0%  ◀  0
                  FALSE             100    0.864664717
         A2 ─────────●  State of Nature
10.35 ─■  0   0.432332358
  Alternative                 S2  50.0%  ◀  0
  0.453358542                        0      0

                              S1  50.0%  ◀  0
                  FALSE              0      0
         A3 ─────────●  State of Nature
                   0   0.312344451
                              S2  50.0%  ◀  0
                                    49     0.624688901
```

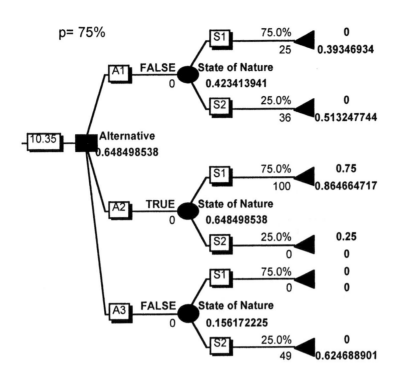

10.36 The optimal policy is not to test for disease A but to treat disease A. (Note: this decision tree is continued on the next page.)

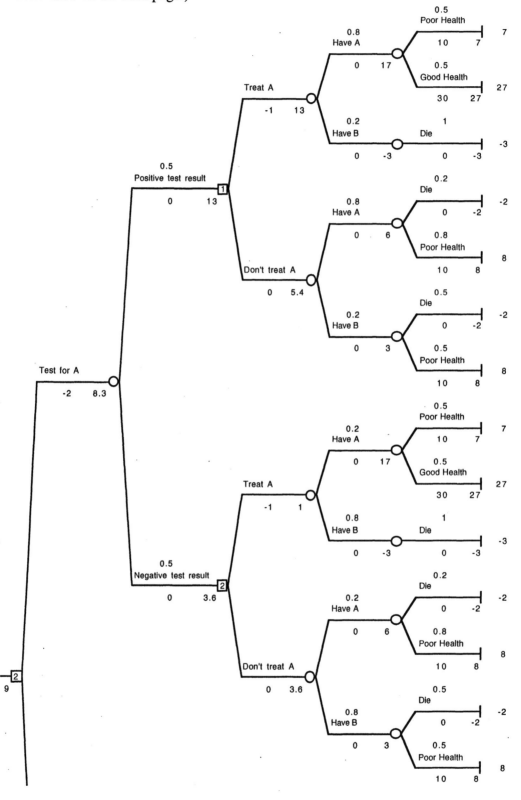

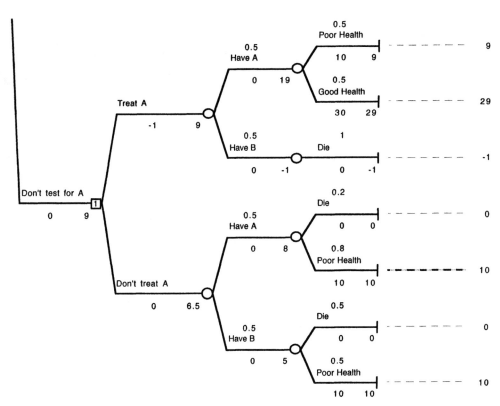

10.37 For the decision-maker to be indifferent between A1 and A2, U(x) must equal 3.5.

So, $x^{\frac{1}{3}} = 3.5$ or x = \$42.88.

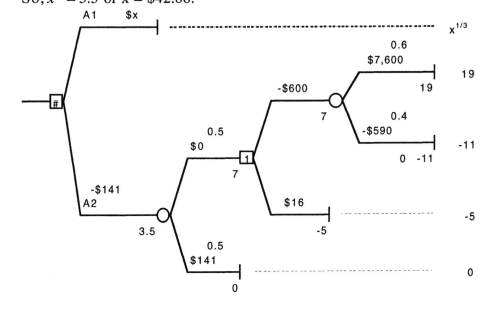

10.38   a)

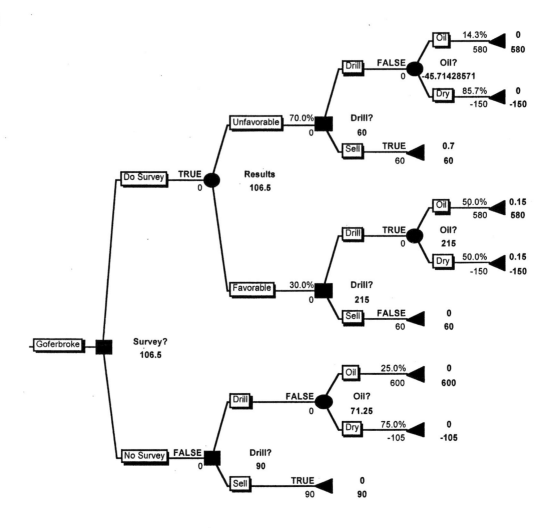

b) Policy Suggestion:

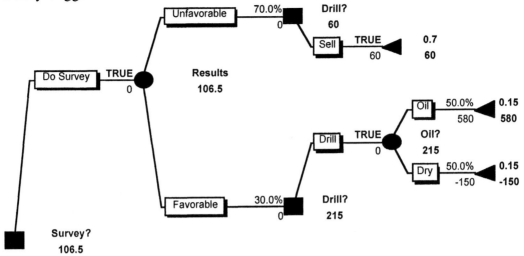

STATISTICS

Mean	106.5
Minimum	-150
Maximum	580
Mode	60
Std Dev	212.1621
Skewness	1.394998
Kurtosis	4.043419

PROFILE:

#	X	P
1	-150	0.15
2	60	0.7
3	580	0.15

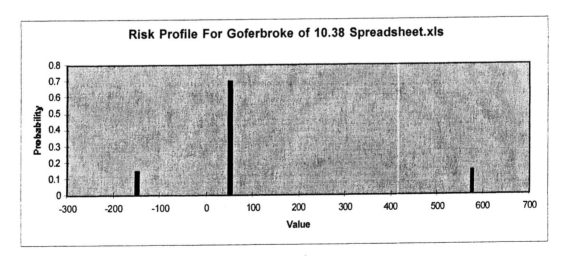

c)

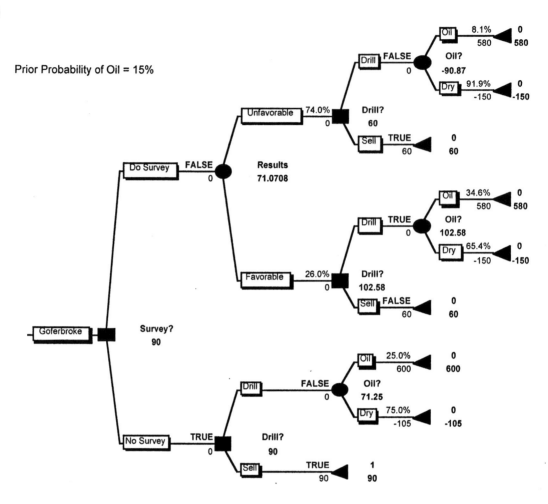

Prior Probability of Oil = 15%

Prior Probability of Oil = 20%

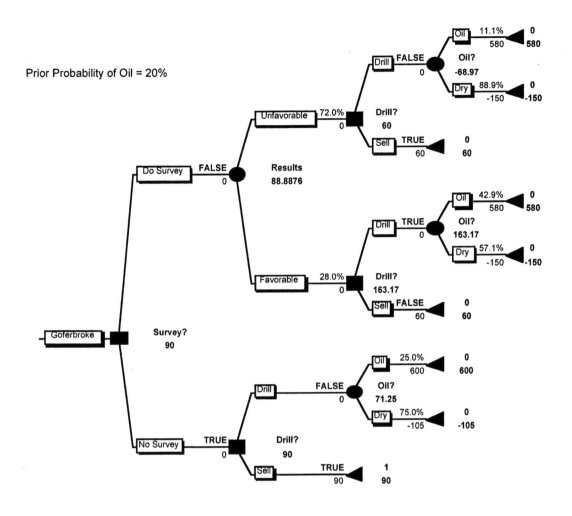

Prior Probability of Oil = 30%

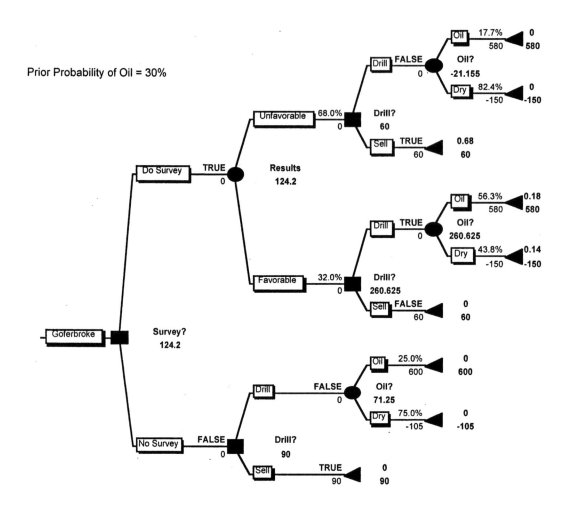

Prior Probability of Oil = 35%

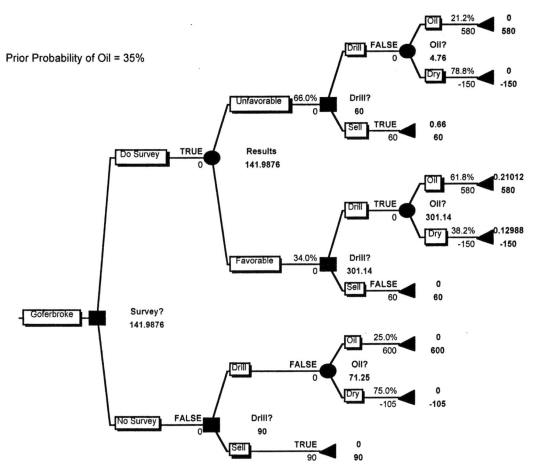

10.39 Answers will vary.

10.40 Answers will vary.

Cases

10.1   a)   The relevant data are summarized in the following spreadsheet.

Data:

Price:

High	Medium	Low
50.00	40.00	30.00

Sales:

High	Medium	Low
50,000	30,000	20,000

Probability tables:

Prior probabilities:

Competition:	Severe	Moderate	Weak
p(competition)	0.20	0.70	0.10

Conditional Probabilities:

Price:	50.00		
Competition:	Severe	Moderate	Weak
50k Units	0.20	0.25	0.30
30k Units	0.25	0.30	0.35
20k Units	0.55	0.45	0.35

Price:	40.00		
Competition:	Severe	Moderate	Weak
50k Units	0.25	0.30	0.40
30k Units	0.35	0.40	0.50
20k Units	0.40	0.30	0.10

Price:	30.00		
Competition:	Severe	Moderate	Weak
50k Units	0.35	0.40	0.50
30k Units	0.40	0.50	0.45
20k Units	0.25	0.10	0.05

b)   The scenario "moderate competition, sales of 30,000 units at a unit price of $30" has the largest total probability. Therefore, under the Maximum Likelihood Criterion, Charlotte should price the product at $30.

If all outcomes have the same probability, then Charlotte should charge the highest price possible in order to maximize her expected revenues. Under the Equally Likely Criterion Charlotte should charge a unit price of $50.

c) The three branches of the decision tree for the decision problem without additional information follow.

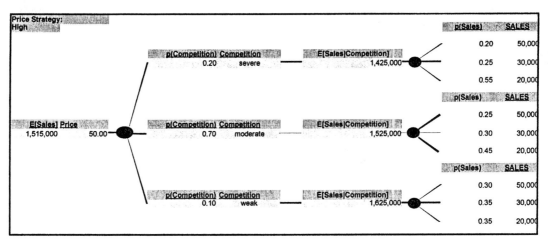

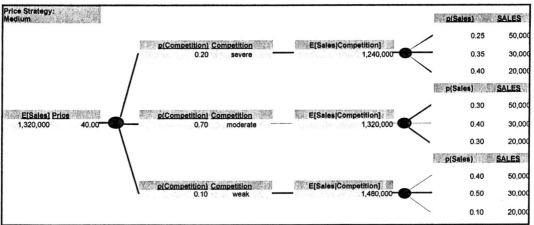

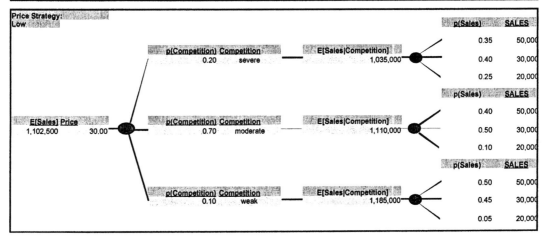

The calculation of the expected revenue for a high price strategy is as follows (please refer to the decision tree). Each final outcome ("Sales") is multiplied by its probability. For example, the expected sales given severe competition (E[Sales|Competition]) equals:

0.2*50,000+0.25*30,000+0.55*20,000 = 1,425,000

The remaining expected values are calculated accordingly.

The decision tree indicates that the alternative with the maximum expected value is the high price strategy. Therefore, Charlotte should price her product at $50.

d) The decision tree for the decision problem with additional information follows in two sections. The branches of the decisions are on the next page. Please note that the decision alternative "Expected Value w/o Information" represents the entire decision tree of part (c). The calculations in this decision tree are performed in the same manner as in part (c).

Decision Tree (with additional info)

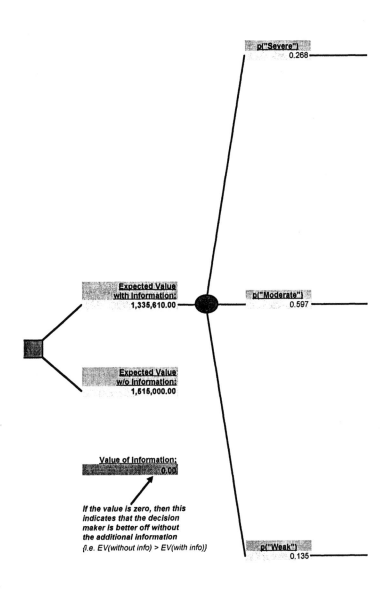

p("Severe")
0.268

Expected Value
with information:
1,335,610.00

p("Moderate")
0.597

Expected Value
w/o Information:
1,515,000.00

Value of information:
0.00

If the value is zero, then this indicates that the decision maker is better off without the additional information
(i.e. EV(without info) > EV(with info))

p("Weak")
0.135

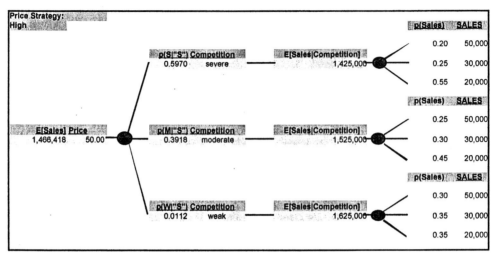

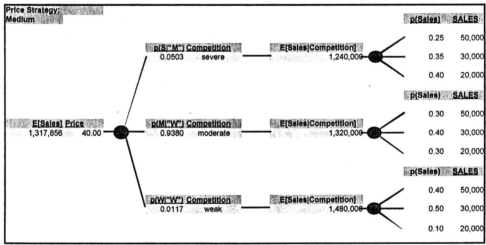

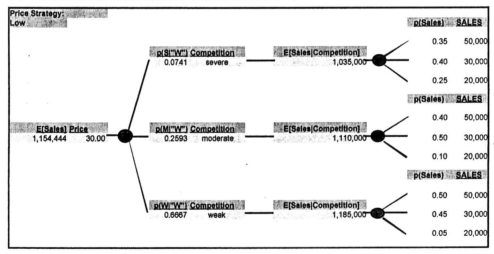

Since the expected value for the decision tree with additional (imperfect) information is less than that without information, Charlotte should not purchase the services of the market research company.

10.2 **a)** The available data are summarized in the table.

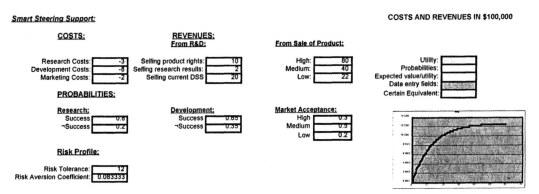

b) The basic decision tree is shown. Rectangular nodes represent decision forks and oval nodes represent chance forks.

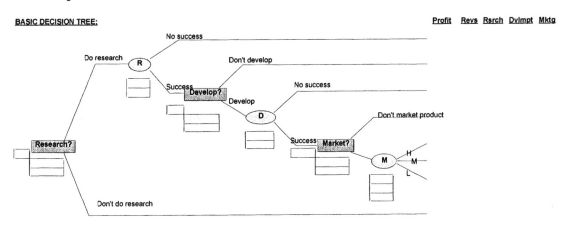

c) The decision tree displays all the expected payoffs.

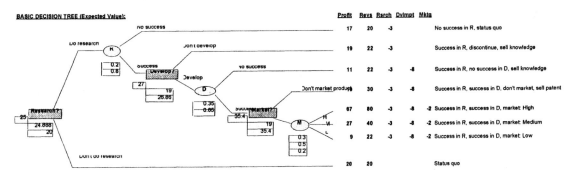

d) The best course of action is to do the research project. The expected payoff equals $2.4888 million.

e) The decision tree with perfect information on research is displayed. The expected value in this case equals $2.5488 million. The difference between the expected values with and without information equals $60,000, which is the value of perfect information on research.

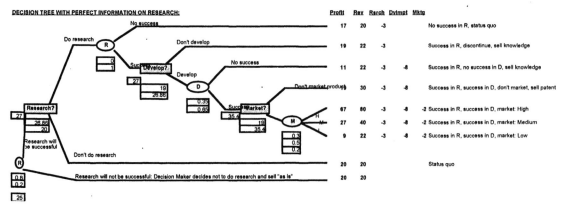

f) The decision tree with perfect information on development is displayed. The expected value in this case equals $2.7618 million. The difference between the expected values with and without information equals $273,000, which is the value of perfect information on development.

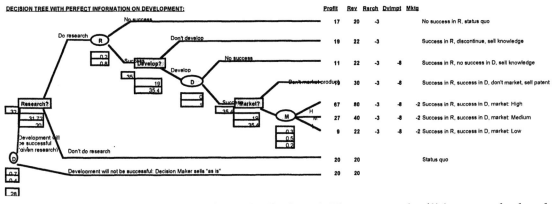

g-i) The decision tree with expected utilities is displayed. The expected utilities are calculated in the following way: for each of the outcome branches of the decision tree (e.g. profit of $6,700,000) the corresponding utility is calculated (e.g. 12.45992). Once this is done, the expected utilities are calculated. The best course of action is not to do the research (expected utility of 10.14469 vs. 9.846267 in the case of "Do research").

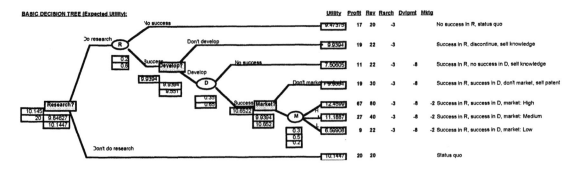

j) The expected utility for perfect information on research equals 9.939397 which is still less than the expected utility of the alternative "Don't do research" (10.14469). Therefore, the best course of action is not to do the research implying a value of zero for perfect information on the outcome of the research effort.

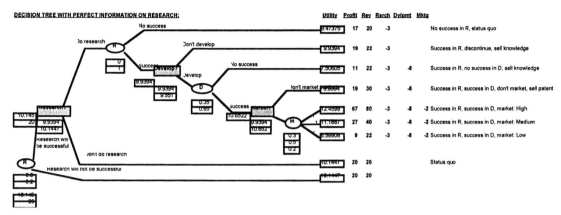

k) The expected utility for perfect information on development equals 10.321347 which is more than the expected utility for the case with no information (10.14469). The value of perfect information on development is calculated as the difference between the inverses of these two utility values (U^{-1}[10.321347] - U^{-1}[10.14469] = 20.93274 – 20 = 0.93274). The value of perfect information on the outcome of the development effort equals $93,274.

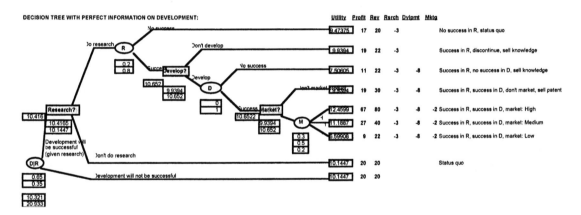

SUPPLEMENT TO CHAPTER 10
DECISION ANALYSIS WITHOUT PROBABILITIES

Review Questions

CD10-1 It might be desirable to use a decision criterion that doesn't rely on the prior probabilities if these probabilities are not reliable.

CD10-2 The maximax criterion is a very optimistic criterion that focuses on the best that can happen by choosing the alternative that can yield the maximum of the maximum payoffs.

CD10-3 The maximin criterion is a very pessimistic criterion that focuses on the worst that can happen by choosing the alternative that can yield the maximum of the minimum payoffs.

CD10-4 The pessimism-optimism index measures where the decision-maker falls on a scale from totally pessimistic to totally optimistic. This index is used with the realism criterion to combine the maximax and maximin criteria.

CD10-5 The maximax and maximin criteria are special cases of the realism criterion where the decision-maker is totally optimistic (index = 1) or totally pessimistic (index = 0).

CD10-6   The regret from having chosen a particular decision alternative is regret = maximum payoff – actual payoff.

CD10-7 The regret that can be felt afterward if the decision does not turn out well is being minimized with the minimax regret criterion.

CD10-8 A totally optimistic person would find the maximax criterion appealing, while a totally pessimistic person would find the maximin criterion appealing. The realism criterion would appeal to someone who wants to be able to choose how aggressive to be. The minimax regret criterion would appeal to someone who spends time regretting past decisions.

CD10-9 There is no uniformly reasonable criterion that doesn't use prior probabilities.

Problems

CD10.1 a)

Alternative	State of Nature S1	State of Nature S2	Maximum in Row
A1	1	7	7 Maximax
A2	6	3	6
A3	4	4	4

A1 should be chosen for a maximum payoff of $7,000.

b)

Alternative	State of Nature S1	S2	Minimum in Row
A1	1	7	1
A2	6	3	3
A3	4	4	4 Maximin

A3 should be chosen with a minimum payoff of $4,000.

c)

Pessimism-Optimism Index = 0.5

Alternative	State of Nature S1	S2	Maximum in Row	Minimum in Row	Weighted Payoff
A1	1	7	7	1	4
A2	6	3	6	3	4.5 Maximum
A3	4	4	4	4	4

Pessimism-Optimism Index = 0.25

Alternative	State of Nature S1	S2	Maximum in Row	Minimum in Row	Weighted Payoff
A1	1	7	7	1	2.5
A2	6	3	6	3	3.75
A3	4	4	4	4	4 Maximum

Pessimism-Optimism Index = 0.75

Alternative	State of Nature S1	S2	Maximum in Row	Minimum in Row	Weighted Payoff
A1	1	7	7	1	5.5 Maximum
A2	6	3	6	3	5.25
A3	4	4	4	4	4

d)

Payoff Table

Alternative	State of Nature				
	S1	S2			
A1	1	7			
A2	6	3			
A3	4	4			
Maximum	6	7	0	0	0

Regret Table

Alternative	State of Nature		Maximum in Row	
	S1	S2		
A1	5	0	5	
A2	0	4	4	
A3	2	3	3	Minimax

Choose A3 to minimize the maximum regret ($3,000).

CD10.2 a)

Alternative	State of Nature			Maximum in Row	
	S1	S2	S3		
A1	15	30	20	30	
A2	12	24	28	28	
A3	5	25	35	35	Maximax
A4	18	20	25	25	

A3 should be chosen for a maximum payoff of 35.

b)

Alternative	State of Nature			Minimum in Row	
	S1	S2	S3		
A1	15	30	20	15	
A2	12	24	28	12	
A3	5	25	35	5	
A4	18	20	25	18	Maximin

A4 should be chosen with a minimum payoff of $18.

c)

Pessimism-Optimism Index = 0.5

Alternative	State of Nature S1	S2	S3	Maximum in Row	Minimum in Row	Weighted Payoff	
A1	15	30	20	30	15	22.5	Maximum
A2	12	24	28	28	12	20	
A3	5	25	35	35	5	20	
A4	18	20	25	25	18	21.5	

Pessimism-Optimism Index = 0.25

Alternative	State of Nature S1	S2	S3	Maximum in Row	Minimum in Row	Weighted Payoff	
A1	15	30	20	30	15	18.75	
A2	12	24	28	28	12	16	
A3	5	25	35	35	5	12.5	
A4	18	20	25	25	18	19.75	Maximum

Pessimism-Optimism Index = 0.75

Alternative	State of Nature S1	S2	S3	Maximum in Row	Minimum in Row	Weighted Payoff	
A1	15	30	20	30	15	26.25	
A2	12	24	28	28	12	24	
A3	5	25	35	35	5	27.5	Maximum
A4	18	20	25	25	18	23.25	

d)

Payoff Table

Alternative	State of Nature S1	S2	S3		
A1	15	30	20		
A2	12	24	28		
A3	5	25	35		
A4	18	20	25		
Maximum	18	30	35	0	0

Regret Table

Alternative	State of Nature S1	S2	S3	Maximum in Row	
A1	3	0	15	15	
A2	6	6	7	7	Minimax
A3	13	5	0	13	
A4	0	10	10	10	

Choose A2 to minimize the maximum regret ($7).

CD10.3 a)

Alternative	State of Nature		Maximum in Row	
	Sell 10,000	Sell 100,000		
Build Computers	0	54	54	Maximax
Sell Rights	15	15	15	

Build computers (maximum profit of $54 million).

b)

Alternative	State of Nature		Minimum in Row	
	Sell 10,000	Sell 100,000		
Build Computers	0	54	0	
Sell Rights	15	15	15	Maximin

Sell the rights ($15 million).

c)

Pessimism-Optimism Index =	0.5

Alternative	State of Nature		Maximum in Row	Minimum in Row	Weighted Payoff	
	Sell 10,000	Sell 100,000				
Build Computers	0	54	54	0	27	Maximum
Sell Rights	15	15	15	15	15	

Build computers

d)

Payoff Table

Alternative	State of Nature				
	Sell 10,000	Sell 100,000			
Build Computers	0	54			
Sell Rights	15	15			
Maximum	15	54	0	0	0

Regret Table

Alternative	State of Nature		Maximum in Row	
	Sell 10,000	Sell 100,000		
Build Computers	15	0	15	Minimax
Sell Rights	0	39	39	

Choose to build computers to minimize the maximum regret ($15 million).

CD10.4 a)

Alternative	State of Nature				Maximum in Row	
	Sell 10	Sell 11	Sell 12	Sell 13		
Buy 10	50	50	50	50	50	
Buy 11	47	55	55	55	55	
Buy 12	44	52	60	60	60	
Buy 13	41	49	57	65	65	Maximax

Buy 13 cases (maximum profit of $65).

b)

Alternative	State of Nature				Minimum in Row	
	Sell 10	Sell 11	Sell 12	Sell 13		
Buy 10	50	50	50	50	50	Maximin
Buy 11	47	55	55	55	47	
Buy 12	44	52	60	60	44	
Buy 13	41	49	57	65	41	

Buy 10 cases (minimum $50).

c)

Alternative	State of Nature				Maximum in Row	Minimum in Row	Weighted Payoff	
	Sell 10	Sell 11	Sell 12	Sell 13				
Buy 10	50	50	50	50	50	50	50	
Buy 11	47	55	55	55	55	47	51	
Buy 12	44	52	60	60	60	44	52	
Buy 13	41	49	57	65	65	41	53	Maximum

Buy 13 cases

d)

Payoff Table

Alternative	State of Nature			
	Sell 10	Sell 11	Sell 12	Sell 13
Buy 10	50	50	50	50
Buy 11	47	55	55	55
Buy 12	44	52	60	60
Buy 13	41	49	57	65
Maximum	50	55	60	65	0

Regret Table

Alternative	State of Nature				Maximum in Row	
	Sell 10	Sell 11	Sell 12	Sell 13		
Buy 10	0	5	10	15	15	
Buy 11	3	0	5	10	10	
Buy 12	6	3	0	5	6	Minimax
Buy 13	9	6	3	0	9	

Choose to buy 12 cases to minimize the maximum regret ($6).

CD10.5 a)

Payoff Table

Alternative	State of Nature	
	S1	S2
A1	12	17
A2	13	15
A3	15	12
A4	0	20
Maximum	15	20	0	0	0

Regret Table

Alternative	State of Nature		Maximum in Row	
	S1	S2		
A1	3	3	3	Minimax
A2	2	5	5	
A3	0	8	8	
A4	15	0	15	

Choose A1 to minimize the maximum regret (3).

b)

Payoff Table

Alternative	State of Nature				
	S1	S2			
A1	1 2	1 7			
A2	1 3	1 5			
A3	1 5	1 2			
Maximum	1 5	1 7	0	0	0

Regret Table

Alternative	State of Nature		Maximum in Row	
	S1	S2		
A1	3	0	3	
A2	2	2	2	Minimax
A3	0	5	5	

Choose A2 to minimize the maximum regret (2).

c) The above answers demonstrate the objection that making choices between serious alternatives can depend on irrelevant alternatives with this criterion.

CD10.6 a)

Alternative	State of Nature			Maximum in Row	
	Improving	Stable	Worsening		
Conservative	30	5	-10	30	
Speculative	40	10	-30	40	Maximax
Counter-cyclical	-10	0	15	15	

Choose the speculative investment.

b)

Alternative	State of Nature			Minimum in Row	
	Improving	Stable	Worsening		
Conservative	30	5	-10	-10	Maximum
Speculative	40	10	-30	-30	
Counter-cyclical	-10	0	15	-10	Maximum

Choose either the conservative or the counter-cyclical investment.

c)

Pessimism-Optimism Index =	0.5

Alternative	Improving	Stable	State of Nature Worsening	Maximum in Row	Minimum in Row	Weighted Payoff	
Conservative	30	5	-10	30	-10	10	Maximum
Speculative	40	10	-30	40	-30	5	
Counter-cyclical	-10	0	15	15	-10	2.5	

Choose the conservative investment.

d)

Payoff Table

Alternative	Improving	Stable	State of Nature Worsening		
Conservative	30	5	-10		
Speculative	40	10	-30		
Counter-cyclical	-10	0	15		
Maximum	40	10	15	0	0

Regret Table

Alternative	Improving	Stable	State of Nature Worsening		Maximum in Row	
Conservative	10	5	25		25	Minimax
Speculative	0	0	45		45	
Counter-cyclical	50	10	0		50	

Choose the conservative investment.

CHAPTER 11
INVENTORY MANAGEMENT WITH KNOWN DEMAND

Teaching notes for this chapter are available in the Teaching Notes section near the front of this Instructor's Manual.

Review Questions

11.1-1 Administrative costs, such as labor charges to place an order, can cause the cost to exceed the purchase price.

11.1-2 Capital tied up in inventory will not be regained until the goods are sold. If the capital were free to be invested it would be able to earn a return from other opportunities. This cost is called an opportunity cost because it reflects the lost return because alternate opportunities must be foregone to carry inventory.

11.1-3 Other costs associated with holding inventory include the cost of leasing warehouse space, the cost of insurance for inventory, labor costs for warehouse personnel, and taxes based on the value of the inventory.

11.1-4 Customer dissatisfaction and the loss of future sales, price decreases to compensate for delays, delayed revenue, and increased record keeping are all cost consequences for inventory shortages.

11.2-1 The four cost components that may be included in an inventory model are acquisition cost, setup cost, holding cost, and shortage cost.

11.2-2 Retailers and wholesalers replenish their inventory and incur a direct cost by purchasing products. Manufacturers replenish their inventory and incur a direct cost by manufacturing more of the product involved.

11.2-3 When the replenishment is done by purchasing the product, the setup cost consists of the various administrative costs. When a manufacturer is replenishing its inventory, the setup cost consists of the cost of setting up the manufacturing process for another production run.

11.2-4 An inventory policy prescribes both when inventory should be replenished and by how much.

11.2-5 The total inventory cost per unit time needs to be minimized to determine an optimal inventory policy.

11.2-6 A fixed cost is a cost that remains the same regardless of the decisions made while a variable cost is a cost that is affected by the decisions made. The variable costs are the only relevant costs since they are the only costs that can be decreased by improving the decisions.

11.3-1 The basic EOQ model is so popular due to a combination of simplicity and wide applicability.

11.3-2 The model assumes a constant demand rate, that the order quantity to replenish inventory arrives all at once just when desired, and that planned shortages are not allowed. The model is sometimes used when these assumptions are not completely satisfied as in the case where constant demand is only a reasonable approximation.

11.3-3 Lead-time is the amount of time between the placement of an order and the delivery of the order quantity. The reorder point is the inventory level at which an order is placed.

11.3-4 In a continuous-review inventory system the current inventory level is monitored on a continuous basis while in a periodic-review system the inventory level is checked only periodically.

11.3-5 A continuous-review inventory system will not fit the basic EOQ model if shortages often occur and it is necessary to carry safety stock.

11.3-6 The single decision variable for the model is the order quantity (Q).

11.3-7 The shape of the pattern of inventory levels over time is a saw-toothed pattern.

11.4-1 The two types of costs included in the total variable cost are the annual setup cost and the annual holding cost. These costs are equal at the point where the order quantity is optimal.

11.4-2 The optimal order quantity increases if the demand rate increases in order to avoid overly large increases in the number of setup costs incurred per year. The optimal order quantity increases if the setup cost increases in order to decrease the number of times this setup cost will be incurred per year. The optimal order quantity decreases if the unit holding cost increases in order to drive down the average inventory level.

11.4-3 The optimal order quantity can change fairly significantly if fairly small changes are made to either the setup cost of the unit holding cost. This change is even larger if the changes are made to both costs in opposite directions.

11.4-4 The optimal order quantity does not change if both the setup cost and the unit holding cost are changed by the same percentage amount in the same direction.

11.4-5 A fairly small error in estimating either the setup cost or the unit holding cost will not increase the total variable cost very much. The same is true if the error occurs in both costs.

11.5-1 If the cost of holding inventory is high relative to the shortage costs then it may make sense to permit planned inventory shortages.

11.5-2 The assumptions for the EOQ model with planned shortages are the same as for the basic EOQ model except that planned shortages are allowed.

11.5-3 The decision variables for the EOQ model with planned shortages are the order quantity (Q) and the maximum shortage (S).

11.5-4 The total variable cost for this model includes annual setup costs, annual holding costs and annual shortage costs.

11.5-5 The optimal order quantity for this model is larger than for the basic EOQ model. The maximum inventory level for this model always will be less than for the basic EOQ model.

11.5-6 Management objects to planned shortages because they will hurt the reputation the company has for providing good customer service.

11.6-1 Quantity discounts are reductions in the unit acquisition costs of a product that are offered for ordering a relatively large quantity.

11.6-2 When quantity discounts are offered annual acquisition costs need to be included in the total variable inventory cost.

11.6-3 The unit holding cost is equal to the price paid for the items in inventory multiplied by the inventory holding cost rate (h=Ic).

11.6-4 The best order quantity for a discount category whose minimum order quantity exceeds Q from the basic EOQ model is the minimum allowed. When the maximum order quantity is less than the Q from the basic EOQ model then the best order quantity is the maximum allowed.

11.7-1 The replenishment of inventory over time is common with manufacturers who replenish their inventory by conducting intermittent production runs.

11.7-2 The assumptions for this model are the same as those for the basic EOQ model except that a production run is scheduled to begin each time the inventory level drops to 0, and this production run replenishes inventory at a constant rate throughout the duration of the run.

11.7-3 The maximum inventory level is less than the production lot size because products are being withdrawn from inventory as the production run is under way.

11.7-4 The square root formula for this model contains the annual production rate if producing continuously (R).

11.7-5 Independent-demand products have demand that does not depend on the demands for all products. Dependent-demand products have demand that is dependent upon the demand for another product, generally because the former product us a component of the latter product.

11.7-6 Material requirements planning (MRP) is a popular technique for managing inventories of components of a final product.

11.7-7 A just-in-time inventory system places great emphasis on reducing inventory levels to a bare minimum.

11.7-8 In more general terms, the focus of the just-in-time philosophy is on avoiding waste wherever it might occur in the production process.

Problems

11.1 a)

Data

D =	676	(demand/year)
K =	$75	(setup cost)
h =	$600.00	(unit holding cost)
L =	3.5	(lead time in days)
WD =	365	(working days/year)

Results

Reorder Point =	6.5
Annual Setup Cost =	$10,140
Annual Holding Cost =	$1,500
Total Variable Cost =	$11,640

Decision

Q =	5	(order quantity)

b)

Q	Annual Setup Cost	Annual Holding Cost	Total Variable Cost
	$10,140	$1,500	$11,640
5	$10,140	$1,500	$11,640
7	$7,243	$2,100	$9,343
9	$5,633	$2,700	$8,333
11	$4,609	$3,300	$7,909
13	$3,900	$3,900	$7,800
15	$3,380	$4,500	$7,880
17	$2,982	$5,100	$8,082
19	$2,668	$5,700	$8,368
21	$2,414	$6,300	$8,714
23	$2,204	$6,900	$9,104
25	$2,028	$7,500	$9,528

c)

Data		
D =	676	(demand/year)
K =	$75	(setup cost)
h =	$600.00	(unit holding cost)
L =	3.5	(lead time in days)
WD =	365	(working days/year)

Results	
Reorder Point =	6.48
Annual Setup Cost =	$3,900
Annual Holding Cost =	$3,900
Total Variable Cost =	$7,800

Decision		
Q =	13	(order quantity)

d)

Data		
D =	676	(demand/year)
K =	$75	(setup cost)
h =	$600	(unit holding cost)
L =	3.5	(lead time in days)
WD =	365	(working days/year)

Results	
Reorder Point =	6.48
Annual Setup Cost =	$3,900
Annual Holding Cost =	$3,900
Total Variable Cost =	$7,800

Decision		
Q =	13	(order quantity)

The results are the same as those obtained in part c).

e) $Q^* = \sqrt{\dfrac{2KD}{h}} = \sqrt{\dfrac{2(75)(676)}{0.2(3000)}} = 13$ computers purchased with each order

f)

Number of orders per year $= \dfrac{D}{Q} = \dfrac{676}{13} = 52$

$ROP = D(LT) = (13)\left(\dfrac{1}{2}\right) = 6.5$ - inventory level when each order is placed

g) The optimal policy reduces the total variable inventory cost by $3,840 per year, which is a 33% reduction.

11.2   a)

Data		
D =	102000	(demand/year)
K =	$1,000	(setup cost)
h =	$0.12	(unit holding cost)
L =	0	(lead time in days)
WD =	365	(working days/year)

Results	
Reorder Point =	0
Annual Setup Cost =	$12,000.00
Annual Holding Cost =	$510.00
Total Variable Cost =	$12,510.00

Decision		
Q =	8500	(order quantity)

b)

Months	Q	Annual Setup Cost	Annual Holding Cost	Total Variable Cost
		$12,000	$510	$12,510
1	8500	$12,000	$510	$12,510
2	17000	$6,000	$1,020	$7,020
3	25500	$4,000	$1,530	$5,530
4	34000	$3,000	$2,040	$5,040
5	42500	$2,400	$2,550	$4,950
6	51000	$2,000	$3,060	$5,060
7	59500	$1,714	$3,570	$5,284
8	68000	$1,500	$4,080	$5,580
9	76500	$1,333	$4,590	$5,923
10	85000	$1,200	$5,100	$6,300

c)

Data		
D =	102000	(demand/year)
K =	$1,000	(setup cost)
h =	$0.12	(unit holding cost)
L =	0	(lead time in days)
WD =	365	(working days/year)

Results	
Reorder Point =	0
Annual Setup Cost =	$2,473.86
Annual Holding Cost =	$2,473.86
Total Variable Cost =	$4,947.73

Decision		
Q =	41231	(order quantity)

d)

Data		
D =	102000	(demand/year)
K =	$1,000	(setup cost)
h =	$0.12	(unit holding cost)
L =	0	(lead time in days)
WD =	365	(working days/year)

Results	
Reorder Point =	0
Annual Setup Cost =	$2,473.86
Annual Holding Cost =	$2,473.86
Total Variable Cost =	$4,947.73

Decision	
Q =	41231 (order quantity)

The results are the same as those obtained in part c).

e)

$$Q^* = \sqrt{\frac{2KD}{h}} = \sqrt{\frac{2(1000)(8500)}{0.01}} = 41,231 \text{ gallons purchased with each order}$$

11.3 a)

Data		
D =	10400	(demand/year)
K =	$20	(setup cost)
h =	$0.20	(unit holding cost)
L =	3.5	(lead time in days)
WD =	365	(working days/year)

Results	
Reorder Point =	99.73
Annual Setup Cost =	$144.22
Annual Holding Cost =	$144.22
Total Variable Cost =	$288.44

Decision	
Q =	1442 (order quantity)

b)

Data		
D =	10400	(demand/year)
K =	$20	(setup cost)
h =	$0.15	(unit holding cost)
L =	3.5	(lead time in days)
WD =	365	(working days/year)

Results	
Reorder Point =	99.73
Annual Setup Cost =	$124.90
Annual Holding Cost =	$124.90
Total Variable Cost =	$249.80

Decision	
Q =	1665 (order quantity)

The order quantity is increased by 223 LCDs. If the order quantity obtained in part a) is still used the TVC increases to $252.39.

c)

Data		
D =	10400	(demand/year)
K =	$20	(setup cost)
h =	$0.25	(unit holding cost)
L =	3.5	(lead time in days)
WD =	365	(working days/year)

Results	
Reorder Point =	99.73
Annual Setup Cost =	$161.25
Annual Holding Cost =	$161.25
Total Variable Cost =	$322.49

Decision	
Q =	1290 (order quantity)

The order quantity is decreased by 152 LCDs. If the order quantity obtained in part a) is still used the TVC increases to $324.49.

d)

Cost of Capital	Unit Holding Cost	Q
		1290
10%	0.15	1665
12%	0.17	1564
14%	0.19	1480
16%	0.21	1407
18%	0.23	1345
20%	0.25	1290

e)

Setup Hours	Setup Cost	Q
		1665
0.5	$10	1178
0.75	$15	1442
1	$20	1665
1.25	$25	1862
1.5	$30	2040

f)

Unit Holding Cost	Optimal Order Quantity (Q)				
			Setup Cost		
1665.33	$10	$15	$20	$25	$30
0.15	1178	1442	1665	1862	2040
0.17	1106	1355	1564	1749	1916
0.19	1046	1281	1480	1654	1812
0.21	995	1219	1407	1574	1724
0.23	951	1165	1345	1504	1647
0.25	912	1117	1290	1442	1580

11.4 Optimal Order Quantity

573.21			Unit Holding Cost				
	$3.15	**$3.36**	**$3.78**	**$4.20**	**$4.62**	**$5.04**	**$5.25**
$86.25	573	555	523	496	473	453	444
$92.00	592	573	540	513	489	468	459
$103.50	628	608	573	544	518	496	486
Setup $115.00	662	641	604	573	547	523	513
Cost $126.50	694	672	634	601	573	549	538
$138.00	725	702	662	628	599	573	562
$143.75	740	717	676	641	611	585	573

Total Variable Cost (with Q = Q*)

2407.49			Unit Holding Cost				
	$3.15	**$3.36**	**$3.78**	**$4.20**	**$4.62**	**$5.04**	**$5.25**
$86.25	$1,806	$1,865	$1,978	$2,085	$2,187	$2,284	$2,331
$92.00	$1,865	$1,926	$2,043	$2,153	$2,258	$2,359	$2,407
$103.50	$1,978	$2,043	$2,167	$2,284	$2,395	$2,502	$2,554
Setup $115.00	$2,085	$2,153	$2,284	$2,407	$2,525	$2,637	$2,692
Cost $126.50	$2,187	$2,258	$2,395	$2,525	$2,648	$2,766	$2,823
$138.00	$2,284	$2,359	$2,502	$2,637	$2,766	$2,889	$2,949
$143.75	$2,331	$2,407	$2,554	$2,692	$2,823	$2,949	$3,009

Total Variable Cost (with Q = 573)

2407.49			Unit Holding Cost				
	$3.15	**$3.36**	**$3.78**	**$4.20**	**$4.62**	**$5.04**	**$5.25**
$86.25	$1,806	$1,866	$1,986	$2,107	$2,227	$2,347	$2,407
$92.00	$1,866	$1,926	$2,046	$2,167	$2,287	$2,407	$2,468
$103.50	$1,986	$2,046	$2,167	$2,287	$2,407	$2,528	$2,588
Setup $115.00	$2,107	$2,167	$2,287	$2,407	$2,528	$2,648	$2,708
Cost $126.50	$2,227	$2,287	$2,407	$2,528	$2,648	$2,769	$2,829
$138.00	$2,347	$2,407	$2,528	$2,648	$2,769	$2,889	$2,949
$143.75	$2,407	$2,468	$2,588	$2,708	$2,829	$2,949	$3,009

The conclusions remain the same for the 25%. In the cases where K and h change in the same direction, there is little or no extra cost incurred. When K and h change in the opposite direction extra cost is incurred, and this extra cost is more than it was for the 10% increase.

11.5 a) Q* will decrease by half.

b) Q* will double.

c) Q* remains the same.

d) Q* will double.

e) Q* remains the same.

11.6 a)

$$Q^* = \sqrt{\frac{2KD}{h}} \Rightarrow 50 = \sqrt{\frac{2(75)(50)}{h}} \Rightarrow \sqrt{h} = \frac{\sqrt{2(75)(50)}}{50} \Rightarrow h = \$3 \text{ per month which}$$

is 15% of the acquisition cost.

b) Optimal Order Quantity h = 20%

Data		
D =	50	(demand/month)
K =	$75	(setup cost)
h =	$4.00	(unit holding cost)
L =	5	(lead time in days)
WD =	25	(working days/month)

Results	
Reorder Point =	10
Annual Setup Cost =	$86.60
Annual Holding Cost =	$86.60
Total Variable Cost =	$173.21

Decision		
Q =	43	(order quantity)

Current Inventory Policy

Data		
D =	50	(demand/month)
K =	$75	(setup cost)
h =	$4.00	(unit holding cost)
L =	5	(lead time in days)
WD =	25	(working days/month)

Results	
Reorder Point =	10
Annual Setup Cost =	$75.00
Annual Holding Cost =	$100.00
Total Variable Cost =	$175.00

Decision		
Q =	50	(order quantity)

c) Reorder point is 10 as shown in the above spreadsheet.

d)

$$ROP = -S* + D(LT) = -5 + (50)\left(\frac{1}{5}\right) = 5 \text{ hammers which adds \$20 to his TVC (5}$$

hammers x $4 holding cost).

11.7 $Q^* = \sqrt{\frac{2KD}{h}} \Rightarrow 10 = \sqrt{\frac{2(200)(D)}{400}} \Rightarrow D = 10^2\left(\frac{400}{2(200)}\right) \Rightarrow D = 100 \text{ per year}$

11.8

$$TVC = K\frac{D}{Q} + h\frac{Q}{2}$$

$$\frac{dTVC}{dQ} = -K\frac{D}{Q^2} + \frac{h}{2} = 0 \qquad \Rightarrow \frac{KD}{Q^2} = \frac{h}{2} \qquad \Rightarrow Q^2 = \frac{2KD}{h} \qquad \Rightarrow Q = \sqrt{\frac{2KD}{h}}$$

11.9 a)

Data		
D =	3000	(demand/year)
K =	$200	(setup cost)
h =	$20	(unit holding cost)
L =	0	(lead time in days)
WD =	365	(working days/year)

Results	
Reorder Point =	0
Annual Setup Cost =	$2,449.49
Annual Holding Cost =	$2,449.49
Total Variable Cost =	$4,898.98

Decision		
Q =	245	(order quantity)

b)

Data		
D =	3000	(demand/year)
K =	$200	(setup cost)
h =	$20.00	(unit holding cost)
p =	$30.00	(unit shortage cost)

Results	
Max Inventory Level =	189.74
Annual Setup Cost =	$1,897.37
Annual Holding Cost =	$1,138.42
Annual Shortage Cost =	$758.95
Total Variable Cost =	$3,794.73

Decision		
Q =	316	(order quantity)
S =	126	(maximum shortage)

c)

Quantity	Basic EOQ Model	EOQ Model with Planned Shortages
Order quantity	244.95	316.23
Maximum shortage	0	126.49
Maximum inventory level	244.95	189.74
Reorder point	0	-126.49
Annual setup cost	$2,449.49	$1,897.37
Annual holding cost	$2,449.49	$1,138.42
Annual shortage cost	0	$758.95
Total variable cost	$4,898.98	$3,794.73

11.10 a)

p	$Q^* = \sqrt{\dfrac{h+p}{p}}\sqrt{\dfrac{2KD}{h}}$	$TVC = K\dfrac{D}{Q} + h\dfrac{(Q-S)^2}{2Q} + p\dfrac{S^2}{2Q}$
$15	649	$2,127.94
$30	612	$2,254.82
$60	593	$2,327.41
$120	583	$2,366.43

b)

p	TVC	% reduction from basic model
$15	$2,127.94	12%
$30	$2,254.82	6%
$60	$2,327.41	3%
$120	$2,366.43	1.5%

c)

p	Max. wait time (days)	Acceptable case
$15	5.91	
$30	3.13	
$60	1.62	***
$120	0.82	

11.11 a)

Data

D =	676	(demand/year)
K =	$75	(setup cost)
h =	$600	(unit holding cost)
p =	$200	(unit shortage cost)

Decision

Q =	26	(order quantity)
S =	20	(maximum shortage)

Results

Max Inventory Level =	6.00
Annual Setup Cost =	$1,950.00
Annual Holding Cost =	$415.38
Annual Shortage Cost =	$1,538.46
Total Variable Cost =	$3,903.85

This TVC is a reduction of $3900 or 50% from the TVC when shortages were not allowed.

b)

Q	Annual Setup Cost	Annual Holding Cost	Annual Shortage Cost	Total Variable Cost
	$1,950	$415	$1,538	$3,904
15	$3,380	$500	$2,667	$6,547
17	$2,982	$159	$2,353	$5,494
19	$2,668	$16	$2,105	$4,789
21	$2,414	$14	$1,905	$4,333
23	$2,204	$117	$1,739	$4,061
25	$2,028	$300	$1,600	$3,928
27	$1,878	$544	$1,481	$3,904
29	$1,748	$838	$1,379	$3,966
31	$1,635	$1,171	$1,290	$4,097
33	$1,536	$1,536	$1,212	$4,285
35	$1,449	$1,929	$1,143	$4,520

c)

S	Annual Setup Cost	Annual Holding Cost	Annual Shortage Cost	Total Variable Cost
	$1,950	$415	$1,538	$3,904
10	$1,950	$2,954	$385	$5,288
12	$1,950	$2,262	$554	$4,765
14	$1,950	$1,662	$754	$4,365
16	$1,950	$1,154	$985	$4,088
18	$1,950	$738	$1,246	$3,935
20	$1,950	$415	$1,538	$3,904
22	$1,950	$185	$1,862	$3,996
24	$1,950	$46	$2,215	$4,212
26	$1,950	$0	$2,600	$4,550
28	$1,950	$46	$3,015	$5,012
30	$1,950	$185	$3,462	$5,596

11.12

ratio of p to h	$Q^* = \sqrt{\dfrac{h+p}{p}}\sqrt{\dfrac{2KD}{h}}$	Maximum Inventory Level	Maximum Shortage
1/3	2,000	500	1,500
1	1,414	707	707
2	1,225	816	408
3	1,155	866	289
5	1,095	913	183
10	1,049	953	95

11.13 a)

Data

D =	5200	(demand/year)
K =	$50	(setup cost)
I =	0.2	(inventory holding cost rate)
N =	3	(# of discount categories)

Category	Price	Range of order quantities Lower Limit	Upper Limit	EOQ	Q*	Annual Purchase Cost	Annual Setup Cost	Annual Holding Cost	Total Variable Cost
1	$100	0	99	161.25	99.00	$520,000.00	$2,626.26	$990.00	$523,616.26
2	$95	100	499	165.43	165.43	$494,000.00	$1,571.62	$1,571.62	$497,143.25
3	$90	500	10000000	169.97	500.00	$468,000.00	$520.00	$4,500.00	$473,020.00

Results

Optimal Q =	500
Total Variable Cost =	$473,020

b) Orders placed per year = $\dfrac{D}{Q} = \dfrac{5200}{500} = 10.4$

Time interval between orders = $\dfrac{Q}{D} = \dfrac{500}{5200} = (0.096 \text{ years})(52) = 5 \text{ weeks}$

11.14 a)

	Data	
D =	365	(demand/year)
K =	$5	(setup cost)
I =	0.2	(inventory holding cost rate)
N =	3	(# of discount categories)

		Range of order quantities				Annual Purchase	Annual Setup	Annual Holding	Total Variable
Category	Price	Lower Limit	Upper Limit	EOQ	Q*	Cost	Cost	Cost	Cost
1	$4.00	0	49	67.55	49.00	$1,460.00	$37.24	$19.60	$1,516.84
2	$3.90	50	99	68.41	68.41	$1,423.50	$26.68	$26.68	$1,476.86
3	$3.80	100	10000000	69.30	100.00	$1,387.00	$18.25	$38.00	$1,443.25

Results	
Optimal Q =	100
Total Variable Cost =	$1,443.25

b) Orders placed per year $= \dfrac{D}{Q} = \dfrac{365}{100} = 3.65$

Time interval between orders $= \dfrac{Q}{D} = \dfrac{100}{365} = (0.274 \text{ years})(52) = 14.25 \text{ weeks}$

11.15 a)

Discount Category	$TVC = cD + K\dfrac{D}{Q} + h\dfrac{Q}{2}$
1	$TVC = (8.50)(400) + (80)\left(\dfrac{400}{Q}\right) + (0.2)(8.50)\left(\dfrac{Q}{2}\right)$
2	$TVC = (8)(400) + (80)\left(\dfrac{400}{Q}\right) + (0.2)(8)\left(\dfrac{Q}{2}\right)$
3	$TVC = (7.50)(400) + (80)\left(\dfrac{400}{Q}\right) + (0.2)(7.50)\left(\dfrac{Q}{2}\right)$

b)

Discount Category	$Q^* = \sqrt{\dfrac{2KD}{h}}$
1	$Q^* = \sqrt{\dfrac{2(80)(400)}{0.2(8.50)}} = 194$
2	$Q^* = \sqrt{\dfrac{2(80)(400)}{0.2(8)}} = 200$
3	$Q^* = \sqrt{\dfrac{2(80)(400)}{0.2(7.50)}} = 207$

c)

Discount Category	Feasible Q	$TVC = cD + K\dfrac{D}{Q} + h\dfrac{Q}{2}$
1	99	$3,807.38
2	200	$3,520.00
3	1,000	$3,782.00

d)

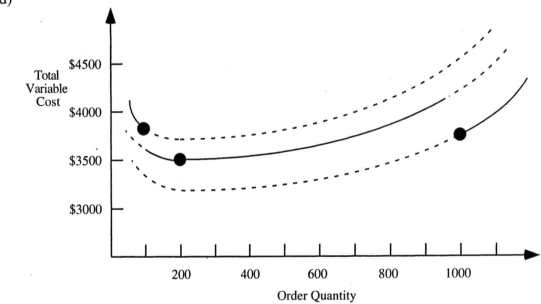

e) $Q^* = 200$ with a TVC of $3,520.

11-14

f)

Data

D =	400	(demand/year)
K =	$80	(setup cost)
I =	0.2	(inventory holding cost rate)
N =	3	(# of discount categories)

Category	Price	Range of order quantities Lower Limit	Range of order quantities Upper Limit	EOQ	Q*	Annual Purchase Cost	Annual Setup Cost	Annual Holding Cost	Total Variable Cost
1	$8.50	0	99	194.03	99.00	$3,400.00	$323.23	$84.15	$3,807.38
2	$8.00	100	999	200.00	200.00	$3,200.00	$160.00	$160.00	$3,520.00
3	$7.50	1000	10000000	206.56	1000.00	$3,000.00	$32.00	$750.00	$3,782.00

Results

Optimal Q =	200
Total Variable Cost =	$3,520

g) Since the value of Q that minimizes TVC for discount category 2 is feasible that means that this order quantity minimizes the annual setup and holding costs. Category 1 could therefore not possibly have lower annual setup and holding costs. Furthermore, since the purchase price per case is higher for category 1, it could not possibly have lower purchasing costs. Thus, we can eliminate category 1 as a candidate for providing the optimal order quantity.

h) Orders placed per year = $\dfrac{D}{Q} = \dfrac{400}{200} = 2$

Time interval between orders = $\dfrac{Q}{D} = \dfrac{200}{400} = (0.5 \text{ years})(12) = 6 \text{ months}.$

11.16 a)

Discount Category	$TVC = cD + K\dfrac{D}{Q} + h\dfrac{Q}{2}$
1	$TVC = (1.00)(2400) + (4)\left(\dfrac{2400}{Q}\right) + (0.17)(1.00)\left(\dfrac{Q}{2}\right)$
2	$TVC = (0.95)(2400) + (4)\left(\dfrac{2400}{Q}\right) + (0.17)(0.95)\left(\dfrac{Q}{2}\right)$
3	$TVC = (0.90)(2400) + (4)\left(\dfrac{2400}{Q}\right) + (0.17)(0.90)\left(\dfrac{Q}{2}\right)$

b)

Discount Category	$Q^* = \sqrt{\dfrac{2KD}{h}}$
1	$Q^* = \sqrt{\dfrac{2(4)(2400)}{0.17(1.00)}} = 336$
2	$Q^* = \sqrt{\dfrac{2(4)(2400)}{0.17(0.95)}} = 345$
3	$Q^* = \sqrt{\dfrac{2(4)(2400)}{0.17(0.90)}} = 354$

c)

Discount Category	Feasible Q	$TVC = cD + K\dfrac{D}{Q} + h\dfrac{Q}{2}$
1	199	$2,465.16
2	345	$2,335.68
3	500	$2,217.45

d)

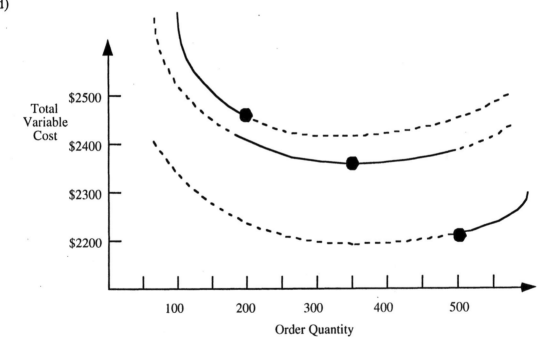

e) $Q^* = 500$ with a TVC of $2,217.45.

f)

Data

D =	2400	(demand/year)
K =	$4	(setup cost)
I =	0.17	(inventory holding cost rate)
N =	3	(# of discount categories)

Category	Price	Range of order quantities Lower Limit	Range of order quantities Upper Limit	EOQ	Q*	Annual Purchase Cost	Annual Setup Cost	Annual Holding Cost	Total Variable Cost
1	$1.00	0	199	336.07	199.00	$2,400.00	$48.24	$16.92	$2,465.16
2	$0.95	200	499	344.80	344.80	$2,280.00	$27.84	$27.84	$2,335.68
3	$0.90	500	10000000	354.25	500.00	$2,160.00	$19.20	$38.25	$2,217.45

Results

Optimal Q =	500
Total Variable Cost =	$2,217.45

g) Since the value of Q that minimizes TVC for discount category 2 is feasible that means that this order quantity minimizes the annual setup and holding costs. Category 1 could therefore not possibly have lower annual setup and holding costs. Furthermore, since the purchase price per bag is higher for category 1, it could not possibly have lower purchasing costs. Thus, we can eliminate category 1 as a candidate for providing the optimal order quantity.

h) Orders placed per year $= \dfrac{D}{Q} = \dfrac{2400}{500} = 4.8$

Time interval between orders $= \dfrac{Q}{D} = \dfrac{500}{2400} = (0.21 \text{ years})(12) = 2.5 \text{ months}$

11.17 a)

Data

D =	6000	(demand/year)
R =	24000	(production rate)
K =	$7,500	(unit setup cost)
h =	$120.00	(unit holding cost)

Results

Annual Setup Cost =	$45,000.00
Annual Holding Cost =	$45,000.00
Total Variable Cost =	$90,000.00

Decision

Q =	1000	(production lot size)

b)

Production run duration $= \dfrac{Q}{R} = \dfrac{1000}{2000} = 0.5 \text{ months}$

Time interval between production runs $= \dfrac{Q}{D} = \dfrac{1000}{6000} = (0.1667 \text{ years})(12) = 2 \text{ months}$

c) Maximum inventory level $= Q - \dfrac{D}{R}Q = 1000 - \left(\dfrac{6000}{24000}\right)(1000) = 750$. This is less than the production lot size since monitors are being withdrawn from inventory while a production run is going on.

11-17

11.18 a)

Data		
D =	52000	(demand/year)
R =	104000	(production rate)
K =	$1,000	(unit setup cost)
h =	$13.00	(unit holding cost)

Decision		
Q =	4000	(production lot size)

Results	
Annual Setup Cost =	$13,000.00
Annual Holding Cost =	$13,000.00
Total Variable Cost =	$26,000.00

b)

$$\text{Time interval between orders } = \frac{Q}{D} = \frac{4000}{52000} = (0.077 \text{ years})(52) = 4 \text{ weeks}$$

$$\text{Delivery duration } = \frac{Q}{R} = \frac{4000}{2000} = 2 \text{ weeks}$$

c) $ROP = D(LT) = 1000(1) = 1000$

11.19 a)

Case	K	h	Q*	TVC	Difference in Q
Base	$12,000	$3.60	50,000	$120,000	
1	$12,000	$2.70	57,735	$103,923	+7,735
2	$12,000	$4.50	44,721	$134,164	-5,279
3	$9,000	$3.60	43,301	$103,923	-6,699
4	$15,000	$3.60	55,901	$134,164	+5,901

b)

Case	K	h	Q*	TVC	Difference in Q
Base	$12,000	$3.60	50,000	$120,000	
5	$9,000	$2.70	50,000	$90,000	0
6	$9,000	$4.50	38,729	$116,190	-11,271
7	$15,000	$2.70	64,550	$116,190	+14,550
8	$15,000	$4.50	50,000	$150,000	0

c) The value of Q* is fairly sensitive to the estimates of K and h in all cases except 5 and 8. When both K and h are increased or decreased by the same proportional amount the value of Q* remains the same.

d) Optimal Order Quantity

		Unit Holding Cost		
	50000	$2.70	$3.60	$4.50
Setup	$9,000	50000	43301	38730
Cost	$12,000	57735	50000	44721
	$15,000	64550	55902	50000

Total Variable Cost (with Q = Q*)

		Unit Holding Cost		
	120000	$2.70	$3.60	$4.50
Setup	$9,000	$90,000	$103,923	$116,190
Cost	$12,000	$103,923	$120,000	$134,164
	$15,000	$116,190	$134,164	$150,000

Total Variable Cost (with Q = 50,000)

		Unit Holding Cost		
	120000	$2.70	$3.60	$4.50
Setup	$9,000	$90,000	$105,000	$120,000
Cost	$12,000	$105,000	$120,000	$135,000
	$15,000	$120,000	$135,000	$150,000

e) Amount that TVC with Q = 50,000 exceeds TVC with Q = Q*:

		Unit Holding Cost		
		$2.70	$3.60	$4.50
Setup	$9,000	$0	$1,077	$3,810
Cost	$12,000	$1,077	$0	$836
	$15,000	$3,810	$836	$0

f) Given the results in part e), it is not too important to improve upon the values of K and h since errors in the estimates of these costs do not increase the value of TVC much from its minimum.

11.20 a)

Data

D =	250000	(demand/year)
R =	1500000	(production rate)
K =	$12,000	(unit setup cost)
h =	$3.60	(unit holding cost)

Decision

Q =	44721	(production lot size)

Results

Annual Setup Cost =	$67,082.04
Annual Holding Cost =	$67,082.04
Total Variable Cost =	$134,164.08

This alternative does not look good since it increases TVC by $14,164.

b) TVC = annual setup cost + annual holding cost = $100,000+0 = $100,000. This looks like a good alternative since it reduces TVC by $20,000.

c) Option 2 is a just-in-time inventory system.

Cases

11.1 a) Robert's problem can be solved using the basic EOQ model. The data for the case is as follows:

$D = 12*250 = 3000$
$K = 18.75/3 = 6.25$
$h = 0.12*1.25 = 0.15$
$L = 0$
$WD = 12*30 = 360$

Basic EOQ Model (Analytical)

	Data			Results	
D =	3000	(demand/year)	Reorder Point =		0
K =	$6.25	(setup cost)			
h =	$0.15	(unit holding cost)	Annual Setup Cost =		$37.50
L =	0	(lead time in days)	Annual Holding Cost =		$37.50
WD =	360	(working days/year)	Total Variable Cost =		$75.00

	Decision	
Q =	500.00	(order quantity)

Robert should order 500 toothbrushes 6 times per year.

b) Now the lead time equals L = 6 days. We can use the basic EOQ model again:

Basic EOQ Model (Analytical)

	Data			Results	
D =	3000	(demand/year)	Reorder Point =		50
K =	$6.25	(setup cost)			
h =	$0.15	(unit holding cost)	Annual Setup Cost =		$37.50
L =	6	(lead time in days)	Annual Holding Cost =		$37.50
WD =	360	(working days/year)	Total Variable Cost =		$75.00

	Decision	
Q =	500.00	(order quantity)

Whenever the inventory of toothbrushes drops down to 50, Robert should place an order for 500 toothbrushes. He needs to place an order 6 times a year.

c) Now we need to consider the EOQ model with planned shortages. The shortage costs are $p = 1.50$.

EOQ Model with Planned Shortages (Analytical)

Data				Results	
D =	3000	(demand/year)		Max Inventory Level =	476.73
K =	$6.25	(setup cost)			
h =	$0.15	(unit holding cost)		Annual Setup Cost =	$35.75
p =	$1.50	(unit shortage cost)		Annual Holding Cost =	$32.50
				Annual Shortage Cost =	$3.25
Decision				Total Variable Cost =	$71.51
Q =	524.40	(order quantity)			
S =	47.67	(maximum shortage)			

Robert should place orders of about 524 toothbrushes. Because of the lead time of L = 6 days the reorder point is $-47.67 + (3000/360)*6 = 2.33$. The maximum shortage that occurs would be roughly 48 toothbrushes.

d) We compute the inventory policies for the two extreme cases p = 0.85 and p = 25.

EOQ Model with Planned Shortages (Analytical)

Data				Results	
D =	3000	(demand/year)		Max Inventory Level =	460.98
K =	$6.25	(setup cost)			
h =	$0.15	(unit holding cost)		Annual Setup Cost =	$34.57
p =	$0.85	(unit shortage cost)		Annual Holding Cost =	$29.39
				Annual Shortage Cost =	$5.19
Decision				Total Variable Cost =	$69.15
Q =	542.33	(order quantity)			
S =	81.35	(maximum shortage)			

The reorder point when p = $0.85 equals $-81.35 + (3000/360)*6 = -31.35$

EOQ Model with Planned Shortages (Analytical)

Data			Results	
D =	3000	(demand/year)	Max Inventory Level =	498.51
K =	$6.25	(setup cost)		
h =	$0.15	(unit holding cost)	Annual Setup Cost =	$37.39
p =	$25.00	(unit shortage cost)	Annual Holding Cost =	$37.17
			Annual Shortage Cost =	$0.22
Decision			Total Variable Cost =	$74.78
Q =	501.50	(order quantity)		
S =	2.99	(maximum shortage)		

The reorder point when p = $25.00 equals –2.99 + (3000/360)*6 = 47.01. We can conclude that as the shortage cost increases, the reorder point increases.

e) Now we need to consider the EOQ model with quantity discounts.

There are 3 discount categories with prices of $1.25, $1.15, and $1.00 respectively. The holding cost rate equals I = 0.12.

EOQ Model with Quantity Discounts (Analytical)

Data		
D =	3000	(demand/year)
K =	$6.25	(setup cost)
I =	0.12	(inventory holding cost rate)
N =	3	(number of discount categories)

		Range of order quantities				Annual Purchase Cost	Annual Setup Cost	Annual Holding Cost	Total Variable Cost
Ctgry	Price	Lower Limit	Upper Limit	EOQ	Q*				
1	$1.25	0	500	500.00	500.00	$3,750.00	$37.50	$37.50	$3,825.00
2	$1.15	501	999	521.29	521.29	$3,450.00	$35.97	$35.97	$3,521.94
3	$1.00	1000	10000000	559.02	1000.00	$3,000.00	$18.75	$60.00	$3,078.75

Results	
Optimal Q =	1000
TVC=	$3,078.75

The optimal order quantity equals Q =1000. Robert should order 3 times a year.

Review Questions

12.1-1   Freddie should consider the trade-off between too much inventory and too little inventory.

12.1-2   Based on Freddie's data, 9, 10, and 11 are the only numbers of copies that he has sold in the past.

12.1-3   The state of nature for each day is the number of requests to purchase a copy that will occur. The number of requests is the state of nature because it is the random variable in the decision to purchase copies from the distributor.

12.2-1   Only a single time period is needed because perishable products cannot be sold later.

12.2-2   The only decision to be made is how many units to order so they can be placed into inventory at the beginning of the period.

12.2-3   It is assumed that the demand during the period is uncertain but that the probability distribution of demand is known.

12.2-4   The unit cost of underordering is the decrease in profit that results from failing to order a unit that could have been sold during the period. The unit cost of overordering is the decrease in profit that results from ordering a unit that could not be sold during the period.

12.2-5   Bayes' decision rule will make the same decision since both approaches are applying Bayes' decision rule, but with different payoffs, where one is to be maximized and the other minimized.

12.2-6   Service level is the probability that no shortage will occur.

12.2-7   Optimal service level $= \dfrac{C_{under}}{C_{under} + C_{over}}$.

12.2-8   The point at which the optimal service level hits the cumulative distribution function gives the optimal order quantity.

12.2-9   There are many types of perishable products.

12.3-1   There have been four stockouts of panoramic disposable cameras during the year with durations ranging from a few days to a couple weeks.

12.3-2   Recent complaints from distributors about delays in shipping the disposable panoramic camera have concerned the Vice President for Marketing and she is suggesting having more frequent production runs to keep the inventory better stocked.

12.3-3   The Division Vice President for Production is concerned about the frequent interruptions in the production of other models caused by setting up for a production run for the disposable panoramic cameras. He is recommending having much longer production runs much less frequently.

12.3-4   The Division President is skeptical about his Vice President's recommendation because it would increase inventory levels. He has been promoting the just-in-time philosophy of minimizing inventory.

12.4-1 The management science team began by trying to diagnose why the frequent stockouts were occurring under the current inventory policy.

12.4-2 Under the old inventory policy, the probability of a stockout is 50% and the maximum size of a stockout is 8,000.

12.4-3 Reorder point = average sales during lead time + amount of safety stock.

12.4-4 Even when the amount of safety stock provided still permits occasional short stockouts, this safety stock can dramatically improve the service to customers by greatly reducing both the number and length of the delays in filling customer orders.

12.4-5 Management made the decision on how much safety stock to provide.

12.4-6 The relevant cost factors for choosing the order quantity are acquisition costs, setup costs, holding costs, and shortage costs.

12.4-7 The main component of shortage costs is lost future profit from lost future sales caused by customer dissatisfaction with delays in filling current orders.

12.4-8 Increasing the order quantity decreases the average monthly setup costs because this decreases the average number of setups required per month. Increasing the order quantity increases the average monthly holding costs, since this increases the average inventory level. Increasing the order quantity decreases the average monthly shortage costs, because this decreases the average number of opportunities for stockout per month.

12.4-9 The management science team used the EOQ model with planned shortages to find the approximately optimal order quantity.

12.4-10 The President is unhappy about the large increase in inventory levels. The Vice President for Marketing is concerned that shortages of various magnitudes still can be expected to occur about once per year. The Vice President for Production is unhappy because the policy would only slightly decrease the frequency of production runs.

12.4-11 The high setup cost, the long lead time, and the high variability in monthly sales were the three factors the caused the cost of this inventory policy to be unusually high.

12.4-12 The setup cost and lead time will be greatly reduced by acquiring some additional production facilities that would be used solely for production of the disposable panoramic cameras.

12.5-1 The camera is considered a stable product because each camera in inventory will remain sellable indefinitely.

12.5-2 A continuous-review inventory system is one where the inventory level of a stable product is monitored on a continuous basis so that a new order can be placed as soon as the inventory level drops to the reorder point.

12.5-3 The traditional method of implementing a continuous-review inventory system was to use a two-bin system.

12.5-4 The common modern method of implementing a continuous-review inventory system is a computerized inventory system.

12.5-5 An (R,Q) inventory policy controls a continuous-review inventory system by using a fixed reorder point (R) and a fixed order quantity (Q).

12.5-6 Except for the setup cost, the cost of the order is proportional to the order quantity Q. A certain holding cost is incurred for each unit in inventory per unit time. When a stockout occurs, a certain shortage cost is incurred for each unit backordered per unit time until the backorder is filled.

12.5-7　The EOQ model with planned shortages is used to approximate the optimal order quantity.

12.5-8　The key difference between the models is that rather than having known demand with a fixed rate, the model in this chapter assumes uncertain demand. The main difference in the results from the two models is that because of the uncertain demand for the current model, some safety stock needs to be added when setting the reorder point to provide some cushion for having well-above-average demand during the lead time.

12.5-9　The most convenient measure of the service level is the probability that a stockout will not occur between the time an order is placed and the order quantity is received.

12.5-10　$R = \mu + K_L \sigma$

12.6-1　The products in the A group are the particularly important ones that are to be carefully monitored according to a formal inventory model. Products in the C group are the least important, so they are only monitored informally on a very occasional basis. Group B products receive an intermediate treatment.

12.6-2　Occasionally it is not appropriate to apply a single-product inventory model because of interactions between the products.

12.6-3　A multiechelon inventory system is a system with multiple echelons of inventory where each echelon (except the bottom one) is used to replenish the inventories at the various sites of the next lower echelon.

12.6-4　The echelons of IBM's system start with the manufacture of the parts, then national or regional warehouses, then field distribution centers, then parts stations, and finally many thousands of outside locations.

12.6-5　The three factors that proved to be especially important were the inclusion of a user team as advisors to the project team, a very extensive user acceptance test whereby users could identify problem areas that needed rectifying prior to full implementation, and that the new system was phased in gradually, with careful testing at each phase.

12.6-6　The cost savings were about $20 million per year through improved operational efficiency and even larger annual savings in holding costs.

12.6-7　A supply chain spans procurement, manufacturing, and distribution.

12.6-8　HP faced inventories mounting into the billions of dollars and alarming customer dissatisfaction with its order fulfillment process.

12.6-9　WINO deals with inventories of finished products as well as inventories of incoming goods and departing goods at each site along the supply chain.

12.6-10　A key intangible benefit was to enhance HP's reputation as a progressive company that can be counted on by its customers to fill their orders promptly.

Problems

12.1 a)

| | State of Nature (Purchase Requests) | | | | Expected |
Alternative	15	16	17	18	Payoff
Order 15 copies	15	15	15	15	$15.00
Order 16 copies	14	16	16	16	$15.20 Maximum
Order 17 copies	13	15	17	17	$15.00
Order 18 copies	12	14	16	18	$14.20
Prior Probability	0.4	0.2	0.3	0.1	

Freddie's most profitable alternative is to order 16 copies.

b)

| | State of Nature (Purchase Requests) | | | | Expected |
Alternative	15	16	17	18	Cost
Order 15 copies	0	1	2	3	1.10
Order 16 copies	1	0	1	2	0.90 Minimum
Order 17 copies	2	1	0	1	1.10
Order 18 copies	3	2	1	0	1.90
Prior Probability	0.4	0.2	0.3	0.1	

Freddie's most profitable alternative is to order 16 copies.

c) Service level if order 15 copies = 0.4
Service level if order 16 copies = 0.6
Service level if order 17 copies = 0.9
Service level if order 18 copies = 1

$$\text{Optimal service level} = \frac{C_{under}}{C_{under} + C_{over}} = \frac{1}{1+1} = 0.5$$

Freddie should order 16 copies.

d)

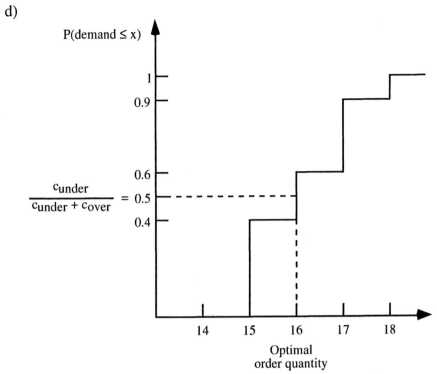

$P(\text{demand} \le x)$

Optimal
order quantity

12.2   a) $C_{under} = (\$3) - (\$1) = \$2$ $C_{over} = (\$1) - (\$.50) = \$.50$

b)

Alternative	State of Nature (Purchase Requests)						Expected Cost
	0	1	2	3	4	5	
Make 0	0.0	2.0	4.0	6.0	8.0	10.0	5.10
Make 1	0.5	0.0	2.0	4.0	6.0	8.0	3.35
Make 2	1.0	0.5	0.0	2.0	4.0	6.0	1.98
Make 3	1.5	1.0	0.5	0.0	2.0	4.0	1.10
Make 4	2.0	1.5	1.0	0.5	0.0	2.0	0.98 Minimum
Make 5	2.5	2.0	1.5	1.0	0.5	0.0	1.23
Prior Probability	0.1	0.15	0.2	0.3	0.15	0.1	

Prepare 4 doughnuts each day to minimize costs.

c) Service level if 0 made = 0.1
   Service level if 1 made = 0.25
   Service level if 2 made = 0.45
   Service level if 3 made = 0.75
   Service level if 4 made = 0.9
   Service level if 5 made = 1

$$\text{Optimal service level} = \frac{C_{under}}{C_{under} + C_{over}} = \frac{2}{2 + 0.5} = 0.8$$

Prepare 4 doughnuts each day.

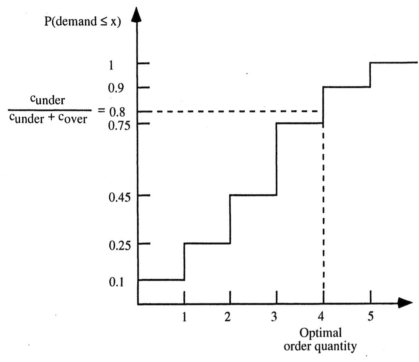

d) The probability of running short will be $1 - 0.9 = 0.1 = 10\%$

e) Before 5 doughnuts are prepared, the optimal service level needs to exceed 0.9.

   Let g be the cost of lost customer goodwill. Then $C_{under} = \$2 + g$.

   Thus $\dfrac{C_{under}}{C_{under} + C_{over}} > 0.9 \quad \Leftrightarrow \quad \dfrac{\$2 + g}{\$2.5 + g} > 0.9 \quad \Leftrightarrow \quad g > \$2.50$

   The goodwill cost would need to be at least \$2.50 before 5 doughnuts should be prepared.

12.3 a)

$$\text{Optimal service level} = \frac{C_{under}}{C_{under} + C_{over}} = \frac{1}{1 + 0.5} = 0.667$$

b)

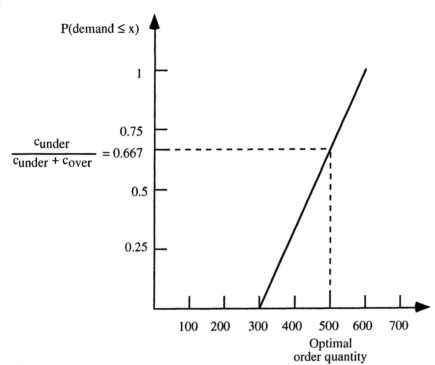

$$\frac{c_{under}}{c_{under} + c_{over}} = 0.667$$

P(demand ≤ x)

Optimal order quantity

c) $Q^* = 300 + 0.667(600-300) = 500$

d) The probability of running short is $1-0.667 = 0.333 = 33.3\%$

e)

$$\text{Optimal service level} = \frac{C_{under}}{C_{under} + C_{over}} = \frac{1+1.5}{1+1.5+0.5} = 0.833$$

$Q^* = 300 + 0.833(600-300) = 550$
The probability of running short is $1-0.833 = 0.167 = 16.7\%$

12.4 a) Revenue (w/ shortages) = 500 ($3.00) = $1,500

b) Average number of loaves sold (w/out shortages) = $300 + \dfrac{500-300}{2} = 400$
Average daily revenue (w/out shortages) = 400($3.00) = $1,200

c) $1,500 x 0.333 = $500 (w/ shortages)
$1,200 x 0.667 = $800 (w/out shortages)
Average daily revenue over all days = $500 + $800 = $1,300

d) Average number of loaves not sold = $\dfrac{200-0}{2} = 100$
Average number of day-old loaves obtained over all days = 100 x 0.667 = 66.7
Average daily revenue from day-old bread = 66.7 x $1.50 = $100

e) Average total daily revenue = $1,300 + $100 = $1,400
Average daily profit = $1,400 – $2(500) = $400

f) Average daily profit (600 loaves)= $3(450)-$2(600)+$1.50(150) = $375

g) Average daily profit (550 loaves) = $375 + \dfrac{\$400 - \$375}{2} = \$387.50$

h) Average size of shortage (550 loaves) = $\dfrac{600 - 550}{2} = 25$ loaves

Average daily shortage over all days = 25 x 0.167 = 4.167
Average daily cost of loss of goodwill = 4.167 x $1.50 = $6.25
Average daily profit (550 loaves & loss of goodwill) = $387.50 - $6.25 = $381.25

i) Average size of shortage (500 loaves) = $\dfrac{100 - 0}{2} = 50$ loaves

Average daily shortage over all days = 50 x 0.333 = 16.67
Average daily cost of loss of goodwill = 16.67 x $1.50 = $25
Average daily profit (500 loaves & loss of goodwill) = $400 - $25 = $375

12.5 a) $Q^* = a + (\text{service level}) (b-a) = a + (0.667)(75) = a + 50$

b) Probability of incurring shortage = 1 - 0.667 = 33.3% which is the same as in problem 13.3.

c) Maximum shortage = $b - (a + 50) = 25$
Maximum number of loaves that won't be sold = 50

The corresponding numbers for problem 13.3 are 100 and 200 respectively which are four times the amounts here.

d) The average daily costs of underordering and overordering for the new plan are 25% of the original costs. Thus, it is quite valuable to obtain as much information as possible about demand before placing the final order for a perishable product.

e) $Q^* = a + (\text{service level}) (b-a) = a + (0.833)(75) = a + 62.5$
Probability of incurring shortage = 1 - 0.833 = 16.67%
Maximum shortage = $b - (a + 62.5) = 12.5$
Maximum number of loaves that won't be sold = 62.5

12.6 a) This problem can be interpreted as an inventory problem with uncertain demand for a perishable product with euro-traveler's checks as the product. Once Stan gets back from his trip the checks are not good anymore so they are a perishable product. He can redeposit the amount into his savings account but will incur a fee of lost interest. Stan must decide how many checks to buy without knowing how many he will need.

C_{under} = value of 1 day – cost of 1 day – cost of 1 check = $49

C_{over} = cost of check + lost interest = $3

b)

| | State of Nature (Amount Needed) | | | | | | | | Expected |
Alternative	1000	1100	1200	1300	1400	1500	1600	1700	Cost
Buy 0	0	0	0	50	100	150	200	250	80.00
Buy 1	3	3	3	0	50	100	150	200	45.90
Buy 2	6	6	6	3	0	50	100	150	25.05
Buy 3	9	9	9	6	3	0	50	100	14.80
Buy 4	12	12	12	9	6	3	0	50	9.85 Minimum
Buy 5	15	15	15	12	9	6	3	0	10.20
Prior Probability	0.05	0.1	0.15	0.25	0.2	0.1	0.1	0.05	

Purchase 4 additional checks.

c) Service level for buying 0 = 0.3
Service level for buying 1 = 0.55
Service level for buying 2 = 0.75
Service level for buying 3 = 0.85
Service level for buying 4 = 0.95
Service level for buying 5 = 1

$$\text{Optimal service level} = \frac{C_{under}}{C_{under} + C_{over}} = \frac{49}{49+3} = 0.94$$

Buy 4 additional checks.

d)

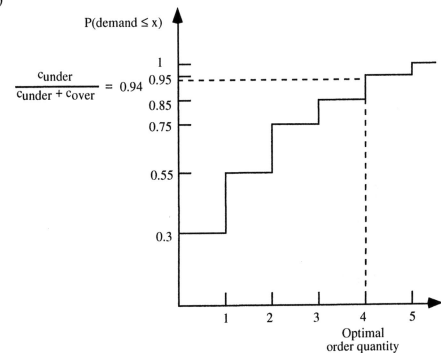

12.7 a) $\text{Optimal service level} = \dfrac{C_{under}}{C_{under} + C_{over}} = \dfrac{3000}{3000 + 1000} = 0.75$

b) When the demand is less-than-or-equal-to Q, no shortage will occur. Therefore the probability that the demand is less-than-or-equal-to Q gives us the service level that corresponds to choosing the order quantity Q. Increasing Q increases this probability. Therefore the smallest order quantity that provides the service level L is the value of Q such that $P(\text{demand} \le Q) = L$.

c) $Q = \mu + K_L \sigma = 50 + (0.675)(15) = 60$

12.8 a) When interpreting this problem as an inventory problem, overbooked reservations are the perishable products that are being placed into inventory.

b) C_{under} = lost fare = \$250
C_{over} = cost of certificate = \$150

c) Service level for accepting 0 = 0.05
Service level for accepting 1 = 0.15
Service level for accepting 2 = 0.3
Service level for accepting 3 = 0.45
Service level for accepting 4 = 0.6
Service level for accepting 5 = 0.75
Service level for accepting 6 = 0.85
Service level for accepting 7 = 0.95
Service level for accepting 8 = 1

$$\text{Optimal service level} = \frac{C_{under}}{C_{under} + C_{over}} = \frac{250}{250 + 150} = 0.625$$

Accept 5 overbooked reservation.

d)

12.9 a)

Data		
D =	8000	(average demand/unit time)
K =	3000	(setup cost)
h =	0.3	(unit holding cost)
p =	10	(unit shortage cost)
L =	0.75	(service level)

Results	
Q =	12837
R =	12000

Demand During Lead Time

Distribution =	Uniform	
a =	0	(lower endpoint)
b =	16000	(upper endpoint)

Q^* is cut in half. R is unchanged. This will reduce the average monthly holding cost. However, it will increase the average monthly shortage cost (since the number of order cycles per month increases). The smaller setup cost reduces the average monthly setup cost.

b)

Data		
D =	8000	(average demand/unit time)
K =	12000	(setup cost)
h =	0.3	(unit holding cost)
p =	10	(unit shortage cost)
L =	0.75	(service level)

Results	
Q =	25675
R =	10000

Demand During Lead Time

Distribution =	Uniform	
a =	4000	(lower endpoint)
b =	12000	(upper endpoint)

Q^* is unchanged. R is reduced from 12,000 to 10,000. This will reduce the average monthly holding cost (less safety stock to hold). The average monthly shortage costs and setup costs will be unchanged.

c)

	Data		Results	
D =	8000	(average demand/unit time)	Q =	25675
K =	12000	(setup cost)	R =	2300
h =	0.3	(unit holding cost)		
p =	10	(unit shortage cost)		
L =	0.75	(service level)		

Demand During Lead Time

Distribution =	Uniform	
a =	200	(lower endpoint)
b =	3000	(upper endpoint)

Q^* is unchanged. R is reduced from 12,000 to 2300. This will reduce the average monthly holding cost. The average monthly shortage costs and setup costs will be unchanged.

d)

	Data		Results	
D =	8000	(average demand/unit time)	Q =	12837
K =	3000	(setup cost)	R =	2300
h =	0.3	(unit holding cost)		
p =	10	(unit shortage cost)		
L =	0.75	(service level)		

Demand During Lead Time

Distribution =	Uniform	
a =	200	(lower endpoint)
b =	3000	(upper endpoint)

Q^* is cut in half. R is reduced from 12,000 to 2300. This will reduce the average monthly holding cost. However, it will increase the average monthly shortage cost (since the number of order cycles per month increases). The smaller setup cost reduces the average monthly setup cost.

e) Average inventory just before an order is received = 2300 − 1600 = 700.
Average inventory just after an order is received = 700 + 12,837 = 13,537.
Average inventory = (700 + 13,537) / 2 = 7119.
Average monthly holding cost = 7119 ($0.30) = $2136.

Average number of orders per year = (8000) / (12,837) = 0.62.
Probability of stockout before order received = 0.25.
Expected number of stockouts per month = (0.25)(0.62) = 0.155.
Average stockout size = 700 / 2 = 350.
Estimate of average delay per camera delayed = 1/15 week = 0.015 months.
Average monthly shortage cost = (0.155)(350)(0.015)($10) = $8

Average number of setups per month = 8000 / 12,837 = 0.62.
Average monthly setup cost = (0.62)($3,000) = $1860.

Average monthly cost = $2136 + $8 + $1860 = $4004.
This is less than half the cost before the changes ($8896).

12.10 a) $Q = \sqrt{\dfrac{h+p}{p}} \sqrt{\dfrac{2KD}{h}} = \sqrt{\dfrac{3000+1000}{1000}} \sqrt{\dfrac{2(1500)(900)}{3000}} = 60$

b) $R = \mu + K_L \sigma = 50 + 0.675(15) = 60$

c)

Data		
D =	900	(average demand/unit time)
K =	1500	(setup cost)
h =	3000	(unit holding cost)
p =	1000	(unit shortage cost)
L =	0.75	(service level)

Results	
Q =	60
R =	60.1173555

Demand During Lead Time	
Distribution =	Normal
mean =	50
stand. dev. =	15

d) Safety Stock = R − mean = 60 − 50 = 10

e) If demand during the delivery time exceeds 60 (the order quantity), then the reorder point will be hit again before the order arrives, triggering another order.

12.11 a) $Q = \sqrt{\dfrac{h+p}{p}} \sqrt{\dfrac{2KD}{h}} = \sqrt{\dfrac{8+1}{1}} \sqrt{\dfrac{2(40)(40)}{8}} = 60$

$R = a + L(b - a) = 5 + 0.8(15 - 5) = 13$

b)

Data		
D =	40	(average demand/unit time)
K =	40	(setup cost)
h =	8	(unit holding cost)
p =	1	(unit shortage cost)
L =	0.8	(service level)

Results	
Q =	60
R =	13

Demand During Lead Time		
Distribution =	Uniform	
a =	5	(lower endpoint)
b =	15	(upper endpoint)

c) Average number of orders per year = $(40)(12) / 60 = 8$.
Probability of a stockout before order received?? = 0.2.
Average number of stockouts per year = $(8)(0.2) = 1.6$.

12.12 a)

	EMBED Equation			
	Case 1	Case 2	Case 3	Case 4
L	h=$1, σ=1	h=$100, σ=1	h=$1, σ=100	h=$100, σ=100
0.5	0	0	0	0
0.75	0.675	67.5	67.5	6750
0.9	1.282	128.2	128.2	12,820
0.95	1.645	164.5	164.5	16,450
0.99	2.327	232.7	232.7	23,270
0.999	3.098	309.8	309.8	30,980

b)

	ΔC ($)			
	Case 1	Case 2	Case 3	Case 4
ΔL	h=$1, σ=1	h=$100, σ=1	h=$1, σ=100	h=$100, σ=100
0.25	0.675	67.5	67.5	6750
0.15	0.607	60.7	60.7	6070
0.05	0.363	36.3	36.3	3630
0.04	0.682	68.2	68.2	6820
0.009	0.771	77.1	77.1	7710

c) As the service level gets higher, increasing the service level further costs more for smaller increases. Thus, there will be diminishing returns when raising the service level further and further. You should balance the cost of the safety stock with the cost of stockouts to determine the best service level.

12.13 a) $C = hK_L\sigma = (\$100)(1.282)(100) = \$12,820$.

b) $\sigma = \sqrt{d}\sigma_1 \Rightarrow 100 = \sqrt{4}\sigma_1 \Rightarrow \sigma_1 = 50$.

If the lead time were 1 day, then $C = hK_L\sigma_1 = (\$100)(1.282)(50) = \$6410$.

This is a 50% reduction in the cost of the safety stock.

c) $\sigma = \sqrt{d}\sigma_1 = \sqrt{8}(50) = 141.4$.
$C = hK_L\sigma = (\$100)(1.282)(141.4) = \$18,127$. This is a 41% increase.

d) The lead time would need to quadruple to 16 days.

12.14 a) The safety stock would drop to zero.

b) The safety stock would decrease.

c) The safety stock is unchanged for a given service level. However, with higher shortage costs, there will be an incentive to increase the service level (with a correspondingly higher level of safety stock).

d) The safety stock increases.

e) The safety stock doubles.

f) The safety stock doubles.

12.15 a) Ground Chuck:

Data

D =	26000	(average demand/unit time)
K =	25	(setup cost)
h =	0.3	(unit holding cost)
p =	3	(unit shortage cost)
L =	0.95	(service level)

Results

Q =	2183
R =	145

Demand During Lead Time

Distribution =	Uniform	
a =	50	(lower endpoint)
b =	150	(upper endpoint)

Chuck Wagon:

Data

D =	26000	(average demand/unit time)
K =	200	(setup cost)
h =	0.3	(unit holding cost)
p =	3	(unit shortage cost)
L =	0.95	(service level)

Results

Q =	6175
R =	829

Demand During Lead Time

Distribution =	Normal	
mean =	500	
stand. dev. =	200	

b) Ground Chuck: $R = a + L(b - a) = 50 + 0.95(150 - 50) = 145$.
Chuck Wagon: $R = \mu + K_L\sigma = 500 + 1.645(200) = 829$.

c) Ground Chuck: Safety Stock = R – mean = 145 – 100 = 45.
Chuck Wagon: Safety Stock = R – mean = 829 – 500 = 329.

d) Ground Chuck: Average annual holding cost = ($0.30)$\left(\dfrac{45 + (2183 + 45)}{2}\right)$ = $340.95

Chuck Wagon:

$$\text{Average annual holding cost} = (\$0.30)\left(\frac{329 + (6175 + 329)}{2}\right) = \$3,416.50$$

e) Ground Chuck:

$$\text{Annual shipping cost} = K\left(\frac{D}{Q}\right) = (\$25)\left(\frac{26,000}{2183}\right) = \$297.76.$$

Annual purchase cost = $(26,000)(\$1.49) = \$38,740$

Average annual acquisition cost = $\$297.76 + \$38,740 = \$39,037.76$.

Chuck Wagon:

$$\text{Annual shipping cost} = K\left(\frac{D}{Q}\right) + (\$0.10)D$$

$$= (\$200)\left(\frac{26,000}{6175}\right) + (\$0.10)(26,000) = \$3442.11.$$

Annual purchase cost = $(26,000)(\$1.35) = \$35,100$.

Average annual acquisition cost = $\$3442.11 + \$35,100 = \$38,542.11$.

f) Ground Chuck: $340.95 + $39,037.76 = $39,378.71.
Chuck Wagon: $3416.50 + $38,542.11 = $41,958.61.

Jed should choose Ground Chuck as their supplier.

g) If Jed would like to use the beef within a month of receiving it, then Ground Chuck is the better choice. The order quantity with Ground Chuck is roughly one month's supply, whereas with Chuck Wagon the optimal order quantity is roughly three month's supply.

12.16. a) Option 1:

Data		
D =	26000	(average demand/unit time)
K =	130	(setup cost)
h =	6	(unit holding cost)
p =	100	(unit shortage cost)
L =	0.99	(service level)

Results	
Q =	1093
R =	366

Demand During Lead Time

Distribution =	Normal
mean =	250
stand. dev. =	50

Option 2:

Data		
D =	26000	(average demand/unit time)
K =	50	(setup cost)
h =	6	(unit holding cost)
p =	100	(unit shortage cost)
L =	0.99	(service level)

Results	
Q =	678
R =	995

Demand During Lead Time

Distribution =	Uniform	
a =	500	(lower endpoint)
b =	1000	(upper endpoint)

b) Option 1: $R = \mu + K_L \sigma = 250 + 2.327(50) = 366$.
Option 2: $R = a + L(b - a) = 500 + 0.99(1000 - 500) = 995$.

c) Option 1: Safety Stock = R – mean = $366 - 250 = 116$.
Option 2: Safety Stock = R – mean = $995 - 750 = 245$.

d) Option 1: Average annual holding cost = $(\$6)\left(\dfrac{116 + (1093 + 116)}{2}\right) = \$3975$.

Option 2: Average annual holding cost = $(\$6)\left(\dfrac{245 + (678 + 245)}{2}\right) = \$3504$.

e) Option 1:

$$\text{Annual shipping cost} = K\left(\frac{D}{Q}\right) + (\$3)D$$

$$= (\$130)\left(\frac{26,000}{1093}\right) + (\$3)(26,000) = \$81,092.$$

Annual purchase cost $= (26,000)(\$30) = \$780,000.$

Average annual acquisition cost $= \$81,092 + \$780,000 = \$861,092.$

Option 2:

$$\text{Annual shipping cost} = K\left(\frac{D}{Q}\right) + (\$3)D$$

$$= (\$50)\left(\frac{26,000}{678}\right) + (\$2)(26,000) = \$53,917.$$

Annual purchase cost $= (26,000)(\$30) = \$780,000.$

Average annual acquisition cost $= \$53,917 + \$780,000 = \$833,917.$

f) Option 1: $\$3975 + \$861,092 = \$865,067.$
   Option 2: $\$3504 + \$833,917 = \$837,421.$

Option 2 should be selected.

Cases

12.1   For the analysis of this case we use the template for perishable products.

a)   First we need to determine the optimal service level for Howie. The unit sale price equals $5, the unit purchase cost equal $3, and the unit salvage value equals 0.5*$3 - 0.5 = $1.

Data		Results	
Unit sale price =	5	Cost of overordering =	2
Unit purchase cost =	3	Cost of underordering =	2
Unit salvage value =	1		
		Optimal Service Level =	0.5

Since Talia assumes that demand is uniformly distributed between 120 and 420 sets, Howie should order 120 + 0.5*300 = 270 sets.

b) If Leisure Limited refunds 75% of the purchase cost, then the unit salvage value for a returned set equals 0.75*$3-$0.5 = $1.75. We determine the new optimal service level:

Data	
Unit sale price =	5
Unit purchase cost =	3
Unit salvage value =	1.75

Results	
Cost of overordering =	1.25
Cost of underordering =	2
Optimal Service Level =	0.615385

The order quantity is now 120 + 0.615385*300 = 304.62. Note that Howie can now order more sets at one time than he could under the scenario of part (a) because he is not punished as severely as before when he fails to sell all sets.

For the case of a 25% refund the unit salvage value equals $0.25.

Data	
Unit sale price =	5
Unit purchase cost =	3
Unit salvage value =	0.25

Results	
Cost of overordering =	2.75
Cost of underordering =	2
Optimal Service Level =	0.421053

Now the order quantity equals 120 + 0.421053*300 = 246.32. Howie must now purchase fewer sets at one time (compared to the previous scenarios) because he is punished more severely if he fails to sell sets.

c) For a unit sale price of $6 and a 50% refund on returned firecracker sets, the optimal service level can be determined as follows:

Data	
Unit sale price =	6
Unit purchase cost =	3
Unit salvage value =	1

Results	
Cost of overordering =	2
Cost of underordering =	3
Optimal Service Level =	0.6

However, if Howie raises the price of a firecracker set, one would expect that the demand for his sets will decrease. Therefore, Talia should not use the same uniform demand distribution that she used for her previous calculations of the optimal order quantity.

d) Talia's strategy for estimating the demand is overly simplistic. She makes the very simplifying assumption that the demand is uniformly distributed between 120 and 420 sets. However, she does not take into account that the demand depends on the price of a firecracker set. She should expect that stands charging less than the average price of $5 per set typically sell more sets than stands charging $5 or even more than $5 per set. Talia should call Buddy again to try to obtain more detailed information, such as the range of sales and the average sale of stands charging $5 or $6 per set.

Talia should also reevaluate her assumption that the demand is uniformly distributed. She should check how her forecasts change if she uses other demand distributions, such as, for example, a normal distribution.

12.2 a) We can use the statistical functions in Excel to compute the sample mean and sample variance:

25
31
18
22
40
19
38
21
25
36
34
28
27

28   **Average**
7.29154762   **stand.dev**

The sample mean equals 28, and the sample variance equals 53.1667.

b) Based on the findings of Scarlett Windermere, American Aerospace can use a (R,Q) policy for the inventory of part 10003487. The assumptions of this model are satisfied:

1. The part is a stable product
2. Its inventory level is under continuous review.
3. While the production of this part itself has no lead time, it is typically delayed by the lead time of one and a half months of the little steel part. Therefore, we can use this lead time for our analysis.
4. The demand for this part is the same as for the jet engine MX332, since it is only used for this particular engine. We therefore assume that the demand for the part is approximately normally distributed with a mean of 28 and a variance of 53.1667.
5. Excess demand is backlogged.
6. There is a fixed setup cost K = 5800, a holding cost h = 750 and a shortage cost of p = 3250.

Note that the average demand per year equals D = 12*28 = 336. The average demand during the one and a half months of lead time equals 1.5*28 = 42, and its standard deviation equals 1.5* 7.29154762 = 10.9373214.

Data			Results	
D =	336	(average demand/unit time)	Q =	79.9753808
K =	5800	(setup cost)	R =	53.3357995
h =	750	(unit holding cost)		
p =	3250	(unit shortage cost)		
L =	0.85	(service level)		

Demand During Lead Time

Distribution =	N	(U=uniform; N=Normal)
mean =	42	
stand. dev. =	10.9373214	

American Aerospace should implement an (R,Q) policy with R = 53.34 and Q = 79.98.

c) For the computation of the approximate holding and setup cost we use the rounded values Q = 80 and R = 53.

The average inventory just before an order arrives equals 53 – 42 = 11, and just after the order has arrived it equals 11+80 = 91. So, the average inventory level equals 51 resulting in average yearly holding cost of (approximately) 51*750 = 38250.

The average number of setups per year equals 336/80 = 4.2 resulting in average yearly setup cost of 4.2*5800 = 24360.

d) The new service level equals L = 0.95.

Data   **Results**

D =	336	(average demand/unit time)	Q =	79.9753808
K =	5800	(setup cost)	R =	59.990286
h =	750	(unit holding cost)		
p =	3250	(unit shortage cost)		
L =	0.95	(service level)		

Demand During Lead Time

Distribution =	N	(U=uniform; N=Normal)
mean =	42	
stand. dev. =	10.9373214	

Again, we round and use Q = 80 and R = 60.

The average inventory just before an order arrives equals 80 – 60 = 20, and just after the order has arrived it equals 20+80 = 100. So, the average inventory level equals 60 resulting in average yearly holding cost of (approximately) 60*750 = 45000. Notice that the average yearly holding cost has increased substantially. This should come as no surprise due to the increased safety stock (20 instead of 11).

The average number of setups per year is still 336/80 = 4.2, resulting again in an average yearly setup cost of 4.2*5800 = 24360.

e) Scarlett's independent analysis of the stationary part 10003487 can only be justified since there is only a single jet engine that needs this part, and this part appears to be the bottleneck in the production process. But more often, the same stationary part will be used for several jet engines. As a result the demand for stationary parts will depend on the demand for several jet engines, and a stockout in one stationary part affects the demand for other parts. These interdependencies cannot be captured by an independent analysis of each part. Therefore, Scarlett's approach will most likely result in rather inaccurate inventory policies for many other stationary parts.

f) Scarlett could try to forecast the demand for jet engines based on sales data from previous years.

Review Questions

13.1-1 Substantially underestimating demand is likely to lead to many lost sales, unhappy customers, and perhaps allowing the competition to gain the upper hand in the marketplace. Significantly overestimating the demand is very costly due to excessive inventory costs, forced price reductions, unneeded production or storage capacity, and lost opportunity to market more profitable goods.

13.1-2 A forecast of the demand for spare parts is needed to provide good maintenance service.

13.1-3 In cases where the yield of a production process is less than 100%, it is useful to forecast the production yield in order to determine an appropriate value of reject allowance and, consequently, the appropriate size of the production run.

13.1-4 Statistical models to forecast economic trends are commonly called econometric models.

13.1-5 Providing too few agents leads to unhappy customers, lost calls, and perhaps lost business. Too many agents cause excessive personnel costs.

13.2-1 The company mails catalogs to its customers and prospective customers several times per year, as well as publishing mini-catalogs in computer magazines. They then take orders for products over the phone at the company's call center.

13.2-2 Customers who receive a busy signal or are on hold too long may not call back and business may be lost. If too many agents are on duty there may be idle time, which wastes money because of labor costs.

13.2-3 The manager of the call center is Lydia Ann Weigelt. Her current major frustration is that each time she has used her procedure for setting staffing levels for the upcoming quarter, based on her forecast of the call volume, the forecast usually has turned out to be considerably off.

13.2-4 Assume that each quarter's call volume will be the same as for the preceding quarter, except for adding 25% for quarter 4.

13.2-5 The average forecasting error is commonly called MAD, which stands for Mean Absolute Deviation.

13.2-6 A time series is a series of observations over time of some quantity of interest.

13.3-1 In general, the seasonal factor for any period of a year measures how that period compares to the overall average for an entire year.

13.3-2 Seasonally adjusted call volume $= \dfrac{\text{Actual call volume}}{\text{Seasonal factor}}$

13.3-3 Forecast of the actual call volume = (Seasonal factor)(Seasonally adjusted forecast)

13.3-4 The last-value forecasting method sometimes is called the naïve method because statisticians consider it naïve to use just a sample size of one when additional relevant data are available.

13.3-5 Conditions affecting the CCW call volume were changing significantly over the past three years.

13.3-6 Rather than using old data that may no longer be relevant, this method averages the data for only the most recent periods.

13.3-7 This method modifies the moving-average method by placing the greatest weight on the last value in the time series and then progressively smaller weights on the older values.

13.3-8 A small value is appropriate if conditions are remaining relatively stable. A larger value is needed if significant changes in the conditions are occurring relatively frequently.

13.3-9 Forecast $= \alpha(\text{last value}) + (1 - \alpha)(\text{last forecast})$. Estimated trend is added to this formula when using exponential smoothing with trend.

13.3-10 The one big factor that drives total sales up or down is whether there are any hot new products being offered.

13.4-1 The next value that will occur in a time series is a random variable.

13.4-2 The goal of time series forecasting methods is to estimate the mean of the underlying probability distribution of the next value of the time series as closely as possible.

13.4-3 No, the probability distribution is not the same for every quarter.

13.4-4 Each of the forecasting methods, except for the last-value method, placed at least some weight on the observations from Year 1 to estimate the mean for each quarter in Year 2. These observations, however, provide a poor basis for estimating the mean of the Year 2 distribution.

13.4-5 A time series is said to be stable if its underlying probability distribution usually remains the same from one time period to the next. A time series is unstable if both frequent and sizable shifts in the distribution tend to occur.

13.4-6 Since sales drive call volume, the forecasting process should begin by forecasting sales.

13.4-7 The major components are the relatively stable market base of numerous small-niche products and each of a few major new products.

13.5-1 Causal forecasting obtains a forecast of the quantity of interest by relating it directly to one or more other quantities that drive the quantity of interest.

13.5-2 The dependent variable is call volume and the independent variable is sales.

13.5-3 When doing causal forecasting with a single independent variable, linear regression involves approximating the relationship between the dependent variable and the independent variable by a straight line.

13.5-4 In general, the equation for the linear regression line has the form $y = a + bx$. If there is more than one independent variable, then this regression equation has a term, a constant times the variable, added on the right-hand side for each of these variables.

13.5-5 The procedure used to obtain a and b is called the method of least squares.

13.5-6 The new procedure gives a MAD value of only 120 compared with the old MAD value of 400 with the 25% rule.

13.6-1 Statistical forecasting methods cannot be used if no data are available, or if the data are not representative of current conditions.

13.6-2 Even when good data are available, some managers prefer a judgmental method instead of a formal statistical method. In many other cases, a combination of the two may be used.

13.6-3 The jury of executive opinion method involves a small group of high-level managers who pool their best judgment to collectively make a forecast rather than just the opinion of a single manager.

13.6-4 The sales force composite method begins with each salesperson providing an estimate of what sales will be in his or her region.

13.6-5 A consumer market survey is helpful for designing new products and then in developing the initial forecasts of their sales. It is also helpful for planning a marketing campaign.

13.6-6 The Delphi method normally is used only at the highest levels of a corporation or government to develop long-range forecasts of broad trends.

13.7-1 Generally speaking, judgmental forecasting methods are somewhat more widely used than statistical methods.

13.7-2 Among the judgmental methods, the most popular is a jury of executive opinion. Manager's opinion is a close second.

13.7-3 The survey indicates that the moving-average method and linear regression are the most widely used statistical forecasting methods.

Problems

13.1 a) Forecast = last value = 39

b) Forecast = average of all data to date = $\dfrac{5+17+29+41+39}{5} = \dfrac{131}{5} = 26$

c) Forecast = average of last 3 values = $\dfrac{29+41+39}{3} = \dfrac{109}{3} = 36$

d) It appears as if demand is rising so the average forecasting method seems inappropriate because it uses older, out of date data.

13.2 a) Forecast = last value = 13

b) Forecast = average of all data to date = $\dfrac{15+18+12+17+13}{5} = \dfrac{75}{5} = 15$

c) Forecast = average of last 3 values = $\dfrac{12+17+13}{3} = \dfrac{42}{3} = 14$

d) The averaging method seems best since all five months of data are relevant in determining the forecast of sales for next month.

13.3

Quarter	Forecast	True Value	Error
1	327	345	18
2	332	317	15
3	328	336	8
4	330	311	19

$$\text{MAD} = \frac{\text{Sum of forecasting errors}}{\text{Number of forecasts}} = \frac{18+15+8+19}{4} = \frac{60}{4} = 15$$

13.4 a) Method 1 MAD $= \dfrac{258 + 499 + 560 + 809 + 609}{5} = \dfrac{2735}{5} = 547$

Method 2 MAD $= \dfrac{374 + 471 + 293 + 906 + 396}{5} = \dfrac{2440}{5} = 488$

b) She can use the older data to calculate more forecasting errors and compare MAD for a longer time span. This may make her feel more comfortable with her decision.

13.5 a)

Quarter	Call Volume	Seasonal Factor
1	6809	$\dfrac{6809}{7027} = 0.97$
2	6465	$\dfrac{6465}{7027} = 0.92$
3	6569	$\dfrac{6569}{7027} = 0.93$
4	8266	$\dfrac{8266}{7027} = 1.18$

b)

Quarter	Seasonal Factor	Actual Call Volume	Seasonally Adjusted Call Volume
1	0.97	7257	$\dfrac{7257}{0.97} = 7481$
2	0.92	7064	$\dfrac{7064}{0.92} = 7678$
3	0.93	7784	$\dfrac{7784}{0.93} = 8370$
4	1.18	8724	$\dfrac{8724}{1.18} = 7393$

c)

Quarter	Two-Year Average	Seasonal Factor
1	7033	$\dfrac{7033}{7367} = 0.95$
2	6765	$\dfrac{6765}{7367} = 0.92$
3	7177	$\dfrac{7177}{7367} = 0.97$
4	8495	$\dfrac{8495}{7367} = 1.15$

d)

Quarter	Seasonal Factor	Actual Call Volume	Seasonally Adjusted Call Volume
1	0.95	6992	$\dfrac{6992}{0.95} = 7360$
2	0.92	6822	$\dfrac{6822}{0.92} = 7415$
3	0.97	7949	$\dfrac{7949}{0.97} = 8195$
4	1.15	9650	$\dfrac{9650}{1.15} = 8391$

13.6 a)

Quarter	Unemployment Rate	Seasonal Factor
1	0.062	$\dfrac{0.062}{0.063} = 0.98$
2	0.06	$\dfrac{0.06}{0.063} = 0.95$
3	0.075	$\dfrac{0.075}{0.063} = 1.19$
4	0.055	$\dfrac{0.055}{0.063} = 0.87$

b)

Quarter	Seasonal Factor	Actual Unemployment Rate	Seasonally Adjusted Call Volume
1	0.98	0.078	$\dfrac{0.078}{0.98} = 0.08$
2	0.95	0.074	$\dfrac{0.074}{0.95} = 0.078$
3	1.19	0.087	$\dfrac{0.087}{1.19} = 0.073$
4	0.87	0.061	$\dfrac{0.061}{0.87} = 0.07$

This progression indicates that the state's economy is improving with the unemployment rate decreasing from 8% to 7% (seasonally adjusted) over the four quarters.

13.7 a)

Quarter	Three-Year Average	Seasonal Factor
1	21	$\dfrac{21}{25} = 0.84$
2	23	$\dfrac{23}{25} = 0.92$
3	30	$\dfrac{30}{25} = 1.2$
4	26	$\dfrac{26}{25} = 1.04$

b) Seasonally adjusted value = $\dfrac{28}{1.04} = 27$, so the actual forecast = $(27)(0.84) = 23$.

c) Q1 = 23 as shown in part b)

$$Q2 = \frac{23}{0.84} = 27, \text{ so the actual forecast} = (27)(0.92) = 25$$

$$Q3 = \frac{25}{0.92} = 27, \text{ so the actual forecast} = (27)(1.2) = 33$$

$$Q4 = \frac{33}{1.2} = 27, \text{ so the actual forecast} = (27)(1.04) = 28$$

d)

Quarter	Seasonal Factor	Average House Sales	Seasonally Adjusted Forecast
1	0.84	25	(25)(0.84)=21
2	0.92	25	(25)(0.92)=23
3	1.2	25	(25)(1.2)=30
4	1.04	25	(25)(1.04)=26

13.8 Forecast = $\dfrac{1977 - 1945}{4} = 8 + 2083 = 2091$

13.9 Forecast = $\dfrac{793 - 805}{3} = -4 + 782 = 778$

13.10 Forecast = $\dfrac{1532 - 1632}{10} = -10 + 1551 = 1541$

13.11 Forecast (0.1) = α(last value) + $(1-\alpha)$(last forecast) = $(0.1)(792) + (1-0.1)(782) = 783$
Forecast (0.3) = α(last value) + $(1-\alpha)$(last forecast) = $(0.3)(792) + (1-0.3)(782) = 785$
Forecast (0.5) = α(last value) + $(1-\alpha)$(last forecast) = $(0.5)(792) + (1-0.5)(782) = 787$

13.12 Forecast $(0.1) = \alpha(\text{last value}) + (1-\alpha)(\text{last forecast}) = (0.1)(1973) + (1-0.1)(2083) = 2072$
Forecast $(0.3) = \alpha(\text{last value}) + (1-\alpha)(\text{last forecast}) = (0.3)(1973) + (1-0.3)(2083) = 2050$
Forecast $(0.5) = \alpha(\text{last value}) + (1-\alpha)(\text{last forecast}) = (0.5)(1973) + (1-0.5)(2083) = 2028$

13.13 a) Forecast (year 1) = initial estimate = 5000
Forecast (year 2) $= \alpha(\text{last value}) + (1-\alpha)(\text{last forecast})$
$= (0.25)(4600) + (1-0.25)(5000) = 4900$
Forecast (year 3) $= (0.25)(5300) + (1-0.25)(4900) = 5000$

b) MAD $= \dfrac{400 + 400 + 1000}{3} = 600$

c) Forecast (next year) $= (0.25)(6000) + (1-0.25)(5000) = 5250$

13.14 Forecast =
$\alpha(\text{last value}) + (1-\alpha)(\text{last forecast})$

$+\beta\big[(\alpha)(\text{last value - next to last value}) + (1-\alpha)(\text{last forecast - next to last forecast})\big]$

$+(1-\beta)(\text{last est. of trend})$

Forecast (year 1) = initial average + initial trend = 3900 + 700 = 4600

Forecast (year 2) = (0.25)(4600)+(1-0.25)(4600)+(0.25)[(0.25)(4600-3900)
+(1-0.25)(4600-3900)]+(1-0.25)(700) = 5300

Forecast (year 3) = (0.25)(5300)+(1-0.25)(5300)+(0.25)[(0.25)(5300-4600)
+(1-0.25)(5300-4600)]+(1-0.25)(700) = 6000

13.15 Forecast =
$\alpha(\text{last value}) + (1-\alpha)(\text{last forecast})$

$+\beta\big[(\alpha)(\text{last value - next to last value}) + (1-\alpha)(\text{last forecast - next to last forecast})\big]$

$+(1-\beta)(\text{last est. of trend})$

= (0.2)(550) + (1-0.2)(540) + (0.3)[(0.2)(550 − 535) + (1-0.2)(540 − 530)] + (1-0.3)(10)
= 552

13.16 Forecast =
$\alpha(\text{last value}) + (1-\alpha)(\text{last forecast})$

$+\beta\big[(\alpha)(\text{last value - next to last value}) + (1-\alpha)(\text{last forecast - next to last forecast})\big]$

$+(1-\beta)(\text{last est. of trend})$

= (0.1)(4935) + (1-0.1)(4975) + (0.2)[(0.1)(4935 − 4655) + (1-0.1) (4975 − 4720)]
+ (1-0.2)(240)
= 5215

13.17 a) Since sales are relatively stable, the averaging method would be appropriate for
forecasting future sales. This method uses a larger sample size than the last-value
method, which should make it more accurate and since the older data is still relevant, it
should not be excluded, as would be the case in the moving-average method.

b)

Time Period	Data	Last-Value Forecast	Forecasting Error
1	23		
2	24	23	1
3	22	24	2
4	28	22	6
5	22	28	6
6	27	22	5
7	20	27	7
8	26	20	6
9	21	26	5
10	29	21	8
11	23	29	6
12	28	23	5

Mean Absolute Deviation

MAD = 5.182

c)

Time Period	Data	Averaging Forecast	Forecasting Error
1	23		
2	24	23	1
3	22	24	2
4	28	23	5
5	22	24	2
6	27	24	3
7	20	24	4
8	26	24	2
9	21	24	3
10	29	24	5
11	23	24	1
12	28	24	4

Mean Absolute Deviation

MAD = 3

d)

Time Period	Data	Moving-Average Forecast	Forecasting Error
1	23		
2	24		
3	22		
4	28	23	5
5	22	25	3
6	27	24	3
7	20	26	6
8	26	23	3
9	21	24	3
10	29	22	7
11	23	25	2
12	28	24	4

Number of previous periods to consider

n = 3

Mean Absolute Deviation

MAD = 3.926

e) Considering the MAD values, the averaging method is the best one to use.

f) Unless there is reason to believe that sales will not continue to be relatively stable, the averaging method should be the most accurate in the future as well.

13.18

Smoothing Constant	MAD
0.1	2.70
0.2	2.82
0.3	2.97
0.4	3.13
0.5	3.32

Ben Swanson should choose 0.1 for the smoothing constant.

13.19 a) Since the sales level is shifting significantly from month to month, and there is no consistent trend, the last-value method seems like it will perform well. The averaging method will not do as well because it places too much weight on old data. The moving-average method will be better than the averaging method but will lag any short-term trends. The exponential smoothing method will also lag trends by placing too much weight on old data. Exponential smoothing with trend will likely not do well because the trend is not consistent.

b) last-value method

Time Period	Data	Last-Value Forecast	Forecasting Error	Mean Absolute Deviation
1	126			MAD = 5.273
2	137	126	11	
3	142	137	5	
4	150	142	8	
5	153	150	3	
6	154	153	1	
7	148	154	6	
8	145	148	3	
9	147	145	2	
10	151	147	4	
11	159	151	8	
12	166	159	7	

averaging method

Time Period	Data	Averaging Forecast	Forecasting Error	Mean Absolute Deviation
1	126			MAD = 10
2	137	126	11	
3	142	132	11	
4	150	135	15	
5	153	139	14	
6	154	142	12	
7	148	144	4	
8	145	144	1	
9	147	144	3	
10	151	145	6	
11	159	145	14	
12	166	147	19	

moving-average method

Time Period	Data	Moving-Average Forecast	Forecasting Error
1	126		
2	137		
3	142		
4	150	135	15
5	153	143	10
6	154	148	6
7	148	152	4
8	145	152	7
9	147	149	2
10	151	147	4
11	159	148	11
12	166	152	14

Number of previous periods to consider

$n = 3$

Mean Absolute Deviation

MAD = 8.111

Comparing MAD values, the last-value method is the best to use of these three options.

c)

Smoothing Constant	MAD
0.1	18.5
0.2	13.0
0.3	10.1
0.4	8.66
0.5	7.96

It appears that a high value for the smoothing constant is appropriate.

d)

α	β	MAD
0.1	0.1	25.4
0.1	0.3	21.2
0.1	0.5	17.7
0.3	0.1	13.5
0.3	0.3	9.75
0.3	0.5	8.80
0.5	0.1	8.42
0.5	0.3	6.70
0.5	0.5	6.49

It appears that a high value for both smoothing constants is appropriate.

e) Management should use the last-value method to forecast sales. Using this method the forecast for January of the new year will be 166.

13.20 a) Shift in total sales may be due to the release of new products on top of a stable product base, as was seen in the CCW case study.

b) Forecasting might be improved by breaking down total sales into stable and new products. Exponential smoothing with a relatively small smoothing constant can be used for the stable product base. Exponential smoothing with trend, with a relatively large smoothing constant, can be used for forecasting sales of each new product.

c) Managerial judgment is needed to provide the initial estimate of anticipated sales in the first month for new products. In addition, a manger should check the exponential smoothing forecasts and make any adjustments that may be necessary based on knowledge of the marketplace.

13.21 a)

Smoothing Constant	MAD
0.1	1.51
0.2	1.62
0.3	1.73
0.4	1.84
0.5	1.95

Choose $\alpha = 0.1$

b)

Smoothing Constant	MAD
0.1	1.84
0.2	1.88
0.3	1.92
0.4	2
0.5	2.1

Choose $\alpha = 0.1$

c)

Smoothing Constant	MAD
0.1	2.82
0.2	2.54
0.3	2.26
0.4	2.06
0.5	1.9

Choose $\alpha = 0.5$

13.22 a)

Smoothing Constant	MAD
0.1	0.740
0.2	0.749
0.3	0.759
0.4	0.77
0.5	0.782

Choose $\beta = 0.1$

b)

Smoothing Constant	MAD
0.1	2.61
0.2	2.76
0.3	2.87
0.4	2.99
0.5	3.05

Choose $\beta = 0.1$

c)

Smoothing Constant	MAD
0.1	5.66
0.2	6.02
0.3	6.23
0.4	6.36
0.5	6.54

Choose $\beta = 0.1$

13.23 a) The time series is not stable enough for the moving-average method.

b)

Time Period	Data	Moving-Average Forecast	Forecasting Error
1	382		
2	405		
3	398		
4	421	395	26
5	426	408	18
6	415	415	0
7	443	421	22
8	451	428	23
9	446	436	10
10	464	447	17
11		454	

Number of previous periods to consider

n = 3

Mean Absolute Deviation

MAD = 16.619

c)

Time Period	Data	Exponential Smoothing Forecast	Forecasting Error
1	382	380	2
2	405	381	24
3	398	393	6
4	421	389	32
5	426	401	26
6	415	403	12
7	443	398	46
8	451	412	40
9	446	416	31
10	464	413	51
11		422	

Smoothing Constant

α = 0.5

Initial Estimate

Average = 380

Mean Absolute Deviation

MAD = 26.75

d)

Time Period	Data	Latest Trend	Estimated Trend	Exponential Smoothing Forecast	Forecasting Error
1	382		10	380	2
2	405	11	10	391	14
3	398	14	11	405	7
4	421	9	11	414	7
5	426	12	11	427	1
6	415	11	11	438	23
7	443	5	10	441	2
8	451	10	10	451	0
9	446	10	10	461	15
10	464	6	9	466	2
11		8	9	474	

Smoothing Constants

α = 0.25
β = 0.25

Initial Estimates

Average = 370
Trend = 10

Mean Absolute Deviation

MAD = 7.285

e) Exponential smoothing with trend should be used in the future.

13.24

Time Period	Data	Latest Trend	Estimated Trend	Exponential Smoothing Forecast	Forecasting Error
1	15		5	15	0
2	21	5	5	20	1
3	24	5	5	25	1
4	32	5	5	30	2
5	37	5	5	35	2
6	41	5	5	41	0
7	40	5	5	46	6
8	47	4	5	50	3
9	51	4	5	54	3
10	53	4	5	58	5
11		4	4	62	

Smoothing Constants

$\alpha =$	0.2
$\beta =$	0.2

Initial Estimates

Average =	10
Trend =	5

Mean Absolute Deviation

MAD =	2.272

Forecast for next production yield = 62%.

13.25 a)

Year	Quarter	True Value
1	1	25
1	2	47
1	3	68
1	4	42
2	1	27
2	2	46
2	3	72
2	4	39
3	1	24
3	2	49
3	3	70
3	4	44

Type of Seasonality

Quarterly

Month	Estimate for Seasonal Factor
1	0.550
2	1.027
3	1.519
4	0.904

b)

Year	Quarter	True Value	Seasonally Adjusted Value	Seasonally Adjusted Forecast	Actual Forecast	Forecasting Error
1	1	25	45			
1	2	47	46	45	47	0
1	3	68	45	46	70	2
1	4	42	46	45	40	2
2	1	27	49	46	26	1
2	2	46	45	49	50	4
2	3	72	47	45	68	4
2	4	39	43	47	43	4
3	1	24	44	43	24	0
3	2	49	48	44	45	4
3	3	70	46	48	72	2
3	4	44	49	46	42	2
4	1			49	27	
4	2					
4	3					
4	4					
5	1					
5	2					

Type of Seasonality

Quarterly

Quarter	Seasonal Factor
1	0.550
2	1.027
3	1.519
4	0.904

Mean Absolute Deviation

MAD =	2.392

Forecast = 27 acre-feet

c) Winter = (49)(0.55) = 27
    Spring = (49)(1.03) = 50
    Summer = (49)(1.52) = 74
    Fall = (49)(0.9) = 44

d)

Year	Quarter	True Value	Seasonally Adjusted Value	Seasonally Adjusted Forecast	Actual Forecast	Forecasting Error
1	1	25	45			
1	2	47	46	45	47	0
1	3	68	45	46	69	1
1	4	42	46	45	41	1
2	1	27	49	46	25	2
2	2	46	45	46	48	2
2	3	72	47	46	70	2
2	4	39	43	46	42	3
3	1	24	44	46	25	1
3	2	49	48	46	47	2
3	3	70	46	46	70	0
3	4	44	49	46	41	3
4	1			46	25	
4	2					
4	3					
4	4					
5	1					
5	2					

Type of Seasonality
Quarterly

Quarter	Seasonal Factor
1	0.550
2	1.027
3	1.519
4	0.904

Mean Absolute Deviation
MAD = 1.570

Forecast = 25 acre-feet

e)

Year	Quarter	True Value	Seasonally Adjusted Value	Seasonally Adjusted Forecast	Actual Forecast	Forecasting Error
1	1	25	45			
1	2	47	46			
1	3	68	45			
1	4	42	46			
2	1	27	49	46	25	2
2	2	46	45	47	48	2
2	3	72	47	46	70	2
2	4	39	43	47	42	3
3	1	24	44	46	25	1
3	2	49	48	45	46	3
3	3	70	46	45	69	1
3	4	44	49	45	41	3
4	1			47	26	
4	2					
4	3					
4	4					
5	1					
5	2					
5	3					
5	4					
6	1					

Number of previous periods to consider
n = 4

Type of Seasonality
Quarterly

Quarter	Seasonal Factor
1	0.550
2	1.027
3	1.519
4	0.904

Mean Absolute Deviation
MAD = 2.169

Forecast = 26 acre-feet

f)

Year	Quarter	True Value	Seasonally Adjusted Value	Seasonally Adjusted Forecast	Actual Forecast	Forecasting Error		
1	1	25	45	46	25	0		Smoothing Constant
1	2	47	46	46	47	0		$\alpha = $ 0.1
1	3	68	45	46	70	2		
1	4	42	46	46	41	1		Initial Estimate
2	1	27	49	46	25	2		Average = 46
2	2	46	45	46	47	1		
2	3	72	47	46	70	2		Type of Seasonality
2	4	39	43	46	42	3		Quarterly
3	1	24	44	46	25	1		
3	2	49	48	46	47	2		
3	3	70	46	46	70	0		
3	4	44	49	46	41	3		
4	1			46	25			
4	2							
4	3							
4	4							
5	1							
5	2							
5	3							
5	4							
6	1							
6	2							
6	3							
6	4							

Type of Seasonality
Quarterly

Quarter	Seasonal Factor
1	0.550
2	1.027
3	1.519
4	0.904

Mean Absolute Deviation
MAD = 1.420

Forecast = 25 acre-feet

g) The exponential smoothing method results in the lowest MAD value (1.420).

13.26 a)

Year	Quarter	Value
1	1	23
1	2	22
1	3	31
1	4	26
2	1	19
2	2	21
2	3	27
2	4	24
3	1	21
3	2	26
3	3	32
3	4	28

Type of Seasonality
Quarterly

Quarter	Estimate for Seasonal Factor
1	0.840
2	0.920
3	1.200
4	1.040

b)

Year	Quarter	True Value	Seasonally Adjusted Value	Seasonally Adjusted Forecast	Actual Forecast	Forecasting Error
1	1	23	27			
1	2	22	24	27	25	3
1	3	31	26	24	29	2
1	4	26	25	26	27	1
2	1	19	23	25	21	2
2	2	21	23	23	21	0
2	3	27	23	23	27	0
2	4	24	23	23	23	1
3	1	21	25	23	19	2
3	2	26	28	25	23	3
3	3	32	27	28	34	2
3	4	28	27	27	28	0
4	1			27	23	
4	2					
4	3					
4	4					
5	1					
5	2					

Type of Seasonality
Quarterly

Quarter	Seasonal Factor
1	0.840
2	0.920
3	1.200
4	1.040

Mean Absolute Deviation
MAD = 1.485

c)

Year	Quarter	True Value	Seasonally Adjusted Value	Seasonally Adjusted Forecast	Actual Forecast	Forecasting Error
1	1	23	27			
1	2	22	24	27	25	3
1	3	31	26	26	31	0
1	4	26	25	26	27	1
2	1	19	23	26	21	2
2	2	21	23	25	23	2
2	3	27	23	25	30	3
2	4	24	23	24	25	1
3	1	21	25	24	20	1
3	2	26	28	24	22	4
3	3	32	27	25	30	2
3	4	28	27	25	26	2
4	1			25	21	
4	2					
4	3					
4	4					
5	1					
5	2					

Type of Seasonality
Quarterly

Quarter	Seasonal Factor
1	0.840
2	0.920
3	1.200
4	1.040

Mean Absolute Deviation
MAD = 1.942

d)

Year	Quarter	True Value	Seasonally Adjusted Value	Seasonally Adjusted Forecast	Actual Forecast	Forecasting Error
1	1	23	27			
1	2	22	24			
1	3	31	26			
1	4	26	25			
2	1	19	23	26	21	2
2	2	21	23	24	22	1
2	3	27	23	24	29	2
2	4	24	23	23	24	0
3	1	21	25	23	19	2
3	2	26	28	23	21	5
3	3	32	27	25	30	2
3	4	28	27	26	27	1
4	1			27	22	
4	2					
4	3					
4	4					
5	1					
5	2					
5	3					
5	4					
6	1					

Number of previous periods to consider

n = 4

Type of Seasonality

Quarterly

Quarter	Seasonal Factor
1	0.840
2	0.920
3	1.200
4	1.040

Mean Absolute Deviation

MAD = 1.983

e)

Year	Quarter	True Value	Seasonally Adjusted Value	Seasonally Adjusted Forecast	Actual Forecast	Forecasting Error
1	1	23	27	25	21	2
1	2	22	24	26	24	2
1	3	31	26	25	30	1
1	4	26	25	25	26	0
2	1	19	23	25	21	2
2	2	21	23	25	23	2
2	3	27	23	24	29	2
2	4	24	23	24	25	1
3	1	21	25	24	20	1
3	2	26	28	24	22	4
3	3	32	27	25	30	2
3	4	28	27	25	26	2
4	1			26	22	
4	2					
4	3					
4	4					
5	1					
5	2					
5	3					
5	4					
6	1					
6	2					
6	3					
6	4					

Smoothing Constant

α = 0.25

Initial Estimate

Average = 25

Type of Seasonality

Quarterly

Quarter	Seasonal Factor
1	0.840
2	0.920
3	1.200
4	1.040

Mean Absolute Deviation

MAD = 1.661

f)

Year	Qtr	True Value	Seasonally Adjusted Value	Latest Trend	Est. Trend	Seasonally Adjusted Forecast	Actual Forecast	Forecasting Error
1	1	23	27		0	25	21	2
1	2	22	24	1	0	26	24	2
1	3	31	26	0	0	25	30	1
1	4	26	25	0	0	26	27	1
2	1	19	23	0	0	25	21	2
2	2	21	23	-1	0	25	23	2
2	3	27	23	-1	0	24	29	2
2	4	24	23	-1	0	23	24	0
3	1	21	25	0	0	23	19	2
3	2	26	28	0	0	23	21	5
3	3	32	27	1	0	25	29	3
3	4	28	27	1	0	25	26	2
4	1			1	0	26	22	

Smoothing Constants

α =	0.25
β =	0.25

Initial Estimates

Average =	25
Trend =	0

Mean Absolute Deviation

MAD =	1.778

Type of Seasonality

Quarterly

Quarter	Seasonal Factor
1	0.840
2	0.920
3	1.200
4	1.040

g) Using the last-value method with seasonality (MAD=1.485), the forecast for Q1 is 23 houses.

h) Q2 = (27)(0.92) = 25
Q3 = (27)(1.2) = 32
Q4 = (27)(1.04) = 28

13.27 a)

Method	MAD
Last-value	3.07
Averaging	3.12
Moving-average	2.18
Exponential smoothing	2.34

b)

Year	Month	True Value	Seasonally Adjusted Value	Seasonally Adjusted Forecast	Actual Forecast	Forecasting Error
1	Jan	68	76			
1	Feb	71	81			
1	Mar	66	73			
1	Apr	72	77	76	71	1
1	May	77	80	77	74	3
1	June	85	78	77	84	1
1	July	94	80	79	92	2
1	Aug	96	83	80	91	5
1	Sep	80	82	81	78	2
1	Oct	73	80	82	75	2
1	Nov	84	80	82	88	2
1	Dec	89	82	81	87	2
2	Jan			81	73	
2	Feb					
2	Mar					
2	Apr					
2	May					
2	June					
2	July					
2	Aug					
2	Sep					

Number of previous periods to consider

n = 3

Type of Seasonality

Monthly

Month	Seasonal Factor
Jan	0.90
Feb	0.88
Mar	0.91
Apr	0.93
May	0.96
June	1.09
July	1.17
Aug	1.15
Sep	0.97
Oct	0.91
Nov	1.05
Dec	1.08

Mean Absolute Deviation

MAD = 2.183

According to the moving-average method, the forecast for Jan. is 73 passengers.

13.28 a)

Method	MAD
Last-value	2.49
Averaging	7.06
Moving-average	2.79
Exponential smoothing	4.28

b)

Year	Month	True Value	Seasonally Adjusted Value	Latest Trend	Est. Trend	Seasonally Adjusted Forecast	Actual Forecast	Forecasting Error
1	Jan	75	83		2	82	74	1
1	Feb	76	86	2	2	84	74	2
1	Mar	81	89	2	2	87	79	2
1	Apr	84	90	3	2	90	83	1
2	May	85	89	2	2	92	88	3
2	Jun	99	91	2	2	93	102	3
2	Jul	107	91	2	2	95	111	4
2	Aug	108	94	1	2	96	110	2
3	Sep	94	97	1	2	97	95	1
3	Oct	90	99	2	2	99	90	0
3	Nov	106	101	2	2	101	106	0
3	Dec	110	102	2	2	103	111	1
4	Jan			2	2	104	94	

Type of Seasonality

Monthly

Month	Seasonal Factor
Jan	0.90
Feb	0.88
Mar	0.91
Apr	0.93
May	0.96
Jun	1.09
Jul	1.17
Aug	1.15
Sep	0.97
Oct	0.91
Nov	1.05
Dec	1.08

Smoothing Constants

$\alpha =$	0.2
$\beta =$	0.2

Initial Estimates

Average =	80
Trend =	2

Mean Absolute Deviation

MAD =	1.656

MAD here is lower that all those found in part a).

c)

Year	Month	True Value	Seasonally Adjusted Value	Latest Trend	Est. Trend	Seasonally Adjusted Forecast	Actual Forecast	Forecasting Error
1	Jan	68	76		0	80	72	4
1	Feb	71	81	-1	0	79	69	2
1	Mar	66	73	0	0	79	72	6
1	Apr	72	77	-1	0	77	72	0
2	May	77	80	0	0	77	74	3
2	Jun	85	78	0	0	77	84	1
2	Jul	94	80	0	0	77	90	4
2	Aug	96	83	0	0	78	89	7
3	Sep	80	82	1	0	79	77	3
3	Oct	73	80	1	0	80	73	0
3	Nov	84	80	0	0	80	84	0
3	Dec	89	82	0	0	80	87	2
4	Jan	75	83	1	0	81	73	2
4	Feb	76	86	1	0	83	73	3
4	Mar	81	89	2	1	86	79	2
4	Apr	84	90	3	1	89	83	1
5	May	85	89	2	1	90	87	2
5	Jun	99	91	1	1	89	97	2
5	Jul	107	91	-1	1	91	106	1
5	Aug	108	94	2	1	91	105	3
6	Sep	94	97	1	1	94	91	3
6	Oct	90	99	3	1	97	88	2
6	Nov	106	101	3	2	99	104	2
6	Dec	110	102	2	2	101	109	1
7	Jan			2	2	102	92	

Type of Seasonality

Monthly

Month	Seasonal Factor
Jan	0.90
Feb	0.88
Mar	0.91
Apr	0.93
May	0.96
Jun	1.09
Jul	1.17
Aug	1.15
Sep	0.97
Oct	0.91
Nov	1.05
Dec	1.08

Smoothing Constants

$\alpha =$	0.2
$\beta =$	0.2

Initial Estimates

Average =	80
Trend =	0

Mean Absolute Deviation

MAD =	2.289

d) Exponential smoothing with trend should be used.

13.29 a)

Month	Estimate for Seasonal Factor
Jan	0.808
Feb	0.807
Mar	0.876
Apr	0.921
May	1.016
June	1.105
July	1.018
Aug	1.189
Sep	0.806
Oct	0.761
Nov	1.437
Dec	1.256

b)

Year	Month	True Value	Seasonally Adjusted Value	Seasonally Adjusted Forecast	Actual Forecast	Forecasting Error
1	Jan					
1	Feb					
1	Mar					
1	Apr					
1	May					
1	June					
1	July					
1	Aug					
1	Sep					
1	Oct	335	440			
1	Nov	594	413	440	633	39
1	Dec	527	420	427	536	9
2	Jan	364	450	424	343	21
2	Feb	343	425	428	345	2
2	Mar	391	446	432	378	13
2	Apr	437	474	441	406	31
2	May	458	451	449	456	2
2	June	494	447	457	505	11
2	July	468	460	457	466	2
2	Aug	555	467	453	538	17
2	Sep	387	480	458	369	18
2	Oct	364	478	469	357	7
2	Nov	662	461	475	683	21
2	Dec	581	463	473	594	13
3	Jan			467	377	

Number of previous periods to consider
$n = 3$

Type of Seasonality
Monthly

Month	Seasonal Factor
Jan	0.808
Feb	0.807
Mar	0.876
Apr	0.921
May	1.016
June	1.105
July	1.018
Aug	1.189
Sep	0.806
Oct	0.761
Nov	1.437
Dec	1.256

Mean Absolute Deviation
MAD = 14.761

c)

Year	Month	True Value	Seasonally Adjusted Value	Seasonally Adjusted Forecast	Actual Forecast	Forecasting Error
1	Jan	364	450	420	339	25
1	Feb	343	425	426	344	1
1	Mar	391	446	426	373	18
1	Apr	437	474	430	396	41
1	May	458	451	439	446	12
1	June	494	447	441	488	6
1	July	468	460	442	450	18
1	Aug	555	467	446	530	25
1	Sep	387	480	450	363	24
1	Oct	364	478	456	347	17
1	Nov	662	461	461	662	0
1	Dec	581	463	461	578	3
2	Jan			461	372	
2	Feb					
2	Mar					
2	Apr					
2	May					
2	June					
2	July					
2	Aug					
2	Sep					
2	Oct					
2	Nov					
2	Dec					

Smoothing Constant

α = 0.2

Initial Estimate

Average = 420

Type of Seasonality

Monthly

Month	Seasonal Factor
Jan	0.808
Feb	0.807
Mar	0.876
Apr	0.921
May	1.016
June	1.105
July	1.018
Aug	1.189
Sep	0.806
Oct	0.761
Nov	1.437
Dec	1.256

Mean Absolute Deviation

MAD = 15.777

d)

Year	Month	True Value	Seasonally Adjusted Value	Latest Trend	Est. Trend	Seasonally Adjusted Forecast	Actual Forecast	Forecasting Error
1	Jan	364	450		0	420	339	25
1	Feb	343	425	6	1	427	345	2
1	Mar	391	446	1	1	428	375	16
1	Apr	437	474	5	2	434	399	38
2	May	458	451	10	4	445	452	6
2	Jun	494	447	5	4	450	497	3
2	Jul	468	460	3	4	453	461	7
2	Aug	555	467	5	4	458	545	10
3	Sep	387	480	6	4	464	374	13
3	Oct	364	478	7	5	472	359	5
3	Nov	662	461	6	5	479	688	26
3	Dec	581	463	2	4	479	602	21
4	Jan				1	4	480	388

Type of Seasonality

Monthly

Month	Seasonal Factor
Jan	0.808
Feb	0.807
Mar	0.876
Apr	0.921
May	1.016
Jun	1.105
Jul	1.018
Aug	1.189
Sep	0.806
Oct	0.761
Nov	1.437
Dec	1.256

Smoothing Constants

$\alpha =$	0.2
$\beta =$	0.2

Initial Estimates

Average =	420
Trend =	0

Mean Absolute Deviation

MAD =	14.200

e) Exponential smoothing with trend results in the best MAD value (14.2).

f)

Month	Avg. Forecast	Forecasting Error
January	340	24
February	345	2
March	375	16
April	400	37
May	451	7
June	497	7
July	459	9
August	538	17
September	369	18
October	354	10
November	678	16
December	591	12

MAD = 14.58

g) Exponential smoothing with trend performed better than the average of all three so it should be used next year.

13.30 a)

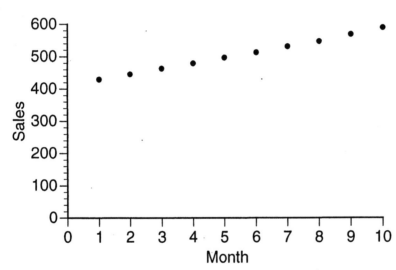

b) $y = 410 + 17.6x$

c)
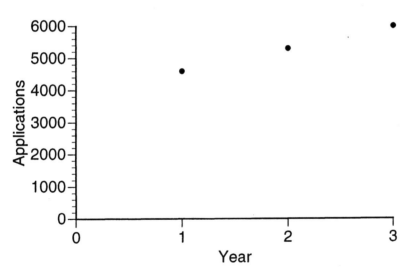

d) $y = 410 + (17.6)(11) = 604$

e) $y = 410 + (17.6)(20) = 762$

f) The average growth in sales per month is 17.6.

13.31 a)

b)

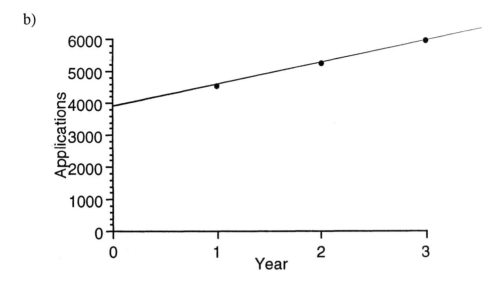

c) $y = 3900 + 700x$

d) y (year 4) = $3900 + (700)(4) = 6700$
   y (year 5) = $3900 + (700)(5) = 7400$
   y (year 6) = $3900 + (700)(6) = 8100$
   y (year 7) = $3900 + (700)(7) = 8800$
   y (year 8) = $3900 + (700)(8) = 9500$

e) It does not make sense to use the forecast obtained earlier of 9500. The relationship between the variable has changed and, thus, the linear regression that was used is no longer appropriate.

f)

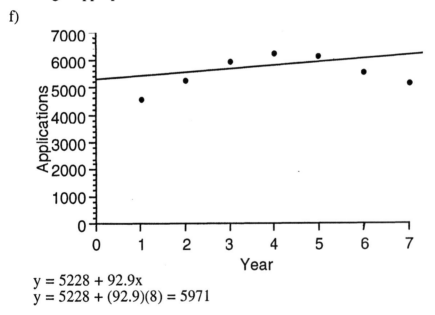

$y = 5228 + 92.9x$
$y = 5228 + (92.9)(8) = 5971$

The linear regression line does not provide a close fit to the data. Consequently, the forecast that it provides for year 8 is not likely to be accurate. It does not make sense to continue to use a linear regression line when changing conditions cause a large shift in the underlying trend in the data.

g)

Time Period	Data	Latest Trend	Estimated Trend	Exponential Smoothing Forecast	Forecasting Error
1	4600		700	4600	0
2	5300	700	700	5300	0
3	6000	700	700	6000	0
4	6300	700	700	6700	400
5	6200	500	600	7100	900
6	5600	150	375	7025	1425
7	5200	-338	19	6331	1131
8		-547	-264	5502	
9					

Smoothing Constants

$\alpha =$	0.5
$\beta =$	0.5

Initial Estimates

Average =	3900
Trend =	700

Mean Absolute Deviation

MAD =	550.893

Causal forecasting takes all the data into account, even the data from before changing conditions cause a shift. Exponential smoothing with trend adjusts to shifts in the underlying trend.

13.32 a)

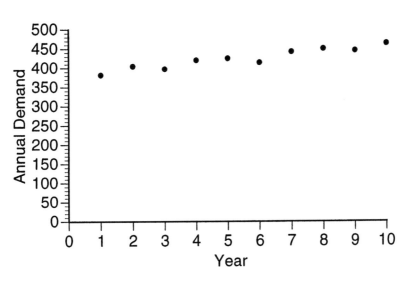

b) $y = 380 + 8.15x$

c)

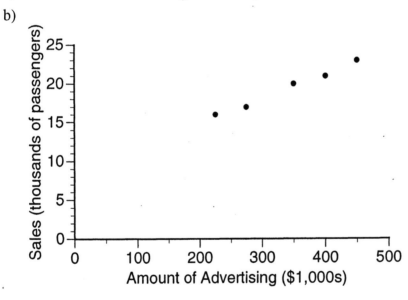

d) $y = 380 + (8.15)(11) = 470$

e) $y = 380 = (8.15)(15) = 503$

f) The average growth per year is 8.15 tons.

13.33 a) The amount of advertising is the independent variable and sales is the dependent variable.

b)

c) y = 8.71 + 0.031x

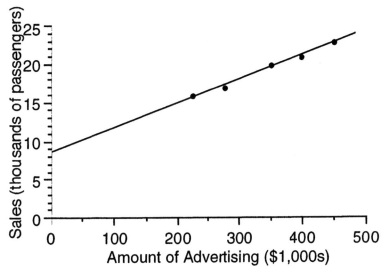

d) y = 8.71 + (0.031)(300) = 18,000 passengers

e) 22 = 8.71 + (0.031)(x)   x = $429,000

f) An increase of 31 passengers can be attained.

13.34 a) The number of flying hours is the independent variable and the number of wing flaps needed is the dependent variable.

b)

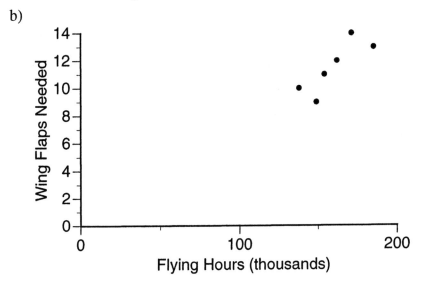

c)   y = -3.38 + 0.093x

d)

e) $y = -3.38 + (0.093)(150) = 11$

f) $y = -3.38 + (0.093)(200) = 15$

13.35

Time Period	Independent Variable	Dependent Variable	Estimate	Estimation Error	Square of Error	Linear Regression Line $y = a + bx$	
1	323	24	22	2.48	6	a =	-9.954
2	359	23	25	2.02	4	b =	0.097
3	396	28	29	0.63	0		
4	421	32	31	0.93	1		
5	457	34	35	0.57	0	Estimator	
6	472	37	36	0.97	1	If x =	200
7	446	33	34	0.50	0	then y=	9.533
8	407	30	30	0.30	0		
9	374	27	26	0.51	0		
10	343	22	23	1.47	2		

Joe should use the linear regression line $y = -9.95 + 0.097x$ to develop a forecast for jobs in the future.

Cases

13.1   a)   We need to forecast the call volume for each day separately.

1) To obtain the seasonally adjusted call volume for the past 13 weeks, we first have to determine the seasonal factors. Because call volumes follow seasonal patterns within the week, we have to calculate a seasonal factor for Monday, Tuesday, Wednesday, Thursday, and Friday. We calculate the seasonal factors using the following formula:

$$\frac{\text{Average for the Day}}{\text{Overall Average}}$$

The spreadsheet used to calculate the seasonal factors follows.

	Monday	Tuesday	Wednesday	Thursday	Friday	Total
Week 44	1130	851	859	828	726	4394
Week 45	1085	1042	892	840	799	4658
Week 46	1303	1121	1003	1113	1005	5545
Week 47	2652	2825	1841	0	0	7318
Week 48	1949	1507	989	990	1084	6519
Week 49	1260	1134	941	847	714	4896
Week 50	1002	847	922	842	784	4397
Week 51	823	0	0	401	429	1653
Week 52/1	1209	830	0	1082	841	3962
Week 2	1362	1174	967	930	853	5286
Week 3	924	954	1346	904	758	4886
Week 4	886	878	802	945	610	4121
Week 5	910	754	705	729	772	3870
Average	1268.846	1070.538	866.692	803.923	721.154	946.231
Seasonal Factors	**1.341**	**1.131**	**0.916**	**0.850**	**0.762**	

Now that we have found the seasonal factors, we can obtain the seasonally adjusted series. For each day within each of the 13 weeks, we need to calculate the seasonally adjusted daily call volumes using the following formula:

$$\frac{\text{Actual Daily Call Volume}}{\text{Seasonal Factor for the Corresponding Day of the Week}}$$

The spreadsheet for the seasonally adjusted call volumes follows.

	Monday	Tuesday	Wednesday	Thursday	Friday
Week 44	842.69	752.18	937.83	974.57	952.59
Week 45	809.13	921.01	973.86	988.69	1048.37
Week 46	971.70	990.83	1095.05	1310.02	1318.67
Week 47	1977.71	2496.97	2009.95	0.00	0.00
Week 48	1453.45	1332.01	1079.76	1165.25	1422.32
Week 49	939.63	1002.32	1027.36	996.93	936.84
Week 50	747.23	748.65	1006.61	991.05	1028.69
Week 51	613.74	0.00	0.00	471.98	562.89
Week 52/1	901.60	733.62	0.00	1273.53	1103.48
Week 2	1015.70	1037.68	1055.74	1094.63	1119.23
Week 3	689.06	843.22	1469.53	1064.02	994.58
Week 4	660.73	776.05	875.60	1112.28	800.39
Week 5	678.62	666.45	769.70	858.05	1012.95

2) To forecast the call volume for the next week using the last-value forecasting method, we need to use the Last Value with Seasonality template. However, we need to modify this template because it does not provide the option for daily seasonality. The modified spreadsheet follows.

Week	Day	True Value	Seasonally Adjusted Value	Seasonally Adjusted Forecast	Actual Forecast	Forecasting Error
44	Mon	1130	843			
44	Tues	851	753	843	952	101
44	Wed	859	938	753	690	169
44	Thurs	828	974	938	797	31
44	Fri	726	955	974	740	14
45	Mon	1085	809	955	1281	196
45	Tues	1042	922	809	914	128
45	Wed	892	974	922	845	47
45	Thurs	840	988	974	828	12
45	Fri	799	1051	988	751	48
46	Mon	1303	972			
46	Tues	1121	992			
46	Wed	1003	1095			
46	Thurs	1113	1309			
46	Fri	1005	1322			
47	Mon	2652	1978			
47	Tues	2825	2500			
47	Wed	1841	2010			
47	Thurs	0	0			
47	Fri	0	0			
48	Mon	1949	1453			
48	Tues	1507	1334			
48	Wed	989	1080			
48	Thurs	990	1165			
48	Fri	1084	1426			
49	Mon	1260	940			
49	Tues	1134	1004			
49	Wed	941	1027			
49	Thurs	847	996			
49	Fri	714	939			
50	Mon	1002	747			
50	Tues	847	750			
50	Wed	922	1007			
50	Thurs	842	991			
50	Fri	784	1032			
51	Mon	823	614			
51	Tues	0	0			
51	Wed	0	0			
51	Thurs	401	472			
51	Fri	429	564			
52/1	Mon	1209	902			
52/1	Tues	830	735			
52/1	Wed	0	0			
52/1	Thurs	1082	1273			
52/1	Fri	841	1107			
2	Mon	1362	1016			
2	Tues	1174	1039			
2	Wed	967	1056			
2	Thurs	930	1094			
2	Fri	853	1122			
3	Mon	924	689			
3	Tues	954	844			
3	Wed	1346	1469			
3	Thurs	904	1064			
3	Fri	758	997			
4	Mon	886	661			
4	Tues	878	777			
4	Wed	802	876			
4	Thurs	945	1112			
4	Fri	610	803			
5	Mon	910	679			
5	Tues	754	667			
5	Wed	705	770			
5	Thurs	729	858			
5	Fri	772	1016			
6	Mon	1362	1016	1016	1362	0
6	Tues	1148	1016	1016	1148	0
6	Wed	931	1016	1016	931	0
6	Thurs	864	1016	1016	864	0
6	Fri	773	1017	1016	773	0

Type of Seasonality
Daily

Day	Seasonal Factor
Mon	1.34
Tues	1.13
Wed	0.92
Thurs	0.85
Fri	0.76

Weekly Demand for the Next We   5077

The forecasted call volume for the next week is 5077 calls: 1362 calls are received on Monday, 1148 calls are received on Tuesday, 931 calls are received on Wednesday, 864 calls are received on Thursday, and 773 calls are received on Friday.

3) To forecast the call volume for the next week using the averaging forecasting method, we need to use the Averaging with Seasonality template. However, we need to modify this template because it does not provide the option for daily seasonality. The modified spreadsheet follows.

Week	Day	True Value	Seasonally Adjusted Value	Seasonally Adjusted Forecast	Actual Forecast	Forecasting Error
44	Mon	1130	843			
44	Tues	851	753			
44	Wed	859	938			
44	Thurs	828	974			
44	Fri	726	955			
45	Mon	1085	809			
45	Tues	1042	922			
45	Wed	892	974			
45	Thurs	840	988			
45	Fri	799	1051			
46	Mon	1303	972			
46	Tues	1121	992			
46	Wed	1003	1095			
46	Thurs	1113	1309			
46	Fri	1005	1322			
47	Mon	2652	1978			
47	Tues	2825	2500			
47	Wed	1841	2010			
47	Thurs	0	0			
47	Fri	0	0			
48	Mon	1949	1453			
48	Tues	1507	1334			
48	Wed	989	1080			
48	Thurs	990	1165			
48	Fri	1084	1426			
49	Mon	1260	940			
49	Tues	1134	1004			
49	Wed	941	1027			
49	Thurs	847	996			
49	Fri	714	939			
50	Mon	1002	747			
50	Tues	847	750			
50	Wed	922	1007			
50	Thurs	842	991			
50	Fri	784	1032			
51	Mon	823	614			
51	Tues	0	0			
51	Wed	0	0			
51	Thurs	401	472			
51	Fri	429	564			
52/1	Mon	1209	902			
52/1	Tues	830	735			
52/1	Wed	0	0			
52/1	Thurs	1082	1273			
52/1	Fri	841	1107			
2	Mon	1362	1016			
2	Tues	1174	1039			
2	Wed	967	1056			
2	Thurs	930	1094			
2	Fri	853	1122			
3	Mon	924	689			
3	Tues	954	844			
3	Wed	1346	1469			
3	Thurs	904	1064			
3	Fri	758	997			
4	Mon	886	661			
4	Tues	878	777			
4	Wed	802	876			
4	Thurs	945	1112			
4	Fri	610	803			
5	Mon	910	679			
5	Tues	754	667			
5	Wed	705	770			
5	Thurs	729	858			
5	Fri	772	1016			
6	Mon	1270	947	947	1270	0
6	Tues	1070	947	947	1070	0
6	Wed	867	947	947	867	0
6	Thurs	805	947	947	805	0
6	Fri	720	947	947	720	0

	Type of Seasonality
	Daily

Day	Seasonal Factor
Mon	1.34
Tues	1.13
Wed	0.92
Thurs	0.85
Fri	0.76

Weekly Demand for the Next Week   4732

The forecasted call volume for the next week is 4732 calls: 1270 calls are received on Monday, 1070 calls are received on Tuesday, 867 calls are received on Wednesday, 805 calls are received on Thursday, and 720 calls are received on Friday.

4) To forecast the call volume for the next week using the moving-average forecasting method, we need to use the Moving Averaging with Seasonality template. However, we need to modify this template because it does not provide the option for daily seasonality. The modified spreadsheet follows.

Week	Day	True Value	Seasonally Adjusted Value	Seasonally Adjusted Forecast	Actual Forecast	Forecasting Error
44	Mon	1130	843			
44	Tues	851	753			
44	Wed	859	938			
44	Thurs	828	974			
44	Fri	726	955			
45	Mon	1085	809			
45	Tues	1042	922			
45	Wed	892	974			
45	Thurs	840	988			
45	Fri	799	1051			
46	Mon	1303	972			
46	Tues	1121	992			
46	Wed	1003	1095			
46	Thurs	1113	1309			
46	Fri	1005	1322			
47	Mon	2652	1978			
47	Tues	2825	2500			
47	Wed	1841	2010			
47	Thurs	0	0			
47	Fri	0	0			
48	Mon	1949	1453			
48	Tues	1507	1334			
48	Wed	989	1080			
48	Thurs	990	1165			
48	Fri	1084	1426			
49	Mon	1260	940			
49	Tues	1134	1004			
49	Wed	941	1027			
49	Thurs	847	996			
49	Fri	714	939			
50	Mon	1002	747			
50	Tues	847	750			
50	Wed	922	1007			
50	Thurs	842	991			
50	Fri	784	1032			
51	Mon	823	614			
51	Tues	0	0			
51	Wed	0	0			
51	Thurs	401	472			
51	Fri	429	564			
52/1	Mon	1209	902			
52/1	Tues	830	735			
52/1	Wed	0	0			
52/1	Thurs	1082	1273			
52/1	Fri	841	1107			
2	Mon	1362	1016			
2	Tues	1174	1039			
2	Wed	967	1056			
2	Thurs	930	1094			
2	Fri	853	1122			
3	Mon	924	689			
3	Tues	954	844			
3	Wed	1346	1469			
3	Thurs	904	1064			
3	Fri	758	997			
4	Mon	886	661			
4	Tues	878	777			
4	Wed	802	876			
4	Thurs	945	1112			
4	Fri	610	803			
5	Mon	910	679			
5	Tues	754	667			
5	Wed	705	770			
5	Thurs	729	858			
5	Fri	772	1016			
6	Mon	1070	798	798	1070	0
6	Tues	928	822	822	928	0
6	Wed	781	853	853	781	0
6	Thurs	739	869	869	739	0
6	Fri	662	871	871	662	0

Number of previous periods to consider	
n =	5
Type of Seasonality	Daily
Day	Seasonal Factor
Mon	1.34
Tues	1.13
Wed	0.92
Thurs	0.85
Fri	0.76

Weekly Demand for the Next Week   4189

The forecasted call volume for the next week is 4189 calls: 1070 calls are received on Monday, 928 calls are received on Tuesday, 781 calls are received on Wednesday, 739 calls are received on Thursday, and 662 calls are received on Friday.

13-37

5) To forecast the call volume for the next week using the exponential smoothing forecasting method, we need to use the Exponential with Seasonality template. However, we need to modify this template because it does not provide the option for daily seasonality. The modified spreadsheet follows.

Week	Day	True Value	Seasonally Adjusted Value	Seasonally Adjusted Forecast	Actual Forecast	Forecasting Error
44	Mon	1130	843			
44	Tues	851	753			
44	Wed	859	938			
44	Thurs	828	974			
44	Fri	726	955			
45	Mon	1085	809			
45	Tues	1042	922			
45	Wed	892	974			
45	Thurs	840	988			
45	Fri	799	1051			
46	Mon	1303	972			
46	Tues	1121	992			
46	Wed	1003	1095			
46	Thurs	1113	1309			
46	Fri	1005	1322			
47	Mon	2652	1978			
47	Tues	2825	2500			
47	Wed	1841	2010			
47	Thurs	0	0			
47	Fri	0	0			
48	Mon	1949	1453			
48	Tues	1507	1334			
48	Wed	989	1080			
48	Thurs	990	1165			
48	Fri	1084	1426			
49	Mon	1260	940			
49	Tues	1134	1004			
49	Wed	941	1027			
49	Thurs	847	996			
49	Fri	714	939			
50	Mon	1002	747			
50	Tues	847	750			
50	Wed	922	1007			
50	Thurs	842	991			
50	Fri	784	1032			
51	Mon	823	614			
51	Tues	0	0			
51	Wed	0	0			
51	Thurs	401	472			
51	Fri	429	564			
52/1	Mon	1209	902			
52/1	Tues	830	735			
52/1	Wed	0	0			
52/1	Thurs	1082	1273			
52/1	Fri	841	1107			
2	Mon	1362	1016			
2	Tues	1174	1039			
2	Wed	967	1056			
2	Thurs	930	1094			
2	Fri	853	1122			
3	Mon	924	689			
3	Tues	954	844			
3	Wed	1346	1469			
3	Thurs	904	1064			
3	Fri	758	997			
4	Mon	886	661			
4	Tues	878	777			
4	Wed	802	876			
4	Thurs	945	1112			
4	Fri	610	803			
5	Mon	910	679			
5	Tues	754	667			
5	Wed	705	770			
5	Thurs	729	858			
5	Fri	772	1016	946		
6	Mon	1278	953	953	1278	0
6	Tues	1077	953	953	1077	0
6	Wed	873	953	953	873	0
6	Thurs	810	953	953	810	0
6	Fri	724	953	953	724	0

Smoothing Constant
α = 0.1

Initial Estimate
Average = 946.2307692

Type of Seasonality
Daily

Day	Seasonal Factor
Mon	1.34
Tues	1.13
Wed	0.92
Thurs	0.85
Fri	0.76

Weekly Demand for the Next Week   4763

The forecasted call volume for the next week is 4763 calls: 1278 calls are received on Monday, 1077 calls are received on Tuesday, 873 calls are received on Wednesday, 810 calls are received on Thursday, and 724 calls are received on Friday.

b) To obtain the mean absolute deviation for each forecasting method, we simply need to subtract the true call volume from the forecasted call volume for each day in the sixth week. We then need to take the absolute value of the five differences. Finally, we need to take the average of these five absolute values to obtain the mean absolute deviation.

The spreadsheet for the calculation of the mean absolute deviation for the last-value forecasting method follows.

LAST VALUE

Week	Day	True Value	Actual Forecast	Forecasting Error
6	Mon	723	1362	639
6	Tues	677	1148	471
6	Wed	521	931	410
6	Thurs	571	864	293
6	Fri	498	773	275

Mean Absolute Deviation

MAD =	417

This method is the least effective of the four methods because this method depends heavily upon the <u>average</u> seasonality factors. If the average seasonality factors are not the true seasonality factors for week 6, a large error will appear because the average seasonality factors are used to transform the Friday call volume in week 5 to forecasts for <u>all</u> call volumes in week 6. We calculated in part (a) that the call volume for Friday is 0.76 times lower than the overall average call volume. In week 6, however, the call volume for Friday is only 0.83 times lower than the average call volume over the week. Also, we calculated that the call volume for Monday is 1.34 times higher than the overall average call volume. In Week 6, however, the call volume for Monday is only 1.21 times higher than the average call volume over the week. These differences introduce a large error.

The spreadsheet for the calculation of the mean absolute deviation for the averaging forecasting method appears below.

Averaging

Week	Day	True Value	Actual Forecast	Forecasting Error
6	Mon	723	1270	547
6	Tues	677	1070	393
6	Wed	521	867	346
6	Thurs	571	805	234
6	Fri	498	720	222

Mean Absolute Deviation

MAD =	348

This method is the second-most effective of the four methods. Again, the reason lies in the average seasonality factors. Applying the average seasonality factors to an average call volume yields a much more accurate result than applying average seasonality factors to only one call volume. This method is not the most effective method, however, because the centralized call center experiences not only daily seasonality, but also weekly seasonality. For example, the call volumes in weeks 45 and 46 are much greater than the call volumes in week 6. Therefore, these larger call volumes inflate the average call volume, which in turn inflates the forecasts for Week 6.

The spreadsheet for the calculation of the mean absolute deviation for the moving-average forecasting method appears below.

MOVING AVERAGE

Week	Day	True Value	Actual Forecast	Forecasting Error
6	Mon	723	1070	347
6	Tues	677	928	251
6	Wed	521	781	260
6	Thurs	571	739	168
6	Fri	498	662	164

Mean Absolute Deviation

MAD = 238

This method is the most effective of the four methods because this method only uses the average week 5 call volume to forecast the call volumes for week 6. Again, applying the average seasonality factors to an average call volume yields a much more accurate result than applying average seasonality factors to only one call volume. Also, the average call volume used in this method is not overly inflated since it is an average of the week 5 call volumes, which are closer to the week 6 call volumes than any other of the 13 weeks.

The spreadsheet for the calculation of the mean absolute deviation for exponential forecasting method follows.

EXPONENTIAL SMOOTHING

Week	Day	True Value	Actual Forecast	Forecasting Error
6	Mon	723	1278	555
6	Tues	677	1077	400
6	Wed	521	873	352
6	Thurs	571	810	239
6	Fri	498	724	226

Mean Absolute Deviation

MAD = 355

This method is almost as effective as the averaging forecasting method because the smoothing constant used is 0.1. Therefore, the call volumes from earlier weeks are still weighted in calculating the call volume average. This method is a little less effective than the averaging forecasting method because the smoothing constant causes less weight to be placed on the call volumes in weeks 44 and 45. These call volumes are lower than volumes in weeks 46, 48, and 49, however, and they help lower the already inflated average call volume.

c) This problem is simply a linear regression problem.

   1) To find a mathematical relationship, we use the Linear Regression template. The decentralized case volumes are the independent variables, and the centralized case volumes are the dependent variables. Substituting the case volume data, we obtain the following spreadsheet:

Week	Independent Variable	Dependent Variable	Estimate	Estimation Error	Square of Error	Linear Regression Line y = a + bx
44	612	2052	2038	13.84	192	a = 1575.516778
45	721	2170	2121	49.45	2445	b = 0.755947559
46	693	2779	2099	679.61	461872	
47	540	2334	1984	350.27	122690	
48	1386	2514	2623	109.26	11938	Estimator
49	577	1713	2012	298.70	89221	If x = 613
50	405	1927	1882	45.32	2054	then y= 2038.912632
51	441	1167	1909	741.89	550400	
52/1	655	1549	2071	521.66	272132	
2	572	2126	2008	118.08	13943	
3	475	2337	1935	402.41	161932	
4	530	1916	1976	60.17	3620	
5	595	2098	2025	72.69	5284	

   2) To forecast the week 6 call volume for the centralized call center, we simply input the week 6 decentralized case volume for the value of x in the Estimator section of the Linear Regression Spreadsheet. The value of y then represents the week 6 centralized case volume. We multiply this value of y by 1.5 to obtain the week 6 centralized call volume. The calculations in Excel appear below.

Estimator

If x =	613
then y=	2038.912632

Calls = 1.5 * y
          3058.36894ε

We then break this weekly call volume into daily call volume. We do this conversion by dividing the weekly call volume by the sum of the seasonal factors calculated in part (a) and then multiplying this weekly call volume by the appropriate seasonal factor to find the call volume for each of the five days of the week. The spreadsheet showing these calculations follows:

Seasonal Factors		1.341	1.131	0.916	0.850	0.762

Week 6 Call Volume	3058
Sum of Seasonal Factors	5.000

Converted Week 6 Call Volume	611.6

Call Volume for:	
Monday	820.1237
Tuesday	691.9468
Wednesday	560.19
Thursday	519.6189
Friday	466.1206
Week 6 Call Volume	3058

The forecasted call volume for week 6 is 3058 calls: 820 calls are received on Monday, 692 calls are received on Tuesday, 560 calls are received on Wednesday, 520 calls are received on Thursday, and 466 calls are received on Friday.

3) To calculate the mean absolute deviation, we need to subtract the true call volume from the forecasted call volume for each day in the sixth week. We then need to take the absolute value of the five differences. Finally, we need to take the average of these five absolute values to obtain the mean absolute deviation.

The spreadsheet for the calculation of the mean absolute deviation follows.

CAUSAL FORECASTING

Week	Day	True Value	Actual Forecast	Forecasting Error
6	Mon	7 23	820	97
6	Tues	6 77	692	15
6	Wed	5 21	560	39
6	Thurs	5 71	520	51
6	Fri	4 98	466	32

Mean Absolute Deviation

MAD =	47

This forecasting method is by far the most effective method. The centralized center performs the same services and serves the same population as the decentralized center. Therefore, the call volume trends are the same. Once we have a factor to scale the decentralized call volumes to the centralized call volumes, we have a very effective forecasting method.

d) We would definitely recommend using the causal forecasting method implemented in part (c) because it yields the lowest error. The causal method shows us that the call volume trends remain relatively the same year after year. We had to convert between case volumes and call volumes in part (c), however, and such a conversion introduces error. For example, what if a case generates a higher or lower number of calls? We therefore recommend that call volume data be meticulously recorded as the centralized center continues its operation. Once one year's worth of call volumes have been collected, the causal forecasting model should be updated. The model should be updated to use the historical centralized call volume data instead of the historical decentralized case volume data.

Teaching notes for this chapter are available in the Teaching Notes section near the front of this Instructor's Manual.

Review Questions

14.1-1   Customers might be vehicles, machines, or other items.

14.1-2   It might be a crew of people working together, a machine, a vehicle, or an electronic device.

14.1-3   Mean arrival rate = $\dfrac{1}{\text{mean interarrival time}}$.

14.1-4

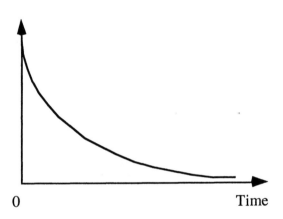

14.1-5   The mean equals the standard deviation of the exponential distribution.

14.1-6   Having random arrivals means that arrival times are completely unpredictable in the sense that the chance of an arrival in the next minute always is just the same as for any other minute. The only distribution of interarrival times that fits having random arrivals is the exponential distribution.

14.1-7   The number of customers in the queue is the number of customers waiting for service to begin. The number of customers in the system is the number in the queue plus the number currently being served.

14.1-8   Queueing models conventionally assume that the queue is an infinite queue and that the queue discipline is first come first served.

14.1-9   Mean service time = $\dfrac{1}{\text{mean service rate}}$.

14.1-10 For the exponential distribution, the standard deviation equals the mean. For the degenerate distribution, the standard deviation equals zero. For the Erlang distribution, the standard deviation = $\dfrac{1}{\sqrt{k}}$ mean.

14.1-11 The three parts of a label for queueing models provide information on the distribution of service times, the number of servers, and the distribution of interarrival times.

14.2-1 In commercial service systems, outside customers receive service from commercial organizations. Many examples are possible.

14.2-2 In internal service systems, the customers receiving service are internal to the organization. Many examples are possible.

14.2-3 In transportation service systems, either the customers or the servers are vehicles. Many examples are possible.

14.3-1 When the customers are internal to the organization providing the service, it is more important how many customers typically are waiting in the queueing system.

14.3-2 Commercial service systems tend to place a greater importance on how long customers typically have to wait.

14.3-3 L = expected number of customers in the system
L_q = expected number of customers in the queue
W = expected waiting time in the system
W_q = expected waiting time in the queue

14.3-4 A queueing system is in a steady state condition if it is in its normal condition after operating for some time.

14.3-5 $W = W_q + \dfrac{1}{\mu}$

14.3-6 $L = \lambda W$ and $L_q = \lambda W_q$

14.3-7 $L = L_q + \dfrac{\lambda}{\mu}$

14.3-8 Steady-state probabilities can also be used as measures of performance.

14.4-1 Each Tech Rep should be assigned enough machines so that the Tech Rep will be active repairing machines approximately 75% of the time.

14.4-2 The issue is the increased number of complaints about intolerable waits for repairs on the new copier.

14.4-3 The average waiting time of customers before the Tech Rep begins the trip to the customer site to repair the machine should not exceed two hours.

14.4-4 Four alternative approaches have been suggested.

14.4-5 A team of management scientist and John Phixitt will analyze these approaches.

14.4-6 The machines needing repair are the customers and the Tech Reps are the servers.

14.5-1 λ = expected number of arrivals per unit time
μ = expected number of service completions per unit time
$\dfrac{1}{\lambda}$ = expected interarrival time
$\dfrac{1}{\mu}$ = expected service time
$\rho = \dfrac{\lambda}{\mu}$ = utilization factor

14.5-2 1. Interarrival times have an exponential distribution with a mean of $\frac{1}{\lambda}$.

    2. Service times have an exponential distribution with a mean of $\frac{1}{\mu}$.

    3. The queueing system has 1 server.

14.5-3   Formulas are available for L, W, W_q, L_q, P_n, $P(W>t)$, $P(W_q>t)$, and $P(W_q=0)$.

14.5-4 $\rho<1$.

14.5-5   The average waiting time until service begins is 6 hours.

14.5-6   It would cost approximately \$300 million annually.

14.5-7   The M/G/1 model differs in the assumption about service time. In this model the service times can have any probability distribution. It is not even necessary to determine the form of this distribution. It is only necessary to estimate the mean and standard deviation of the distribution.

14.5-8   The M/D/1 model assumes a degenerate service-time distribution. The $M/E_k/1$ model assumes an Erlang distribution with shape parameter k.

14.5-9   Decreasing the standard deviation decreases L_q, L, W, and W_q.

14.5-10 The total additional cost is a one-time cost of approximately \$500 million.

14.6-1 $\rho = \dfrac{\lambda}{s\mu}$ which is the average fraction of time that individual servers are being utilized serving customers.

14.6-2 $\rho <1$.

14.6-3   Explicit formulas are available for all the measures of performance considered for the M/M/1 model.

14.6-4   Three territories need to be combined in order to satisfy the new service standard.

14.6-5   The M/M/s model has a great amount of variability in service times. The M/D/s model has no variability. The $M/E_k/s$ model provides a middle ground between the other two with some variability in service times.

14.7-1   When using priorities, more important customers are served ahead of others who have waited longer.

14.7-2   With nonpreemptive priorities, once a server has begun serving a customer, the service must be completed without interruption even if a higher priority customer arrives while this service is in process. With preemptive priorities, the lowest priority customer being served is ejected back into the queue whenever a higher priority customer enters the queueing system.

14.7-3   Except for using preemptive priorities, the assumptions are the same as for the M/M/1 model.

14.7-4   Except for using nonpreemptive priorities, the assumptions are the same as for the M/M/s model.

14.7-5 $\rho<1$.

14.7-6　Priority class 1 consists of printer-copiers and priority class 2 consists of all other machines.

14.7-7　Two-person territories would be needed to reduce waiting times to acceptable levels.

14.7-8　Management decided to change to two-person territories, with priority given to the printer-copiers for repairs.

14.8-1　Giving a relatively high utilization factor to the server provides surprisingly poor measures of performance for the system.

14.8-2　As ρ is increased above 0.9, L_q and L grow astronomically.

14.8-3　Decreasing the variability of service times improves the performance of a single-server queueing system substantially.

14.8-4　Cutting the variability of service times in half provides most of the improvement from completely eliminating the variability.

14.8-5　Combining separate single-server queueing systems into one multiple-server queueing system greatly improves the measures of performance.

14.8-6　Applying priorities when selecting customers to begin service can greatly improve the measures of performance for high-priority customers.

14.8-7　Applying preemptive priorities improves the measures of performance for customers in the top priority class even more than applying nonpreemptive priorities.

14.9-1　When choosing the number of servers there is a tradeoff between the cost of the servers and the amount of waiting by the customers.

14.9-2　Making one's own employees wait causes lost productivity, which results in lost profit which is the waiting cost.

14.9-3　$WC = C_w L$ where C_w is the waiting cost per unit time for each customer in the queueing system, and L is the expected number of customers in the queueing system.

14.9-4　A relatively high utilization factor for the servers in a queueing system can actually be more costly and therefore not advisable.

14.10-1　Previous one-person territories were replaced by larger three-person territories.

14.10-2　Queueing models were used to find the minimum number of servers that would provide satisfactory measures of performance for the queueing system.

14.10-3　Decisions needed to be made on the number of telephone trunk lines, telephone agents, and hold positions.

14.10-4　The city's arrestees were the customers in New York City.

14.10-5　More than $750 million in annual profits were obtained by the business customers of AT&T.

Problems

14.1　a)　A hospital emergency room is a queueing system with patients as the customers and care providers as the servers.

　　　b)　The queue is the waiting room and it would operate on a priority procedure.

　　　c)　Arrivals would be random since arrival times are completely unpredictable.

d) The service times in this context would be the amount of time it takes for a patient to receive care, which would be highly variable.

14.2

	customer	server
a)	shoppers	checkout clerk
b)	fires	fire fighters
c)	cars	toll collectors
d)	bikes	bicycle repair people
e)	ships	longshoremen
f)	machines	operator
g)	loads	handling equipment
h)	clogged pipes	plumber
i)	custom orders	customized process
j)	employees	secretary

14.3 a) True. The only distribution of interarrival times that fits having random arrivals is the exponential distribution.

b) False. The probability of an arrival in the next minute is completely uninfluenced by when the last arrival occurred.

c) True. Most queueing models assume that the form of the probability distribution of interarrival times is an exponential distribution.

14.4 a) False. Depending on the nature of the queueing system, the exponential distribution can provide either a reasonable approximation or a gross distortion of the true service-time distribution.

b) False. The mean and standard deviation are always equal.

c) True. The exponential and degenerate distributions represent two rather extreme cases regarding the amount of variability in the service times.

14.5 a) False. The queue is where customers wait before being served.

b) False. Queueing models conventionally assume that the queue is an infinite queue.

c) True. The most common is first come first served.

14.6 a) A bank is a queueing system with people as the customers, and tellers as the servers.

b)

$W_q = 1$ minute

$W = W_q + \dfrac{1}{\mu} = 1 + 2 = 3$ minutes

$L_q = \lambda W_q = \dfrac{40}{60}(1) = 0.667$ customers

$L = \lambda W = \dfrac{40}{60}(3) = 2$ customers

14.7 a) A parking lot is a queueing system for providing parking with cars as the customers, and parking spaces as the servers. The service time is the amount of time a car spends in a space. The queue capacity is 0.

b)

$$L = 0(P_0) + 1(P_1) + 2(P_2) + 3(P_3) = 0(0.2) + 1(0.3) + 2(0.3) + 3(0.2) = 1.5 \text{ cars}$$

$$L_q = 0 \text{ cars}$$

$$W = \left(\frac{L}{\lambda}\right) = \left(\frac{1.5}{2}\right) = 0.75 \text{ hours}$$

$$W_q = \left(\frac{L_q}{\lambda}\right) = \left(\frac{0}{2}\right) = 0 \text{ hours}$$

c) A car spends an average of 45 minutes in a parking space.

14.8   a) $L = 0\left(\frac{1}{16}\right) + 1\left(\frac{4}{16}\right) + 2\left(\frac{6}{16}\right) + 3\left(\frac{4}{16}\right) + 4\left(\frac{1}{16}\right) = 2$ which represents the average number of customers in the shop, including those getting their hair cut.

b)

n	# in queue	probability	product
0	0		
1	0		
2	0		
3	1	0.25	0.25
4	2	0.0625	0.125

Lq = 0.375 which represents the average number of customers in the shop waiting to get a haircut.

c)

$$W = \frac{L}{\lambda} = \frac{2}{4} = 0.5 = 30 \text{ minutes}$$

$$W_q = \frac{L_q}{\lambda} = \frac{0.375}{4} = 0.094 = 5.625 \text{ minutes}$$

These quantities mean that customers will be in the shop an average of half an hour, including the time to get a haircut, and will have to wait an average of 5.625 minutes before their haircut will begin.

d) W - Wq = 0.5 – 0.094 = 0.406 hours = 24.375 minutes

14.9   The utilization factor ρ represents the fraction of time that the server is busy. The server is busy except when there are zero people in the system. P_0 is the probability of having 0 customers in the system. Hence, $\rho = 1 - P_0$.

14.10 a)

$$L = \frac{\lambda}{\mu - \lambda} = \frac{30}{40 - 30} = 3 \text{ customers}$$

$$W = \frac{1}{\mu - \lambda} = \frac{1}{40 - 30} = 0.1 \text{ hours}$$

$$W_q = \frac{\lambda}{\mu(\mu - \lambda)} = \frac{30}{40(40 - 30)} = 0.075 \text{ hours}$$

$$L_q = \lambda W_q = 30(0.075) = 2.25 \text{ customers}$$

$$P_0 = 1 - \rho = 1 - 0.75 = 0.25$$

$$P_1 = (1 - \rho)\rho = (1 - 0.75)0.75 = 0.188$$

$$P_2 = (1 - \rho)\rho^2 = (1 - 0.75)0.75^2 = 0.141$$

There is a 42% chance of having more than 2 customers at the checkout stand.

b)

Data		
$\lambda =$	30	(mean arrival rate)
$\mu =$	40	(mean service rate)
s =	1	(# servers)

Pr(ω>t) =	3.975E-31
when t =	7

Prob(ω_q>t) =	1.447E-22
when t =	5

P0+P1+P2=   0.578125

Results	
L =	3
$L_q =$	2.25
W =	0.1
$W_q =$	0.075
$\rho =$	0.75
$P_0 =$	0.25
$P_1 =$	0.1875
$P_2 =$	0.140625

c)

$$L = \frac{\lambda}{\mu - \lambda} = \frac{30}{60 - 30} = 1 \text{ customer}$$

$$W = \frac{1}{\mu - \lambda} = \frac{1}{60 - 30} = 0.033 \text{ hours}$$

$$W_q = \frac{\lambda}{\mu(\mu - \lambda)} = \frac{30}{60(60 - 30)} = 0.017 \text{ hours}$$

$$L_q = \lambda W_q = 30(0.075) = 0.5 \text{ customer}$$

$$P_0 = 1 - \rho = 1 - 0.5 = 0.5$$

$$P_1 = (1 - \rho)\rho = (1 - 0.5)0.5 = 0.25$$

$$P_2 = (1 - \rho)\rho^2 = (1 - 0.5)0.5^2 = 0.125$$

There is a 12.5% chance of having more than 2 customers at the checkout stand.

d)

Data		
$\lambda =$	30	(mean arrival rate)
$\mu =$	60	(mean service rate)
$s =$	1	(# servers)

$Pr(\omega > t) =$	6.283E-92
when t =	7

$Prob(\omega_q > t) =$	3.588E-66
when t =	5

P0+P1+P2=   0.875

Results	
$L =$	1
$L_q =$	0.5
$W =$	0.03333333
$W_q =$	0.01666667
$\rho =$	0.5
$P_0 =$	0.5
$P_1 =$	0.25
$P_2 =$	0.125

e) The manager should adopt the new approach of adding another person to bag the groceries.

14.11 a) $P_0+P_1+P_2+P_3+P_4 = 0.5+0.25+0.125+0.0625+0.03125 = 0.96875$ or 97% of the time.

b)

$P_0 =$	0.5
$P_1 =$	0.25
$P_2 =$	0.125
$P_3 =$	0.0625
$P_4 =$	0.03125

Total = 0.968 or 97%

14.12 a)

Data		
$\lambda =$	4	(mean arrival rate)
$\mu =$	5	(mean service rate)
$s =$	1	(# servers)

$Pr(\omega > t) =$	0.3678794
when t =	1

$Prob(\omega_q > t) =$	0.2943036
when t =	1

P0+P1+P2+P3+P4=   0.67232

Results	
$L =$	4
$L_q =$	3.2
$W =$	1
$W_q =$	0.8
$\rho =$	0.8
$P_0 =$	0.2
$P_1 =$	0.16
$P_2 =$	0.128
$P_3 =$	0.1024
$P_4 =$	0.08192

The train does not meet any of the criteria.

b)

Data		
$\lambda =$	4	(mean arrival rate)
$\mu =$	6.67	(mean service rate)
s =	1	(# servers)

Pr(ω>t) = 0.0692522
when t = 1

Prob(ω_q>t) = 0.0415306
when t = 1

P0+P1+P2+P3+P4=   0.922434109

Results	
L =	1.49812734
L_q =	0.89842719
W =	0.37453184
W_q =	0.2246068
ρ=	0.59970015
P_0 =	0.40029985
P_1 =	0.24005988
P_2 =	0.14396395
P_3 =	0.0863352
P_4 =	0.05177523

The forklift truck meets all the criteria.

c) Tractor-trailer train: L($20)+$50 = $130/hour
   Forklift truck: L($20)+$150 = $180/hour

d) The forklift truck should be chosen.

14.13

$$\lambda = \frac{L}{W} = \frac{8}{120} = 0.0667$$

$$\mu = \frac{1}{W} + \lambda = \frac{1}{120} + 0.0667 = 0.075$$

Data		
$\lambda =$	0.0666667	(mean arrival rate)
$\mu =$	0.075	(mean service rate)
s =	1	(# servers)

Pr(ω>t) = 0.9917013
when t = 1

Results	
L =	8
L_q =	7.11111111
W =	120
W_q =	106.666667

14.14 a) The customers are trucks to be loaded or unloaded and the servers are crews. The system
           currently has 1 server.

b)

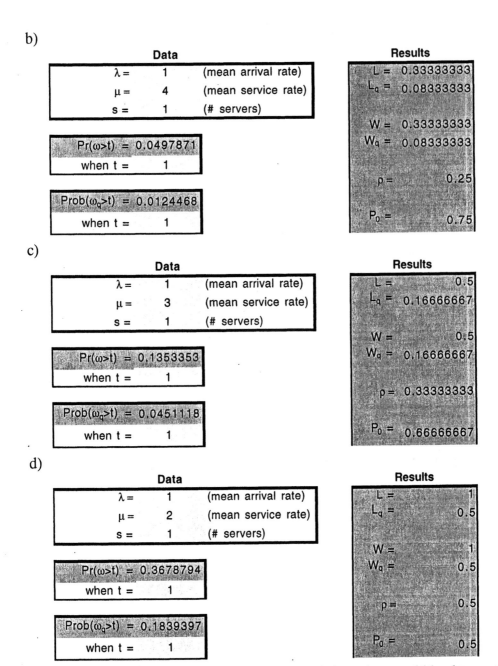

Data

$\lambda =$	1	(mean arrival rate)
$\mu =$	4	(mean service rate)
$s =$	1	(# servers)

Pr(ω>t) =	0.0497871
when t =	1

Prob(ω_q>t) =	0.0124468
when t =	1

Results

L =	0.33333333
L_q =	0.08333333
W =	0.33333333
W_q =	0.08333333
ρ =	0.25
P_0 =	0.75

c)

Data

$\lambda =$	1	(mean arrival rate)
$\mu =$	3	(mean service rate)
$s =$	1	(# servers)

Pr(ω>t) =	0.1353353
when t =	1

Prob(ω_q>t) =	0.0451118
when t =	1

Results

L =	0.5
L_q =	0.16666667
W =	0.5
W_q =	0.16666667
ρ =	0.33333333
P_0 =	0.66666667

d)

Data

$\lambda =$	1	(mean arrival rate)
$\mu =$	2	(mean service rate)
$s =$	1	(# servers)

Pr(ω>t) =	0.3678794
when t =	1

Prob(ω_q>t) =	0.1839397
when t =	1

Results

L =	1
L_q =	0.5
W =	1
W_q =	0.5
ρ =	0.5
P_0 =	0.5

e) A one person team should not be considered since that would lead to a utilization factor of $\rho=1$ which does not enable the qeueuing system to reach a steady-state condition with a manageable load for the team.

f &g) Total cost = ($20)(# on crew)+($30)(L_q)
       TC(4 members) = (20)(4)+(30)(0.0833) = $82.50/hour
       TC(3 members) = (20)(3)+(30)(0.167) = $65/hour
       TC(2 members) = (20)(2)+(30)(0.5) = $55/hour

   A crew of 2 people will minimize the expected total cost per hour.

14.15 a) For $\mu = 1$

Data		
$\lambda =$	0.5	(mean arrival rate)
$\mu =$	1	(mean service rate)
$s =$	1	(# servers)

$Pr(\omega > t) =$	0.082085	
when t =	5	

$Prob(\omega_q > t) =$	0.0410425	
when t =	5	

Results

$L =$	1
$L_q =$	0.5
$W =$	2
$W_q =$	1
$\rho =$	0.5
$P_0 =$	0.5

For $\mu = 0.667$

Data		
$\lambda =$	0.5	(mean arrival rate)
$\mu =$	0.6666667	(mean service rate)
$s =$	1	(# servers)

$Pr(\omega > t) =$	0.4345982	
when t =	5	

$Prob(\omega_q > t) =$	0.3259487	
when t =	5	

Results

$L =$	3
$L_q =$	2.25
$W =$	6
$W_q =$	4.5
$\rho =$	0.75
$P_0 =$	0.25

For $\mu = 0.5$ – this is not a feasible alternative since $\rho = 1$.

b) TC (mean = 1) = \$1.60 + (\$0.80)(1) = \$2.40
TC (mean = 1.5) = \$0.90 + (\$0.80)(3) = \$3.30

The grinder should be set so that the mean service time is 1 minute.

14.16 a)

Data		
$\lambda =$	10	(mean arrival rate)
$\mu =$	20	(mean service rate)
$s =$	1	(# servers)

$Pr(\omega > t) =$	0.0067379
when $t =$	0.5

$Prob(\omega_q > t) =$	0.003369
when $t =$	0.5

P0+P1+P2+P3+P4+P5=   0.984375

Results	
$L =$	1
$L_q =$	0.5
$W =$	0.1
$W_q =$	0.05
$\rho =$	0.5
$P_0 =$	0.5
$P_1 =$	0.25
$P_2 =$	0.125
$P_3 =$	0.0625
$P_4 =$	0.03125
$P_5 =$	0.015625

All the criteria are currently being satisfied.

b)

Data		
$\lambda =$	15	(mean arrival rate)
$\mu =$	20	(mean service rate)
$s =$	1	(# servers)

$Pr(\omega > t) =$	0.082085
when $t =$	0.5

$Prob(\omega_q > t) =$	0.0615637
when $t =$	0.5

P0+P1+P2+P3+P4+P5=   0.822021484

Results	
$L =$	3
$L_q =$	2.25
$W =$	0.2
$W_q =$	0.15
$\rho =$	0.75
$P_0 =$	0.25
$P_1 =$	0.1875
$P_2 =$	0.140625
$P_3 =$	0.10546875
$P_4 =$	0.07910156
$P_5 =$	0.05932617

None of the criteria are now satisfied.

c)

Data		
$\lambda =$	25	(mean arrival rate)
$\mu =$	20	(mean service rate)
$s =$	2	(# servers)

$Pr(\omega > t) =$	0.0010217
when $t =$	0.5

$Prob(\omega_q > t) =$	0.0002659
when $t =$	0.5

P0+P1+P2+P3+P4+P5 = 0.926640437

Results	
$L =$	2.05128205
$L_q =$	0.80128205
$W =$	0.08205128
$W_q =$	0.03205128
$\rho =$	0.625
$P_0 =$	0.23076923
$P_1 =$	0.28846154
$P_2 =$	0.18028846
$P_3 =$	0.11268029
$P_4 =$	0.07042518
$P_5 =$	0.04401574

In this case, the first and third criteria are satisfied but the second is not.

14.17 L_q is unchanged and W_q is reduced by half.

14.18 a)

Data		
$\lambda =$	0.2	(mean arrival rate)
$1/\mu =$	4	(expected service time)
$\sigma =$	4	(standard deviation)
$s =$	1	(# servers)

Results	
$L =$	4
$L_q =$	3.2
$W =$	20
$W_q =$	16

Data		
$\lambda =$	0.2	(mean arrival rate)
$1/\mu =$	4	(expected service time)
$\sigma =$	3	(standard deviation)
$s =$	1	(# servers)

Results	
$L =$	3.3
$L_q =$	2.5
$W =$	16.5
$W_q =$	12.5

Data		
$\lambda =$	0.2	(mean arrival rate)
$1/\mu =$	4	(expected service time)
$\sigma =$	2	(standard deviation)
$s =$	1	(# servers)

Results	
$L =$	2.8
$L_q =$	2
$W =$	14
$W_q =$	10

Data		
$\lambda =$	0.2	(mean arrival rate)
$1/\mu =$	4	(expected service time)
$\sigma =$	1	(standard deviation)
$s =$	1	(# servers)

Results	
$L =$	2.5
$L_q =$	1.7
$W =$	12.5
$W_q =$	8.5

Data		
$\lambda =$	0.2	(mean arrival rate)
$1/\mu =$	4	(expected service time)
$\sigma =$	0	(standard deviation)
$s =$	1	(# servers)

Results	
$L =$	2.4
$L_q =$	1.6
$W =$	12
$W_q =$	8

b) L_q is half with $\sigma = 0$ therefore it is quite important to reduce the variability of the service times.

c)

σ	L_q	Change	
4	3.2		
3	2.5	0.7	largest reduction
2	2	0.5	
1	1.7	0.3	
0	1.6	0.1	smallest reduction

d) μ needs to be increased 0.05 to achieve the same L_q.

14.19 a) False. When L increases, W also increases.

b) False. When μ and σ^2 are small, L_q is not necessarily small.

c) True. For exponential service time $L_q = \dfrac{\rho^2}{1-\rho}$

   For constant service time $L_q = \dfrac{1}{2}\dfrac{\rho^2}{1-\rho}$.

14.20 a)

Data		
λ =	30	(mean arrival rate)
$1/\mu$ =	0.0208333	(expected service time)
σ =	0.0208333	(standard deviation)
s =	1	(# servers)

Results	
L =	1.66666667
L_q =	1.04166667
W =	0.05555556
W_q =	0.03472222

b)

Data		
λ =	30	(mean arrival rate)
$1/\mu$ =	0.0208333	(expected service time)
σ =	0	(standard deviation)
s =	1	(# servers)

Results	
L =	1.14583333
L_q =	0.52083333
W =	0.03819444
W_q =	0.01736111

c) L_q in part b) is half of L_q in part a).

d) Marsha needs to reduce her service time to approximately 61 seconds.

14.21 a)

Data		
λ =	0.05	(mean arrival rate)
$1/\mu$ =	15	(expected service time)
σ =	15	(standard deviation)
s =	1	(# servers)

Results	
L =	3
L_q =	2.25
W =	60
W_q =	45

b)

Data		
λ =	0.05	(mean arrival rate)
$1/\mu$ =	16	(expected service time)
σ =	9.49	(standard deviation)
s =	1	(# servers)

Results	
L =	2.96287563
L_q =	2.16287563
W =	59.2575125
W_q =	43.2575125

c) The new proposal shows that they will be slightly better off if they switch to the new queueing system.

d) TC (status quo) = $40 + (L_q)($20) = $85/hour
   TC (proposal) = $40 + (L_q)($20) = $83/hour

14.22 a) $L = L_q + \rho = \dfrac{\lambda^2 \sigma^2 + \rho^2}{2(1-\rho)} + \rho = \dfrac{(1)^2(0.354)^2 + 0.5^2}{2(1-0.5)} + 0.5 = 0.875$

b) $W = W_q + \dfrac{1}{\mu} = \dfrac{L_q}{\lambda} + \dfrac{1}{\mu} = \dfrac{0.375}{1} + \dfrac{1}{2} = 0.875$

c)

Data		
$\lambda =$	1	(mean arrival rate)
$1/\mu =$	0.5	(expected service time)
$\sigma =$	0.354	(standard deviation)
$s =$	1	(# servers)

Results	
$L =$	0.875316
$L_q =$	0.375316
$W =$	0.875316
$W_q =$	0.375316

d)

Data		
$\lambda =$	1	(mean arrival rate)
$\mu =$	2	(mean service rate)
$k =$	2	(shape parameter)
$s =$	1	(# servers)

Results	
$L =$	0.875
$L_q =$	0.375
$W =$	0.875
$W_q =$	0.375

14.23 a & b) Current policy:

Data		
$\lambda =$	1	(mean arrival rate)
$\mu =$	2	(mean service rate)
$s =$	1	(# servers)

Results	
$L =$	1
$L_q =$	0.5
$W =$	1
$W_q =$	0.5

Proposal:

Data		
$\lambda =$	0.25	(mean arrival rate)
$\mu =$	0.5	(mean service rate)
$k =$	4	(shape parameter)
$s =$	1	(# servers)

Results	
$L =$	0.8125
$L_q =$	0.3125
$W =$	3.25
$W_q =$	1.25

Under the current policy an airplane looses 1 day of flying time as opposed to 3.25 days under the proposed policy.

Under the current policy 1 airplane is loosing flying time per day as opposed to 0.8125 airplanes.

c) The comparison in part b) is the appropriate one for making the decision since it takes into account that airplanes will not have to come in for service as often.

14.24 a)

Data		
$\lambda =$	2	(mean arrival rate)
$\mu =$	1	(mean service rate)
$s =$	4	(# servers)

$Pr(\omega>t) =$	0.0079019
when t =	5

$Prob(\omega_q>t) =$	7.896E-06
when t =	5

P0+P1+P2+P3+P4+P5+P6+P7+P8+P9=

0.997282609

Results	
$L =$	2.17391304
$L_q =$	0.17391304
$W =$	1.08695652
$W_q =$	0.08695652
$\rho =$	0.5
$P_0 =$	0.13043478
$P_1 =$	0.26086957
$P_2 =$	0.26086957
$P_3 =$	0.17391304
$P_4 =$	0.08695652
$P_5 =$	0.04347826
$P_6 =$	0.02173913
$P_7 =$	0.01086957
$P_8 =$	0.00543478
$P_9 =$	0.00271739

All the guidelines are currently being met.

b)

Data		
$\lambda =$	3	(mean arrival rate)
$\mu =$	1	(mean service rate)
$s =$	4	(# servers)

Results	
$L =$	4.52830189
$L_q =$	1.52830189
$W =$	1.50943396
$W_q =$	0.50943396
$\rho =$	0.75
$P_0 =$	0.03773585
$P_1 =$	0.11320755
$P_2 =$	0.16981132
$P_3 =$	0.16981132
$P_4 =$	0.12735849
$P_5 =$	0.09551887
$P_6 =$	0.07163915
$P_7 =$	0.05372936
$P_8 =$	0.04029702
$P_9 =$	0.03022277

$Pr(\omega > t) = 0.0239006$ when $t = 5$

$Prob(\omega_q > t) = 0.0034325$ when $t = 5$

P0+P1+P2+P3+P4+P5+P6+P7+P8+P9=

0.9093317

The first two guidelines will not be satisfied in one year but the third will be.

c) Five tellers will be needed in a year,

14.25 a)

λ	L	L_q	W	W_q	P(W>5)
0.5	1	0.5	2	1	0.082
0.9	9	8.1	10	9	0.607
0.99	99	98	100	99	0.951

Increasing the utilization factor increases the length and duration of the queue. The increases are huge when ρ gets very close to 1.

b)

λ	L	L_q	W	W_q	P(W>5)
0.5	1.33	0.333	2.67	0.667	0.150
0.9	9.47	7.67	10.5	8.53	0.641
0.99	99.5	97.5	100.5	98.5	0.956

Increasing the utilization factor increases the length and duration of the queue. The increases are huge when ρ gets very close to 1.

14.26

Data		
$\lambda =$	10	(mean arrival rate)
$\mu =$	12	(mean service rate)
$s =$	1	(# servers)

Pr(ω>t) =	2.061E-09
when t =	10

Prob(ω_q>t) =	0.8333333
when t =	0

P0+P1=   0.305555556

Results	
L =	5
$L_q =$	4.16666667
W =	0.5
$W_q =$	0.41666667
$\rho =$	0.83333333
$P_0 =$	0.16666667
$P_1 =$	0.13888889
$P_2 =$	0.11574074
$P_3 =$	0.09645062

Data		
$\lambda =$	10	(mean arrival rate)
$\mu =$	12	(mean service rate)
$s =$	2	(# servers)

Pr(ω>t) =	1.894E-52
when t =	10

Prob(ω_q>t) =	0.245098
when t =	0

P0+P1+P2=   0.897875817

Results	
L =	1.00840336
$L_q =$	0.17507003
W =	0.10084034
$W_q =$	0.017507
$\rho =$	0.41666667
$P_0 =$	0.41176471
$P_1 =$	0.34313725
$P_2 =$	0.14297386
$P_3 =$	0.05957244

Data		
$\lambda =$	10	(mean arrival rate)
$\mu =$	12	(mean service rate)
$s =$	3	(# servers)

Pr(ω>t) =	8.047E-53
when t =	10

Prob(ω_q>t) =	0.0577101
when t =	0

P0+P1+P2+P3=   0.983969426

Results	
L =	0.85552951
$L_q =$	0.02219618
W =	0.08555295
$W_q =$	0.00221962
$\rho =$	0.27777778
$P_0 =$	0.43213296
$P_1 =$	0.3601108
$P_2 =$	0.15004617
$P_3 =$	0.04167949

Data		
$\lambda =$	10	(mean arrival rate)
$\mu =$	12	(mean service rate)
$s =$	4	(# servers)

Results	
L =	0.83623441
L_q =	0.00290108
W =	0.08362344
W_q =	0.00029011
ρ =	0.20833333
P_0 =	0.43433168
P_1 =	0.36194306
P_2 =	0.15080961
P_3 =	0.04189156
P_4 =	0.00872741

$Pr(\omega > t)$ =	7.707E-53
when t =	10

$Prob(\omega_q > t)$ =	0.0110241
when t =	0

P0+P1+P2+P3+P4=   0.997703314

Data		
$\lambda =$	10	(mean arrival rate)
$\mu =$	12	(mean service rate)
$s =$	5	(# servers)

Results	
L =	0.83368262
L_q =	0.00034929
W =	0.08336826
W_q =	3.4929E-05
ρ =	0.16666667
P_0 =	0.43457121
P_1 =	0.36214268
P_2 =	0.15089278
P_3 =	0.04191466
P_4 =	0.00873222
P_5 =	0.00145537

$Pr(\omega > t)$ =	7.672E-53
when t =	10

$Prob(\omega_q > t)$ =	0.0017464
when t =	0

P0+P1+P2+P3+P4+P5=   0.999708926

a) 2 servers

b) 3 servers

c) 2 servers

d) 1 server

e) 5 servers

f) 1 server

g) 3 servers

14.27 a) Option 1:

Data				Results	
$\lambda =$	150	(mean arrival rate)		$L =$	6.01123596
$\mu =$	60	(mean service rate)		$L_q =$	3.51123596
$s =$	3	(# servers)			
				$W =$	0.04007491
				$W_q =$	0.02340824

Option 2:

Data				Results	
$\lambda =$	150	(mean arrival rate)		$L =$	5
$\mu =$	180	(mean service rate)		$L_q =$	4.16666667
$s =$	1	(# servers)			
				$W =$	0.03333333
				$W_q =$	0.02777778

b) W and L are smaller for Option 2 because it is a more efficient system. This is true because when there are only 1 or 2 customers in the system Option 2 is operating at full efficiency, while Option 1 will have idle servers. W_q and L_q are larger for Option 2 because there are fewer people in service (only 1 register) and therefore more people in line.

c) W should be the most important measure to customers since they should be most concerned with the total time spent in the system. Given this, Option 2 is better.

14.28 a) Deposits:

Data				Results	
$\lambda =$	16	(mean arrival rate)		$L =$	4
$\mu =$	20	(mean service rate)		$L_q =$	3.2
$s =$	1	(# servers)			
				$W =$	0.25
				$W_q =$	0.2

Withdrawals:

Data				Results	
$\lambda =$	14	(mean arrival rate)		$L =$	2.33333333
$\mu =$	20	(mean service rate)		$L_q =$	1.63333333
$s =$	1	(# servers)			
				$W =$	0.16666667
				$W_q =$	0.11666667

Combined expected wait time = 0.211

b)

Data		
$\lambda =$	30	(mean arrival rate)
$\mu =$	20	(mean service rate)
$s =$	2	(# servers)

Results	
$L =$	3.42857143
$L_q =$	1.92857143
$W =$	0.11428571
$W_q =$	0.06428571

c) An expected processing time of 3.43 minutes would cause the expected waiting times to be the same for the two procedures.

14.29 This year:

Data		
$\lambda =$	10	(mean arrival rate)
$\mu =$	7.5	(mean service rate)
$s =$	2	(# servers)

Results	
$L =$	2.4
$L_q =$	1.06666667
$W =$	0.24
$W_q =$	0.10666667

Next year:

Data		
$\lambda =$	5	(mean arrival rate)
$\mu =$	7.5	(mean service rate)
$s =$	1	(# servers)

Results	
$L =$	2
$L_q =$	1.33333333
$W =$	0.4
$W_q =$	0.26666667

This years system yields smaller values for all measure except L.

14.30 a) <u>Exponential distribution:</u>
Status quo:

Data		
$\lambda =$	24	(mean arrival rate)
$\mu =$	30	(mean service rate)
$s =$	1	(# servers)

Results	
$L =$	4
$L_q =$	3.2
$W =$	0.16666667
$W_q =$	0.13333333

Proposal:

Data		
$\lambda =$	48	(mean arrival rate)
$\mu =$	30	(mean service rate)
$s =$	2	(# servers)

Results	
$L =$	4.44444444
$L_q =$	2.84444444
$W =$	0.09259259
$W_q =$	0.05925926

<u>Erlang distribution, k=2:</u>
Status quo:

Data		
$\lambda =$	24	(mean arrival rate)
$\mu =$	30	(mean service rate)
$k =$	2	(shape parameter)
$s =$	1	(# servers)

Results	
$L =$	3.2
$L_q =$	2.4
$W =$	0.13333333
$W_q =$	0.1

Proposal:
L=3.5 and W=0.0729

<u>Erlang distribution, k=8:</u>
Status quo:

Data		
$\lambda =$	24	(mean arrival rate)
$\mu =$	30	(mean service rate)
$k =$	8	(shape parameter)
$s =$	1	(# servers)

Results	
$L =$	2.6
$L_q =$	1.8
$W =$	0.10833333
$W_q =$	0.075

Proposal:
L=2.5 and W=0.0521

<u>Degenerate distribution:</u>
Status quo:

Data		
$\lambda =$	24	(mean arrival rate)
$\mu =$	30	(mean service rate)
$s =$	1	(# servers)

Results	
$L =$	2.4
$L_q =$	1.6
$W =$	0.1
$W_q =$	0.06666667

Proposal:
L=3.5 and W=0.0729

b) The proposal is better regardless of the distribution used. (Note that the L shown in the spreadsheets for the status quo needs to be doubled since there are two tool cribs.)

c) Insight three is illustrated.

14.31 a) L = 1.5

$$W = \frac{L}{\lambda} = \frac{1.5}{0.2} = 7.5$$

$$W_q = W - \frac{1}{\mu} = 7.5 - \frac{1}{0.167} = 1.5$$

$$L_q = \lambda W_q = 0.2(1.5) = 0.3$$

b)

Data		
$\lambda =$	0.2	(mean arrival rate)
$\mu =$	0.3333333	(mean service rate)
$s =$	1	(# servers)

Results	
$L =$	1.05
$L_q =$	0.45
$W =$	5.25
$W_q =$	2.25

c) TC(Alternative 1) = \$70 + (\$100)(L) = \$220
TC(Alternative 2) = \$100 + (\$100)(L) = \$205

Alternative 2 should be adopted.

14.32 a) L = 2

$$W = \frac{L}{\lambda} = \frac{2}{0.3} = 6.67$$

$$W_q = W - \frac{1}{\mu} = 6.67 - 5 = 1.67$$

$$L_q = \lambda W_q = 0.3(1.67) = 0.5$$

b)

Data		
$\lambda =$	0.3	(mean arrival rate)
$1/\mu =$	3	(expected service time)
$\sigma =$	1.19	(standard deviation)
$s =$	1	(# servers)

Results	
$L =$	5.587245
$L_q =$	4.687245
$W =$	18.62415
$W_q =$	15.62415

c) TC(Alternative 1) = \$3000 + (\$150)(L) = \$3,300
    TC(Alternative 2) = \$2750 + (\$150)(L) = \$3,589

Alternative 1 should be adopted.

14.33 a) This system is an example of a nonpreemptive priority queueing system.

b)

n =	2	(# of priority classes)
μ =	20	(mean service rate)
s =	1	(# servers)

	λ_i	L	Lq	W	Wq
Priority Class 1	2	0.1666667	0.0666667	0.0833333	0.0333333
Priority Class 2	10	1.3333333	0.8333333	0.1333333	0.0833333

λ =	12
ρ =	0.6

c) $$\frac{W_q(\text{first - class passengers})}{W_q(\text{coach - class passengers})} = \frac{0.033}{0.083} = 0.4$$

d) $\rho(12) = 0.6 = 7.2$ hours

14.34 a) A preemptive priorities queueing model fits this system.

b)

n =	3	(# of priority classes)
μ =	3	(mean service rate)
s =	1	(# servers)

	λ_i	L	Lq	W	Wq
Priority Class 1	0.2	0.0714286	0.0047619	0.3571429	0.0238095
Priority Class 2	0.6	0.2922078	0.0922078	0.487013	0.1536797
Priority Class 3	1.2	1.6363636	1.2363636	1.3636364	1.030303

λ =	2
ρ =	0.6666667

Guidelines will be satisfied next year with a single doctor.

c)

Data		
$\lambda =$	2	(mean arrival rate)
$\mu =$	3	(mean service rate)
$s =$	1	(# servers)

Results	
$L =$	2
$L_q =$	1.33333333
$W =$	1
$W_q =$	0.66666667

The guideline for stable cases would be satisfied but the other two would not be.

d)

$n =$	3	(# of priority classes)
$\mu =$	3	(mean service rate)
$s =$	1	(# servers)

	λ_i	L	Lq	W	Wq
Priority Class 1	0.225	0.0810811	0.0060811	0.3603604	0.027027
Priority Class 2	0.675	0.3474903	0.1224903	0.5148005	0.1814672
Priority Class 3	1.35	2.5714286	2.1214286	1.9047619	1.5714286

$\lambda =$	2.25
$\rho =$	0.75

The guidelines are still met.

14.35 a) s=4

n =	3	(# of priority classes)
μ =	4	(mean service rate)
s =	4	(# servers)

	λ_i	L	Lq	W	Wq
Priority Class 1	6	1.8056604	0.3056604	0.3009434	0.0509434
Priority Class 2	4	1.5433962	0.5433962	0.3858491	0.1358491
Priority Class 3	2	1.1792453	0.6792453	0.5896226	0.3396226

λ =	12
ρ =	0.75

s=5

n =	3	(# of priority classes)
μ =	4	(mean service rate)
s =	5	(# servers)

	λ_i	L	Lq	W	Wq
Priority Class 1	6	1.6012078	0.1012078	0.266868	0.016868
Priority Class 2	4	1.1349438	0.1349438	0.2837359	0.0337359
Priority Class 3	2	0.6180758	0.1180758	0.3090379	0.0590379

λ =	12
ρ =	0.6

The guidelines are met with 4 lathes.

b) TC (4 lathes) = \$250(4) + \$750(L_1) + \$450(L_2) + \$150(L_3) = \$3227.50
TC (5 lathes) = \$250(5) + \$750(L_1) + \$450(L_2) + \$150(L_3) = \$3051.50

5 lathes should be obtained to minimize the expected total cost.

14.36 a) 1 server is optimal.

Data		
$\lambda =$	8	(mean arrival rate)
$\mu =$	10	(mean service rate)
$s =$	1	(# servers)

$Pr(\omega > t) =$	0.1353353
when $t =$	1

$Prob(\omega_q > t) =$	0.1082682
when $t =$	1

$C_s =$	100	(cost/server/unit time)
$C_w =$	10	(waiting cost/unit time)
Cost of Service =	100	
Cost of Waiting =	40	
Total Cost =	140	

Results	
$L =$	4
$L_q =$	3.2
$W =$	0.5
$W_q =$	0.4
$\rho =$	0.8
$P_0 =$	0.2
$P_1 =$	0.16
$P_2 =$	0.128
$P_3 =$	0.1024
$P_4 =$	0.08192
$P_5 =$	0.065536
$P_6 =$	0.0524288

b) 2 servers are optimal.

Data		
$\lambda =$	8	(mean arrival rate)
$\mu =$	10	(mean service rate)
$s =$	2	(# servers)

$Pr(\omega > t) =$	0.0024788
when $t =$	1

$Prob(\omega_q > t) =$	0.0009915
when $t =$	1

$C_s =$	100	(cost/server/unit time)
$C_w =$	100	(waiting cost/unit time)
Cost of Service =	200	
Cost of Waiting =	95.238095	
Total Cost =	295.2381	

Results	
$L =$	0.95238095
$L_q =$	0.15238095
$W =$	0.11904762
$W_q =$	0.01904762
$\rho =$	0.4
$P_0 =$	0.42857143
$P_1 =$	0.34285714
$P_2 =$	0.13714286
$P_3 =$	0.05485714
$P_4 =$	0.02194286
$P_5 =$	0.00877714
$P_6 =$	0.00351086

c) 3 servers are optimal.

Data			Results	
$\lambda =$	8	(mean arrival rate)	L =	0.81892092
$\mu =$	10	(mean service rate)	$L_q =$	0.01892092
s =	3	(# servers)		
			W =	0.10236511
$Pr(\omega>t) =$	0.0006534		$W_q =$	0.00236511
when t =	1			
			$\rho =$	0.26666667
$Prob(\omega_q>t) =$	0.0001742			
when t =	1		$P_0 =$	0.44715447
			$P_1 =$	0.35772358
$C_s =$	10	(cost/server/unit time)	$P_2 =$	0.14308943
$C_w =$	100	(waiting cost/unit time)	$P_3 =$	0.03815718
Cost of Service =	30		$P_4 =$	0.01017525
Cost of Waiting =	81.892092		$P_5 =$	0.0027134
Total Cost =	111.89209		$P_6 =$	0.00072357

14.37 Jim should operate 4 cash registers during the lunch hour.

Data			Results	
$\lambda =$	66	(mean arrival rate)	L =	2.4771986
$\mu =$	30	(mean service rate)	$L_q =$	0.2771986
s =	4	(# servers)		
			W =	0.03753331
$Pr(\omega>t) =$	1.371E-06		$W_q =$	0.00419998
when t =	1			
			$\rho =$	0.55
$Prob(\omega_q>t) =$	7.54E-07			
when t =	1		$P_0 =$	0.104562
			$P_1 =$	0.2300364
$C_s =$	9	(cost/server/unit time)	$P_2 =$	0.25304004
$C_w =$	18	(waiting cost/unit time)	$P_3 =$	0.1855627
Cost of Service =	36		$P_4 =$	0.10205948
Cost of Waiting =	44.589575		$P_5 =$	0.05613272
Total Cost =	80.589575		$P_6 =$	0.03087299

14.38 Garrett-Tompkins should have 6 copiers.

Data				Results	
$\lambda =$	30	(mean arrival rate)		L =	2.53388915
$\mu =$	12	(mean service rate)		L_q =	0.03388915
s =	6	(# servers)			
				W =	0.08446297
$Pr(\omega > t) =$	0.0009119			W_q =	0.00112964
when t =	1				
				$\rho =$	0.41666667
$Prob(\omega_q > t) =$	0.00038				
when t =	1			P_0 =	0.08162026
				P_1 =	0.20405065
$C_s =$	1.5	(cost/server/unit time)		P_2 =	0.25506331
$C_w =$	25	(waiting cost/unit time)		P_3 =	0.21255276
Cost of Service =	9			P_4 =	0.13284547
Cost of Waiting =	63.347229			P_5 =	0.06642274
Total Cost =	72.347229			P_6 =	0.02767614

Case Problems

14.1   The operations of the records and benefits call center can be modeled as an M/M/s queueing system. We, therefore, use the template for the M/M/s queueing model throughout this case. The mean arrival rate equals 70 per hour, and the mean service rate of every representative equals 6 per hour. Mark needs at least s = 12 representatives answering phone calls to ensure that the queue does not grow indefinitely.

a) In order to solve this problem we have to determine the number of servers by "trial and error" until we find a number s such that the probability of waiting more than 4 minutes in the queue is above 35%.

For 13 servers we obtain the following results:

Template for M/M/s Queueing Model

Data			Results	
$l =$	70	(mean arrival rate)	$L =$	17.07963527
$m =$	6	(mean service rate)	$L_q =$	5.4129686
$s =$	13	(# servers)		
			$W =$	0.24399479
$Pr(w>t) =$	0.825608		$W_a =$	0.077328123
when $t =$	0.066667			
			$r =$	0.897435897
$Prob(w_a>t) =$	0.362914			
when $t =$	0.066667		$P_0 =$	5.32592E-06
			$P_1 =$	6.21358E-05
			$P_2 =$	0.000362459
			$P_3 =$	0.001409561
			$P_4 =$	0.004111221
			$P_5 =$	0.009592849
			$P_6 =$	0.018652761
			$P_7 =$	0.031087935
			$P_8 =$	0.045336573
			$P_9 =$	0.058769631
			$P_{10} =$	0.06856457
			$P_{11} =$	0.072719998
			$P_{12} =$	0.070699998
			$P_{13} =$	0.063448716
			$P_{14} =$	0.056941156
			$P_{15} =$	0.051101037
			$P_{16} =$	0.045859905
			$P_{17} =$	0.041156325
			$P_{18} =$	0.036935163
			$P_{19} =$	0.033146942
			$P_{20} =$	0.029747255
			$P_{21} =$	0.026696255
			$P_{22} =$	0.023958177
			$P_{23} =$	0.021500928
			$P_{24} =$	0.019295705
			$P_{25} =$	0.017316658

For 13 servers, the probability that a customer has to wait more than 4 minutes equals 36.3%.

If there are 12 servers, this probability would be 78%:

Template for M/M/s Queueing Model

Data

l =	70	(mean arrival rate)
m =	6	(mean service rate)
s =	12	(# servers)

Pr(w>t) =	0.944173
when t =	0.066667

Prob(w_q>t) =	0.779968
when t =	0.066667

If there are 14 servers, this probability would be less than 16.4%:

Template for M/M/s Queueing Model

Data

l =	70	(mean arrival rate)
m =	6	(mean service rate)
s =	14	(# servers)

Pr(w>t) =	0.75683
when t =	0.066667

Prob(w_q>t) =	0.163704
when t =	0.066667

It appears that Mark currently employs 13 servers.

b) Using the same procedure as in part (a) we find that for s = 18 servers the probability of waiting more than 1 minute drops below 5%:

Template for M/M/s Queueing Model

	Data			Results	
$l =$	70	(mean arrival rate)	$L =$	11.77798802	
$m =$	6	(mean service rate)	$L_q =$	0.111321353	
$s =$	18	(# servers)			
			$W =$	0.168256972	
$Pr(w>t) =$	0.909075		$W_q =$	0.001590305	
when $t =$	0.016667				
			$r =$	0.648148148	
$Prob(w_q>t) =$	0.032078				
when $t =$	0.016667		$P_0 =$	8.49029E-06	
			$P_1 =$	9.90534E-05	
			$P_2 =$	0.000577812	
			$P_3 =$	0.002247045	
			$P_4 =$	0.006553882	
			$P_5 =$	0.015292391	
			$P_6 =$	0.029735204	
			$P_7 =$	0.049558673	
			$P_8 =$	0.072273065	
			$P_9 =$	0.093687307	
			$P_{10} =$	0.109301858	
			$P_{11} =$	0.115926213	
			$P_{12} =$	0.11270604	
			$P_{13} =$	0.101146446	
			$P_{14} =$	0.084288705	
			$P_{15} =$	0.065557882	
			$P_{16} =$	0.047802622	
			$P_{17} =$	0.032805721	
			$P_{18} =$	0.021262967	
			$P_{19} =$	0.013781553	
			$P_{20} =$	0.008932488	
			$P_{21} =$	0.005789576	
			$P_{22} =$	0.003752503	
			$P_{23} =$	0.002432178	
			$P_{24} =$	0.001576411	
			$P_{25} =$	0.001021748	

c) Using the same "trial and error" method as before, we find the minimal number of servers necessary to ensure that 80% of customers wait one minute or less to be s = 15.

Template for M/M/s Queueing Model

Data

l =	70	(mean arrival rate)
m =	6	(mean service rate)
s =	15	(# servers)

Pr(w>t) =	0.926712
when t =	0.016667

Prob(w_a>t) =	0.194213
when t =	0.016667

The minimal number of servers to ensure that 95% of customers wait 90 seconds or less is s = 17.

Template for M/M/s Queueing Model

Data

l =	70	(mean arrival rate)
m =	6	(mean service rate)
s =	17	(# servers)

Pr(w>t) =	0.870524
when t =	0.025

Prob(w_a>t) =	0.046459
when t =	0.025

When an employee of Cutting Edge calls the benefits center from work and has to wait on the phone, the company loses valuable work time for this customer. Mark should try to estimate the amount of work time employees lose when they have to wait on the phone. Then he could determine the cost of this waiting time and try to choose the number of representatives in such a fashion that he reaches a reasonable trade-off between the cost of employees waiting on the phone and the cost of adding new representatives.

Clearly, Mark's criteria would be different if he were dealing with external customers. While the internal customers might become disgruntled when they have to wait on the phone, they cannot call somewhere else. Effectively, the benefits center holds monopolistic power. On the contrary, if Mark were running a call center dealing with external customers, these customers could decide to do business with a competitor if they become angry from waiting on the phone.

d) If the representatives can only handle 6 calls per hour, then Mark needs to employ 18 representatives (see part b). If a representative can handle 8 calls per hour, then the minimal number of representatives equals 14:

Template for M/M/s Queueing Model

Data

$l =$	70	(mean arrival rate)
$m =$	8	(mean service rate)
$s =$	14	(# servers)

$Pr(w>t) =$	0.881748
when $t =$	0.016667

$Prob(w_q>t) =$	0.036649
when $t =$	0.016667

The cost of training 14 employees equals 14*$2500 = $35000 and saves Mark 4*$30000 = $120000 in annual salary. In the first year alone Mark would save $85000 if he chose to train all his employees so that they can handle 8 instead of 6 phone calls per hour.

e) Mark needs to carefully check the number of calls arriving at the call center per hour. In this case we have made the simplifying assumption that the arrival rate is constant. That assumption is unrealistic; clearly we would expect more calls during certain times of the day, during certain days of the week, and during certain weeks of the year. We might want to collect data on the number of calls received depending on the time. This data could then be used to forecast the number of calls the center will receive in the near future, which in turn would help to forecast the number of representatives needed.

Also, Mark should carefully check the number of phone calls a representative can answer per hour. Clearly, the length of a call will depend on the issue the caller wants to discuss. We might want to consider training representatives for special issues. These representatives could then always answer those particular calls. Using specialized representatives might increase the number of phone calls the entire center can handle.

Finally, using an M/M/s model is clearly a great simplification. We need to evaluate whether the assumptions for an M/M/s model are at least approximately satisfied. If this is not the case, we should consider more general models such as M/G/s or G/G/s.

14.2 a) Status quo at the presses – 7.517 sheets of in-process inventory.

Data			Results	
$\lambda =$	7	(mean arrival rate)	$L =$	7.51737284
$\mu =$	1	(mean service rate)	$L_q =$	0.51737284
$s =$	10	(# servers)		

Status quo at the inspection station – 7 wing sections of in-process inventory.

Data			Results	
$\lambda =$	7	(mean arrival rate)	$L =$	7
$\mu =$	8	(mean service rate)	$L_q =$	6.125
$s =$	1	(# servers)		

Inventory cost = (7.517 + 7)(8) = $116.14 / hour
Machine cost = (10)(7) = $70 / hour
Inspector cost = $17 / hour

Total cost = $203.14 / hour

b) Proposal 1 will increase the in-process inventory at the presses to 11.147 sheets since the mean service rate has decreased.

Data		
$\lambda =$	7	(mean arrival rate)
$\mu =$	0.8333333	(mean service rate)
$s =$	10	(# servers)

Results	
$L =$	11.0474066
$L_q =$	2.64740664

The in-process inventory at the inspection station will not change.

Inventory cost = $(11.147 + 7)(8) = \$145.18$ / hour
Machine cost = $(10)(6.5) = \$65$ / hour
Inspector cost = $\$17$ / hour

Total cost = $\$227.18$ / hour

This total cost is higher than for the status quo so should not be adopted. The main reason for the higher cost is that slowing down the machines won't change in-process inventory for the inspection station.

c) Proposal 2 will decrease the in-process inventory at the inspection station to 4.148 wing sections since the mean service rate has increased.

Data		
$\lambda =$	7	(mean arrival rate)
$\mu =$	8.3333333	(mean service rate)
$k =$	2	(shape parameter)
$s =$	1	(# servers)

Results	
$L =$	4.1475
$L_q =$	3.3075
$W =$	0.5925
$W_q =$	0.4725

The in-process inventory at the presses will not change.

Inventory cost = $(7.517 + 4.148)(8) = \$90.44$ / hour
Machine cost = $(10)(7) = \$70$ / hour
Inspector cost = $\$19$ / hour

Total cost = $\$179.44$ / hour

This total cost is lower than for the status quo so should be adopted. The main reason for the lower cost is the increase in the service rate and the resulting decrease in the in-process inventory.

d) As seen above, proposal 2 should be adopted to reduce the average level of in-process inventory at the inspection station from 7 to 4.148 wing sections. Inventory cost will be reduced by $\$25.70$ / hour while inspector costs only increase $\$2$ / hour for a total savings of $\$23.70$ / hour.

Case 14.3

KEYCORP
Teaching Note

Basic Issue

KeyCorp, a major US bank with 1300 branches, was seeking to improve customer service by reducing customer waiting times in its branches while maintaining cost effective staffing.

Techniques and Concepts

Queuing theory, particularly the M/M/k model..

Suggested Assignment Questions

How can KeyCorp provide a report for branch managers which details customer waiting times, and reviews branch performance against KeyCorp's service objectives?

Suggested Discussion Questions

1. Could KeyCorp collect customer waiting time data directly?
2. How can waiting times be estimated from the available data?
3. What assumptions are necessary to make these estimates?

Analysis

To assist the branch managers, KeyCorp wanted to provide them with a system that would measure branch activities and generate reports on customer wait times and teller productivity levels. Since KeyCorp had stabilized the environment in which tellers operated and had reengineered various service activities, this system would focus on branch controllable elements of service.

Professor Peter C. Bell, Richard Ivey School of Business, prepared this teaching note, with assistance from Binu Koshy, as an aid to instructors in the classroom use of the case *KeyCorp*, © INFORMS, 1998.

KeyCorp management introduced the Customer Wait-time Model to report on customer waiting times at each branch during each half hour period. This enabled them to establish separate service level targets for individual branches by calendar day. Customer waiting times, however, were not measured directly by the Performance Capture System (PCS), and KeyCorp had to estimate these from available data.

KeyCorp's bank branches were multiple-channel queuing systems and KeyCorp used multiple-server waiting line models to estimate waiting times. To do this, several assumptions are necessary.

First, to use the M/M/k model requires assumptions of a Poisson arrival rate and exponential customer service times. Second, the parameters (*service rate, arrival rate,* and *number of tellers available*) must be estimated from data available in PCS.

Customer Service Rate

PCS recorded the customer service time for each customer by the start and the end of the customer function the teller used on the teller system. Since each customer session began and ended with human interaction away from the teller system (including greeting the customer, customer identification, counting out cash, and thanking the customer) additional time had to be added to the average system time. KeyCorp determined appropriate beginning and end times using time studies, and validated the resulting service times against actual time studies of a sample of 5,000 customers taken from 25 branches over 36 business days. Service times were found to be close to being distributed exponentially (with mean service rate μ).

Customer Arrival Rate

Data from PCS was used to determine the arrival rate for each hour at the branch level:

1. C_b is the number of customers in the queue at the beginning of each half hour, and C_e is the number of customers in the queue at the end of each half hour (The teller enters both numbers directly in response to a statistical prompt).

2. C_d is the number of customers served in each half hour (taken from the customer count collected by PCS).

3. The arrival rate $(\lambda) = C_d + C_e - C_b$

Furthermore, using time studies to evaluate at the interarrival time between customers, KeyCorp determined that the interarrival times were distributed approximately exponentially, hence the arrival process was assumed to be Poisson

Number Of Tellers Available

Observation and time study analysis demonstrated that the number of open and available tellers could not be deduced directly from the number signed on to the teller system since tellers performed non-customer-related activities while still logged on to the teller system. The time studies involving 5000 customers at over 25 branches showed that in 98 percent of the cases, the time between two consecutive customers for any particular teller was less than 10 minutes, providing that the teller was continuously available for serving customers. Using this the number of open tellers was estimated using the following heuristic:

1. Determine the number of open tellers using PCS for any half-hour interval. For example, three tellers A, B, and C are open between 10:00 and 10:30.

2. Use PCS transaction data to determine if the time between two consecutive customers is greater than 10 minutes for an open teller. For example, if teller B does not perform any customer transactions between 10:12 and 10:30 B is consider to be unavailable for these 18 minutes.

Subtract the time unavailable to determine the average number of tellers open in any given half hour (k). For the above example, 3 - 18/30 = 2.4, or k = 2.4.

Primary Wait-Time Estimates using the M/M/k Model

Once the model has been paramaterized (λ, μ, k) standard M/M/k results were used to determine the steady-state wait-time statistics for the half hour, such as:

- Probability of zero customers waiting;
- Average length of queue; and
- Average wait time.

The M/M/k model required k be a nonzero integer but KeyCorp's k values were real numbers. Two sets of wait time statistics, $w(k^+)$ and $w(k^-)$, using M/M/k^+ and M/M/k^- where k^+ was integer (k) and k^- was integer (k+1) were computed and KeyCorp used logarithmic interpolation between M/M/k^+ and M/M/k^- results to arrive at the final set of statistics for the half hour.

Estimation of the Distribution of Waiting Times

With the final wait-time average for a half hour established, KeyCorp's final step was to determine the appropriate distribution of wait times: the number and percent of customers waiting in each time interval. From empirical data, they determined that the gamma distribution was the best fit for the distribution of wait times per half hour, regardless of the parameters μ, λ and k.

All the data inputs such as the number of tellers serving customers (k), the customer service time (μ), and the customer arrival rate (λ) were derived from Performance Capture and validated with actual time study observations of 5000 customers at 25 branches over 36 business days.

Textbook formulae for the M/M/k queue provide the following results (from Hillier and Lieberman):

$$P_0 = 1 / \left[\sum_{n=0}^{k-1} (\lambda/\mu)^n / n! + (\lambda/\mu)^k / k! \times 1/(1 - (\lambda/k\mu)) \right]$$

$$P_n = \begin{cases} [(\lambda/\mu)^n / n!] P_0, & \text{if } 0 \leq n \leq k \\ [(\lambda/\mu)^n / k!k^{n-k}] P_0, & \text{if } n \geq k \end{cases}$$

Using the notation $\rho = \lambda/\mu k$,

$$L_q = [P_0(\lambda/\mu)^k \rho] / [k!(1-\rho)^2]$$

$$W_q = L_q / \lambda$$

$$W = W_q + 1/\mu$$

$$L = L_q + \lambda/\mu$$

$$P\{W_q > t\} = [1 - P\{W_q = 0\}]e^{-k\mu(1-\rho)t}$$

$$P\{W_q = 0\} = \sum_{n=0}^{k-1} P_n$$

The number of tellers serving customers (k) was not an integer in the branch environment. For example, it could be 3.5 for the time interval 11:00 AM to 11:30 AM in any of the following situations:

- The branch had three tellers throughout the time interval and an additional part time teller starting at 11:15 AM.

- The branch had four tellers at 11:00 AM; one of the tellers leaves for lunch at 11:25 AM and another teller begins to perform administrative activities at 11:20 AM.

Since the M/M/k results required k to be an integer and since k was a real number, they calculated two sets of wait time statistics $w(k^+)$ and $w(k^-)$. To include a dynamic arrival pattern (for example on Social Security payment day a bus from a retirement community might bring multiple customers at one time), they developed a dynamic arrival rate compensation algorithm examining the difference between the number of customers waiting at the beginning of the half-hour interval and the expected length of the queue $L_{(q)}$ for the half-hour interval to modify the expected wait time w(k). To determine the expected wait time distribution, they further adjusted the w(k) using a gamma distribution parameter estimation based on 200 half-hour interval observations, representing thousands of customer session observations. They validated the results at each step against 5000 actual customer wait-time stop-watch observations. In at least 90 percent of cases, the value of w(k) was unchanged with or without the described heuristic algorithms. Nonetheless, in the other 10 percent of the cases, the algorithms enhanced the value of w(k) substantially.

Implementation

KeyCorp wanted to foster pride and competition at the branch level, with empowerment of branch management to control decisions that would lead to improved customer service. They developed a number of reports to help branch management meet service level objectives.

Wait Time by Branch: Report W1

Report W1 provided each branch with information about the branches in its district regarding the numbers of customers served, tellers available to serve customers, customers waiting in line to be served, and the customers served in less than one minute, one to five minutes, five to 10 minutes, and more than 10 minutes. By integrating this information with teller productivity information, districts and regions could recognize outstanding performers and develop plans to improve under performers.

REPORT: W1

WAIT TIME BY BRANCH
BANK - DISTRICT
MONTH YEAR

	BRANCH	LOBBY CUSTOMERS SERVED	OPEN LOBBY TELLERS	WAIT TIME IN MINUTES								% OF CUST SERVED <5 MIN	& DAYS SERVICE MET
				<1 #	%	1 TO 5 #	%	5 TO 10 #	%	10+ #	%		
TOTAL	DISTRICT	121,429	2.2	66,660	53%	48,359	38%	8,713	7%	3,221	3%	91%	65%
9062	MAUI	7,117	2.2	4,069	57%	2,104	30%	345	5%	572	8%	87%	64%
9108	HONOLULU	7,394	2.5	4,821	65%	2,328	32%	166	2%	64	1%	97%	95%
*****	*****	*****	*****	****	***	****	***	****	***	****	***	***	***
*****	*****	*****	*****	****	***	****	***	****	***	****	***	***	***
9147	EM ORY	5,115	1.7	3,208	63%	1,610	32%	162	3%	104	2%	95%	84%

Wait Time by Day at the Branch Level: Report W2

Report W2 provided branch managers with the same information for their particular branches as report W1, but it provided the information for each day of the month as well as for the average weekday. By viewing customer wait times in conjunction with branch productivity reports, managers gained valuable insight into the need for staffing and/or scheduling changes.

REPORT: W2

WAIT TIME BY DAY AT BRANCH LEVEL
BANK - DISTRICT
BRANCH # - NAME
MONTH YEAR

WEEKDAY	DATE	LOBBY CUSTOMERS SERVED	OPEN LOBBY TELLERS	WAIT TIME IN MINUTES								% OF CUST SERVED <5 MINUTES
				<1 #	%	1 TO 5 #	%	5 TO 10 #	%	10+ #	%	
TOTAL-BRANCH	ALL	7,394	2.5	4,821	65%	2,328	32%	166	2%	64	1%	97%
MONDAY	ALL	848	2.4	529	63%	260	31%	41	5%	14	2%	93%
MONDAY	9/12/94	256	2.1	140	55%	84	33%	26	10%	4	2%	88%
*****	*****	***	***	***	***	***	***	***	***	***	***	***

★★★★★	★★★★★	★★★	★★★	★★★	★★★	★★★	★★★	★★★	★★★	★★★	★★★		★★★
FRIDAY	9/30/94	524	3.2	353	68%	163	31%	5	1%	0	0%		99%

Wait Time by Half-Hour Interval at the Branch Level: Report W3

Report W3 identified those instances in which the branch daily wait time failed to meet the target. Management used this report to identify failures to meet service standards, to understand why, and to rectify the problem.

REPORT: W3

WAIT TIME BY HALF-HOUR INTERVAL AT BRANCH LEVEL
BANK - DISTRICT
BRANCH # - NAME
DAYS OF WEEK, DATE

TIME INTERVAL	CUST IN LOBBY LINE	CUST SERVED	OPEN LOBBY TELLERS	AVG CUST TIME (SEC)	WAIT TIME IN MINUTES								% OF CUST SERVED <5 MINUTES
					<1		1 TO 5		5 TO 10		10+		
					#	%	#	%	#	%	#	%	
09:00AM-09:29AM	1	14	3.1	207	10	71%	4	29%	0	0%	0	0%	100%
09:30AM-09:59AM	3	9	1.70	222	0	0%	3	33%	5	56%	1	11%	33%
★★★★★	★★★	★★★	★★★	★★★	★★★	★★★	★★★	★★★	★★★	★★★	★★★	★★★	★★★
★★★★★	★★★	★★★	★★★	★★★	★★★	★★★	★★★	★★★	★★★	★★★	★★★	★★★	★★★
04:30PM-04:59PM	2	21	2.3	126	8	36%	13	59%	1	5%	0	0%	95%
ALL TIME INTERVALS	1/1/00	256	2.1	127	140	55%	84	33%	5	10%	4	2%	88%

Impact of the Work

In 1983, KeyCorp introduced its Service Excellence Management System (SEMS) models throughout its 1,332 branches without receiving a single complaint or challenge to the validity or integrity of the data. SEMS reports measured proficiency and service management for nearly 6,000 of KeyCorp's 29,000 person work force.

KeyCorp was projected to save over $98 million between 1995 and 1999 as a direct result of the SEMS models. KeyCorp spent less than $500,000 for the system including training, giving it a 3,500 percent internal rate of return over five years. The project payback period was less than 10 days! Improved scheduling and reduced personnel freed up an additional 15 percent of branch capacity, which KeyCorp could use to pursue value-added activities, such as new product sales.

As the branches improved their customer service, customers perceived KeyCorp as "easy to do business with." The number of branches serving 90 percent of customers in less than five minutes improved from 42 to 94 percent, the number of days on which 90 percent of customers waited less than five minutes improved from 55 to 89 percent and the number of customers waiting more than five minutes decreased from 14 to four percent. As of August 1995, the average customer session time lasted 115 seconds, a reduction of 131 seconds or 53 percent from the initial benchmark level of 246 seconds from April 1992. This service improvement, in conjunction with better scheduling and staffing, created more satisfied customers.

Available Videotape:

A short videotape is available which shows the SEMS system and describes the impact of SEMS on the bank and its customers. Impact statements are provided by Yank Heisler, Group Executive VP of KeyCorp, Henry L. Meyer III, Chief banking Officer, KeyCorp, Dennis Long, EVP Retail Services, Key Bank of Washington, branch managers and customers. (Run time, about 11 mins).

Sources:

S.K. Kotha, M.P. Barnum and D.A. Bowen, KeyCorp Service Excellence Management System, **Interfaces** 26: 1 January-February 1996, pp.54-74.

Videotape: 95.03: KeyCorp, INFORMS/CPMS Edelman Award for Management Science Achievement, INFORMS, 1995 (47:00 mins. approx.).

Review Questions

CD14-1 When the system is full with K customers, any new arriving customers leave without entering the system.

CD14-2 P_K is the probability that the system is full.

CD14-3 Average fraction of time that servers are busy = $\dfrac{\lambda(1 - P_K)}{s\mu}$.

CD14-4 The calling population for a queueing system is the population of all potential customers who might need to come to the system for service. A finite calling population is one that is small enough that the number of customers already in the queueing system affects the mean arrival rate of new customers.

CD14-5 Upon completing service, the time until a member of the calling population needs service again has an exponential distribution with a mean of $\dfrac{N}{\lambda}$.

CD14-6 $\bar{\lambda} = \displaystyle\sum_{n=0}^{N} \frac{N-n}{N} \lambda P_n$

CD14-7 Utilization of servers = $\dfrac{\bar{\lambda}}{s\mu}$.

CD14-8 No, this approximation should not be used when ρ is nearly 1 unless K or N is huge.

Problems

CD14-1 a)

Data		
$\lambda =$	0.25	(mean arrival rate)
$\mu =$	0.3333333	(mean service rate)
$s =$	1	(# servers)
$K =$	1	(max customers)

Results	
$L =$	0.42857143
$L_q =$	0
$W =$	3
$W_q =$	0
$\rho =$	0.75
$P_0 =$	0.57142857
$P_1 =$	0.42857143

b)

Data		
$\lambda =$	0.25	(mean arrival rate)
$\mu =$	0.3333333	(mean service rate)
$s =$	1	(# servers)
$K =$	3	(max customers)

Results

$L =$ 1.34285714
$L_q =$ 0.70857143

$W =$ 6.35135135
$W_q =$ 3.35135135

$\rho =$ 0.75

$P_0 =$ 0.36571429
$P_1 =$ 0.27428571
$P_2 =$ 0.20571429
$P_3 =$ 0.15428571

c)

Data		
$\lambda =$	0.25	(mean arrival rate)
$\mu =$	0.3333333	(mean service rate)
$s =$	1	(# servers)
$K =$	5	(max customers)

Results

$L =$ 2.02630103
$L_q =$ 1.33042933

$W =$ 8.73566652
$W_q =$ 5.73566652

$\rho =$ 0.75

$P_0 =$ 0.3041283
$P_1 =$ 0.22809623
$P_2 =$ 0.17107217
$P_3 =$ 0.12830413
$P_4 =$ 0.0962281
$P_5 =$ 0.07217107

CD14-2   a & b)

Data		
$\lambda =$	20	(mean arrival rate)
$\mu =$	30	(mean service rate)
s =	1	(# servers)
K =	2	(max customers)

Results	
L =	0.73684211
$L_q =$	0.21052632
W =	0.04666667
$W_q =$	0.01333333
$\rho =$	0.66666667
$P_0 =$	0.47368421
$P_1 =$	0.31578947
$P_2 =$	0.21052632

Data		
$\lambda =$	20	(mean arrival rate)
$\mu =$	30	(mean service rate)
s =	1	(# servers)
K =	3	(max customers)

Results	
L =	1.01538462
$L_q =$	0.43076923
W =	0.05789474
$W_q =$	0.0245614
$\rho =$	0.66666667
$P_0 =$	0.41538462
$P_1 =$	0.27692308
$P_2 =$	0.18461538
$P_3 =$	0.12307692

Data		
$\lambda =$	20	(mean arrival rate)
$\mu =$	30	(mean service rate)
s =	1	(# servers)
K =	4	(max customers)

Results	
L =	1.24170616
$L_q =$	0.62559242
W =	0.06717949
$W_q =$	0.03384615
$\rho =$	0.66666667
$P_0 =$	0.38388626
$P_1 =$	0.25592417
$P_2 =$	0.17061611
$P_3 =$	0.11374408
$P_4 =$	0.07582938

Data		
$\lambda =$	20	(mean arrival rate)
$\mu =$	30	(mean service rate)
$s =$	1	(# servers)
$K =$	5	(max customers)

Results	
$L =$	1.42255639
$L_q =$	0.78796992
$W =$	0.07472354
$W_q =$	0.04139021
$\rho =$	0.66666667
$P_0 =$	0.36541353
$P_1 =$	0.24360902
$P_2 =$	0.16240602
$P_3 =$	0.10827068
$P_4 =$	0.07218045
$P_5 =$	0.0481203

c)

spaces	rate customers are lost (P_k)	change in P_k	profit/hour ($4)($\lambda$)(1-$P_k$)	change in profit/hour
2	0.21		$63.20	
3	0.12	0.09	$70.40	$7.20
4	0.08	0.04	$73.60	$3.20
5	0.05	0.03	$76.00	$2.40

d) Since it cost $200 per month per car length rented, each additional space must bring at least $200 per month (or $1 per hour) in additional profit. Five spaces still bring more than that so 5 should be provided.

CD14-3

Data		
$\lambda =$	15	(mean arrival rate)
$\mu =$	15	(mean service rate)
$s =$	2	(# servers)
$K =$	3	(max customers)

Results	
$L =$	0.96969697
$L_q =$	0.06060606
$W =$	0.07111111
$W_q =$	0.00444444
$\rho =$	0.5
$P_0 =$	0.36363636
$P_1 =$	0.36363636
$P_2 =$	0.18181818
$P_3 =$	0.09090909

a) $P_0 + P_1 = 0.72$

b) $P_2 = 0.18$

c) $P_3 = 0.09$

CD14-4 a)   The M/M/s model with a finite calling population fits this queueing system.

b)

Data		
$\lambda =$	**0.333333**	(max arrival rate)
$\mu =$	**0.5**	(mean service rate)
$s =$	**1**	(# servers)
$N =$	**3**	(size of population)

Results	
$L =$	0.71805274
$L_q =$	0.21095335
$W =$	2.832
$W_q =$	0.832
$\rho =$	0.66666667
$\lambda\text{-bar} =$	0.2535497
$P_0 =$	0.49290061
$P_1 =$	0.32860041
$P_2 =$	0.14604462
$P_3 =$	0.03245436

The probabilities that there are 0, 1, 2, or 3 machines not running are P_0, P_1, P_2, and P_3 respectively as shown in the spreadsheet above. The mean of this distribution is L=0.718 as shown above.

c) $$W = \frac{L}{\bar{\lambda}} = \frac{0.718}{0.253} = 2.832 \text{ hours.}$$

d)   The expected fraction of time that the repair technician will be busy is the system utilization, which is 0.667.

e)   M/M/s model:

Data		
$\lambda =$	0.3333333	(mean arrival rate)
$\mu =$	0.5	(mean service rate)
$s =$	1	(# servers)

Results	
$L =$	2
$L_q =$	1.33333333

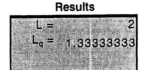

Finite queue variation of the M/M/s model with K=3:

Data		
$\lambda =$	0.3333333	(mean arrival rate)
$\mu =$	0.5	(mean service rate)
$s =$	1	(# servers)
$K =$	3	(max customers)

Results	
$L =$	1.01538462
$L_q =$	0.43076923
$W =$	3.47368421

f)

Data		
$\lambda =$	**0.333333**	(max arrival rate)
$\mu =$	**0.5**	(mean service rate)
s =	**2**	(# servers)
N =	**3**	(size of population)

Results	
L =	0.55280899
L_q =	0.00898876
W =	2.03305785
W_q =	0.03305785
ρ =	0.33333333
λ-bar =	0.27191011
P_0 =	0.54606742
P_1 =	0.36404494
P_2 =	0.08089888
P_3 =	0.00898876

The probabilities that there are 0, 1, 2, or 3 machines not running are P_0, P_1, P_2, and P_3 respectively as shown in the spreadsheet above. The mean of this distribution is L=0.553 as shown above.

The expected fraction of time that the repair technician will be busy is the system utilization, which is 0.333.

CD14-5   a)   Alternative 1:

Data		
$\lambda =$	**1.2**	(max arrival rate)
$\mu =$	**4**	(mean service rate)
s =	**1**	(# servers)
N =	**3**	(size of population)

Results	
L =	0.32064422
L_q =	0.05270864
W =	0.29918033
W_q =	0.04918033

Three machines are the maximum that can be assigned to an operator while still achieving the required production rate. The average number not running is L=0.32. Thus, 1 − (0.32/3) = 89.7% of machines are running on the average.

$$\text{Utilization of servers} = \frac{\bar{\lambda}}{s\mu} = \frac{1.072}{(1)(4)} = 0.268.$$

b) Alternative 2:

Data				Results	
$\lambda =$	4.8	(max arrival rate)		L =	1.12461693
$\mu =$	4	(mean service rate)		$L_q =$	0.03708214
s =	3	(# servers)			
N =	12	(size of population)		W =	0.25852352
				$W_q =$	0.00852433

Three operators are required to achieve the required production rate. The average number not running is L=1.125. Thus, $1 - (1.125/12) = 90.6\%$ of machines are running on the average.

$$\text{Utilization of servers} = \frac{\overline{\lambda}}{s\mu} = \frac{4.350}{(3)(4)} = 0.363.$$

c) Alternative 3:

Data				Results	
$\lambda =$	4.8	(max arrival rate)		L =	1.03519555
$\mu =$	8	(mean service rate)		$L_q =$	0.48698409
s =	1	(# servers)			
N =	12	(size of population)		W =	0.23602691
				$W_q =$	0.11103346

Two operators are required to achieve the required production rate. The average number not running is L=1.035. Thus, $1 - (1.035/12) = 91.4\%$ of machines are running on the average.

$$\text{Utilization of servers} = \frac{\overline{\lambda}}{s\mu} = \frac{4.386}{(1)(8)} = 0.548.$$

Teaching notes for this chapter are available in the Teaching Notes section near the front of this Instructor's Manual.

Review Questions

15.1-1 Computer simulation imitates the operation of a stochastic system by using the corresponding probability distributions to randomly generate the various events that occur in the system.

15.1-2 Computer simulation typically takes a lot of time and effort, which tends to be relatively expensive.

15.1-3 Computer simulation typically is used when the stochastic system involved is too complex to be analyzed satisfactorily by mathematical models.

15.1-4 A random number is a number between 0 and 9 which is generated in such a way that every possible number within this interval has an equal chance of occurring. These numbers are the used to generate random occurrences from probability distributions.

15.1-5 The inverse transformation method is a method for generating random observations from a probability distribution. The first step is to generate a uniform random number r. The second step is to find the value of x such that $F(x)=r$. The value of x is the desired random observation from the probability distribution.

15.2-1 Herr Cutter must decide whether or not to hire an associate.

15.2-2 The first rule of thumb is that in a well run barbershop with a long-established clientele, these loyal customers are willing to tolerate an average waiting time of about 20 minutes until the haircut begins. The second rule of thumb is that is a well run barbershop, new customers are willing to tolerate an average waiting time of about 10 minutes before the haircut begins.

15.2-3 The probability distributions for service times and interarrival times need to be estimated.

15.2-4 Uniform random numbers and the inverse transformation method are used to generate random observations from these distributions.

15.2-5 A simulation clock is a variable in the computer program that records how much simulated time has elapsed.

15.2-6 The main procedure for advancing the time on the simulation clock is called next-event time advance.

15.2-7 The state of the system is $N(t)$=number of customers in the system at time t.

15.2-8 The only difference comes when the next-event time-advance procedure is determining which event occurs next. Instead of just two possibilities for this next event, there are three.

15.3-1 Fritz began by simulating the current operation of the shop. This was largely to test the validity of his simulation model.

15.3-2 The Queueing Simulator obtains a point estimate and a 95% confidence interval.

15.3-3 Fritz compared the results from the simulation run with the analytical results available. He also asked Herr Cutter whether the numbers seem consistent with what he has been experiencing in the barbershop.

15.3-4 Fritz's simulation model assumes that the system has an infinite queue and that once started, the system operates continually without ever closing and reopening. A simulation model does not need to be a completely realistic representation of the real system.

15.3-5 It is estimated that Herr Cutter's income would eventually increase if he adds an associate.

15.4-1 The case study is an example of queueing system simulation.

15.4-2 The management science team simulated various redesigns of the company's entire supply chain.

15.4-3 The probability of meeting a deadline is being estimated when computer simulation is used to supplement the PERT three-estimate approach.

15.4-4 How many machines of each type should be provided?

15.4-5 A new distribution system with central dispatching was being designed.

15.4-6 Computer simulation provides a probability distribution of the return from the investment.

15.4-7 Simulating the use of hospital resources when treating patients with coronary heart disease has been done.

15.4-8 An automated system to handle mail was being planned. It was projected to achieve labor savings of over $4 billion per year.

15.5-1 The management science team needs to begin by meeting with management.

15.5-2 A simulation model often is formulated in terms of a flow diagram.

15.5-3 Before constructing a computer program, the management science team should engage the people most intimately familiar with how the system will operate in checking the accuracy of the simulation model.

15.5-4 A general-purpose simulation language is capable of programming almost any kind of simulation model. Applications-oriented simulators are designed for simulating fairly specific types of systems.

15.5-5 In an animation, key elements of a system are represented in a computer display by icons that change shape, color or position when there is a change in the state of the simulation system.

15.5-6 Will the measures of performance for the real system be closely approximated by the values of these measures generated by the simulation model?

15.5-7 Each simulation run can be viewed as a statistical experiment that is generating statistical observations of the performance of the simulated system.

15.5-8 The output from the simulation run now provide statistical estimates of the desired measures of performance for each system configuration of interest.

15.5-9 Presentation is usually done through both a written report and a formal oral presentation to the managers responsible for making the decisions regarding the system under study.

15.6-1 Three simulation add-ins are @Risk, Crystal Ball, and RiskSim.

15.6-2 Instead of entering a single number in an input cell where there is uncertainty, a probability distribution that describes the uncertainty is entered instead.

15.6-3 A spreadsheet computer simulation generates random observations from the probability distributions.

15.6-4 The RISKDISCRETE function is used to generate random observation from a discrete probability distribution.

15.6-5 One key advantage of computer simulation is that it does not need to make the most of the simplifying approximations that may be required by analytical methods. Another is that there is great flexibility about which probability distributions to use.

Problems

15.1   a)   Let the numbers 0.0000 to 0.4999 correspond to heads and the numbers 0.5000 to 0.9999 correspond to tails. The random observations for throwing an unbiased coin are 0.7520 = tails, 0.4184 = heads, 0.4189 = heads, 0.5982 = tails, 0.9559 = tails, and 0.1403 = heads.

       b)   Let the numbers 0.0000 to 0.5999 correspond to strikes and the numbers 0.6000 to 0.9999 correspond to balls. The random observations for pitches are 0.7520 = ball, 0.4184 = strike, 0.4189 = strike, 0.5982 = strike, 0.9559 = ball, and 0.1403 = strike.

       c)   Let the numbers 0.0000 to 0.3999 correspond to green lights, the numbers 0.4000 to 0.4999 correspond to yellow lights, and the numbers 0.5000 to 0.9999 correspond to red lights. The random observations for lights are 0.7520 = red, 0.4184 = yellow, 0.4189 = yellow, 0.5982 = red, 0.9559 = red, and 0.1403 = green.

15.2   a)   Answers will vary.

       b)   The formula in cell D10 is =VLOOKUP(C10, $J$8:$K$9, 2).

	B	C	D	E	F	G	H	I	J	K
3	Summary of Game							Distribution of		
4	Number of Flips =			2				Coin Flips		
5	Winnings =			$6						Result
6										(0=Tails,
7				Result				Probability	Cumulative	1=Heads)
8		Random	(0=Tails,	Total	Total			0.5	0	0
9	Flip	Number	1=Heads)	Heads	Tails	Stop?		0.5	0.5	1
10	1	0.1921	0	0	1					
11	2	0.4894	0	0	2					
12	3	0.4593	0	0	3	Stop				
13	4	0.1960	0	0	4	NA				
14	5	0.4498	0	0	5	NA				
58	49	0.4746	0	21	28	NA				
59	50	0.7349	1	22	28	NA				

c) A simulation with 14 replications:

Play	Number of Flips	Winnings
	7	$1
1	11	-$3
2	5	$3
3	5	$3
4	9	-$1
5	7	$1
6	7	$1
7	5	$3
8	3	$5
9	17	-$9
10	5	$3
11	5	$3
12	3	$5
13	9	-$1
14	7	$1
Average	7	$1.00

d) A simulation with 1000 replications:

Play	Number of Flips	Winnings
	11	-$3
1	5	$3
2	13	-$5
3	15	-$7
4	5	$3
5	19	-$11
6	11	-$3
7	3	$5
8	3	$5
9	3	$5
10	7	$1
995	5	$3
996	3	$5
997	3	$5
998	3	$5
999	21	-$13
1000	5	$3
Average	9.15	-$1.15

15.3   a) Answers will vary.

b) Let the numbers 0.0000 to 0.4999 correspond to heads and the numbers 0.5000 to 0.9999 correspond to tails.

Group 1: $0.4871 = H, 0.3611 = H, 0.1249 = H$
Group 2: $0.2439 = H, 0.7743 = T, 0.9157 = T$
Group 3: $0.1998 = H, 0.4170 = H, 0.7533 = T$
Group 4: $0.2436 = H, 0.5289 = T, 0.6148 = T$
Group 5: $0.8597 = T, 0.6120 = T, 0.8045 = T$
Group 6: $0.5311 = T, 0.8138 = T, 0.5914 = T$
Group 7: $0.3464 = H, 0.7329 = T, 0.2593 = H$
Group 8: $0.1147 = H, 0.0193 = H, 0.1572 = H$

Groups with 0 heads=2, with 1 heads=2, with 2 heads=2, with 3 heads=2

c)

Flip	Random Number	Result (0=Tails, 1=Heads)
1	0.6447	1
2	0.6897	1
3	0.1961	0

Total Number of Heads =   2

d) Answers will vary. The following 8 replications have 2 replications with 0 heads (1/4), 4 replications with 1 head (1/2), 1 replication with 2 heads (1/8), and 1 replication with 3 heads (1/8). This is not very close to the expected probability distribution.

Replication	Number of Heads
	1
1	1
2	3
3	2
4	0
5	1
6	1
7	1
8	0

e) Answers will vary. With the following 800 replications, 93 have 0 heads (93/800), 303 have 1 head (303/800), 309 have 2 heads (309/800), and 95 have 3 heads (95/800). This is quite close to the expected probability distribution.

Replication	Number of Heads
	1
1	1
2	2
3	1
4	1
5	1
798	0
799	2
800	1

Number with 0 heads =	93
Number with 1 head =	303
Number with 2 heads =	309
Number with 3 heads =	95

15.4 a) If it is raining then let the numbers 0.0000 to 0.5999 correspond to rain for the next day and 0.6000 to 0.9999 correspond to clear for the next day. If it is clear then let the numbers 0.0000 to 0.7999 correspond to clear for the next day and the numbers 0.8000 to 0.9999 correspond to rain for the next day.

Day	Random Number	Weather
1	0.9559	rain
2	0.1403	rain
3	0.9345	clear
4	0.0801	clear
5	0.6892	clear
6	0.5146	clear
7	0.6290	clear
8	0.1612	clear
9	0.0989	clear
10	0.1155	clear

b)

Day	Random Number	Weather
		Clear
1	0.8212	Rain
2	0.1449	Rain
3	0.1762	Rain
4	0.7318	Clear
5	0.9218	Rain
6	0.1237	Rain
7	0.2881	Rain
8	0.8235	Clear
9	0.5954	Clear
10	0.8405	Rain

15.5 a)

Summary of Results:

Win? (1=Yes, 0=No)	0
Number of Tosses =	3

Simulated Tosses

Toss	Die 1	Die 2	Sum
1	4	2	6
2	3	2	5
3	6	1	7
4	5	2	7
5	4	4	8
6	1	4	5
7	2	6	8

Results

Win?	Lose?	Continue?
0	0	Yes
0	0	Yes
0	1	No
NA	NA	No
NA	NA	No
NA	NA	No
NA	NA	No

b) Answers will vary. Here is one simulation of 25 replications.

Game	Win?
	0
1	0
2	0
3	1
4	0
5	0
6	0
7	0
8	1
9	0
10	0
11	0
12	0
13	0
14	0
15	0
16	1
17	0
18	1
19	0
20	1
21	1
22	1
23	1
24	1
25	0

c) Answers will vary.

15.6 a) $P(2) = \dfrac{4}{25}$, $P(3) = \dfrac{7}{25}$, $P(4) = \dfrac{8}{25}$, $P(5) = \dfrac{5}{25}$, $P(6) = \dfrac{1}{25}$

b) Mean $= (2)\dfrac{4}{25} + (3)\dfrac{7}{25} + (4)\dfrac{8}{25} + (5)\dfrac{5}{25} + (6)\dfrac{1}{25} = 3.68$ stoves

c) Random numbers can be assigned to the various sales levels to simulate daily sales. Let the numbers 0.000 to 0.1599 correspond to 2 stoves being sold in a day, the numbers 0.1600 to 0.4399 correspond to 3 stoves, the numbers 0.4400 to 0.7599 correspond to 4 stoves, the numbers 0.7600 to 0.9599 correspond to 5 stoves, and the numbers 0.9600 to 0.9999 correspond to 6 stoves.

d) Sales are 4 stoves, 6 stoves, and 2 stoves on the three days. The average is 4, which is 0.32 higher than the mean obtained in part (b).

e) Answers will vary. The following 300-day simulation yielded an average demand of 3.72.

Day	Random Number	Demand
1	0.5475	4
2	0.3597	3
3	0.6539	4
4	0.6263	4
5	0.9576	5
6	0.8396	5
7	0.1005	2
297	0.5809	4
298	0.3673	3
299	0.4453	4
300	0.1361	2

Distribution of Demand

Probability	Cumulative	Demand
0.16	0	2
0.28	0.16	3
0.32	0.44	4
0.20	0.76	5
0.04	0.96	6

Average = 3.720

15.7 a)

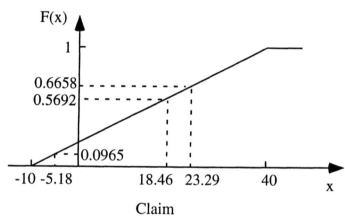

b)

$$F(x) = \frac{x+10}{50} = 0.0965 \text{ when } x = -5.18$$

$$F(x) = \frac{x+10}{50} = 0.5692 \text{ when } x = 18.46$$

$$F(x) = \frac{x+10}{50} = 0.6658 \text{ when } x = 23.29$$

c) $= -10 + 50*\text{RAND}()$

15.8 a)

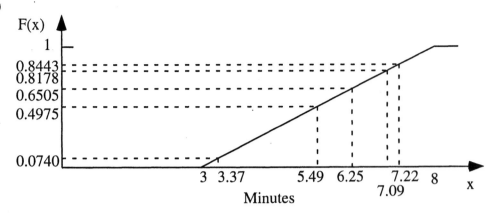

b)

$$F(x) = \frac{x-3}{5} = 0.6505 \text{ when } x = 6.25$$

$$F(x) = \frac{x-3}{5} = 0.0740 \text{ when } x = 3.37$$

$$F(x) = \frac{x-3}{5} = 0.8443 \text{ when } x = 7.22$$

$$F(x) = \frac{x-3}{5} = 0.4975 \text{ when } x = 5.49$$

$$F(x) = \frac{x-3}{5} = 0.8178 \text{ when } x = 7.09$$

c) Average = 5.88 which is higher that the mean of 5.5

d) Results will vary. The following 500-day simulation yielded an average of 5.479.

Day	Random Number	Service Time
1	0.1348	3.674
2	0.6798	6.399
3	0.7941	6.971
4	0.1825	3.913
5	0.6502	6.251
6	0.1088	3.544
497	0.9319	7.660
498	0.6662	6.331
499	0.8760	7.380
500	0.2933	4.467
	Average =	5.479

15.9 a) Let the numbers 0.0000 to 0.3999 correspond to a minor repair and 0.4000 to 0.9999 correspond to a major repair. The random numbers then indicate 0.7256 = major, 0.0817 = minor, 0.4392 = major.

Using the random numbers, the average length of the three repairs is then

1.2243 hours (first major repair)
0.9503 hours (minor repair)
1.6104 hours (second major repair)

The average repair time is then (1.224+ 0.950 + 1.610) / 3 = 1.26 hours.

b)

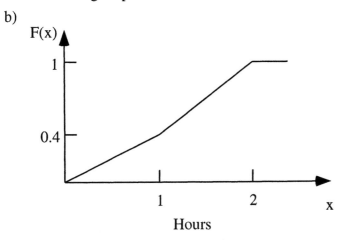

c) $F(x) = \begin{cases} 0.4x & \text{when } 0 \leq x \leq 1 \\ 0.4 + 0.6(x-1) & \text{when } x \geq 1 \end{cases}$

$F(x) = 0.2243$ $\Rightarrow$ $x = 0.561$ hours
$F(x) = 0.9503$ $\Rightarrow$ $x = 1.917$ hours
$F(x) = 0.6104$ $\Rightarrow$ $x = 1.351$ hours

The average repair time is then (0.561 + 1.917 + 1.351) / 3 = 1.28 hours.

d)
$F(x) = 0.7757$ $\Rightarrow$ $x = 1.626$ hours
$F(x) = 0.0497$ $\Rightarrow$ $x = 0.124$ hours
$F(x) = 0.3896$ $\Rightarrow$ $x = 0.974$ hours

The average repair time is then (1.626 + 0.124 + 0.974) / 3 = 0.91 hours.

e) The average repair time is
(0.561 + 1.917 + 1.351 + 1.626 + 0.124 + 0.974) / 6 = 1.09 hours.

f) The method of complementary random numbers in part (e) gave the closest estimate. It performs well because using complements helps counteract the more extreme random numbers (such as 0.9503).

g) Results will vary. The following 300-day simulation using the method of complementary random numbers yielded an overall average service time of 1.095 minutes. This is very close to the true mean of 1.1 minutes.

Day	Random Number	Service Time	Complimentary Random Number	Complimentary Service Time
1	0.1348	0.337	0.8652	1.775
2	0.6798	1.466	0.3202	0.800
3	0.7941	1.657	0.2059	0.515
4	0.1825	0.456	0.8175	1.696
5	0.6502	1.417	0.3498	0.874
6	0.1088	0.272	0.8912	1.819
7	0.1153	0.288	0.8847	1.808
297	0.5456	1.243	0.4544	1.091
298	0.3514	0.878	0.6486	1.414
299	0.8990	1.832	0.1010	0.253
300	0.1544	0.386	0.8456	1.743
	Average =	1.102		1.088

Overall Average = 1.095

15.10 a) Let the numbers 0.0000 to 0.3999 correspond to no claims filed, 0.4000 to 0.7999 correspond to small claims filed, and 0.8000 to 0.9999 correspond to large claims filed. The random numbers then indicate 0.7256 = small, 0.0817 = no, 0.4392 = small.

Using the random numbers, the average size of each claim is then

(0.2243)(2000)=$448.60 (small claim)
$0 (no claim)
(0.6104)(2000)=$1,220.80 (small claim)

The average claim is then (448.60+1,220.80) /2 = $834.70.

b)

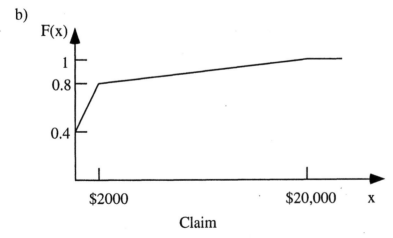

c)

$$F(x) = \begin{cases} 0 & x < 0 \\ 0.4 + \dfrac{0.4x}{2,000} & \text{when } 0 \le x \le 2,000 \\ 0.8 + \dfrac{0.2(x-2,000)}{18,000} & \text{when } 2,000 \le x \le 20,000 \end{cases}$$

$F(x) = 0.2243 \qquad \Rightarrow \qquad x = \$0$

$F(x) = 0.9503 \qquad \Rightarrow \qquad x = \$15,527$

$F(x) = 0.6104 \qquad \Rightarrow \qquad x = \$1,052$

The average claim is then ($0+$15,527+$1052) / 3 = $5526.33.

d)

$F(x) = 0.776 \Rightarrow \qquad x = \$1,880$

$F(x) = 0.050 \Rightarrow \qquad x = \$0$

$F(x) = 0.390 \Rightarrow \qquad x = \$0$

The average claim is then ($1,880 + $0 + $0) / 3 = $626.67 hours.

e) The average claim is
   ($0 + $15,527 + $1052 + $1880 + $0 + $0) / 6 = $3076.50.

f) The method of complementary random numbers in part (e) gave the closest estimate. It performs well because using complements helps counteract the more extreme random numbers (such as 0.9503).

g) Results will vary. The following 300-day simulation using the method of complementary random numbers yielded an overall average claim size of $2547.15. This is quite close to the true mean of $2600.

Day	Random Number	Size of Claim	Complimentary Random Number	Complimentary Size of Claim
1	0.2837	$0.00	0.7163	$1,581.27
2	0.4067	$33.50	0.5933	$966.50
3	0.4202	$101.18	0.5798	$898.82
4	0.3473	$0.00	0.6527	$1,263.54
5	0.9728	$17,550.20	0.0272	$0.00
6	0.8839	$9,547.73	0.1161	$0.00
7	0.6365	$1,182.61	0.3635	$0.00
297	0.1141	$0.00	0.8859	$9,734.86
298	0.3657	$0.00	0.6343	$1,171.49
299	0.7641	$1,820.30	0.2359	$0.00
300	0.0532	$0.00	0.9468	$15,215.71
	Average =	$2,648.11		$2,446.19

Overall Average = $2,547.15

15.11 a)

Uniform Random Number	Random Observation (minutes)
0.2655	9.22
0.3472	9.49
0.0248	7.25
0.9205	12.21
0.6130	10.38

b) If cell C4 contains the uniform random number, then the excel function would be
=IF(C4<0.2, 7+(2/0.2)*C4, IF(C4<0.8, 9+(2/0.6)*(C4-0.2), 11+(2/0.2)*(C4-0.8))).

15.12 a) $F(x) = x^2 = r$ $\Rightarrow$ $x = \sqrt{r}$.

b)

Uniform Random Number	Random Observation
0.0956	0.309
0.5629	0.750
0.6695	0.818
0.7634	0.874
0.8426	0.918

c)

Random Observation	Uniform Random Number Used
0.09	0.0081
0.64	0.4096
0.49	0.2401

d) =SQRT(RAND()).

15.13 a)

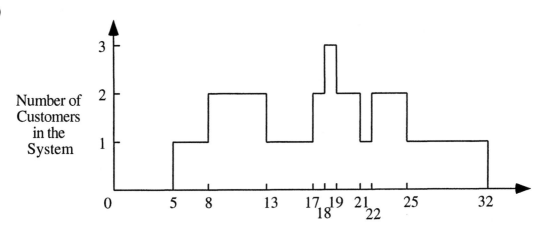

Elapsed Time (minutes)

b)

$$P_0 = \frac{5}{32} = 0.156 \qquad\qquad P_1 = \frac{3+4+1+7}{32} = 0.469$$

$$P_2 = \frac{5+1+2+3}{32} = 0.344 \qquad P_3 = \frac{1}{32} = 0.031$$

$$Est\{L\} = \sum_0^3 nP_n = (0)(0.156)+(1)(0.469)+(2)(0.344)+(3)(0.031) = 1.25 \text{ cust.}$$

$$Est\{L_q\} = \sum_1^3 (n-1)P_n = (1-1)(0.469)+(2-1)(0.344)+(3-1)(0.031) = 0.406 \text{ cust.}$$

Customers	Arrival Time	Service Time	Departure Time	System Time	Wait Time
1	5	8	13	8	0
2	8	6	19	11	5
3	17	2	21	4	2
4	18	4	25	7	3
5	22	7	32	10	3

$$Est\{W_q\} = \frac{\text{sum of observed waiting times}}{\text{number of observed waiting times}} = \frac{13}{5} = 2.6 \text{ minutes}$$

$$Est\{W\} = \frac{\text{sum of observed system times}}{\text{number of observed system times}} = \frac{40}{5} = 8 \text{ minutes}$$

c)

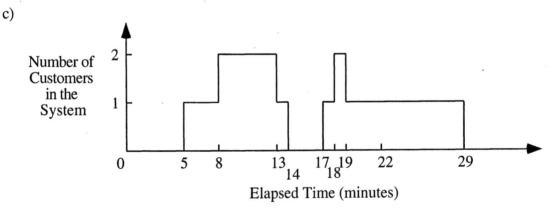

d)

$$P_0 = \frac{5+3}{29} = 0.276 \qquad P_1 = \frac{3+1+1+3+7}{29} = 0.517 \qquad P_2 = \frac{5+1}{29} = 0.207$$

$$Est\{L\} = \sum_0^2 nP_n = (0)(0.276) + (1)(0.517) + (2)(0.207) = 0.931 \text{ customers}$$

$$Est\{L_q\} = \sum_1^2 (n-1)P_n = (1-1)(0.517) + (2-1)(0.207) = 0.207 \text{ customers}$$

Customers	Arrival Time	Service Time	Departure Time	System Time	Wait Time
1	5	8	13	8	0
2	8	6	14	6	0
3	17	2	19	2	0
4	18	4	22	4	0
5	22	7	29	7	0

$$Est\{W_q\} = \frac{\text{sum of observed waiting times}}{\text{number of observed waiting times}} = \frac{0}{5} = 0 \text{ minutes}$$

$$Est\{W\} = \frac{\text{sum of observed system times}}{\text{number of observed system times}} = \frac{27}{5} = 5.4 \text{ minutes}$$

15.14 a) 1. A description of the components of the system. The system is a single-server queueing system with the crew as the server and machines as the customers. The service time has a uniform distribution over the interval from 0 to twice the mean, and interarrival time distribution has an exponential distribution with a mean of 5 hours.

2. A simulation clock will record the amount of simulated time that will elapse.

3. The state of the system will be defined as $N(t)$ = number of machines needing repair at time t.

4. The breakdowns and repairs that occur over time are randomly generated by generating random observations from the distributions of interarrival and service times.

5. Adjust the state of the system when a breakdown or repair occurs by:

$$\text{Reset } N(t) = \begin{cases} N(t)+1, & \text{if a breakdown occurs at time t} \\ N(t)-1, & \text{if a repair occurs at time t} \end{cases}$$

6. Advance the time on the simulation clock by using the next-event time advance procedure.

b) 2 Servers:

Mean Interarrival Time =   5 hours
Size of Crew =   2
Mean Service Time =   4 hours

Average Time in Line (Wq) =	9.1 hours
Average Time in System (W) =	13.5 hours

Customer Arrival	Interarrival Time	Time of Arrival	Time Service Begins	Service Time	Time Service Ends	Time in Line	Time in System
1	23.4	23.4	23.4	7.1	30.4	0.0	7.1
2	5.1	28.5	30.4	2.6	33.0	2.0	4.6
3	6.5	34.9	34.9	1.8	36.7	0.0	1.8
4	1.2	36.1	36.7	6.7	43.3	0.6	7.3
5	0.5	36.6	43.3	7.3	50.6	6.7	14.0
98	2.5	518.3	543.3	6.1	549.4	25.0	31.1
99	0.5	518.8	549.4	6.5	556.0	30.6	37.2
100	1.7	520.5	556.0	2.0	558.0	35.4	37.4

3 Servers:

Mean Interarrival Time =   5 hours
Size of Crew =   3
Mean Service Time =   3 hours

Average Time in Line (Wq) =	2.1 hours
Average Time in System (W) =	5.1 hours

Customer Arrival	Interarrival Time	Time of Arrival	Time Service Begins	Service Time	Time Service Ends	Time in Line	Time in System
1	0.4	0.4	0.4	4.6	5.0	0.0	4.6
2	7.4	7.9	7.9	3.1	10.9	0.0	3.1
3	1.5	9.4	10.9	5.3	16.2	1.5	6.8
4	9.6	19.0	19.0	4.9	23.9	0.0	4.9
5	3.5	22.5	23.9	4.8	28.7	1.4	6.1
98	12.7	583.3	585.7	5.4	591.1	2.4	7.8
99	1.5	584.8	591.1	5.8	596.9	6.3	12.1
100	2.0	586.8	596.9	1.4	598.3	10.1	11.5

4 Servers:

Mean Interarrival Time =   5 hours
Size of Crew =   4
Mean Service Time =   2 hours

Average Time in Line (Wq) =	1.0 hours
Average Time in System (W) =	3.0 hours

Customer Arrival	Interarrival Time	Time of Arrival	Time Service Begins	Service Time	Time Service Ends	Time in Line	Time in System
1	5.6	5.6	5.6	3.9	9.6	0.0	3.9
2	31.4	37.0	37.0	3.6	40.5	0.0	3.6
3	1.2	38.1	40.5	1.1	41.6	2.4	3.5
4	4.9	43.0	43.0	0.3	43.3	0.0	0.3
5	3.9	46.9	46.9	2.7	49.6	0.0	2.7
98	6.0	470.2	470.2	1.9	472.1	0.0	1.9
99	5.5	475.7	475.7	0.4	476.1	0.0	0.4
100	1.1	476.8	476.8	1.8	478.6	0.0	1.8

For these simulation runs, 3 servers was enough to get the average waiting time before repair below 3 hours.

c) <u>2 Servers:</u>

Data

Number of Servers =	1

Interarrival Times

Distribution =	Exponential
Mean =	5

Service Times

Distribution =	Uniform
Minimum =	0
Maximum =	8

Length of Simulation Run

Number of Arrivals =	10,000

Run Simulation

Results

	Point Estimate	95% Confidence Interval Low	High
L =	2.818	2.524	3.112
L_q =	2.016	1.736	2.296
W =	14.045	12.756	15.335
W_q =	10.049	8.778	11.319
P_0 =	0.198	0.181	0.216
P_1 =	0.209	0.194	0.224
P_2 =	0.164	0.153	0.175
P_3 =	0.123	0.114	0.132
P_4 =	0.0879	0.0803	0.0956
P_5 =	0.0637	0.0556	0.0719
P_6 =	0.0473	0.0388	0.0559
P_7 =	0.0342	0.027	0.0415
P_8 =	0.0240	0.0177	0.0304
P_9 =	0.0162	0.0102	0.0222
P_{10} =	0.0128	0.00689	0.0187

<u>3 Servers:</u>

Data

Number of Servers =	1

Interarrival Times

Distribution =	Exponential
Mean =	5

Service Times

Distribution =	Uniform
Minimum =	0
Maximum =	6

Length of Simulation Run

Number of Arrivals =	10,000

Run Simulation

Results

	Point Estimate	95% Confidence Interval Low	High
L =	1.172	1.105	1.24
L_q =	0.0577	0.519	0.634
W =	5.915	5.648	6.182
W_q =	2.909	2.652	3.166
P_0 =	0.404	0.391	0.417
P_1 =	0.291	0.283	0.299
P_2 =	0.16	0.153	0.166
P_3 =	0.0771	0.0712	0.083
P_4 =	0.038	0.0332	0.0427
P_5 =	0.0168	0.0132	0.0203
P_6 =	0.00719	0.00467	0.00972
P_7 =	0.00224	0.00106	0.00342
P_8 =	0.0018	0.000588	0.00309
P_9 =	0.00152	0.000221	0.00282
P_{10} =	0.000428	-0.00021	0.00107

4 Servers:

Data		
Number of Servers =		1

Interarrival Times

Distribution =	Exponential
Mean =	5

Service Times

Distribution =	Uniform
Minimum =	0
Maximum =	4

Length of Simulation Run

Number of Arrivals =	10,000

Run Simulation

Results	Point Estimate	95% Confidence Interval Low	High
L =	0.57	0.549	0.592
L_q =	0.172	0.158	0.187
W =	2.882	2.809	2.956
W_q =	0.87	0.807	0.934
P_0 =	0.602	0.593	0.611
P_1 =	0.273	0.268	0.279
P_2 =	0.0906	0.0862	0.0949
P_3 =	0.246	0.0219	0.0272
P_4 =	0.00766	0.00602	0.0093
P_5 =	0.00178	0.001	0.00255
P_6 =	0.000162	0	0.000329
P_7 =	0.000115	-0.0001	0.000341
P_8 =	0.000058	-0.00006	0.00017
P_9 =	0.000059	-0.00006	0.000174
P_{10} =	0	0	0

For these simulation runs, 3 servers was enough to get the average waiting time before repair below 3 hours.

d) ## 2 Servers:

Data		
λ =	0.2	(mean arrival rate)
$1/\mu$ =	4	(expected service time)
σ =	2.3094011	(standard deviation)
s =	1	(# servers)

Results	
L =	2.93333333
L_q =	2.13333333
W =	14.6666667
W_q =	10.6666667

3 Servers:

Data		
λ =	0.2	(mean arrival rate)
$1/\mu$ =	3	(expected service time)
σ =	1.7320508	(standard deviation)
s =	1	(# servers)

Results	
L =	1.2
L_q =	0.6
W =	6
W_q =	3

4 Servers:

Data		
λ =	0.2	(mean arrival rate)
$1/\mu$ =	2	(expected service time)
σ =	1.1547005	(standard deviation)
s =	1	(# servers)

Results	
L =	0.57777778
L_q =	0.17777778
W =	2.88888889
W_q =	0.88888889

3 servers is enough to get the average waiting time before repair down to 3 hours.

15.15

Customer Arrival	Interarrival Time	Time of Arrival	Time Service Begins	Service Time	Time Service Ends	Time in Line	Time in System
1	4.0	4.0	4.0	19.6	23.6	0	19.6
2	15.6	19.6	19.6	24.9	44.5	0	24.9
3	1.4	21.0	23.6	15.7	39.3	2.6	18.3
4	36.0	56.9	56.9	20.9	77.8	0	20.9
5	41.4	98.3	98.3	16.0	114.3	0	16.0
6	30.2	128.6	128.6	18.9	147.5	0	18.9
7	10.0	138.6	138.6	20.6	159.2	0	20.6
8	35.8	174.4	174.4	23.4	197.8	0	23.4
9	13.0	187.4	187.4	18.8	206.2	0	18.8
10	12.0	199.4	199.4	19.2	218.6	0	19.2

a) Only the third customer has to wait before beginning a haircut. He waits for 2.6 minutes. $W_q = 0.26$ minutes for this simulation.

b)

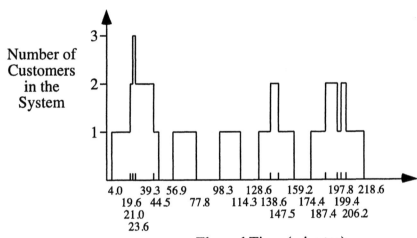

Elapsed Time (minutes)

15.16 a)

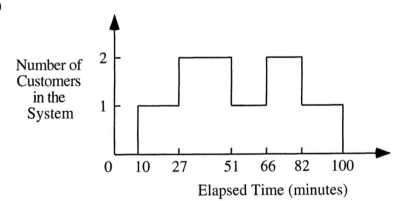

Elapsed Time (minutes)

b)

$$P_0 = \frac{10}{100} = 0.1; \qquad P_1 = \frac{17+15+18}{100} = 0.4;$$

$$P_2 = \frac{24+16}{100} = 0.4; \qquad P_3 = \frac{0}{100} = 0.$$

c) $Est(L) = \sum_{n=1}^{3} nP_n = 1(0.4) + 2(0.4) + 3(0) = 1.2.$

$Est(L_q) = \sum_{n=2}^{3} (n-1)P_n = 1(0.4) + 2(0) = 0.4.$

d) $Est\{W\} = \dfrac{\text{sum of observed system times}}{\text{number of observed system times}} = \dfrac{41+55+34}{3} = 43.33$ minutes.

$Est\{W_q\} = \dfrac{\text{sum of observed waiting times}}{\text{number of observed waiting times}} = \dfrac{0+24+16}{3} = 13.33$ minutes.

15.17 a)

Data

Number of Servers =	2

Interarrival Times

Distribution =	Translated Exp.
Minimum =	0.5
Mean =	1

Service Times

Distribution =	Erlang
Mean =	1.5
k =	4

Length of Simulation Run

Number of Arrivals =	5,000

Run Simulation

Results

	Point Estimate	95% Confidence Interval Low	High
L =	1.796	1.73	1.862
L_q =	0.303	0.26	0.345
W =	1.803	1.748	1.858
W_q =	0.304	0.263	0.345
P_0 =	0.082	0.0742	0.0903
P_1 =	0.343	0.326	0.359
P_2 =	0.352	0.34	0.363
P_3 =	0.161	0.148	0.174
P_4 =	0.0483	0.0382	0.0584
P_5 =	0.012	0.00708	0.017
P_6 =	0.00204	0.000479	0.0036
P_7 =	0.000222	-0.00017	0.000612
P_8 =	0	0	0
P_9 =	0	0	0
P_{10} =	0	0	0

b)

		Data
Number of Servers =		3

Interarrival Times

Distribution =	Translated Exp.
Minimum =	0.5
Mean =	1

Service Times

Distribution =	Erlang
Mean =	1.5
k =	4

Length of Simulation Run

Number of Arrivals =	5,000

Run Simulation

	Results		
	Point Estimate	95% Confidence Interval	
		Low	High
L =	1.498	1.469	1.527
L_q =	0.0101	0.00773	0.0124
W =	1.5075	1.487	1.528
W_q =	0.0101	0.00781	0.0125
P_0 =	0.108	0.1	0.116
P_1 =	0.411	0.4	0.422
P_2 =	0.365	0.355	0.375
P_3 =	0.106	0.0981	0.113
P_4 =	0.00971	0.007551	0.0119
P_5 =	0.00018	0.000003	0.000357
P_6 =	0	0	0
P_7 =	0	0	0
P_8 =	0	0	0
P_9 =	0	0	0
P_{10} =	0	0	0

c) Two Tellers:

Data

Number of Servers =	2

Interarrival Times

Distribution =	Translated Exp.
Minimum =	0.5
Mean =	0.9

Service Times

Distribution =	Erlang
Mean =	1.5
k =	4

Length of Simulation Run

Number of Arrivals =	5,000

Run Simulation

Results

	Point Estimate	95% Confidence Interval Low	High
$L =$	2.355	2.188	2.522
$L_q =$	0.671	0.532	0.809
$W =$	2.103	1.968	2.238
$W_q =$	0.599	0.479	0.718
$P_0 =$	0.04	0.0334	0.0465
$P_1 =$	0.236	0.213	0.259
$P_2 =$	0.343	0.321	0.365
$P_3 =$	0.212	0.198	0.227
$P_4 =$	0.0946	0.0773	0.112
$P_5 =$	0.0427	0.028	0.0573
$P_6 =$	0.0197	0.011	0.0284
$P_7 =$	0.0088	0.00296	0.0146
$P_8 =$	0.00253	0.000469	0.00459
$P_9 =$	0.000453	-0.00018	0.00108
$P_{10} =$	0.000005	-0.000005	0.000016

Three Tellers:

Data

Number of Servers =	3

Interarrival Times

Distribution =	Translated Exp.
Minimum =	0.5
Mean =	0.9

Service Times

Distribution =	Erlang
Mean =	1.5
k =	4

Length of Simulation Run

Number of Arrivals =	5,000

Run Simulation

Results

	Point Estimate	95% Confidence Interval Low	High
$L =$	1.684	1.652	1.716
$L_q =$	0.0217	0.0169	0.0264
$W =$	1.516	1.494	1.538
$W_q =$	0.0195	0.0153	0.0237
$P_0 =$	0.0702	0.064	0.0764
$P_1 =$	0.361	0.349	0.373
$P_2 =$	0.404	0.395	0.414
$P_3 =$	0.143	0.134	0.152
$P_4 =$	0.0196	0.0158	0.0235
$P_5 =$	0.001	0.000342	0.00173
$P_6 =$	0	0	0
$P_7 =$	0	0	0
$P_8 =$	0	0	0
$P_9 =$	0	0	0
$P_{10} =$	0	0	0

d) Two tellers provides reasonable wait times, with both the original arrival wait ($W_q = 0.3$ minutes) and the higher arrival rate in part c ($W_q = 0.6$ minutes).

15.18 a&b)

Mean Interarrival Time =   0.25 days
Mean Service Time =   0.2 days

Average Time in Line (Wq) =	0.68 days
Average Time in System (W) =	0.91 days

Customer Arrival	Interarrival Time	Time of Arrival	Time Service Begins	Service Time	Time Service Ends	Time in Line	Time in System
1	0.41	0.41	0.41	0.83	1.23	0.00	0.83
2	0.21	0.61	1.23	0.32	1.55	0.62	0.93
3	0.11	0.72	1.55	0.28	1.83	0.83	1.11
4	0.21	0.93	1.83	0.04	1.87	0.90	0.95
5	0.31	1.24	1.87	0.05	1.92	0.64	0.69
98	0.08	24.38	24.74	0.52	25.27	0.36	0.89
99	0.19	24.57	25.27	0.27	25.54	0.69	0.97
100	0.30	24.87	25.54	0.14	25.68	0.67	0.81

c)

Mean Interarrival Time =   0.5 days
Mean Service Time =   0.2 days

Average Time in Line (Wq) =	0.13 days
Average Time in System (W) =	0.32 days

Customer Arrival	Interarrival Time	Time of Arrival	Time Service Begins	Service Time	Time Service Ends	Time in Line	Time in System
1	1.46	1.46	1.46	0.18	1.65	0.00	0.18
2	0.13	1.59	1.65	0.04	1.69	0.06	0.10
3	1.80	3.39	3.39	0.33	3.72	0.00	0.33
4	0.43	3.82	3.82	0.12	3.93	0.00	0.12
5	0.16	3.98	3.98	0.53	4.51	0.00	0.53
98	0.23	51.74	51.74	0.06	51.79	0.00	0.06
99	0.12	51.85	51.85	0.53	52.38	0.00	0.53
100	0.15	52.01	52.38	0.04	52.42	0.37	0.41

d) <u>German cars:</u>

Data

Number of Servers =	1

Interarrival Times

Distribution =	Exponential
Mean =	0.25

Service Times

Distribution =	Exponential
Mean =	0.2

Length of Simulation Run

Number of Arrivals =	10,000

[Run Simulation]

Results

	Point Estimate	95% Confidence Interval Low	High
$L =$	3.963	3.302	4.625
$L_q =$	3.165	2.52	3.809
$W =$	0.994	0.84	1.149
$W_q =$	0.794	0.642	0.946
$P_0 =$	0.201	0.179	0.224
$P_1 =$	0.158	0.143	0.174
$P_2 =$	0.128	0.116	0.14
$P_3 =$	0.104	0.0937	0.113
$P_4 =$	0.0849	0.0762	0.0936
$P_5 =$	0.062	0.0542	0.0698
$P_6 =$	0.0518	0.0451	0.0586
$P_7 =$	0.0434	0.0362	0.0507
$P_8 =$	0.033	0.0269	0.0391
$P_9 =$	0.0257	0.0197	0.0316
$P_{10} =$	0.0232	0.0167	0.0297

<u>Japanese cars:</u>

Data

Number of Servers =	1

Interarrival Times

Distribution =	Exponential
Mean =	0.5

Service Times

Distribution =	Exponential
Mean =	0.2

Length of Simulation Run

Number of Arrivals =	10,000

[Run Simulation]

Results

	Point Estimate	95% Confidence Interval Low	High
$L =$	0.639	0.605	0.674
$L_q =$	0.25	0.225	0.276
$W =$	0.325	0.31	0.34
$W_q =$	0.127	0.115	0.139
$P_0 =$	0.611	0.6	0.622
$P_1 =$	0.233	0.228	0.239
$P_2 =$	0.097	0.0919	0.102
$P_3 =$	0.0368	0.033	0.0405
$P_4 =$	0.0131	0.0108	0.0155
$P_5 =$	0.00501	0.00346	0.00657
$P_6 =$	0.00174	0.000963	0.00252
$P_7 =$	0.00104	0.000218	0.00187
$P_8 =$	0.000431	-0.00008	0.000938
$P_9 =$	0.000262	-0.00004	0.000568
$P_{10} =$	0.000042	-0.00004	0.000125

e)

	Data
Number of Servers =	2

Interarrival Times

Distribution =	Exponential
Mean =	0.25

Service Times

Distribution =	Exponential
Mean =	0.2

Length of Simulation Run

Number of Arrivals =	10,000

Run Simulation

Results

	Point Estimate	95% Confidence Interval Low	High
L =	0.925	0.887	0.963
L_q =	0.14	0.1211	0.159
W =	0.234	0.227	0.242
W_q =	0.0355	0.0309	0.0401
P_0 =	0.439	0.427	0.451
P_1 =	0.337	0.329	0.345
P_2 =	0.138	0.133	0.144
P_3 =	0.0516	0.0473	0.0558
P_4 =	0.0213	0.0182	0.0245
P_5 =	0.00766	0.00592	0.0094
P_6 =	0.00343	0.00221	0.00474
P_7 =	0.00122	0.000569	0.00188
P_8 =	0.000407	-0.00014	0.000949
P_9 =	0.000081	-0.00005	0.000211
P_{10} =	0.000025	-0.00002	0.000074

f) This option significantly decreases the waiting time for German cars without the added cost of an additional mechanic.

	Data
Number of Servers =	2

Interarrival Times

Distribution =	Exponential
Mean =	0.1667

Service Times

Distribution =	Exponential
Mean =	0.22

Length of Simulation Run

Number of Arrivals =	20,000

Run Simulation

Results

	Point Estimate	95% Confidence Interval Low	High
L =	2.31	2.175	2.445
L_q =	0.996	0.88	1.111
W =	0.385	0.365	0.405
W_q =	0.166	0.148	0.184
P_0 =	0.208	0.198	0.218
P_1 =	0.27	0.26	0.279
P_2 =	0.178	0.172	0.184
P_3 =	0.119	0.114	0.124
P_4 =	0.0779	0.0731	0.0827
P_5 =	0.05	0.0459	0.0542
P_6 =	0.0345	0.0305	0.0384
P_7 =	0.0224	0.0191	0.0256
P_8 =	0.0141	0.0113	0.0168
P_9 =	0.00925	0.00679	0.0117
P_{10} =	0.0056	0.00384	0.00735

g)

Question Part	Simulated Estimate for W	Analytical Value for W
b	0.91 days	1.00 days
c	0.32 days	0.33 days
d (German)	0.99 days	1.00 days
d (Japanese)	0.33 days	0.33 days
e	0.23 days	0.24 days
f	0.39 days	0.39 days

The results of the simulation were quite accurate for all but part b, where only 100 arrivals were simulated. This suggests that more than 100 arrivals should be simulated.

h) Answers will vary. The option of training the two current mechanics significantly decreases the waiting time for German cars, without a significant impact on the wait for Japanese cars, and does so without the added cost of a third mechanic. Adding a third mechanic lowers the average wait for German cars even more, but comes at an added cost for the third mechanic.

15.19 a & b)

Minimum Interarrival Time = 10 minutes
Maximum Interarrival Time = 20 minutes
Mean Service Time = 10 minutes

Average Time in Line (Wq) = 3.79 days
Average Time in System (W) = 13.52 days

Customer Arrival	Interarrival Time	Time of Arrival	Time Service Begins	Service Time	Time Service Ends	Time in Line	Time in System
1	19.91	19.91	19.91	3.07	22.98	0.00	3.07
2	18.58	38.49	38.49	14.26	52.75	0.00	14.26
3	16.71	55.20	55.20	1.67	56.87	0.00	1.67
4	13.49	68.69	68.69	3.20	71.89	0.00	3.20
5	16.75	85.45	85.45	9.58	95.02	0.00	9.58
98	18.51	1473.63	1480.75	2.83	1483.57	7.12	9.95
99	12.26	1485.88	1485.88	10.60	1496.48	0.00	10.60
100	12.08	1497.96	1497.96	3.12	1501.09	0.00	3.12

c)

Interarrival Time (constant) = 15 minutes
Mean Service Time = 10 minutes

Average Time in Line (Wq) = 4.65 days
Average Time in System (W) = 14.96 days

Customer Arrival	Interarrival Time	Time of Arrival	Time Service Begins	Service Time	Time Service Ends	Time in Line	Time in System
1	15.00	15.00	15.00	11.16	26.16	0.00	11.16
2	15.00	30.00	30.00	23.11	53.11	0.00	23.11
3	15.00	45.00	53.11	1.44	54.55	8.11	9.55
4	15.00	60.00	60.00	11.24	71.24	0.00	11.24
5	15.00	75.00	75.00	27.37	102.37	0.00	27.37
98	15.00	1470.00	1493.42	18.19	1511.62	23.42	41.62
99	15.00	1485.00	1511.62	12.66	1524.28	26.62	39.28
100	15.00	1500.00	1524.28	28.05	1552.33	24.28	52.33

d) Monitors:

Data

Number of Servers =	1

Interarrival Times

Distribution =	Uniform
Minimum =	10
Maximum =	20

Service Times

Distribution =	Exponential
Mean =	10

Length of Simulation Run

Number of Arrivals =	10,000

Run Simulation

Results

	Point Estimate	95% Confidence Interval Low	High
$L =$	1.149	1.083	1.216
$L_q =$	0.488	0.433	0.543
$W =$	17.22	16.226	18.214
$W_q =$	7.31	6.483	8.138
$P_0 =$	0.339	0.325	0.352
$P_1 =$	0.375	0.365	0.386
$P_2 =$	0.16	0.152	0.168
$P_3 =$	0.0762	0.0683	0.084
$P_4 =$	0.0312	0.0253	0.0372
$P_5 =$	0.0131	0.00894	0.0172
$P_6 =$	0.00428	0.00227	0.0063
$P_7 =$	0.00109	0.000123	0.00206
$P_8 =$	0.000164	-0.00009	0.000412
$P_9 =$	0.000041	-0.00004	0.00012
$P_{10} =$	0	0	0

Printers:

Data

Number of Servers =	1

Interarrival Times

Distribution =	Constant
Value =	15

Service Times

Distribution =	Exponential
Mean =	10

Length of Simulation Run

Number of Arrivals =	10,000

Run Simulation

Results

	Point Estimate	95% Confidence Interval Low	High
$L =$	1.178	1.111	1.246
$L_q =$	0.506	0.45	0.563
$W =$	17.675	16.661	18.688
$W_q =$	7.595	6.744	8.446
$P_0 =$	0.328	0.315	0.341
$P_1 =$	0.382	0.372	0.393
$P_2 =$	0.16	0.151	0.168
$P_3 =$	0.0744	0.0664	0.0823
$P_4 =$	0.0356	0.0291	0.0421
$P_5 =$	0.0134	0.00944	0.0174
$P_6 =$	0.0043	0.00237	0.00623
$P_7 =$	0.00129	0.000398	0.00217
$P_8 =$	0.00073	-0.00006	0.00152
$P_9 =$	0.000406	-0.00025	0.00106
$P_{10} =$	0	0	0

e) Monitors:

Data

Number of Servers =	1

Interarrival Times

Distribution =	Uniform
Minimum =	10
Maximum =	20

Service Times

Distribution =	Erlang
Mean =	10
k =	4

Length of Simulation Run

Number of Arrivals =	10,000

Run Simulation

Results

	Point Estimate	95% Confidence Interval Low	High
$L =$	0.753	0.74	0.766
$L_q =$	0.087	0.0796	0.0944
$W =$	11.302	11.114	11.489
$W_q =$	1.305	1.195	1.415
$P_0 =$	0.334	0.327	0.341
$P_1 =$	0.582	0.577	0.587
$P_2 =$	0.0809	0.0749	0.0869
$P_3 =$	0.00291	0.00177	0.00405
$P_4 =$	0.000077	-0.00004	0.00019
$P_5 =$	0	0	0
$P_6 =$	0	0	0
$P_7 =$	0	0	0
$P_8 =$	0	0	0
$P_9 =$	0	0	0
$P_{10} =$	0	0	0

Printers:

Data

Number of Servers =	1

Interarrival Times

Distribution =	Constant
Value =	15

Service Times

Distribution =	Erlang
Mean =	10
k =	4

Length of Simulation Run

Number of Arrivals =	10,000

Run Simulation

Results

	Point Estimate	95% Confidence Interval Low	High
$L =$	0.729	0.718	0.74
$L_q =$	0.0636	0.0579	0.0693
$W =$	10.934	10.767	11.102
$W_q =$	0.954	0.868	1.0393
$P_0 =$	0.335	0.328	0.341
$P_1 =$	0.603	0.598	0.608
$P_2 =$	0.0614	0.0563	0.0665
$P_3 =$	0.00109	0.000496	0.00168
$P_4 =$	0	0	0
$P_5 =$	0	0	0
$P_6 =$	0	0	0
$P_7 =$	0	0	0
$P_8 =$	0	0	0
$P_9 =$	0	0	0
$P_{10} =$	0	0	0

The new inspection equipment would drastically reduce the average waiting time for both monitors (7.3 minutes to 1.3 minutes) and printers (7.6 minutes to less than 1 minute).

15.20 a)

Data

Number of Servers =	1

Interarrival Times

Distribution =	Exponential
Value =	30

Service Times

Distribution =	Erlang
Mean =	20
k =	8

Length of Simulation Run

Number of Arrivals =	100,000

Run Simulation

Results

	Point Estimate	95% Confidence Interval Low	High
$L =$	1.402	1.373	1.432
$L_q =$	0.738	0.711	0.764
$W =$	42.227	41.499	42.956
$W_q =$	22.212	21.498	22.927
$P_0 =$	0.335	0.331	0.34
$P_1 =$	0.3	0.297	0.303
$P_2 =$	0.177	0.175	0.179
$P_3 =$	0.0935	0.0914	0.0957
$P_4 =$	0.0474	0.0455	0.0492
$P_5 =$	0.0234	0.022	0.0248
$P_6 =$	0.0113	0.0103	0.0124
$P_7 =$	0.00588	0.00505	0.00671
$P_8 =$	0.00287	0.00232	0.00341
$P_9 =$	0.00139	0.001	0.00178
$P_{10} =$	0.000789	0.000478	0.0011

b)

Data

Number of Servers =	2

Interarrival Times

Distribution =	Exponential
Value =	14.3

Service Times

Distribution =	Erlang
Mean =	20
k =	8

Length of Simulation Run

Number of Arrivals =	100,000

Run Simulation

Results

	Point Estimate	95% Confidence Interval Low	High
$L =$	2.163	2.122	2.204
$L_q =$	0.769	0.735	0.804
$W =$	31.062	30.6	31.523
$W_q =$	11.048	10.6	11.496
$P_0 =$	0.171	0.168	0.174
$P_1 =$	0.264	0.261	0.268
$P_2 =$	0.225	0.222	0.227
$P_3 =$	0.147	0.145	0.149
$P_4 =$	0.0855	0.0833	0.0877
$P_5 =$	0.0488	0.0468	0.0507
$P_6 =$	0.0265	0.0249	0.0281
$P_7 =$	0.0149	0.0136	0.0163
$P_8 =$	0.00845	0.00734	0.00957
$P_9 =$	0.00423	0.00354	0.00503
$P_{10} =$	0.00212	0.00162	0.00262

15.21 a) $W_q = 0.56$ for the simulation run is smaller than for the queueing model (0.75).

Data

Number of Servers =	1

Interarrival Times

Distribution =	Exponential
Value =	0.3333

Service Times

Distribution =	Translated Exp.
Minimum =	0.0833
Mean =	0.25

Length of Simulation Run

Number of Arrivals =	25,000

Run Simulation

Results

	Point Estimate	95% Confidence Interval Low	High
$L =$	2.446	2.274	2.618
$L_q =$	1.693	1.53	1.856
$W =$	0.813	0.762	0.865
$W_q =$	0.563	0.513	0.613
$P_0 =$	0.246	0.235	0.258
$P_1 =$	0.225	0.216	0.234
$P_2 =$	0.164	0.158	0.17
$P_3 =$	0.111	0.107	0.116
$P_4 =$	0.0763	0.0718	0.0808
$P_5 =$	0.0536	0.0493	0.0579
$P_6 =$	0.0376	0.0336	0.0415
$P_7 =$	0.0271	0.0232	0.0309
$P_8 =$	0.0192	0.0156	0.0227
$P_9 =$	0.0136	0.0105	0.0166
$P_{10} =$	0.00933	0.00687	0.0118

b) $W_q = 0.179$ for the simulation run is smaller than for the queueing model (0.25).

Data

Number of Servers =	1

Interarrival Times

Distribution =	Exponential
Value =	0.5

Service Times

Distribution =	Translated Exp.
Minimum =	0.0833
Mean =	0.25

Length of Simulation Run

Number of Arrivals =	25,000

Run Simulation

Results

	Point Estimate	95% Confidence Interval Low	High
$L =$	0.852	0.823	0.881
$L_q =$	0.355	0.332	0.379
$W =$	0.428	0.416	0.44
$W_q =$	0.179	0.168	0.189
$P_0 =$	0.503	0.496	0.511
$P_1 =$	0.287	0.283	0.291
$P_2 =$	0.126	0.122	0.129
$P_3 =$	0.0493	0.0465	0.0521
$P_4 =$	0.0198	0.0178	0.0218
$P_5 =$	0.00839	0.00698	0.00981
$P_6 =$	0.00349	0.00265	0.00433
$P_7 =$	0.00161	0.000951	0.00226
$P_8 =$	0.000804	0.000328	0.00128
$P_9 =$	0.000371	0.000073	0.000668
$P_{10} =$	0.000222	0.00001	0.000435

c) $W_q = 0.23$ for the simulation run is smaller than for the queueing model (0.32).

	Data	
Number of Servers =		2

Interarrival Times

Distribution =	Exponential
Value =	0.167

Service Times

Distribution =	Translated Exp.
Minimum =	0.0833
Mean =	0.25

Length of Simulation Run

Number of Arrivals =	25,000

Run Simulation

Results

	Point Estimate	95% Confidence Interval Low	High
$L =$	2.91	2.745	3.0755
$L_q =$	1.407	1.257	1.556
$W =$	0.485	0.46	0.509
$W_q =$	0.234	0.211	0.258
$P_0 =$	0.141	0.133	0.149
$P_1 =$	0.215	0.206	0.223
$P_2 =$	0.192	0.185	0.199
$P_3 =$	0.14	0.135	0.146
$P_4 =$	0.0992	0.0942	0.104
$P_5 =$	0.0686	0.064	0.0732
$P_6 =$	0.0478	0.0434	0.052
$P_7 =$	0.0329	0.029	0.0369
$P_8 =$	0.0221	0.0188	0.0255
$P_9 =$	0.0142	0.0113	0.017
$P_{10} =$	0.00863	0.00632	0.0109

d) $W_q = 0.14$ for the simulation run is smaller than for the queueing model (0.19).

	Data	
Number of Servers =		3

Interarrival Times

Distribution =	Exponential
Value =	0.111

Service Times

Distribution =	Translated Exp.
Minimum =	0.0833
Mean =	0.25

Length of Simulation Run

Number of Arrivals =	25,000

Run Simulation

Results

	Point Estimate	95% Confidence Interval Low	High
$L =$	3.432	3.23	3.634
$L_q =$	1.215	1.0386	1.392
$W =$	0.385	0.365	0.405
$W_q =$	0.136	0.117	0.155
$P_0 =$	0.0777	0.0726	0.0829
$P_1 =$	0.174	0.165	0.182
$P_2 =$	0.203	0.195	0.211
$P_3 =$	0.171	0.164	0.177
$P_4 =$	0.12	0.115	0.125
$P_5 =$	0.0813	0.0768	0.0858
$P_6 =$	0.0546	0.0502	0.0591
$P_7 =$	0.0363	0.0323	0.0404
$P_8 =$	0.0231	0.0198	0.0264
$P_9 =$	0.0154	0.0127	0.0181
$P_{10} =$	0.0116	0.00901	0.0143

e) The results from a computer simulation can be quite sensitive to the probability distribution of service times. In a) to d), for example, the waiting times were typically 25% to 35% lower for the computer simulation runs than for the queueing models.

15.22 The simulation spreadsheet is shown below, and the @Risk results follow (1000 iterations). The probability of finishing in 22 months appears to be less than 2%.

	A	B	C	D	E	F	G	H
1		Immediate	Time Estimates			Start	Activity	Finish
2	Activity	Predecessor	o	m	p	Time	Time	Time
3	A	—	1.5	2	15	0	3.575679171	3.575679171
4	B	—	2	3.5	21	0	10.05252124	10.05252124
5	C	A	1	1.5	18	3.575679171	2.730574217	6.306253388
6	D	B	0.5	1	15	10.05252124	0.816185138	10.86870638
7	E	A	3	5	24	3.575679171	13.39355115	16.96923032
8	F	C	1	2	16	6.306253388	8.758827924	15.06508131
9	G	D	0.5	1	14	10.86870638	5.042382869	15.91108925
10	H	B	2.5	3.5	25	10.05252124	6.723277281	16.77579852
11	I	E, F	1	3	18	16.96923032	13.42055391	30.38978423
12	J	G, H	2	3	18	16.77579852	2.915871432	19.69166995
13								
14							Project Completion =	30.38978423
15							Project Deadline =	22
16							Deadline met (1=yes, 0=no)?	0

	F	G	H
1	Start	Activity	Finish
2	Time	Time	Time
3	0	=RiskTriang(C3,D3,E3)	=F3+G3
4	0	=RiskTriang(C4,D4,E4)	=F4+G4
5	=H3	=RiskTriang(C5,D5,E5)	=F5+G5
6	=H4	=RiskTriang(C6,D6,E6)	=F6+G6
7	=H3	=RiskTriang(C7,D7,E7)	=F7+G7
8	=H5	=RiskTriang(C8,D8,E8)	=F8+G8
9	=H6	=RiskTriang(C9,D9,E9)	=F9+G9
10	=H4	=RiskTriang(C10,D10,E10)	=F10+G10
11	=MAX(H7,H8)	=RiskTriang(C11,D11,E11)	=F11+G11
12	=MAX(H9,H10)	=RiskTriang(C12,D12,E12)	=F12+G12
13			
14		Project Completion =	=MAX(H11,H12)
15		Project Deadline =	22
16		Deadline met (1=yes, 0=no)?	=IF(H14<=H15,1,0)

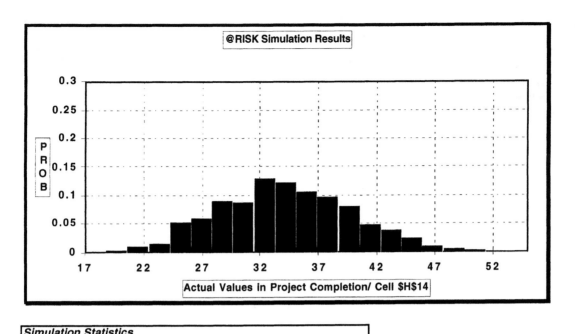

Actual Values in Project Completion/ Cell $H$14

Simulation Statistics		
Date: 7/7/99 at 21:35		
Iterations: 1000		
Simulations: 1		
Worksheet: [Prob22]		[Prob22]
Output Range: Project Completion		Deadline Met?
Cell: $H$14		$H$16
Minimum=	17.96710014	0
Maximum=	54.29407501	1
Mean=	33.42208051	0.019
Std Deviation=	5.911767542	0.136524723
Variance=	34.94899547	0.018639
Skewness=	0.242182767	7.046342806
Kurtosis=	2.90791179	50.65094694
Percentile Values		
5Perc=	24.10403433	0
10Perc=	25.70333328	0
15Perc=	27.18526602	0
20Perc=	28.23194313	0
25Perc=	29.16425562	0
30Perc=	30.25081844	0
35Perc=	31.08764973	0
40Perc=	31.71703453	0
45Perc=	32.37423325	0
50Perc=	33.16358757	0
55Perc=	33.97784405	0
60Perc=	34.6772171	0
65Perc=	35.58364754	0
70Perc=	36.4365715	0
75Perc=	37.35981274	0
80Perc=	38.30871277	0
85Perc=	39.35188961	0
90Perc=	41.20889206	0
95Perc=	43.43574772	0

15.23 The simulation spreadsheet is shown below, and the @Risk results follow (500 iterations). The mean claim appears to be approximately $2625.

	A	B
1	Claim Distribution	
2	0	0.4
3	$ 1,000.00	0.4
4	$ 11,000.00	0.2
5		
6	Claim Amount = $ 1,000.00	

	A	B
1	Claim Distribution	
2	0	0.4
3	=RiskUniform(0,2000)	0.4
4	=RiskUniform(2000,20000)	0.2
5		
6	Claim Amount =	=RiskDiscrete(A2:A4,B2:B4)

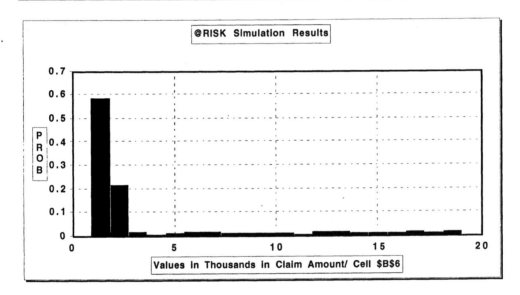

15-36

Simulation Statistics	
Date: 7/7/99 at 21:59	
Iterations: 500	
Simulations: 1	
Worksheet: [Prob23]	
Output Range: Claim Amount	
Cell: $B$6	
Minimum=	0
Maximum=	19849.88281
Mean=	2624.683288
Std Deviation=	4848.025365
Variance=	23503349.94
Skewness=	2.180795137
Kurtosis=	6.595068631
Percentile Values	
5Perc=	0
10Perc=	0
15Perc=	0
20Perc=	0
25Perc=	0
30Perc=	0
35Perc=	0
40Perc=	0
45Perc=	262.7447815
50Perc=	556.0119629
55Perc=	803.9009399
60Perc=	1061.196899
65Perc=	1298.03125
70Perc=	1547.103271
75Perc=	1754.229614
80Perc=	1994.602295
85Perc=	6324.703125
90Perc=	11616.77246
95Perc=	15360.12598

15.24 a) No replacement until breakdown occurs:

	A	B	C	D	E
1				Distribution of Time	
2	Days Until Breakdown =	5		Between Breakdowns	
3	Cost =	$ 11,000.00		Number	
4	Cost / Day =	$ 2,200.00		of Days	Probability
5				4	0.25
6				5	0.5
7				6	0.25

	B
2	=RiskDiscrete(D5:D7,E5:E7)
3	11000
4	=B3/B2

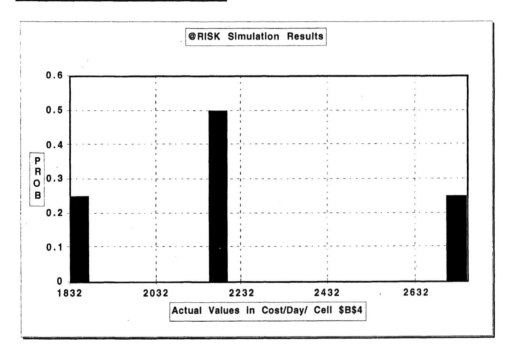

@RISK Simulation Results

Actual Values in Cost/Day/ Cell $B$4

15-38

Simulation Statistics	
Date: 7/7/99 at 22:16	
Iterations: 1000	
Simulations: 1	
Worksheet: [Prob24a]	
Output Range: Cost/Day	
Cell: $B$4	
Minimum=	1833.333374
Maximum=	2750
Mean=	2245.833344
Std Deviation=	327.3154568
Variance=	107135.4083
Skewness=	0.411847187
Kurtosis=	2.038062303
Percentile Values	
5Perc=	1833.333374
10Perc=	1833.333374
15Perc=	1833.333374
20Perc=	1833.333374
25Perc=	1833.333374
30Perc=	2200
35Perc=	2200
40Perc=	2200
45Perc=	2200
50Perc=	2200
55Perc=	2200
60Perc=	2200
65Perc=	2200
70Perc=	2200
75Perc=	2200
80Perc=	2750
85Perc=	2750
90Perc=	2750
95Perc=	2750

b) Scheduled replacement after 4 days:

	A	B	C	D	E
1				Distribution of Time	
2	Days Until Breakdown =	5		Between Breakdowns	
3	Cost =	$ 6,000.00		Number	
4	Cost / Day =	$ 1,500.00		of Days	Probability
5				4	0.25
6				5	0.5
7				6	0.25

	B
2	=RiskDiscrete(D5:D7,E5:E7)
3	=IF(B2=4,11000,6000)
4	=B3/4

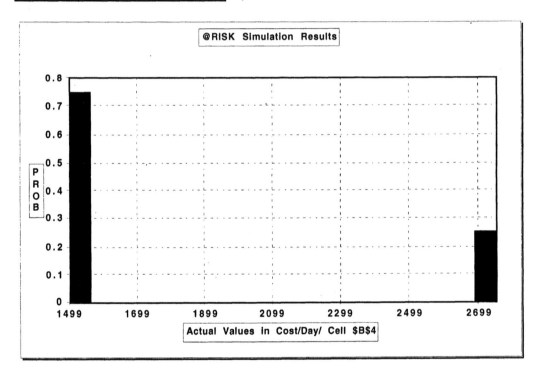

15-40

Simulation Statistics	
Date: 7/8/99 at 0:32	
Iterations: 1000	
Simulations: 1	
Worksheet: [Prob24b]	
Output Range: Cost/Day	
Cell: $B$4	
Minimum=	1500
Maximum=	2750
Mean=	1812.5
Std Deviation=	541.2658774
Variance=	292968.75
Skewness=	1.154700538
Kurtosis=	2.333333333
Percentile Values	
5Perc=	1500
10Perc=	1500
15Perc=	1500
20Perc=	1500
25Perc=	1500
30Perc=	1500
35Perc=	1500
40Perc=	1500
45Perc=	1500
50Perc=	1500
55Perc=	1500
60Perc=	1500
65Perc=	1500
70Perc=	1500
75Perc=	1500
80Perc=	2750
85Perc=	2750
90Perc=	2750
95Perc=	2750

c) Scheduled replacement after 5 days:

	A	B	C	D	E
1				Distribution of Time	
2	Days Until Breakdown =	5		Between Breakdowns	
3	Days Until Replacement =	5		Number	
4	Cost =	$ 11,000.00		of Days	Probability
5	Cost / Day =	$ 2,200.00		4	0.25
6				5	0.5
7				6	0.25

	B
2	=RiskDiscrete(D5:D7,E5:E7)
3	=MIN(5,B2)
4	=IF(B2<=5,11000,6000)
5	=B4/B3

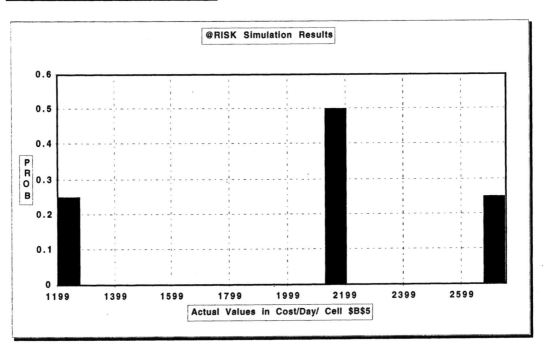

15-42

Simulation Statistics	
Date: 7/7/99 at 22:31	
Iterations: 1000	
Simulations: 1	
Worksheet: [Prob24c]	
Output Range: Cost/Day	
Cell: $B$5	
Minimum=	1200
Maximum=	2750
Mean=	2087.5
Std Deviation=	559.4361
Variance=	312968.75
Skewness=	-0.5788896
Kurtosis=	2.0759727
Percentile Values	
5Perc=	1200
10Perc=	1200
15Perc=	1200
20Perc=	1200
25Perc=	1200
30Perc=	2200
35Perc=	2200
40Perc=	2200
45Perc=	2200
50Perc=	2200
55Perc=	2200
60Perc=	2200
65Perc=	2200
70Perc=	2200
75Perc=	2200
80Perc=	2750
85Perc=	2750
90Perc=	2750
95Perc=	2750

d) The option of scheduling replacement every four days yields the lowest expected cost per day (approximately $1812.50).

15.25 The simulation spreadsheet and @Risk results are shown below. The expected cost with the proposed system of replacing all relays with the first failure is approximately $2.37 / hour. This is cheaper than their current system of replacing each relay as it fails. Therefore, they should replace all four relays with the first failure.

	A	B
1		Time to Failure (hours)
2	Relay 1	1500
3	Relay 2	1500
4	Relay 3	1500
5	Relay 4	1500
6		
7	First Failure Time =	1500
8	Time to End of Shutdown =	1502
9	Cost =	$2,800
10	Cost / Hour =	$1.86

	B
2	=RiskUniform(1000,2000)
3	=RiskUniform(1000,2000)
4	=RiskUniform(1000,2000)
5	=RiskUniform(1000,2000)
6	
7	=MIN(B2:B5)
8	=B7+2
9	2800
10	=B9/B8

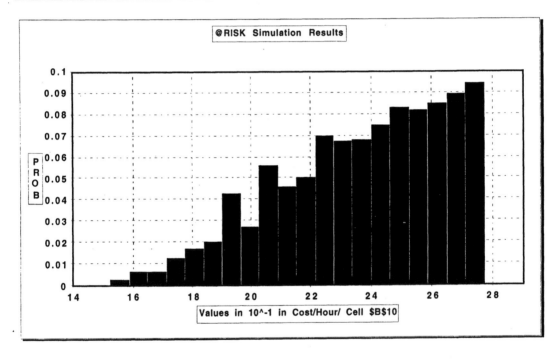

Simulation Statistics	
Date: 7/8/99 at 0:49	
Iterations: 1000	
Simulations: 1	
Worksheet: [Prob25]	
Output Range: Cost/Hour	
Cell: $B$10	
Minimum=	1.5042596
Maximum=	2.7938926
Mean=	2.3702155
Std Deviation=	0.2903318
Variance=	0.0842926
Skewness=	-0.5387744
Kurtosis=	2.4701799
Percentile Values	
5Perc=	1.8312686
10Perc=	1.9456343
15Perc=	2.0391303
20Perc=	2.0948352
25Perc=	2.1654532
30Perc=	2.227929
35Perc=	2.2687374
40Perc=	2.3186806
45Perc=	2.3694554
50Perc=	2.413556
55Perc=	2.4565992
60Perc=	2.4974302
65Perc=	2.5359856
70Perc=	2.5756141
75Perc=	2.6146076
80Perc=	2.6522719
85Perc=	2.6884112
90Perc=	2.7248517
95Perc=	2.7591258

15.26

	A	B	C	D	E
1	Shaft Distribution				Bushing Distribution
2	(Triangular)				(Normal)
3	Minimum =	1.000		Mean =	1.002
4	Most Likely =	1.001		Standard Dev. =	0.001
5	Maximum =	1.002			
6					
7	Shaft Radius =	1.001		Bushing Radius =	1.002
8					
9	Clearance =		0.001		
10	Interference? (1=yes, 0=no)		0		

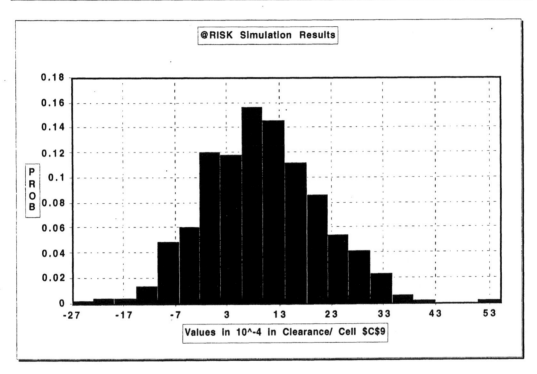

@RISK Simulation Results

Values in 10^-4 in Clearance/ Cell $C$9

Simulation Statistics		
Date: 7/7/99 at 22:52		
Iterations: 500		
Simulations: 1		
Worksheet: [Prob26]		[Prob26]
Output Range: Clearance		Interference
Cell: $C$9		$C$10
Minimum=	-0.002580988	0
Maximum=	0.005446819	1
Mean=	0.001001341	0.174
Std Deviation=	0.001088255	0.379109483
Variance=	1.1843E-06	0.143724
Skewness=	0.129383011	1.719819813
Kurtosis=	3.224675187	3.95778019
Percentile Values		
5Perc=	-0.000767469	0
10Perc=	-0.00032581	0
15Perc=	-6.7149E-05	0
20Perc=	5.32986E-05	0
25Perc=	0.00022788	0
30Perc=	0.000408646	0
35Perc=	0.000573805	0
40Perc=	0.000749844	0
45Perc=	0.000888586	0
50Perc=	0.00099161	0
55Perc=	0.00109613	0
60Perc=	0.001228148	0
65Perc=	0.00137	0
70Perc=	0.001513866	0
75Perc=	0.001731504	0
80Perc=	0.001875703	0
85Perc=	0.002145935	1
90Perc=	0.002475443	1
95Perc=	0.002878371	1

15.27 a) Option 2:

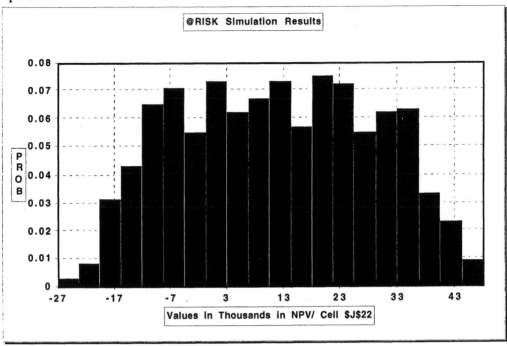

Simulation Statistics	
Date: 7/7/99 at 23:06	
Iterations: 1000	
Simulations: 1	
Worksheet: [Prob27]	
Output Range: NPV	
Cell: $J$22	
Minimum=	-25791.32617
Maximum=	46580.41406
Mean=	11547.39918
Std Deviation=	16386.60767
Variance=	268520911
Skewness=	-0.001998889
Kurtosis=	1.986458314
Percentile Values	
5Perc=	-13890.48525
10Perc=	-10431.59629
15Perc=	-7682.970483
20Perc=	-5201.45332
25Perc=	-2111.829041
30Perc=	501.982785
35Perc=	3289.138159
40Perc=	6137.576953
45Perc=	9038.039697
50Perc=	11793.09717
55Perc=	13929.08638
60Perc=	17264.95313
65Perc=	19709.53594
70Perc=	22204.24961
75Perc=	24534.8125
80Perc=	27785.38398
85Perc=	30690.3582
90Perc=	33634.53438
95Perc=	37353.37305

b) Option 3:

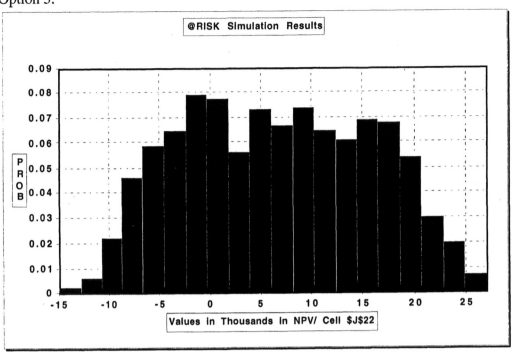

Simulation Statistics	
Date: 7/7/99 at 23:12	
Iterations: 1000	
Simulations: 1	
Worksheet: [Prob27]	
Output Range: NPV	
Cell: $J$22	
Minimum=	-14124.72363
Maximum=	26172.2168
Mean=	6580.300169
Std Deviation=	8834.92538
Variance=	78055906.46
Skewness=	0.035087097
Kurtosis=	1.984228551
Percentile Values	
5Perc=	-7179.637549
10Perc=	-5117.790088
15Perc=	-3601.592346
20Perc=	-2010.522168
25Perc=	-731.961853
30Perc=	626.2370483
35Perc=	1854.629413
40Perc=	3552.943408
45Perc=	4882.023315
50Perc=	6519.886475
55Perc=	8024.979858
60Perc=	9371.307617
65Perc=	10809.82715
70Perc=	12406.08984
75Perc=	14020.00659
80Perc=	15549.94551
85Perc=	16852.32041
90Perc=	18397.16484
95Perc=	20468.98721

c) Option 1 appears to be the best. It has the highest expected NPV ($18,130 vs. $11,547 vs. $6580) *and* there is less chance of losing money (almost 20% vs. greater than 25% for options 2 and 3).

15.28 a-c)

	A	B	C	D	E	F	G
2	Win (1=yes, 0=no)?	1					
3							
4	Toss	Die 1	Die 2	Sum	Win?	Lose?	Continue?
5	1	3	3	6	0	0	Yes
6	2	3	3	6	1	0	No
7	3	3	3	6	NA	NA	No
8	4	3	3	6	NA	NA	No
9	5	3	3	6	NA	NA	No
10	6	3	3	6	NA	NA	No
11	7	3	3	6	NA	NA	No
12	8	3	3	6	NA	NA	No
13	9	3	3	6	NA	NA	No
14	10	3	3	6	NA	NA	No
15	11	3	3	6	NA	NA	No
16	12	3	3	6	NA	NA	No
17	13	3	3	6	NA	NA	No
18	14	3	3	6	NA	NA	No
19	15	3	3	6	NA	NA	No
20	16	3	3	6	NA	NA	No
21	17	3	3	6	NA	NA	No
22	18	3	3	6	NA	NA	No
23	19	3	3	6	NA	NA	No
24	20	3	3	6	NA	NA	No
25	21	3	3	6	NA	NA	No
26	22	3	3	6	NA	NA	No
27	23	3	3	6	NA	NA	No
28	24	3	3	6	NA	NA	No
29	25	3	3	6	NA	NA	No
30	26	3	3	6	NA	NA	No
31	27	3	3	6	NA	NA	No
32	28	3	3	6	NA	NA	No
33	29	3	3	6	NA	NA	No
34	30	3	3	6	NA	NA	No

	B	C	D
5	=RiskDuniform({1,2,3,4,5,6})	=RiskDuniform({1,2,3,4,5,6})	=B5+C5
6	=RiskDuniform({1,2,3,4,5,6})	=RiskDuniform({1,2,3,4,5,6})	=B6+C6
7	=RiskDuniform({1,2,3,4,5,6})	=RiskDuniform({1,2,3,4,5,6})	=B7+C7
8	=RiskDuniform({1,2,3,4,5,6})	=RiskDuniform({1,2,3,4,5,6})	=B8+C8
9	=RiskDuniform({1,2,3,4,5,6})	=RiskDuniform({1,2,3,4,5,6})	=B9+C9

	E	F	G
5	=IF(OR(D5=7,D5=11),1,0)	=IF(OR(D5=2,D5=3,D5=12),1,0)	=IF(E5+F5=1,"No","Yes")
6	=IF(G5="Yes",IF(D6=$D$5,1,0),"NA")	=IF(G5="Yes",IF(D6=7,1,0),"NA")	=IF(G5="Yes",IF(E6+F6=1,"No","Yes"),"No")
7	=IF(G6="Yes",IF(D7=$D$5,1,0),"NA")	=IF(G6="Yes",IF(D7=7,1,0),"NA")	=IF(G6="Yes",IF(E7+F7=1,"No","Yes"),"No")
8	=IF(G7="Yes",IF(D8=$D$5,1,0),"NA")	=IF(G7="Yes",IF(D8=7,1,0),"NA")	=IF(G7="Yes",IF(E8+F8=1,"No","Yes"),"No")
9	=IF(G8="Yes",IF(D9=$D$5,1,0),"NA")	=IF(G8="Yes",IF(D9=7,1,0),"NA")	=IF(G8="Yes",IF(E9+F9=1,"No","Yes"),"No")

d) Answers will vary. There is a fair amount of variability in the number of wins, so a large number of iterations (e.g., 10,000) are necessary to predict the true probability.

Case Problems

15.1 Current Situation: A simulation run (shown below) indicates that the average number of jobs in the system is 1.9. Of these, half will be platen castings (0.95) and half will be housing castings (0.95). The waiting cost is therefore ($200)(0.95) + ($100)(0.95) = $285 / hour.

Current Situation

Data

Number of Servers =	2

Interarrival Times

Distribution =	Exponential
Mean =	15

Service Times

Distribution =	Translated Exponential
Minimum Value =	10
Mean =	20

Length of Simulation Run

Number of Arrivals =	10,000

[**Run Simulation**]

Results

	Point Estimate	95% Confidence Interval Low	High
$L =$	1.90473734	1.81035793	1.99911674
$L_q =$	0.59841056	0.52743245	0.66938867
$W =$	29.0126292	27.9716675	30.0535909
$W_q =$	9.114886	8.1501552	10.0796168
$P_0 =$	0.20397713	0.19264639	0.21530787
$P_1 =$	0.28571897	0.27485167	0.29658627
$P_2 =$	0.2218313	0.2143161	0.22934649
$P_3 =$	0.13716649	0.13013886	0.14419411
$P_4 =$	0.07180874	0.06554342	0.07807405
$P_5 =$	0.03911113	0.03335364	0.04486862
$P_6 =$	0.01984847	0.01572564	0.0239713
$P_7 =$	0.01055801	0.00758385	0.01353217
$P_8 =$	0.00531947	0.00315077	0.00748817
$P_9 =$	0.00231608	0.00116563	0.00346654
$P_{10} =$	0.00146818	0.00041766	0.00251871

Proposal 1: A simulation run (shown below) indicates that the average number of jobs in the system with three planers is approximately 1.46. Of these, half will be platen castings (0.73) and half will be housing castings (0.73). The waiting cost is therefore ($200)(0.73) + ($100)(0.73) = $219 / hour. The savings ($66 / hour) is substantially more than the added cost of the third planer ($30 / hour), so this looks to be worthwhile. The net savings would be $36 / hour.

Proposal 1

Data

Number of Servers =	3

Interarrival Times

Distribution =	Exponential
Mean =	15

Service Times

Distribution =	Translated Exponential
Minimum Value =	10
Mean =	20

Length of Simulation Run

Number of Arrivals =	10,000

[**Run Simulation**]

Results

	Point Estimate	95% Confidence Interval Low	High
$L =$	1.4567689	1.41377127	1.49976653
$L_q =$	0.10973775	0.09249252	0.12698298
$W =$	21.7295877	21.3625419	22.0966335
$W_q =$	1.63688018	1.39559645	1.87816392
$P_0 =$	0.24863392	0.23901401	0.25825383
$P_1 =$	0.33856279	0.33024864	0.34687694
$P_2 =$	0.22994152	0.22306044	0.23682261
$P_3 =$	0.1130194	0.1074762	0.11856259
$P_4 =$	0.04531033	0.04124076	0.0493799
$P_5 =$	0.01487792	0.01250839	0.01724745
$P_6 =$	0.00557272	0.00402145	0.00712399
$P_7 =$	0.00269386	0.00159608	0.00379164
$P_8 =$	0.00118696	0.00037629	0.00199763
$P_9 =$	0.0001609	-2.8773E-05	0.00035057
$P_{10} =$	3.9681E-05	-3.7977E-05	0.00011734

Proposal 2: A simulation run (shown below) indicates that the average number of jobs in the system with constant interarrival times is approximately 1.40. Of these, half will be platen castings (0.70) and half will be housing castings (0.70). The waiting cost is therefore ($200)(0.70) + ($100)(0.70) = $210 / hour. The savings ($75 / hour) is somewhat more than the added cost of changing the preceding production cost ($60 / hour). The net savings ($15) is less than for proposal 1, so this option is less worthwhile.

Proposal 2

Data

Number of Servers =	2

Interarrival Times

Distribution =	Constant
Value =	15

Service Times

Distribution =	Translated Exponential
Minimum Value =	10
Mean =	20

Length of Simulation Run

Number of Arrivals =	10,000

[Run Simulation]

Results

	Point Estimate	95% Confidence Interval Low	High
L =	1.40021685	1.37657912	1.42385458
L_q =	0.06087211	0.04688633	0.07485789
W =	21.0032527	20.6486868	21.3578187
W_q =	0.91308164	0.70329497	1.12286832
P_0 =	0.0507294	0.0485373	0.05292149
P_1 =	0.55919647	0.5490678	0.56932514
P_2 =	0.33758206	0.32938548	0.34577865
P_3 =	0.04717064	0.04194527	0.05239601
P_4 =	0.00402596	0.00223602	0.0058159
P_5 =	0.00037505	-2.6602E-05	0.00077669
P_6 =	0.00026694	-0.00025512	0.000789
P_7 =	0.00046426	-0.0004437	0.00137222
P_8 =	0.00018922	-0.00018084	0.00055929
P_9 =	0	0	0
P_{10} =	0	0	0

Proposal 1 and 2: A simulation run (shown below) indicates that the average number of jobs in the system with both three planers and constant interarrival times is approximately 1.33. Of these, half will be platen castings (0.665) and half will be housing castings (0.665). The waiting cost is therefore ($200)(0.665) + ($100)(0.665) = $200 / hour. The savings ($85 / hour) is less than the combined cost of adding a third planer and changing the preceding production cost ($90 / hour), so this combined option does not appear to be worthwhile.

Proposal 1 and 2

Data

Number of Servers =	3

Interarrival Times

Distribution =	Constant
Value =	15

Service Times

Distribution =	Translated Exponential
Minimum Value =	10
Mean =	20

Length of Simulation Run

Number of Arrivals =	10,000

[Run Simulation]

Results

	Point Estimate	95% Confidence Interval Low	High
L =	1.3337841	1.32084457	1.34672363
L_q =	0.00087734	0.00026928	0.00148541
W =	20.0067615	19.8126686	20.2008545
W_q =	0.01316016	0.00403913	0.0222812
P_0 =	0.05617206	0.05408543	0.05825869
P_1 =	0.58758437	0.5796862	0.59548254
P_2 =	0.32340833	0.31585866	0.330958
P_3 =	0.03197872	0.02902062	0.03493681
P_4 =	0.00083571	0.00026183	0.00140959
P_5 =	2.0817E-05	-1.9966E-05	6.16E-05
P_6 =	0	0	0
P_7 =	0	0	0
P_8 =	0	0	0
P_9 =	0	0	0
P_{10} =	0	0	0

<u>Overall recommendation:</u> Proposal 1 appears to be the most worthwhile, with a net savings of about $36 / hour over the current situation. Other proposals that may be worth looking into should include giving priority to platen castings, because of the higher waiting cost for that type of job.

15.2   a)   Before we begin the formal problem, we must first calculate the mean μ and standard deviation σ of the normally distributed random variable N. We are told that the annual interest rate will be used to estimate μ and the historical annual volatility will be used to estimate σ. Because the case is simulating weekly – not yearly – change, we must convert these yearly values to weekly values.

We first convert the annual interest rate $r = 8$ percent to a weekly interest rate w with the following formula:

$$
\begin{aligned}
w &= (1 + r)^{(1/52)} - 1 \\
&= (1 + 0.08)^{(1/52)} - 1 \\
&= (1.08)^{(1/52)} - 1 \\
&= 0.00148
\end{aligned}
$$

We next convert the annual volatility $V_a = 0.30$ to a weekly volatility V_w with the following formula:

$$
\begin{aligned}
V_w &= V_a / \sqrt{52} \\
&= 0.30 / \sqrt{52} \\
&= 0.0416
\end{aligned}
$$

Once we have the weekly interest rate and volatility, we can calculate μ and σ.

$$
\begin{aligned}
\mu &= w - 0.5(V_w)^2 \\
&= 0.00148 - 0.5(0.0416)^2 \\
&= 0.0006
\end{aligned}
$$

$$
\begin{aligned}
\sigma &= V_w \\
&= 0.0416
\end{aligned}
$$

1.   One component appears in this system: the stock price. The stock price in the previous week is used to calculate the stock price in the next week. The relationship between the stock price in the previous week and the stock price in the next week is given by $s_n = e^N s_c$.

2.   State of the system: $P(t)$ = price of the stock at time t.

3. This simulation requires generating a series of random observations from the normal distribution. Each random observation is a normally distributed random variable that determines the increase or decrease of the stock price at the end of next week. The random variable is substituted for N in the following equation:

$$s_n = e^N s_c$$

To generate a series of random variables, we repeatedly use the function for generating a normally distributed random variable provided by the @RISK software add-in for Excel. This function is RiskNormal(μ, σ) where $\mu = 0.0006$ and $\sigma = 0.0416$.

4. The formula $s_n = e^N s_c$ gives us a procedure for changing the price (the state of the system) when an event occurs.

5. In this simulation, the time periods are fixed. We have a twelve-week period, and we need to calculate the change in the stock price each week. We have a formula $s_n = e^N s_c$ that relates the stock price at the end of the next week to the stock price at the end of the previous week. Thus, we do not have to worry about advancing the clock. We simply have to generate N for each of the twelve weeks.

6. We need to build a spreadsheet using the @RISK software add-in for Excel. We start with the current stock price of $42.00. We then use the formula $s_n = e^N s_c$ to calculate the stock price at the end of each of the twelve weeks. We substitute the @RISK function RiskNormal(μ, σ) for N.

We then use the stock price at the end of the twelfth week to calculate the value of the option at the end of the twelfth week. If the stock price at the end of the twelfth week is greater than the exercise price of $44.00, the value of the option is the difference between the value of the stock at the end of the twelfth week and the exercise price. If the stock price at the end of the twelfth week is less than or equal to the exercise price of $44.00, the value of the option is $0.

Finally, we need to discount the value of the option at the end of the twelfth week to the value of the option in today's dollars using the following formula:

$$\frac{\text{Value of the option at the end of the twelfth week}}{(1.00148)^{12}}$$

The spreadsheet formulas are shown below:

Current Stock Price	42		Annual IR	0.08
Price at End of Week:			Weekly IR	=((1+Annual_IR)^(1/52))-1
One	=EXP(RiskNormal(Mu, Sigma))*B2		Mu	=Weekly_IR-0.5*(Weekly_V^2)
Two	=EXP(RiskNormal(Mu,Sigma))*B4			
Three	=EXP(RiskNormal(Mu,Sigma))*B5		Annual V	0.3
Four	=EXP(RiskNormal(Mu,Sigma))*B6		Weekly V	=Annual_V/(52^(1/2))
Five	=EXP(RiskNormal(Mu,Sigma))*B7		Sigma	=Weekly_V
Six	=EXP(RiskNormal(Mu,Sigma))*B8			
Seven	=EXP(RiskNormal(Mu,Sigma))*B9			
Eight	=EXP(RiskNormal(Mu,Sigma))*B10			
Nine	=EXP(RiskNormal(Mu,Sigma))*B11			
Ten	=EXP(RiskNormal(Mu,Sigma))*B12			
Eleven	=EXP(RiskNormal(Mu,Sigma))*B13			
Twelve	=EXP(RiskNormal(Mu,Sigma))*B14			

| Price of Option at End of Week Twelve | =IF(End_Price>44, End_Price-44, 0) |
| Price of Option Today | =Option/(1+Weekly_IR)^12 |

b) After running the appropriate number of simulation iterations, the mean of the cell labeled the "Price of Option Today" is the price of the option in today's dollars.

Number of Iterations	Price of Option
100	$1.70
500	$1.95
1000	$1.84

c) Using the Black-Scholes Formula, the price of the option is $1.88. The spreadsheet of formulas used to calculate the Black-Scholes Formula in Excel follows:

			Black-Scholes	
Annual IR	0.08		d1	=(LN(Current_Price/(44/(1+Weekly_IR)^12))/(Weekly_V*12^(1/2)) + (Weekly_V*12^(1/2))/2
Weekly IR	=((1+Annual_IR)^(1/52))-1		d2	=_d1-Weekly_V*12^(1/2)
Mu	=Weekly_IR-0.5*(Weekly_V^2)			
			N[d1]	=NORMSDIST(_d1)
Annual V	0.3		N[d2]	=NORMSDIST(_d2)
Weekly V	=Annual_V/(52^(1/2))			
Sigma	=Weekly_V		V	=N_d1*Current_Price-N_d2*(44/(1+Weekly_IR)^12)

The spreadsheet showing the values used in the Black-Scholes formula follows:

		Black-Scholes	
Annual IR	0.08	d1	-0.127503153
Weekly IR	0.001481116	d2	-0.271618491
Mu	0.000615731		
		N[d1]	0.449271051
Annual V	0.3	N[d2]	0.39295775
Weekly V	0.041602515		
Sigma	0.041602515	V	$1.88

The price of the option obtained by simulation and the price of the option obtained by the Black-Scholes formula are amazingly close. The 1000-iteration simulation price is off by just four cents!

d) No, a random walk does not completely describe the price movement of the stock because the random walk assumes a consistent lognormal increase or decrease in the price of the stock. The price of the stock could change according to a different distribution, however, especially if an event occurs to trigger a dramatic increase or decrease in the stock. In this case, the European Space Agency may award Fellare the International Space Station contract. The award notice would most likely trigger a dramatic movement in the stock. The random walk does not take into account this dramatic event.

Review Questions

16.1-1 A corner point is a point that lies at a corner of the feasible region.

16.1-2 The corner point with the best value of the objective function is the optimal solution.

16.1-3 The simplex method has a way of quickly getting to the best corner point and detecting that this point is optimal, so it stops without needing to evaluate the rest of the corner points.

16.1-4 No. It can have one optimal solution, an infinite number of optimal solutions, or no optimal solution.

16.1-5 Yes, and every point of the line segment between these two corner points will be an optimal solution.

16.1-6 The constraints of a linear programming problem can be so restrictive that it is impossible for a solution to satisfy all of the constraints simultaneously.

16.1-7 If some necessary constraint were not included in the linear programming model, it is possible to have no limit on the best objective function value.

16.2-2 The best corner point is always an optimal solution.

16.2-2 The big advantage of searching for an optimal solution simply by finding the best corner point is that it tremendously reduces the number of solutions that need to be considered.

16.2-3 When the simplex method is ready to move from the current corner point to the next one, the adjacent corner points are candidates to be the next one.

16.2-4 If none of the adjacent corner points are better than the current corner point, then the current corner point is an optimal solution.

16.2-5 If the simultaneous solution of a set of constraint boundary equations is feasible then that solution is a corner point.

16.2-6 Two corner points are adjacent to each other if they share all but one of the same constraint boundaries.

16.2-7 The simplex method examines corner points in an order such that each one is adjacent to the preceding one. This greatly streamlines the algebra.

16.2-8 A problem with 20 decision variable and 30 functional constraints might have more than a billion corner points.

16.2-9 The simplex method can solve problems that the enumeration-of-corner-points method cannot because it is able to reach and identify the optimal corner point for a large problem after examining only a small fraction of all the corner points.

16.3-1 The simplex method focuses solely on solutions that are corner points.

16.3-2 Each iteration of the simplex method consists of a prescribed series of steps for moving from the current corner point to a new corner point.

16.3-3 Management science algorithms typically are iterative algorithms.

16.3-4 Whenever possible, the initialization step of the simplex method chooses the origin (0,0) to be the initial corner point to be examined.

16.3-5 When the simplex method finishes examining a corner point it then gathers information about the adjacent corner points. It identifies the rates of improvement in the objective function along the edges that lead to the adjacent corner points.

16.3-6 The optimality test consists simply of checking whether any of the edges give a positive rate of improvement in the objective function. If none do, then the current point is optimal.

16.4-1 A problem with several thousand functional constraints and many thousand decision variables is not considered unusually large for a fast computer.

16.4-2 The software package needs to help formulate, input, and modify the model. In addition is should analyze solutions from the model and present results in the language of management.

16.5-1 Narenda Karmarkar developed a new linear programming algorithm using the interior-point approach.

16.5-2 Today, the more powerful software packages include at least one interior-point algorithm along with the simplex method.

16.5-3 Interior-point algorithms shoot through the interior of the feasible region toward an optimal solution instead of taking a less direct path around the boundary of the feasible region.

16.5-4 The computer time per iteration for an interior-point algorithm is many times longer than for the simplex method.

16.5-5 For fairly small problems, the number of iterations needed by an interior-point algorithm and the simplex method tend to be somewhat comparable. For large problems, interior-point algorithms do not need many more iterations while the simplex method does. The reason for the large difference is the difference in the paths followed.

16.5-6 The simplex method is very well suited for what-if analysis while the interior-point approach currently has limited capability in this area.

16.5-7 The limited capability for performing what-if analysis can be overcome by switching over to the simplex method.

16.5-8 Switching over begins by identifying a corner point that is very close to the final trial solution.

Problems

16.1

Corner Point (A_1, A_2)	Profit = $\$1000A_1 + \$2{,}000A_2$
(0,0)	$0
(8,0)	$8,000
(6,4)	$14,000
(5,5)	$15,000
(0,6.667)	$13,333

Optimal Solution: $(A_1, A_2) = (5,5)$ and profit = $15,000.

16.2

Corner Point (TV,PM)	Cost = TV + 2PM
(0,9)	$18
(4,3)	$12
(8,3)	$14

Optimal Solution: (TV,PM) = (4,3) and cost = $12.

16.3   a & d)

Resource	Resource Usage Per Unit of Each Activity		Totals		Resource Available
	Activity 1	Activity 2			
A	1	0	3.000	≤	5
B	0	1	3.000	≤	4
C	2	1	9.00	≤	9
D	3	4	21	≤	21
Unit Profit	30	20	$ 150.00		
Solution	3.000	3.000			

b & e)   Optimal Solution: $(x_1, x_2) = (3,3)$ and Profit = $150

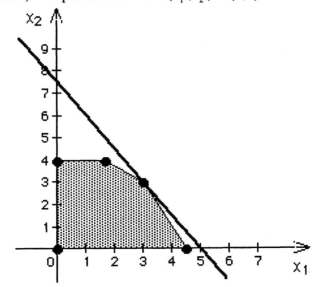

Corner Points: (0,0), (4.5,0), (3,3), (1.667,4), and (0,4).

c)

Corner Point (x_1,x_2)	Profit = $30x_1 + 20x_2$
(0,0)	$0
(4.5,0)	$135
(3,3)	$150
(1.667,4)	$130
(0,4)	$80

Optimal Solution: $(x_1,x_2) = (3,3)$ and Profit = $150

16.4   a & d)

Resource	Resource Usage Per Unit of Each Activity		Totals		Resource Available
	Activity 1	Activity 2			
A	5	3	30.000	≤	30
B	2	3	21.000	≤	21
C	0	1	5	≤	6
Unit Profit	300	200	$ 1,900.00		
Solution	3.000	5.000			

b & e)   Optimal Solution: $(x_1,x_2) = (3,5)$ and Profit = $1900

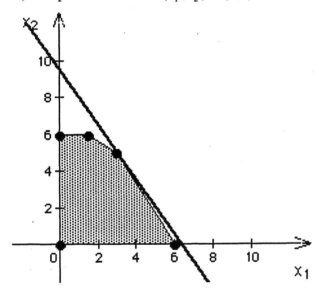

Corner Points: (0,0), (6,0), (3,5), (1.5,6), and (0,6).

c)

Corner Point (x_1,x_2)	Profit = $300x_1 + 200x_2$
(0,0)	$0
(6,0)	$1800
(3,5)	$1900
(1.5,6)	$1650
(0,6)	$1200

Optimal Solution: $(x_1,x_2) = (3,5)$ and Profit = $1900

CD16-4

16.5   a)   Objective Function: Profit = $400x_1 + $400x_2$
              Optimal Solution: $(x_1, x_2) = (2,6)$ and Profit = $3200

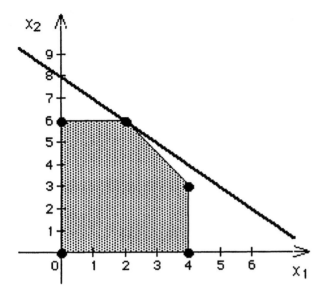

              Objective Function: Profit = $500x_1 + $300x_2$
              Optimal Solution: $(x_1, x_2) = (4,3)$ and Profit = $2900

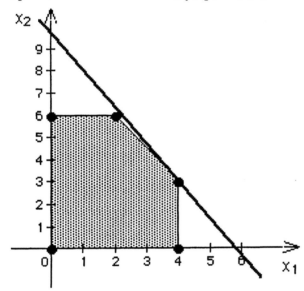

Objective Function: Profit = $300x_1 - $100x_2$
Optimal Solution: $(x_1, x_2) = (4,0)$ and Profit = $1200

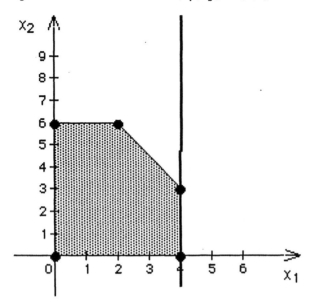

Objective Function: Profit = -$100x_1 + $500x_2$
Optimal Solution: $(x_1, x_2) = (0,6)$ and Profit = $3000

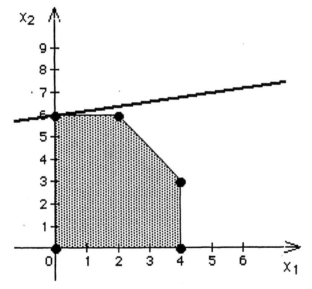

Objective Function: Profit = -100x_1$ - 100x_2$
Optimal Solution: (x_1 ,x_2) = (0,0) and Profit = $0

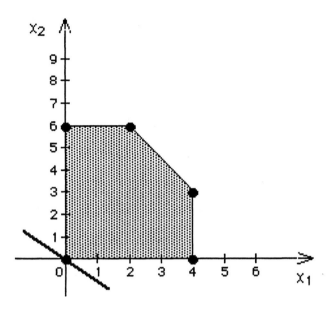

b) Objective Function: Profit = $400x_1 + $400x_2$
    Optimal Solution: $(x_1, x_2) = (2,6)$ and Profit = $3200

Corner Point (x_1, x_2)	Profit = $400x_1 + $400x_2$
(0,0)	$0
(0,6)	$2400
(4,0)	$1600
(2,6)	$3200
(4,3)	$2800

Objective Function: Profit = $500x_1 + $300x_2$
Optimal Solution: $(x_1, x_2) = (4,3)$ and Profit = $2900

Corner Point (x_1, x_2)	Profit = $500x_1 + $300x_2$
(0,0)	$0
(0,6)	$1800
(4,0)	$2000
(2,6)	$2800
(4,3)	$2900

Objective Function: Profit = $300x_1 - $100x_2$
Optimal Solution: $(x_1, x_2) = (4,0)$ and Profit = $1200

Corner Point (x_1, x_2)	Profit = $300x_1 - $100x_2$
(0,0)	$0
(0,6)	-$600
(4,0)	$1200
(2,6)	$0
(4,3)	$900

Objective Function: Profit = -$100x_1 + $500x_2$
Optimal Solution: $(x_1, x_2) = (0,6)$ and Profit = $3000

Corner Point (x_1, x_2)	Profit = -$100x_1 + $500x_2$
(0,0)	$0
(0,6)	$3000
(4,0)	-$400
(2,6)	$2800
(4,3)	$1100

Objective Function: Profit = -$100x_1 - $100x_2$
Optimal Solution: $(x_1, x_2) = (0,0)$ and Profit = $0

Corner Point (x_1, x_2)	Profit = -$100x_1 - $100x_2$
(0,0)	$0
(0,6)	-$600
(4,0)	-$400
(2,6)	-$800
(4,3)	-$700

16.6 a) True. (Ex. Maximize Profit = $-x_1 + 4x_2$)

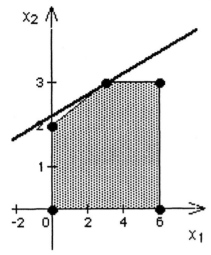

b) True. (Ex. Maximize Profit = $-x_1 + 3x_2$)

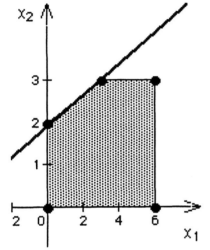

c) False. (Ex. Maximize Profit = $-x_1 - x_2$)

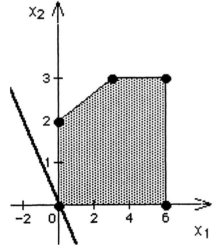

16.7 a)

$$x_1 \leq 6$$
$$x_2 \leq 3$$
$$-x_1 + 3x_2 \leq 6$$

b)

Unit Profit Product 1	Unit Profit Product 2	Objective Function	Multiple Optimal Solutions
-$1	$3	Profit = $-x_1 + 3x_2$	line segment between (0,2) & (3,3)
0	$1	Profit = x_2	line segment between (3,3) & (6,3)
$1	0	Profit = x_1	line segment between (6,3) & (6,0)
0	-$1	Profit = $-x_2$	line segment between (0,0) & (6,0)
-$1	0	Profit = $-x_1$	line segment between (0,0) & (0,2)

c) Objective Function: Profit = $-x_1 + 5x_2$
   Optimal Solution: $(x_1, x_2) = (3,3)$ and Profit = $12

Corner Point (x_1, x_2)	Profit = $-x_1 + 5x_2$
(0,0)	$0
(0,2)	$10
(3,3)	$12
(6,3)	$9
(6,0)	-$6

d) Objective Function: Profit = $-x_1 + 2x_2$
   Optimal Solution: $(x_1, x_2) = (0,2)$ and Profit = $4

Corner Point (x_1, x_2)	Profit = $-x_1 + 2x_2$
(0,0)	$0
(0,2)	$4
(3,3)	$3
(6,3)	$0
(6,0)	-$6

16.8 a)

Resource	Resource Usage Per Unit of Each Activity		Totals		Resource Available
	Activity 1	Activity 2			
A	5	4	16.25	≤	20
B	6	9	30	≤	30
C	2	5	15	≤	15
Unit Profit	20	30	$ 100.00		
Solution	1.25	2.5			

Adjustable Cells

Cell	Name	Final Value	Reduced Cost	Objective Coefficient	Allowable Increase	Allowable Decrease
$B$7	Solution Activity 1	1.25	0.000	20	0	8
$C$7	Solution Activity 2	2.5	0.000	30	20	0

Constraints

Cell	Name	Final Value	Shadow Price	Constraint R.H. Side	Allowable Increase	Allowable Decrease
$D$3	A Totals	16.25	0.000	20	1E+30	3.75
$D$4	B Totals	30	3.333	30	2.647058823	3
$D$5	C Totals	15	0	15	1.666666667	2.142857143

b) The sensitivity report indicates that the problem has other optimal solutions because the allowable increase of Activity 1 and the allowable decrease of Activity 2 are 0.

Resource	Resource Usage Per Unit of Each Activity		Totals		Resource Available
	Activity 1	Activity 2			
A	5	4	20.00	≤	20
B	6	9	30	≤	30
C	2	5	12.85714	≤	15
Unit Profit	20	29.9	$ 99.86		
Solution	2.857	1.429			

c) The other optimal solutions will be located on the line segment connecting the two optimal solutions found in parts a) and b).

d) Optimal Solution: $(x_1, x_2) = (2.857, 1.429)$, $(1.25, 2.5)$ and all points on the connecting line. Profit = $100 million.

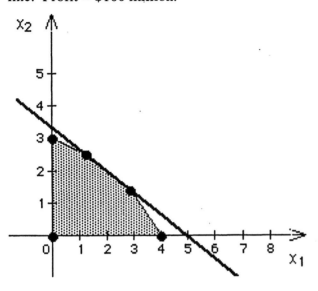

16.9   a)

| Resource | Resource Usage Per Unit of Each Activity | | Totals | Resource Available |
	Activity 1	Activity 2		
A	15	5	300 ≤	300
B	10	6	240 ≤	240
C	8	12	300 ≤	450
Unit Profit	500	300	$ 12,000	
Solution	15	15		

Adjustable Cells

Cell	Name	Final Value	Reduced Cost	Objective Coefficient	Allowable Increase	Allowable Decrease
$B$7	Solution Activity 1	15	0.00	500	400	0
$C$7	Solution Activity 2	15	0.0	300	0	133.3333333

Constraints

Cell	Name	Final Value	Shadow Price	Constraint R.H. Side	Allowable Increase	Allowable Decrease
$D$3	A Totals	300	0.00	300	60	83.33333333
$D$4	B Totals	240	50	240	42.85714286	40
$D$5	C Totals	300	0	450	1E+30	150

b) The sensitivity report indicates that the problem has other optimal solutions because the allowable decrease of Activity 1 and the allowable increase of Activity 2 are 0.

| Resource | Resource Usage Per Unit of Each Activity | | Totals | Resource Available |
	Activity 1	Activity 2		
A	15	5	217 ≤	300
B	10	6	240 ≤	240
C	8	12	450 ≤	450
Unit Profit	500	301	$ 12,036	
Solution	2.5	35.833		

c) The other optimal solutions will be located on the line segment connecting the two optimal solutions found in parts a) and b).

d) Optimal Solution: $(x_1, x_2) = (15,15)$, $(2.5, 35.833)$ and all points on the connecting line. Profit = $12,000.

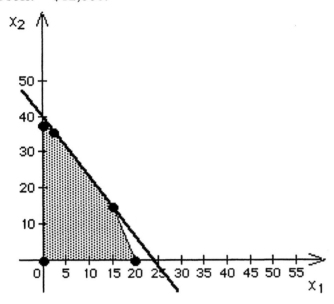

16.10 Feasible Region:

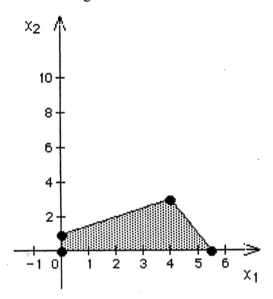

<u>Case 1 ($c_2 = 0$):</u>
If $c_1 > 0$, objective increases as x_1 increases, so the optimal solution is $(x_1, x_2) = (5.5, 0)$.
If $c_2 < 0$, opposite is true, so the optimal solution is $(x_1, x_2) = (0,0)$, $(0, 1)$ and the connecting line.
(Note if $c_1 = 0$, *every* feasible point gives the optimal solution, as $0\ x_1 + 0\ x_2 = 0$).

<u>Case 2 ($c_2 > 0$):</u> (slope of objective function line is $-(c_1 / c_2)$)
If $-(c_1 / c_2) > 1/2$ (or equivalently, $c_1/c_2 < -1/2$), then the optimal solution is $(x_1, x_2) = (0,1)$.
If $-(c_1 / c_2) < -2$, then the optimal solution is $(x_1, x_2) = (5.5, 0)$.
If $1/2 > -(c_1 / c_2) > -2$, then the optimal solution is $(x_1, x_2) = (4,3)$.
(Note, if $-(c_1 / c_2) = 1/2$ or -2, then the optimal solution is at $(4,3)$ and $(0,1)$ or $(5.5,0)$, respectively, along with the connecting line.)

<u>Case 3 ($c_2 < 0$):</u> (slope of objective function line is still $-(c_1 / c_2)$, but the objective function value increases as the line is shifted *down*)
If $-(c_1 / c_2) > 0$ (i.e., $c_1 > 0$), then the optimal solution is $(x_1, x_2) = (5.5, 0)$.
If $-(c_1 / c_2) < 0$ (i.e., $c_1 < 0$), then the optimal solution is $(x_1, x_2) = (0, 0)$.
(Note, if $-(c_1 / c_2) = 0$, then the optimal solution is at $(5.5, 0)$, $(0, 0)$ and the connecting line.)

16.11 a & b)

| Benefit | Benefit Contribution Per Unit of Each Activity | | Totals | | Minimum Level |
	Activity 1	Activity 2			
1	-2	1	0	≥	1
2	1	-2	0	≥	1
Unit Cost	5000	7000	$	-	
Solution	0	0			

Solver could not find a feasible solution.

c)

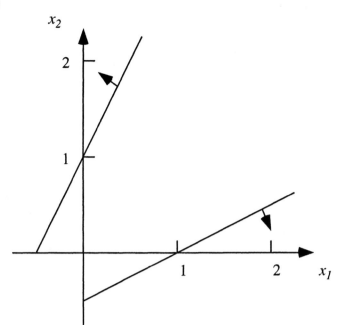

16.12 a & b)

Constraint	Contribution Per Unit of Each Activity		Totals		Resource
	Activity 1	Activity 2			
1	2	1	2	≤	2
2	1	-1	1	≥	2
Unit Profit	90	70	$ 90		
Solution	1	0			

Solver could not find a feasible solution.

c)

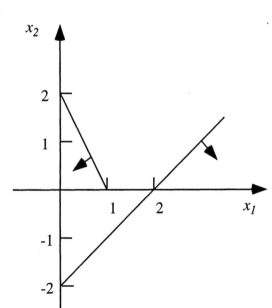

16.13 a)

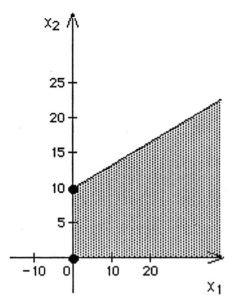

b) Yes. Optimal Solution: $(x_1, x_2) = (0,10)$ and Profit $= 10$.

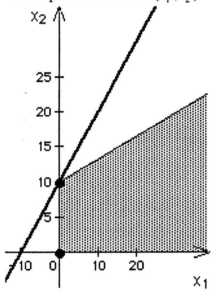

c) No. The objective function value is maximized by sliding the objective function line to the right. This can be done forever, so there is no optimal solution.

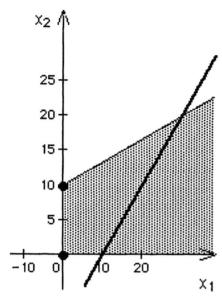

d) No, solutions exist that will make the profit arbitrarily large. This usually occurs when a constraint is left out of the model.

e)

Constraint	Contribution Per Unit of Each Activity		Totals		Resource
	Activity 1	Activity 2			
1	-1	3	0	≤	30
2	-3	1	0	≤	30
Unit Profit	1	-1	$ -		
Solution	0	0			

The Solver message was that the Set Cell values do not converge. There is no optimal solution, because a better solution can always be found.

16.14 a)

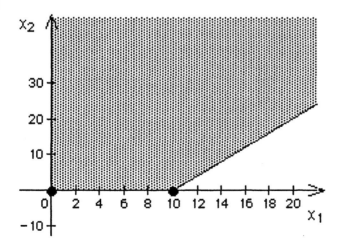

b) No. The objective function value is maximized by sliding the objective function line up. This can be done forever, so there is no optimal solution.

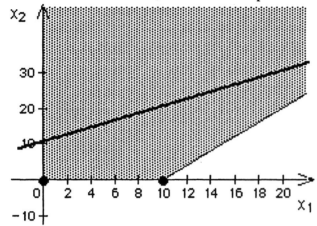

c) Yes. Optimal Solution: $(x_1, x_2) = (10,0)$ and Profit = 10.

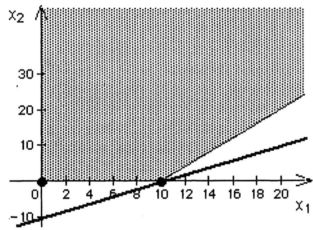

d) No, solutions exist that will make Z arbitrarily large. This usually occurs when a constraint is left out of the model.

e)

| | Contribution Per Unit of Each Activity | | | | Resource |
Resource	Activity 1	Activity 2	Totals		Available
1	2	-1	0	≤	20
2	1	-2	0	≤	20
Unit Profit	-1	1	$		
Solution	0	0			

The Solver message was that the Set Cell values do not converge. There is no optimal solution, because a better solution can always be found.

16.15 a)

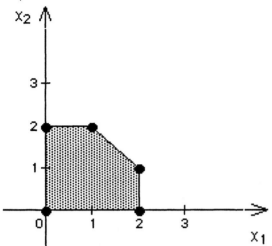

Note: corner points will be called A, B, C, D, and E going clockwise from (0,2).

b) Corner Point   A: $x_1 = 0$, and $x_2 = 2$
                    B: $x_2 = 2$, and $x_1 + x_2 = 3$
                    C: $x_1 + x_2 = 3$, and $x_1 = 2$
                    D: $x_1 = 2$, and $x_2 = 0$
                    E: $x_2 = 0$, and $x_1 = 0$

c) Corner Point   A: $(x_1, x_2) = (0,2)$
                    B: $(x_1, x_2) = (1,2)$
                    C: $(x_1, x_2) = (2,1)$
                    D: $(x_1, x_2) = (2,0)$
                    E: $(x_1, x_2) = (0,0)$

d) Corner Point   A: E and B are adjacent
                    B: A and C are adjacent
                    C: B and D are adjacent
                    D: C and E are adjacent
                    E: D and A are adjacent

e) Corner Points   A and B share $x_2 = 2$
                    B and C share $x_1 + x_2 = 3$
                    C and D share $x_1 = 2$
                    D and E share $x_2 = 0$
                    E and A share $x_1 = 0$

16.16 a) Optimal Solution: $(x_1, x_2) = (0.667, 0.667)$ and Profit = \$6,000.

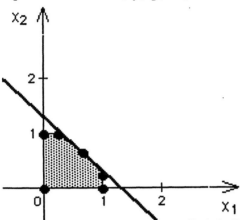

Note: corner points will be called A, B, C, D, E, and F going clockwise from (0,1).

b) Corner Point   A: F and B are adjacent
                   B: A and C are adjacent
                   C: B and D are adjacent
                   D: C and E are adjacent
                   E: D and F are adjacent
                   F: E and A are adjacent

16.17 a) Optimal Solution: $(x_1, x_2) = (2,2)$ and Profit = 10.

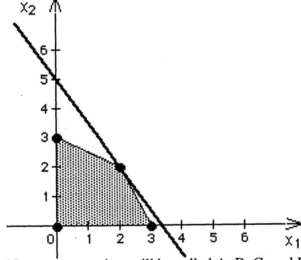

Note: corner points will be called A, B, C, and D going clockwise from (0,3).

b)

Corner Point	Corresponding Constraint Boundary Equations	Corner Point Satisfies the Equations
A: (0,3)	$x_1 = 0$	0=0
	$x_1 + 2x_2 = 6$	0+2(3)=6
B: (2,2)	$x_1 + 2x_2 = 6$	2+2(2)=6
	$2x_1 + x_2 = 6$	2(2)+2=6
C: (3,0)	$2x_1 + x_2 = 6$	2(3)+0=6
	$x_2 = 0$	0=0
D: (0,0)	$x_2 = 0$	0=0
	$x_1 = 0$	0=0

c)

Corner Point	Its Adjacent Corner Points
A: (0,3)	(0,0) and (2,2)
B: (2,2)	(0,3) and (3,0)
C: (3,0)	(2,2) and (0,0)
D: (0,0)	(3,0) and (0,3)

d)

Corner Point (x_1,x_2)	Profit = $3x_1 + 2x_2$
(0,3)	6
(2,2)	10
(3,0)	9
(0,0)	0

Optimal Solution: $(x_1,x_2) = (2,2)$ and Profit = 10.

e)

Corner Point	Profit = $3x_1 + 2x_2$	Next Step
D: (0,0)	0	Check points A and C.
A: (0,3)	6	Move to C.
C: (3,0)	9	Check point B.
B: (2,2)	10	Stop, (2,2) is optimal. *

* the next corner point is A, which has already been checked

16.18 a) Optimal Solution: $(x_1, x_2) = (2,2)$ and Profit $= 6$.

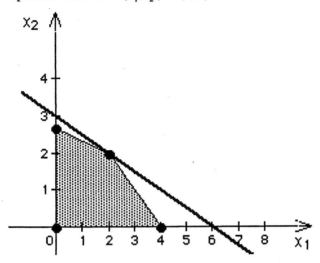

Note: corner points will be called A, B, C, and D going clockwise from (0,2.667).

b)

Corner Point	Corresponding Constraint Boundary Equations	Corner Point Satisfies the Equations
A: (0,2.667)	$x_1 = 0$	0=0
	$x_1 + 3x_2 = 8$	0+3(2.667)=8
B: (2,2)	$x_1 + 3x_2 = 8$	2+3(2)=8
	$x_1 + x_2 = 4$	2+2=4
C: (4,0)	$x_1 + x_2 = 4$	4=4
	$x_2 = 0$	0=0
D: (0,0)	$x_2 = 0$	0=0
	$x_1 = 0$	0=0

c)

Corner Point	Its Adjacent Corner Points
A: (0,2.667)	(0,0) and (2,2)
B: (2,2)	(0,2.667) and (4,0)
C: (4,0)	(2,2) and (0,0)
D: (0,0)	(4,0) and (0,2.667)

d)

Corner Point (x_1, x_2)	Profit $= x_1 + 2x_2$
(0,2.667)	5.333
(2,2)	6
(4,0)	4
(0,0)	0

Optimal Solution: $(x_1, x_2) = (2,2)$ and Profit $= 6$.

e)

Corner Point	Profit = $x_1 + 2x_2$	Next Step
D: (0,0)	0	Check points A and C.
A: (0,2.667)	5.333	Move to A.
C: (4,0)	4	Check point B.
B: (2,2)	6	Stop, (2,2) is optimal. *

* the next corner point is C, which has already been checked

16.19 a) Optimal Solution: $(x_1, x_2) = (3,4)$ and Profit = 17.

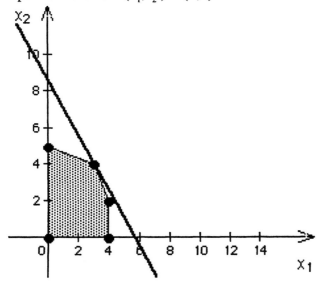

Note: corner points will be called A, B, C, D, and E going clockwise from (0,5).

b)

Corner Point	Corresponding Constraint Boundary Equations	Corner Point Satisfies the Equations
A: (0,5)	$x_1 = 0$	0=0
	$x_1 + 3x_2 = 15$	0+3(5)=15
B: (3,4)	$x_1 + 3x_2 = 15$	3+3(4)=17
	$2x_1 + x_2 = 10$	2(3)+4=10
C: (4,2)	$2x_1 + x_2 = 10$	2(4)+2=10
	$x_1 = 4$	4=4
D: (4,0)	$x_1 = 4$	4=4
	$x_2 = 0$	0=0
E: (0,0)	$x_2 = 0$	0=0
	$x_1 = 0$	0=0

CD16-23

c)

Corner Point	Its Adjacent Corner Points
A: (0,5)	(0,0) and (3,4)
B: (3,4)	(0,5) and (4,2)
C: (4,2)	(3,4) and (4,0)
D: (4,0)	(4,2) and (0,0)
E: (0,0)	(4,0) and (0,5)

d)

Corner Point (x_1, x_2)	Profit $= 3x_1 + 2x_2$
(0,5)	10
(3,4)	17
(4,2)	16
(4,0)	12
(0,0)	0

Optimal Solution: $(x_1, x_2) = (3,4)$ and Profit $= 17$.

e)

Corner Point	Profit $= 3x_1 + 2x_2$	Next Step
E: (0,0)	0	Check points A and C.
A: (0,5)	10	Move to D.
D: (4,0)	12	Check point C.
C: (4,2)	16	Move to C. Check point B.
B: (3,4)	17	Move to B. Stop, (3,4) is optimal. *

* the next corner point is A, which has already been checked

16.20

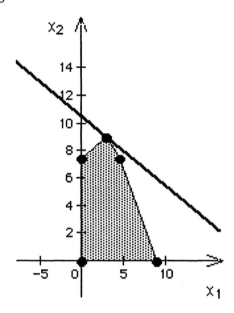

Corner Point	Profit $= 10x_1 + 20x_2$	Next Step
(0,0)	0	Check (0,7.5) and (9,0).
(0,7.5)	150	Move to (0,7.5).
(9,0)	90	Check (3,9).
(3,9)	210	Move to (3,9) Check (4.5,7.5).
(4.5,7.5)	195	Stop, (3,9) is optimal.

16.21

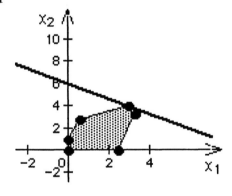

Corner Point	Profit $= 2x_1 + 3x_2$	Next Step
(0,0)	0	Check (2.5,0) and (0,1).
(2.5,0)	5	Move to (2.5,0)
(0,1)	3	Check (3.333,3.333).
(3.333,3.333)	16.667	Move to (3.333,3.333) Check (3,4).
(3,4)	18	Move to (3,4) Check (0.6,2.8).
(0.6,2.8)	9.6	Stop, (3,4) is optimal.

16.22

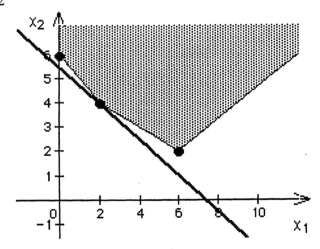

Corner Point	Cost = $15x_1 + 20x_2$	Next Step
(2,4)	110	Check (0,6) and (6,2).
(0,6)	120	Stop, (2,4) is optimal.
(6,2)	130	

16.23

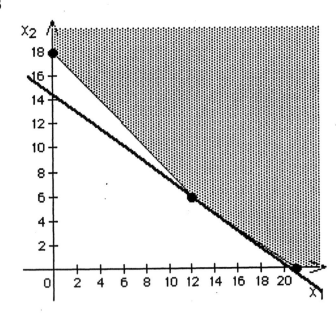

Corner Point	Cost = $5x_1 + 7x_2$	Next Step
(12,6)	102	Check (21,0) and (0,18).
(21,0)	105	Stop, (12,6) is optimal.
(0,18)	126	

16.24 a) True (see solution concept number 6).

    b) False, there can be an infinite number of optimal solutions, such as the set of solutions along a line segment between two corner points.

    c) True, if the objective function line is parallel to the constraint boundary line that connects the two.

16.25 a) If the feasible region is unbounded then there may be no optimal solution.

    b) An optimal solution may contain all points on a line segment between two corner points.

    c) If an adjacent corner point has an equal objective function value then all the points on the connecting line segment will also be optimal.

16.26 a) The problem may not have an optimal solution.

    b) The optimality test checks whether the current corner point is optimal. The iterative step only moves to a new corner point.

    c) The simplex method only chooses the origin as the initial corner point when it is a feasible point.

    d) One of the adjacent points is likely to be better, not necessarily optimal.

    e) The simplex method only identifies the rate of improvement, not all the adjacent corner points.

16.27 a & c)

	Resource Usage Per Unit of Each Activity			Resource
Resource	Activity 1	Activity 2	Totals	Available
A	3	1	15 ≤	15
B	1	2	10 ≤	10
Unit Profit	2	1	$ 11	
Solution	4	3		

b)

Corner Point (x_1, x_2)	Profit $= 2x_1 + x_2$
(0,0)	0
(5,0)	10
(4,3)	11
(0,5)	5

Optimal Solution: $(x_1, x_2) = (4,3)$ and Profit $= \$11$ million

d)

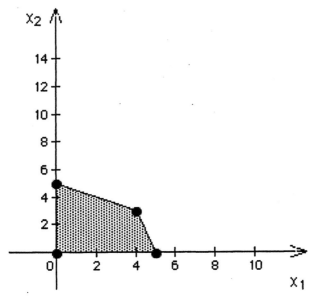

Corner Point	Profit $= 2x_1 + x_2$	Next Step
(0,0)	0	Check (5,0) and (0,5).
(5,0)	10	Move to (5,0).
(0,5)	5	Check (4,3).
(4,3)	11	Move to (4,3). Stop, (4,3) is optimal. *

* the next corner point is (0,5) which has already been checked

16.28 a)

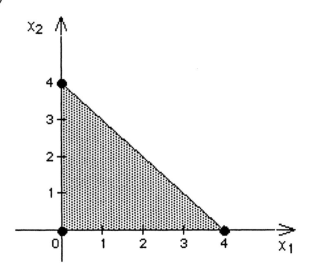

Corner Points: (0,0), (4,0), and (0,4).

b)

Corner Point	Profit = $3x_1 + x_2$	Next Step
(0,0)	0	Check (4,0) and (0,4).
(4,0)	12	Move to (4,0).
(0,4)	4	Stop, (4,0) is optimal. *

* the next corner point is (0,4) which has already been checked

c)

Iteration	x_1	x_2	Z
0	1.00000	1.00000	4.0000
1	1.87500	1.12500	6.7500
2	2.69810	0.80190	8.8962
3	3.34396	0.40095	10.4328
4	3.66710	0.20047	11.2018
5	3.83305	0.10024	11.5994
6	3.91648	0.05012	11.7996
7	3.95824	0.02506	11.8998
8	3.97912	0.01253	11.9499
9	3.98956	0.00626	11.9749
10	3.99478	0.00313	11.9875

16.29 a) Optimal Solution: $(x_1, x_2) = (3,3)$ and Profit = 6.

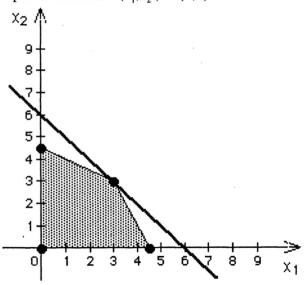

b) Corner points: (0,0), (4.5,0), (0,4.5), and (3,3).

c) Examine (4.5,0) first.

Corner Point	Profit = $x_1 + x_2$	Next Step
(0,0)	0	Check (4.5,0) and (0,4.5).
(4.5,0)	4.5	Move to (4.5,0).
(0,4.5)	4.5	Check (3,3)
(3,3)	6	Move to (3,3) Stop, (3,3) is optimal. *

* the next corner point is (0,4.5) which has already been checked

Examine (0,4.5) first.

Corner Point	Profit = $x_1 + x_2$	Next Step
(0,0)	0	Check (4.5,0) and (0,4.5).
(4.5,0)	4.5	Move to (0,4.5).
(0,4.5)	4.5	Check (3,3)
(3,3)	6	Move to (3,3) Stop, (3,3) is optimal. *

* the next corner point is (4.5,0) which has already been checked

d)

Iteration	x_1	x_2	Z
0	1.00000	1.00000	2.0000
1	2.00000	2.00000	4.0000
2	2.50000	2.50000	5.0000
3	2.75000	2.75000	5.5000
4	2.87500	2.87500	5.7500
5	2.93750	2.93750	5.8750
6	2.96875	2.96875	5.9375
7	2.98437	2.98437	5.9688
8	2.99219	2.99219	5.9844
9	2.99609	2.99609	5.9922
10	2.99805	2.99805	5.9961

e)

Iteration	x_1	x_2	Z
0	3.00000	1.00000	4.0000
1	3.38066	1.23867	4.6193
2	3.33770	1.82460	5.1623
3	3.07911	2.45717	5.5363
4	2.96654	2.76509	5.7316
5	2.94424	2.90206	5.8463
6	2.96055	2.95681	5.9174
7	2.97907	2.97901	5.9581
8	2.98952	2.98952	5.9790
9	2.99476	2.99476	5.9895
10	2.99738	2.99738	5.9948

16.30 a)

Requirement	Contribution Toward Required Amount Per Unit				Required Amount
	Activity 1	Activity 2	Activity 3	Totals	
A	1	2	3	6 =	6
Unit Profit	2	5	7	15	
Solution	0	3	0		

b)

Iteration	x_1	x_2	x_3	Z
0	1.00000	1.00000	1.00000	14.0000
1	0.50000	1.40000	0.90000	14.3000
2	0.25969	2.19516	0.45000	14.6452
3	0.17947	2.57276	0.22500	14.7978
4	0.10690	2.77780	0.11250	14.8903
5	0.05595	2.88765	0.05625	14.9439
6	0.02810	2.94376	0.02812	14.9719
7	0.01406	2.97188	0.01406	14.9859
8	0.00703	2.98594	0.00703	14.9930
9	0.00352	2.99297	0.00352	14.9965
10	0.00176	2.99648	0.00176	14.9982

16.31 a)

Resource	Resource Usage Per Unit of Each Activity				Totals		Resource Available
	Activity 1	Activity 2	Activity 3	Activity 4			
A	3	5	2	3	130	≤	130
B	4	3	5	1	130	≤	130
C	2	6	4	7	118.182	≤	190
Unit Profit	50	60	40	30	1890.91		
Solution	23.636	11.818	0	0			

b)

Iteration	x_1	x_2	x_3	x_4	Z
0	5.0000	6.0000	4.00000	3.00000	860.00
1	7.7865	10.4121	5.15582	3.42273	1322.97
2	9.6707	12.6928	5.25147	3.34029	1555.37
3	11.6525	13.3676	5.08441	3.17856	1683.41
4	14.2623	12.9152	4.64514	3.03224	1764.80
5	17.4541	11.9087	3.51576	2.90497	1815.01
6	20.9150	10.8139	1.83662	2.72815	1849.90
7	22.6670	10.3784	0.91831	2.48589	1867.37
8	23.4697	10.3745	0.45916	2.11734	1877.84
9	23.7466	10.6603	0.22958	1.59018	1883.84
10	23.7621	11.0802	0.11479	0.98935	1887.19

IRWIN/McGRAW-HILL

Instructor's Manual to accompany Introduction to Management Science, by Hillier, Hillier, and Lieberman.

Please use this postage-paid form to report any errors that you find in this material. Be as complete as possible noting specifically which changes should be made. We will address them in subsequent printings and future editions. Thank You.

Attention: Scott Isenberg

Name _____   School _____

Office Phone _____

Please fold and seal so that our address is visible.

BUSINESS REPLY MAIL
FIRST-CLASS MAIL   PERMIT NO. 204   OAKBROOK, IL

NO POSTAGE
NECESSARY
IF MAILED
IN THE
UNITED STATES

ATTENTION: Scott Isenberg

THE McGRAW-HILL COMPANIES
RICHARD D. IRWIN
1333 BURR RIDGE PKY.
BURR RIDGE, IL 60521-0085

(fold)

(fold)

IRWIN/McGRAW-HILL

Instructor's Manual to accompany Introduction to Management Science, by Hillier, Hillier, and Lieberman.

Please use this postage-paid form to report any errors that you find in this material. Be as complete as possible noting specifically which changes should be made. We will address them in subsequent printings and future editions. Thank You.

Attention: Scott Isenberg

Name _____   School _____

Office Phone _____

Please fold and seal so that our address is visible.

BUSINESS REPLY MAIL
FIRST-CLASS MAIL   PERMIT NO. 204   OAKBROOK, IL

POSTAGE WILL BE PAID BY ADDRESSEE

ATTENTION: Scott Isenberg

THE McGRAW-HILL COMPANIES
RICHARD D. IRWIN
1333 BURR RIDGE PKY.
BURR RIDGE, IL 60521-0085

(fold)

(fold)